Biochemical Applications
of
Gas Chromatography

Biochemical Applications
of
Gas Chromatography

H. P. BURCHFIELD

Southwest Research Institute
San Antonio, Texas

ELEANOR E. STORRS

Boyce Thompson Institute
Yonkers, New York

1962

ACADEMIC PRESS · *New York and London*

ACADEMIC PRESS INC.
111 Fifth Avenue
New York 3, N. Y.

United Kingdom Edition
Published by
ACADEMIC PRESS INC. (London) Ltd.
Berkeley Square House
Berkeley Square, London, W.1.

Library of Congress Catalog Card Number 62-13963

PRINTED IN THE UNITED STATES OF AMERICA

IN MEMORY OF

COLONEL
WILLIAM BOYCE THOMPSON
1869–1936

WHO ENDOWED THE INSTITUTE
WHICH MADE THIS WORK POSSIBLE

PREFACE

This book was written to fulfill a need for a text on gas chromatography that would supply both the theoretical background and details of the applications of this technique to biochemical problems. Several excellent books exist which review theory and instrumentation, but these do not contain sufficient experimental detail to be useful as laboratory manuals. On the other hand, the field has not matured sufficiently to make it possible to present a set of routine methods that can be used with confidence in every application. Therefore, experimental details of the most promising procedures are set forth together with enough theoretical background to enable the experimentalist to improvise adaptations without an extensive study of the literature.

Material is included that will be of interest to analytical biochemists working in a variety of fields. These fields include foods, essential oils, amino acids, carbohydrates, pesticides, clinical chemistry, and others. Although the book is organized along biochemical lines, information is included that will be of value to workers in other disciplines. For example, specific instructions are given for the analysis of atmospheric gases and for the resolution of isomeric aliphatic and aromatic hydrocarbons. This information should be useful in the solution of problems in air pollution and petroleum chemistry. In fact, it was necessary to draw upon the literature from these fields to round out the text in areas where biochemical applications were few or lacking altogether.

This book contains methods for the analysis of the principal groups of compounds of biochemical interest. However, the gas chromatographic method is so versatile that the material could not be organized coherently according to the functional groups occurring in the various compounds. For example, alcohols, aldehydes, and esters often coexist in a sample and can frequently be resolved in a single operation. Classification according to vapor pressure is also possible, but this does not allow for a logical presentation of biochemical data. Therefore, the methods employed for sample collection and pre-fractionation are used as the primary basis for chapter organization, since this permits an orderly arrangement of the material from the viewpoint of experimental techniques. Thus volatile components of tissues, essential oils, lipids, and nonvolatile components of tissues, are each treated as distinct groups, since the methods used for sample preparation within each group are similar. The chapters are then arranged in approximate order of decreasing vapor pressure of the compounds discussed in them, and subdivisions within chapters made according to elements and functional groups where this is feasible. As a consequence of this arrangement, procedures for the analysis of compounds with the same functional groups may appear in several sections of the text. Thus methods for the chromatography of organic acids are found in the chapters on volatile compounds, resin acids, lipids, nonvolatile compounds, etc. Consequently anyone interested in compiling methods according to functional group should make liberal use of the subject indexes.

Although gas chromatography is the pivotal analytical technique described in this book it is not the only one. Other methods have been included, where required, to make the book as self-sufficient as possible within the scope of a single volume. Detailed methods for sample collection are provided for each group of compounds, and often pre-fractionation of samples by liquid-solid chromatography or ion exchange techniques is described. Finally, methods are provided for the preparation of stationary liquids and chromatographic columns, subtraction of unwanted compounds from the gas stream, and for the synthesis of derivatives of nonvolatile compounds which are amenable to gas chromatography.

The operating parameters used for gas chromatography are tabulated in standard form throughout the book. The conventions used are simple, and for the most part are self-explanatory. However, the meaning of the entries used to describe columns in series, in parallel, and multiply-packed columns may not be immediately clear. Therefore, the reader is strongly urged to consult pages 20 through 23 for a detailed account of the conventions employed.

In a number of cases, insufficient information was given in original research papers to allow for an adequate compilation of experimental methods. Therefore, it was decided that a more complete as well as a more accurate and up-to-date set of procedures could be obtained by submitting excerpts from the first draft of the manuscript to authors of the original papers for corrections and additions. About 320 methods were sent out and replies were received on 87% of them. Methods which have been verified by the original authors are marked with asterisks to acknowledge their contributions. Many valuable corrections and additions were obtained. In a number of cases, improved methods were submitted in advance of journal publication.

To insure further that the book would be reasonably up to date on publication, the manuscript was prepared during a relatively short time period—between August 1960 and February 1961. Additional material of major importance appearing through September 1961 was added in galley proofs, but coverage of the literature during this period was incomplete.

San Antonio, Texas   H. P. BURCHFIELD
Yonkers, New York   ELEANOR E. STORRS
January, 1962

ACKNOWLEDGMENTS

Most of the text was read for clarity by Dr. E. A. Prill of Boyce Thompson Institute for Plant Research and Dr. Richard Murie of the Diamond Alkali Co. Individual chapters and sections were reviewed by Dr. Richard C. Staples, Dr. L. P. Miller, and Dr. Clark A. Porter of Boyce Thompson Institute, and Mr. Nathaniel Brenner and L. S. Ettre of the Perkin Elmer Corporation. Thanks are also due to Mr. James Broderick and the Wilkens Instrument and Research Corp. for supplying many of the chromatograms and methods included in Chapter 5. Mr. Broderick also reviewed this chapter for us.

Acknowledgments are made to the management of Boyce Thompson Institute for Plant Research, where much of the book was written. Southwest Research Institute has been most cooperative in supplying time and facilities for making revisions in the manuscript and editing the text. The help of Mrs. Ethyl Allison and Miss Sara Joyce Haynie in carrying out these latter tasks is greatly appreciated.

We greatly appreciate the suggestions of Dr. Richard J. Block who first perceived the need for such a book, and encouraged its completion.

CONTENTS

Chapter 1

General Techniques, Conventions, and Instrumentation

Chapter 2

Permanent Gases and Condensable
Organic Vapors

Chapter 3

Volatile Components of Tissues
and Biological Fluids

Chapter 4

Cyclic Compounds

Chapter 5

Essential Oils

Chapter 6

Resin Acids

Chapter 7

Lipids

Chapter 8

Nonvolatile Components of Tissues

Chapter 9

Review of Miscellaneous Applications
Related to Biochemistry

Appendix 1

Appendix 2

Appendix 3

Appendix 4

Chapter 1

General Techniques, Conventions, and Instrumentation

General Introduction

Chromatography has become an invaluable adjunct in so many fields of biochemical research that almost all workers are familiar with it. Consequently, there is no need to reintroduce the subject here. Gas chromatography differs from liquid–liquid chromatography or liquid–solid chromatography primarily in that a gas is used as the mobile phase, and the solute travels through the column as a plug of gas or vapor which is partly dissolved in, or adsorbed on, the stationary phase. The suggestion to use a gas as the mobile phase was made by Martin and Synge in 1941, but it was not implemented until the work of James and Martin (1952) on gas–liquid chromatography and the work of Cremer and Prior (1951) and Cremer and Müller (1951a,b) on gas–solid chromatography. Since then, the use of the technique has penetrated almost every area of analytical and biochemical research.

A. Theory and Nomenclature

I. Forms and Advantages of Gas Chromatography

Gas chromatography can be accomplished with either a liquid sorbed on an inert particulate support or an active solid as the stationary phase. Alternatively, the liquid can be coated on the internal surface of a long capillary tube with very small bore. Each of these procedures has special advantages that overlap only slightly. However, all forms of gas chromatography are more efficient in many respects than methods where a liquid is the mobile phase, because of unique features conferred by the low viscosity and high diffusivity of gases and vapors.

a. Gas–Liquid Chromatography (GLC)

The column in gas–liquid chromatography is a glass or metal tube, usually about 0.5 cm in internal diameter and 1 to 20 meters long. The tube is packed uniformly with a finely divided free-flowing powder prepared by impregnating an inert solid with a liquid of low volatility. The solid support should be absorbent in the sense that it is capable of imbibing and holding the stationary liquid without becoming greasy, but not adsorbent in the sense that it will bind components of the sample being analyzed by secondary

1

valence bonds. The main physical requirement for the liquid is that it must not be eluted from the column at the operating temperature employed.

A sample of the mixture to be separated is flash-evaporated at one end of the column and swept into it by a constantly flowing stream of carrier gas such as hydrogen, helium, or nitrogen (Fig. 1). The components of the

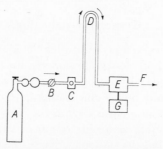

FIG. 1. Basic design of a gas chromatograph, arrows showing the direction of gas flow: (A) gas cylinder with reducing valve; (B) constant-pressure regulator; (C) port for injection of sample; (D) chromatographic column; (E) detector; (F) exit line; (G) strip chart recorder.

sample are carried through the column at different rates, which are governed by their partition coefficients between the gas phase and the stationary liquid phase. Ideally, they emerge from the other end of the column at different times. Their presence in the emerging carrier gas is detected by chemical or physical means, and the response of the detector is fed into a strip chart recorder. Generally, differential detectors are used, and the data are presented as a series of peaks spread out along a longitudinal time axis (Fig. 2). Each peak represents a discrete chemical compound, or a mixture

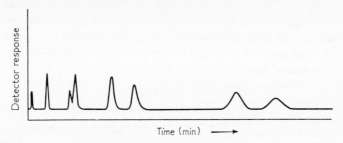

FIG. 2. Typical chromatogram showing separation of a hydrocarbon mixture. Note peak broadening at increased retention times.

of compounds with identical partition coefficients. The time required for each component to emerge from the column is characteristic of the compound and is known as its retention time. The area under the peak is proportional to its concentration in the sample. This constitutes the principal primary information derived from the chromatogram.

It may be helpful to review briefly some elementary principles governing the rate of travel of chemical compounds through columns packed with a stationary liquid phase. Each compound has a characteristic partition coefficient, which is given by equation 1. Therefore, if the partition coefficient

$$K = \frac{\text{Weight of solute/ml stationary phase}}{\text{Weight of solute/ml mobile (gas) phase}} \qquad (1)$$

of compound A is small, the amount of compound dissolved in the stationary liquid phase will be small compared to that in the gas phase. Consequently, the compound passes through the column rapidly, since it is not retarded by the stationary liquid. If the partition coefficient of compound B is large, the greater proportion of it resides in the solvent (stationary phase); therefore, passage through the column is slow, and this material passes through the detector and registers a peak at a later time than compound A. It must be remembered that the solute present in the gas phase is in dynamic equilibrium with the same solute in the liquid phase at all times. The vapor molecules cannot be swept through the column with the carrier gas, leaving the dissolved molecules behind; the only effect is to retard passage in proportion to the partition coefficient of the compound. This situation can be likened, however inaccurately, to a group of sailing ships of different draft being carried along by a high wind at sea. The vessels with greater displacement are slowed down by the drag of the water, whereas those with shallow draft skim along on the surface and pull ahead in the race.

The basic principles governing the separation of chemical compounds by gas chromatography are simple, but unfortunately, like in most other systems, behavior is not ideal. Therefore mathematical treatment of conditions as they supposedly occur in columns is moderately complex. This topic has been dealt with adequately by Keulemans (1959) and others and so will not be repeated here. Nevertheless, it may be worth while to point out a few consequences of departures from ideality, since they affect the symmetry and shape of chromatographic peaks and often must be dealt with experimentally. These are:

1. *Tailing.* Under ideal conditions, peaks on gas chromatograms should be symmetrical and resemble Gaussian distribution curves. This situation is often approximated in GLC, but sometimes the recorder pen does not return to the base line as rapidly on the descending side of the peak as it leaves it on the ascending side. This results in asymmetric peaks and is called tailing. Generally, tailing in GLC arises from adsorption of the solute on active sites of the solid support. It can be reduced and sometimes eliminated by deactivating the support (see this chapter, Section C.III). Peak asymmetry

occurs when adsorption isotherms are nonlinear—that is to say, when the partition coefficient of a compound between the mobile and stationary phases varies with the amount present. However, at the low solute concentrations used in GLC, solutions generally behave ideally, and tailing arises mostly from interaction of the solute and the solid support.

2. *Leading.* Leading is said to occur when the front or leading edge of the chromatographic peak is elongated and the rear or descending side is straight. It occurs when the column is overloaded to such an extent that the solute molecules interact with one another within the stationary liquid. The concentrations in gas chromatography are usually too low for leading to be a serious problem. However, if 2 to 3 mg of a polar compound is chromatographed on a nonpolar stationary phase, asymmetry of this type is observed frequently.

3. *Peak Broadening.* If samples injected into a chromatograph were carried through the column as homogeneous plugs of vapor, peak width would be independent of the time they remain in the column. In practice this is not true. Peaks broaden perceptibly, so those recorded first are high and narrow, whereas those representing slower-moving components tend to become lower and wider, even though the areas under them remain the same. This results from the fact that the vapor molecules diffuse longitudinally as the sample moves through the columns; thus the longer the sample remains in the column, the broader will be the peaks. This problem has been treated mathematically by van Deemter *et al.* (1956) and later by Kieselbach (1961). The simplest form of the van Deemter equation is given by equation 2, where

$$HETP = A + B/u + Cu \qquad (2)$$

HETP is the height equivalent to a theoretical plate;[1] u is the velocity of the carrier gas; A is a constant that accounts for the effect of "eddy" diffusion of the vapor; B is a constant that accounts for the effect of molecular diffusion of the vapor in the direction of the long axis of the column; and C is a constant proportional to the resistance of the column packing to mass transfer of solute through it.

Therefore, it is seen that peak broadening (as measured by high values for *HETP*) results from diffusion of the solute, certain physical characteristics of the column, and flow rate of the carrier gas. This latter quantity, of course, is related directly to the length of time the sample remains in the column.

b. Gas–Solid Chromatography (GSC)

Gas–solid chromatography differs from gas–liquid chromatography in that the stationary phase is an active solid or adsorbent, such as charcoal or silica gel, instead of a liquid. Consequently, the passage of gases and vapors

[1] For a definition of this term, see Section A.IV.b.

through the column is retarded differentially by adsorption rather than by partition. Adsorption isotherms are rarely linear; hence peaks in GSC are asymmetric more often than in GLC. This can be corrected sometimes by treating the active solid with a small amount (about 0.5 to 1.5%) of non-volatile liquid. Sometimes larger volumes are used, in which case the method becomes a hybrid of adsorption and partition chromatography.

Historically, gas–solid chromatography was developed a short time before gas–liquid chromatography (Cremer and Prior, 1951; Cremer and Müller, 1951a,b). GSC has been used to some extent recently for the separation of fairly high-molecular-weight hydrocarbons (Scott and Rowell, 1960), but its main value is for the analysis of permanent gases. Therefore an extended discussion of this topic, and of techniques used only for handling gases and vapors associated with them, will be deferred until Chapter 2.

The method of chromatography described in the preceding section is termed elution analysis, since a compact plug of vapor is applied to a column and swept through it or eluted with carrier gas. This same technique is used in GSC. However, two other methods, "frontal analysis" and "displacement analysis," are possible. They are not employed in any of the methods described in this book, or for that matter in analytical work generally, and consequently will not be discussed here. The reader who is interested in details of these techniques can find them in general texts such as those of Keulemans (1959) or Phillips (1956).

c. Chromatography Using Capillary Columns

Capillary column chromatography is a branch of gas–liquid chromatography in which the stationary phase is coated on the inside surface of a capillary, the wall of the tube thus serving as the solid support in lieu of an inert particulate solid (Golay, 1958). It is given special notice here, since it is developing rapidly into an independent technique from both a theoretical and an experimental point of view. Capillary columns are efficient and can be made very long, since they are coiled in the form of helices which occupy a relatively small amount of space. Glass and metal columns 100 to 300 feet in length are used routinely, and nylon capillaries a mile long with efficiencies of a million theoretical plates have been evaluated (Zlatkis and Kaufman, 1959). With these, separations are achieved rapidly and precisely, that would be impossible by ordinary physicochemical methods.

The roles of capillary and conventionally packed GLC columns overlap only to a minor extent. The methods tend to supplement one another rather than compete. Packed columns[2] can be prepared with a greater variety of selective stationary liquids and will yield fractions of pure compounds large enough for identification by ordinary chemical and physical methods. By

---

[2] Packed columns contain a stationary liquid sorbed on a particulate solid support.

contrast, capillary columns have been used with a smaller variety of stationary liquids, are more difficult to prepare reproducibly, and yield samples too small for characterization by the usual methods. However, they have high plate efficiencies and are suitable for separating mixtures having wide boiling-point ranges without programming the temperature. Many of the defects of capillary columns are likely to be overcome in the near future. Methods for coating them are improving continually, and new physical means for characterizing trace components, such as measurement of electron affinity (Lovelock and Lipsky, 1960), are appearing.

d. Comparison of Gas Chromatography with Other Chromatographic Methods

The concept of replacing the moving liquid phase in conventional chromatography with a gas is a simple one, yet it has led to revolutionary changes in techniques, and vastly improved efficiencies of separations because of the unique physical properties possessed by gases as opposed to liquids. Some of the operating parameters that have been altered drastically by this innovation are summarized below.

1. *Column Dimensions.* Gas chromatography columns can be much longer and narrower than those used when a liquid is the mobile phase, because of the comparatively low viscosity of gases. Packed columns are generally about 0.5 cm in diameter and 1 to 20 meters in length. Glass and metal capillary columns are 100 to 300 feet long, and preliminary results have been reported with a nylon capillary a mile long (Zlatkis and Kaufman, 1959).

2. *Column Efficiencies.* Equilibration of the solute between solvent and carrier occurs rapidly when a gas is the mobile phase. This results in high column efficiencies. Packed and capillary columns having a thousand theoretical plates per foot are commonplace. By combining high efficiency with length, capillary columns having a million theoretical plates have been constructed.

3. *Analysis Times.* Because of the low viscosities of gases, rapid analyses are possible even with long columns. Most GSC analyses are done in 5 minutes or less, whereas most GLC methods require 5 minutes to an hour. As many as eight to ten components can be resolved cleanly in capillary columns in less than a minute.

4. *Operating Temperatures.* Permanent gases can be used without encountering problems caused by freezing and boiling, normally associated with liquids. Consequently, temperatures between $-200°C$ and $+1000°C$ have been used for chromatography, and the range seems destined to expand toward higher temperature through the use of eutectic mixtures of inorganic salts as stationary phases.

5. *Complex Circuitry.* Gases do not wet or stick to materials of construction and by their nature must be handled at all times in gastight apparatus.

Therefore, rapid advances have been made with compact coiled columns and multiple-column arrangements that would not be practicable with liquids as the mobile phase. Furthermore, it is possible to carry out simple chemical transformations such as oxidation, reduction, and dehydration directly in the gas stream.

6. *Detection of Solutes.* Methods for the detection and measurement of trace components in gases are vastly more varied, universal, and sensitive than corresponding methods for the detection of foreign materials in liquids. In this book, twenty-four different methods of detection are listed, some of which will respond to all the components of complex mixtures.

7. *Sample Size.* Thermal detectors will respond to as little as 10^{-9} mole of solute in the carrier gas, and ionization detectors to as little as 10^{-15} mole. Consequently, a complete analysis can be obtained on a 1-μg sample containing as many as twenty components if a capillary column combined with an ionization detector is used. Samples of a few microliters or less are large enough for analyses on packed columns if thermal detectors are used.

8. *Fraction Collection and Analysis.* Fraction collection is greatly simplified, since most organic vapors can be condensed without danger of contamination from the carrier.

9. *Choice of the Mobile Phase.* The selection of the mobile phase is not so critical as it is with liquids. Most permanent gases do not dissolve in liquids to a major extent, so interactions between the two phases are at a minimum. Consequently the separations obtained are largely independent of the nature of the carrier gas. This reduces the number of variables that must be considered in devising new methods of analysis.

10. *Compressibility.* Unlike liquids, gases are compressible. Therefore linear flow rate is higher at the exit of a column than at the inlet, if a constant volumetric rate is assumed. Consequently, column efficiency may vary along its length.

11. *Automation.* Because of the nature of the detection devices, almost all gas chromatograms are recorded automatically on a strip chart, and consequently the operation requires no attention on the part of the analyst once operating parameters have been set and the sample introduced. If desired, equipment is available for automatically computing areas under curves and for adjusting instrument sensitivity when components are present in greatly different amounts. This dispenses with manual titrations, individual colorimetric analyses, etc., so often required in liquid–liquid or liquid–solid chromatography.

II. Nomenclature

A committee appointed by the Analytical Section of the International Union of Pure and Applied Chemistry (IUPAC) has recommended standard terms and units for gas chromatography (Ambrose *et al.*, 1960). These are employed in this book in so far as is practicable. However, in a number of cases, equivalent expressions have been substituted to avoid redundancy, particularly where the meaning is unambiguous. Thus, adsorbent has been used interchangeably with active solid, and the expressions stationary liquid, partition liquid, partition medium, and solvent have been used in various places instead of liquid phase. However, in all tabulated data the IUPAC terminology has been followed. The recommendations are as follows and are quoted without change except for the numbering system and several notes inserted in brackets.

a. Name of Techniques

1. "*Gas chromatography* comprises all chromatographic methods in which the moving phase is a gas [the word chromatography itself implies that a stationary phase is present in addition to the moving phase].

2. "*Gas–liquid chromatography* comprises all chromatographic methods in which the stationary phase is a liquid distributed on a solid support. Separation is achieved by partition of the components of a sample between the phases.

3. "*Gas–solid chromatography* comprises all gas chromatographic methods in which the stationary phase is an active solid [e.g., charcoal, molecular sieves]. Separation is achieved by adsorption of the components of a sample."

b. Apparatus

1. "A *sample injector* is a device by which a liquid or gaseous sample is introduced into the apparatus. The sample can be introduced directly into the carrier gas stream, or into a chamber temporarily isolated from the system by valves which can be changed so as to make an instantaneous switch of the gas stream through the chamber. The latter is a *by-pass injector*.

2. "*Solid volume* is the volume occupied by the solid support or the active solid in the column.

3. "*Liquid volume*, V_L, is the volume occupied by the liquid phase in the column. $V_L = W_L/\rho_L$, where W_L is the weight of the liquid in the column, and ρ_L is its density at the column temperature.

4. "*Interstitial volume* is the volume of the column not occupied by the liquid phase and its solid support, or by the active solid. It does not include any volume external to the column, such as the volume of the sample injector or of the detector.

5. "A *detector* is a device that measures the change of composition of the effluent. A detector that measures instantaneous concentration is called a *differential detector*. An *integral detector* continuously measures the sample accumulated from the beginning of the analysis."

c. Reagents

1. "*Carrier gas* or eluent gas is gas that is used to elute the sample as it passes through the column. The carrier gas forms the *mobile phase*.

2. "*Liquid phase* is a liquid which is relatively nonvolatile at the column temperature and is sorbed on the solid support, where it acts as a solvent for the sample. Separation depends on differences of volatility of the various components of the sample in the liquid phase.

3. "*Solid support* is normally an inert porous solid, which sorbs the liquid phase. The particle size range of the support affects column efficiency and the pressure differential necessary to achieve a given flow rate. Modifications of the method have been introduced for the achievement of special separations, in which the solid support is not inert but is an active solid. In capillary columns the inner wall of the column serves as the solid support and obviates the use of additional porous solids for this purpose.

4. "*Active solid* is a porous solid with adsorptive properties by means of which chromatographic separations may be achieved. The separations resulting from this action follow laws different from those deriving from the partitioning action of the liquid phase.

5. "In gas–liquid chromatography the *stationary phase* comprises the liquid phase without the solid support.[3] In gas–solid chromatography the stationary phase is the active solid."

d. Chromatogram Records

1. "A *chromatogram* is a plot of the detector response versus time or volume of carrier gas. Idealized chromatograms obtained with differential and integral detectors for one component are shown" in Fig. 3.

2. "The *base line* is that portion of a chromatogram recorded (differentially) when only carrier gas emerges from the column.

3. "A *peak* is the portion of the chromatogram recording the detector response [differential type] while a single component emerges from the column [if separation of a mixed sample is incomplete, two or more components may appear as one peak].

4. "The peak base *CD* [Fig. 3*A*] is an interpolation of the base line between the extremities of the peak. The area enclosed between the peak and the peak base is the *peak area* and the distance *BE* from the peak maximum to the peak base measured parallel to the axis representing detector response is the peak height. The segment of peak base *FG* intercepted by tangents to the inflection points on either side of the peak is the *peak width*. The line

---

[3] *Authors' note:* The stationary phase (or liquid) combined with the solid support is usually termed the *column packing*.

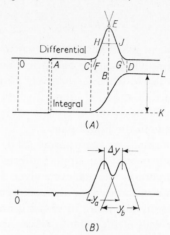

FIG. 3. Chromatogram parameters: (*A*) relation between differential and integral curves; (*B*) incompletely resolved peaks (Ambrose *et al.*, 1960).

parallel to the peak base, bisecting the peak height, and terminated at the sides of the peak *HJ* is the *peak width at half height*.

5. "The following definitions apply to chromatograms obtained with integral detectors. As a sample component passes through the detector, a sigmoid curve is obtained and the base line is displaced to a new position. The change in base line position caused by the sample component is known as a *step*, and the difference in heights of the two base lines is the *step height*."

III. CALCULATION OF RETENTION VALUES

Every chemical compound that can be eluted unchanged from a gas chromatograph has a characteristic retention time, or residence time in the instrument, if operating parameters such as column length, nature of the packing, flow rate of carrier gas, and temperature are held constant. From the standpoint of the practical analyst with only his own instrument and needs to consider, this is a useful measurement, for it will tell him whether compounds can be separated and, if so, how long the analysis will take. However, from a broader point of view, uncorrected retention times are too unstable to be meaningful. To eliminate the flow rate of the carrier gas as a variable, retention volumes are generally used. These are obtained by multiplying retention times by the volumetric flow rate of carrier gas, so they represent the total volume of mobile phase necessary to sweep the solute through the column. However, retention volumes obtained in this way must be corrected in turn to account for the fact that the mobile phase is compressible.

Another factor to be considered is that the volumes of the detector and sample injector as well as the interstitial column volume are included in the uncorrected retention volume, and these may vary from instrument to instrument. This difficulty can be overcome by subtracting the retention volume of a material which is not bound by the packing (air, for example) from the observed value; thus the observed value represents only the amount of carrier required for elution, excluding the internal volume of the instrument.

Corrections also can be made for the amount of liquid phase within the column. As a result, it is possible to calculate a specific retention volume or, alternatively, a value for the partition coefficient of the solute between the solvent and carrier that is independent of everything but the nature of the sample, the partitioning system, and the temperature.

Because of the variety of corrections that can be made, a considerable amount of confusion has arisen concerning the precise meaning of retention volume in any individual case, and in many publications it is not made clear exactly what term is being used. This situation could be improved if all authors would follow the recommendations made by the IUPAC committee on terminology for gas chromatography, which are reproduced with minor changes below.

a. Retention Parameters

1. "*Retention volume* [uncorrected] V_R is the volume of gas required to elute the compound under study and is given by

$$V_R = t_R F_c \tag{3}$$

where t_R is the retention time, the time for the emergence of the peak maximum after injection of the sample, and F_c is the volumetric flow rate of the carrier gas measured at the outlet pressure and the temperature of the column. V_R, t_R correspond to OB in Fig. 3A which, in the remaining definitions, is assumed to have the carrier gas volume as the horizontal axis.

2. "*Gas holdup* V_M is the uncorrected retention volume of a non-absorbed sample and is the volume of carrier gas required to transport such a sample from the point of injection to the point of detection at column outlet pressure. It includes contributions due to the interstitial volume of the column, and the effective volumes of the sample injector and the detector. It can readily be determined for any column by elution of some material for which the partition coefficient is very small compared with its value for other solutes. Gases such as nitrogen, air, or the noble gases are normally employed for this purpose. The peak often produced by the presence of small amounts of air during the sample injection gives this information, and is referred to as the 'air peak.'

"For a capillary column the interstitial volume may be calculated from the dimensions. The interstitial volume divided by j [see equation 6] is the contribution to V_M due to the column and the contribution due to the apparatus may therefore be determined.

3. "*Adjusted retention volume V'_R is given by*

$$V'_R = V_R - V_M = AB \quad \text{(see Fig. 3A)} \tag{4}$$

4. "*Corrected retention volume $V°_R$ is given by*

$$V°_R = jV_R = j(OB) \tag{5}$$

This quantity is of limited use because it is influenced by the volumes of the sample injector and detector as well as by the interstitial volume of the column. The symbol j in equation 5 is the *pressure gradient correction factor* for a homogeneously filled column of constant diameter and is given by

$$j = \frac{3}{2} \frac{(p_i/p_o)^2 - 1}{(p_i/p_o)^3 - 1} \tag{6}$$

where p_i, p_o are the pressures of the carrier gas at the inlet and the outlet of the column, respectively. Use of the factor j allows for the fact that in gas chromatography the mobile phase is compressible. If in fact the flow rate is measured at the inlet of the column the corrected retention volume may be obtained by using a suitably modified expression for j.

5. "*Net retention volume V_N is given by*

$$V_N = jV'_R = j(AB) \tag{7}$$

6. "*Specific retention volume V_g is the net retention volume at 0°C per gram of liquid phase and is given by*

$$V_N/w_L = V_g T/273 \tag{8}$$

where T is the temperature of the column. V_N/w_L is the net retention volume per gram at the column temperature."

7. *Relative Retentions.* "Retention volumes may be expressed relative to the retention volume of a standard component on the same column at the same temperature. *Relative retention r is given by*

$$r_{1,2} = \frac{V_{g1}}{V_{g2}} = \frac{V_{N1}}{V_{N2}} = \frac{V'_{R1}}{V'_{R2}} = \frac{V_{R1}}{V_{R2}} \tag{9}$$

where the subscripts refer to components 1 and 2. Component 2 is the standard. Relative retentions measured from the point of injection can only be considered independent of column dimensions if $V_M \ll V_{R1}$, V_{R2}. When, as is usual and desirable, relative retentions are determined from one chromatogram in which experimental conditions are constant and identical for both components, the determination is simplified to the measurement of the appropriate distances on the recorder chart [i.e., the distances corresponding to the adjusted retention volume]."

8. *Partition coefficient, K* (equation 1), "is assumed to be independent of concentration at the concentrations prevailing in gas chromatography.

"According to elementary theory, which has been adequately verified by experiment, the partition coefficient is related to the retention volume by

$$K = \frac{V_N}{V_L} = \frac{V_N \rho_L}{w_L} = \frac{V_g T \rho_L}{273} \tag{10}$$

where V_N is the net retention volume, V_L is the volume occupied by the liquid phase in the column, ρ_L is the density of the liquid at column temperature, w_L is the weight of the liquid in the column, V_g is the net retention volume at 0°C per gram of liquid phase, and T is the temperature of the column.

"The specific retention volume, the relative retention, and the partition coefficient are independent of column parameters, but they do depend upon the samples involved, the partitioning system, and the temperature.

9. "*Meaning of Qualifying Signs.* In definitions of retention parameters the superscript ° indicates that the pressure correction factor has been applied, and the prime ', that measurements are made from the air peak. However the symbol for net retention volume in accordance with this scheme is unduly cumbersome, and V_N has been substituted for it."

b. *Recommendations*

1. *Retention Data.* "Measurements of retention data should be reported in such a manner that they can be converted for use in experiments with other apparatus and under different conditions. This can be done on an absolute basis by measurement of the partition coefficient or specific retention volume; or on a relative basis by measurement of relative retentions, relative to a standard solute. For determining the relative retentions of a series of substances a standard should be chosen such that its retention volume falls near the middle of the series. Standards with very small retention volumes should not be used."

2. *Standards for Relative Retention Measurement.* "The following substances are suggested as suitable standards for medium temperature work (i.e., up to 150°C): n-butane, 2,2,4-trimethylpentane (isoöctane), benzene, p-xylene, naphthalene, methyl ethyl ketone, cyclohexanone, and cyclohexanol. All these substances can be obtained easily in adequate purity and they cover a wide range of retention volumes, but if none of them is suitable for a particular problem some other easily available laboratory chemical should be used."

3. *Temperature Effects.* See Section F.III.a.

4. *Experimental Details.* See Section A.V.

c. *Discussion* (reprinted from IUPAC report, 1959)

"The partition coefficient for a given solute–solvent system is [for conditions prevailing in gas–liquid chromatography] a physical constant dependent only on the temperature, and gas–liquid chromatography provides a convenient method for its determination. The specific retention volume V_g has the same character of a general constant, and can easily be converted to K by relation 10. In the determination of K it is necessary to determine the density of the solvent at the column temperature (to about 1%) while this is not necessary for the determination of V_g. The other column variables and operating conditions, however, have to be accurately known since they enter into the computation of K and V_g, as can be seen from the relations given above.

"In the determination of relative retentions, it is not necessary to know any column variables (e.g., F_c, w, p_i, p_o) except the temperature; all that is necessary is that they remain constant. Furthermore, relative retentions do not vary with temperature as much as do absolute measurements and they are therefore to be preferred unless the variables listed can be determined with accuracy. Relative retentions, used with standard substances as suggested above, are immediately useful for the identification of compounds if tables of retentions including the compounds in question are available.

"It is important to specify the ratio of liquid phase to solid support precisely. The activity of the latter can be such as to influence appreciably the chromatographic separations achieved; this effect will be more pronounced the lower the amount of liquid phase covering the solid."

1. *Errors.* "The following factors can affect the retention parameters and will cause errors unless they are corrected for: sample size, method of injection, and detector dead volume. These factors affect not only the retention parameters but also the peak shape, and therefore can give misleading results also in the calculation of efficiency and resolution. These calculations then should not be relied on unless the distorting factors are small, and the peaks obtained nearly Gaussian."

2. *Experimental Considerations.* "The flow rate F_c is required at the temperature and outlet pressure of the column whereas measurements of flow are usually made at room temperature. Suitable corrections must therefore be made: if a capillary flowmeter is used, the pressure drop across the meter must be considered; with wet flowmeters allowance must be made for the vapor pressure of water. If F is the flow rate of the saturated gas determined from the flowmeter at pressure p, and p_w is the vapor pressure of water at the temperature of the flowmeter, the partial pressure of the carrier gas p_M is given by

$$p_M = p - p_w$$

and   (11)

$$F_c = F(p - p_w)/p$$

"The carrier gas should enter the column at column temperature; the sample should be made to vaporize very rapidly on injection in order to avoid artifacts of efficiency or resolution.

"In absolute measurements, account must be taken of the temperature of operation in assessing the life of the column before a significant change in w_L occurs. The rate of variation of the partition coefficient with temperature is similar in magnitude to that of vapor pressure, and the accuracy of temperature control, both with time and along the column, needs to be specified."

IV. Factors Influencing Resolution of Solutes

Two independent factors determine whether any given pair of compounds can be separated from one another by gas chromatography. These are the separation factor (equivalent to relative retention) and the column efficiency. Both must be taken into account in selecting stationary phases, column length, temperature, and other parameters. The separation factor is a measure of the relative *positions* of two peaks on a chromatogram, and column efficiency is a measure of the *narrowness* of the peaks. Once the separation factor for any pair of compounds is known, it is possible to calculate the number of theoretical plates required to achieve any specified degree of resolution.

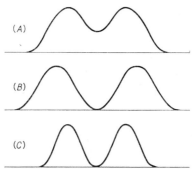

Fig. 4. Factors influencing peak resolution; (A) unresolved peaks; (B) resolution by change in separation factor; (C) resolution by increase in column efficiency.

The interplay between these two factors is illustrated in Fig. 4. Chromatogram A shows two peaks that are not resolved satisfactorily. Better separation can be achieved by shifting the relative positions of the two peaks (chromatogram B) while keeping peak width constant, or alternatively by maintaining the peaks at the same positions and making them narrower (chromatogram C). The first procedure requires a change in separation factor; the second, a change in column efficiency.

a. Separation Factor

The separation factor, α, is the ratio of the retention volumes of the two compounds to be separated, or

$$\alpha = \frac{V_{g1}}{V_{g2}} \tag{12}$$

where the subscripts refer to components 1 and 2.

The separation factor is a measure of the distance between the apices of the two peaks to be separated. If this value is unity, the compounds cannot be resolved no matter how efficient the column. However, the separation factor may be quite large and the peaks still not be resolved because they are too broad, and therefore overlap. This situation can be corrected by improving the column efficiency, or increasing the column length, or both, so that narrower peaks are obtained in relation to their distance from the air peak.

Separation factors can be adjusted by changing the stationary phase or the column temperature. They depend only on the ratio of the partition coefficients of the two solutes between solvent and carrier. If this value cannot be improved by adjusting the temperature, it is necessary to change the stationary liquid. Fortunately, liquids are available having a great deal of selectivity based on polarity (see Section C.II). Consequently, it is usually possible to find a liquid that will provide the required degree of separation even though the boiling points of the solutes are practically identical, since their partial vapor pressures when dissolved in the solvent may differ.

When the peak widths as well as the retention volumes of the two compounds are taken into consideration, it is possible to calculate the resolution of the components. This is given by equation 13, where y_1 is the width of the

$$\text{Resolution} = \frac{2 \ (\text{Difference between retention volumes})}{\text{Sum of peak widths}}$$

$$= 2\Delta y/(y_1 + y_2) \tag{13}$$

peak arising from component 1, and y_2 is the width of the peak arising from component 2 (Fig. 3B).

b. Column Efficiency

Column efficiency is measured by the number of theoretical plates. In a separation process that can be carried out in discrete steps, such as countercurrent extraction, perfect equilibration of the solute between two phases is established at each step, and the phases then are separated. Each step is termed a theoretical plate. However, in a chromatographic column the solute is in constant motion down the column, and perfect equilibrium cannot be established at any one point. Consequently, the best that can be done is to calculate the height of column that will give a separation equivalent to one theoretical plate. This quantity is termed the height equivalent to a theoretical plate (usually abbreviated as *HETP*). The number of theoretical plates in a gas chromatographic column depends on a number of factors, including the rates of diffusion of the solute in the two phases, the uniformity of column packing, the thickness of the layers of stationary liquid, and the nature and flow rate of the mobile phase. The number of theoretical plates can be increased within limits, by increasing the column length, and it is reduced slightly by an increase in diameter.

The number of theoretical plates can be calculated from fundamental column parameters by the van Deemter equation, but from the standpoint of establishing practical operating conditions for any given column it is necessary to calculate it from values determined experimentally. Several equations have been developed for doing this, but they all do not give the same results. However, each is a measure of peak sharpness in relation to retention volume, and they all give about the same relative values. The IUPAC committee on gas chromatographic terminology (Ambrose *et al.*, 1960) recommends equation 14. The theoretical plate number varies with

$$n = 16 \left(\frac{\text{Retention volume}}{\text{Peak width}} \right)^2 \tag{14}$$

the nature of the solute giving rise to the peak used for measurement, as well as with column characteristics. Therefore the compound used to make the calculation should be specified in reports of results, since differences in the number of theoretical plates can be obtained on the same column during the same run if values are calculated from two different peaks. The units for retention and peak width in the above equation must be consistent so that their ratio, n, is dimensionless. If the corrected retention volume is used, the observed peak width also must be corrected for pressure drop across the column.

When the number of theoretical plates is known, the height equivalent to a theoretical plate can be calculated from equation 15, where L is the

$$HETP = L/n \tag{15}$$

effective length of the chromatographic column.

An expression for calculating the performance of capillary columns, as proposed by Golay (1958), is given by equation 16, where P.I. is the perform-

$$\text{P.I.} = \frac{(\Delta t)^4 t_a \, \Delta p}{t_R^3 (t_R - 15 t_a/16)} \tag{16}$$

ance index of the column, Δt is the peak width at half height, t_R is the retention time of a sample component, t_a is the retention time of air, and Δp is the pressure drop across the column.

According to Golay, P.I. is a measure of "the intrinsic goodness of capillary columns operated at optimum flow rate," the theoretical lower limit of this value being 0.1 poise. The smallest value reported for a capillary column is 2.3 poise, and the smallest value for a packed column 5.55 poise. This latter value was calculated from performance data obtained on a 50-foot column packed with Apiezon on firebrick (5:95) and having an efficiency of 30,000 theoretical plates calculated from the o-xylene peak (Scott, 1958).

c. Calculation of Column Efficiency Required for Peak Resolution

The number of theoretical plates required to obtain a specified resolution is given by equation 17, where r is the relative retention (or separation

$$n = \left[2(\text{Resolution}) \frac{r+1}{r-1} \right]^2 \tag{17}$$

factor) of the two components, and the resolution is calculated from equation 13.

An expression relating the impurity of chromatographic peaks to the retention volumes of two adjacent peaks and to column efficiency has been developed by Glueckauf (1955). This expression takes the form of equation 18, where f is the fraction of impurity, m_1 and m_2 are the milliequivalents

$$f = \frac{2m_1 m_2}{m_1{}^2 + m_2{}^2} \left\{ 0.5 - A_\epsilon \left[\frac{V_n(\sqrt{V_{g2}} - \sqrt{V_{g1}})}{\sqrt[4]{V_{g1} V_{g2}}} \right] \right\} \tag{18}$$

of components 1 and 2 loaded onto the column, V_{g1} and V_{g2} are the specific retention volumes of components 1 and 2, n is the column efficiency in theoretical plates, and A_ϵ is the area of the normal error curve, which is defined by equation 19. Values for A_ϵ as a function of t are tabulated in the *Handbook of Chemistry and Physics*.

$$A_\epsilon(t) = (2\pi)^{-1/2} \int_0^t e^{-\frac{t^2}{2}} dt \tag{19}$$

By use of equation 19, a family of curves can be constructed showing the number of theoretical plates required to separate pairs of solutes having known separation factors (V_{g2}/V_{g1}), and mass ratios (m_1/m_2) with any desired product purity. Figure 5 shows that excellent resolution of components can be obtained if separation factors are above 1.2. On the other hand, impractically long columns must be used to separate compounds with values for α approaching unity.

To use this graph, a value for f must be calculated from equation 20.

$$f = f_0 \frac{m_1^2 + m_2^2}{2m_1m_2} \tag{20}$$

Thus if the two solutes are present in a 20:80 ratio, and it is necessary to separate them so that the fractional impurity in each band is 0.05%, the value for f is

$$f = 0.0005 \frac{(0.2)^2 + (0.8)^2}{2(0.2)(0.8)} = 1 \times 10^{-3}$$

The point corresponding to 1×10^{-3} is located on the abscissa of Fig. 5, and an imaginary line is extended vertically to intersect with the diagonal

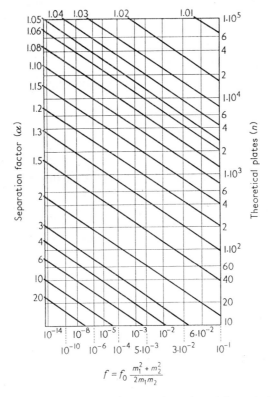

$$f = f_0 \frac{m_1^2 + m_2^2}{2m_1m_2}$$

Fig. 5. Relation between separation factor and number of theoretical plates required to separate two peaks so that the fraction of impurity equals f_0 (Glueckauf, 1955).

corresponding to the separation factor for the pair of solutes to be separated. A line parallel with the abscissa is then extended to the right to intersect the ordinate. The point of intersection gives the number of theoretical plates required for the separation.

For example, if $\alpha = 1.05$, then 15,000 theoretical plates will be required to obtain the separation described above. However if $\alpha = 2.0$, the same result can be obtained with a column having only 70 to 80 theoretical plates.

V. PRESENTATION OF CHROMATOGRAPHIC DATA

The IUPAC committee on terminology for gas chromatography (Ambrose *et al.*, 1960) recommends that the following variables be published with any set of results laying claim to being quantitative in nature: "(1) Nature and particle size range of solid support; (2) Nature, concentration, and amount of liquid phase in the column; (3) Sample size; (4) Column dimensions (length and internal diameter); (5) Column inlet and outlet pressures; (6) Flow rate of carrier gas and method of measurement; (7) Temperature of column and accuracy of temperature control; and (8) Description of detector, e.g., type of sensing element, cell geometry, cell volume, response time."

In arriving at a method for tabulating data for this book, a compromise was sought between the recommendations of the committee, the needs of the practical analyst, and the actual amount of detail contained in published papers on this subject. As the work progressed, it became evident that the end product would fall far short of the minimum required to provide adequate directions for analysis unless steps were taken to supplement the information available in the literature. Accordingly, letters were sent to all the authors whose work is used in this volume, requesting corrections and supplementary information. The response was surprisingly good, and to this we owe any merit the book may have as a practical guide for analysis. Methods that have been checked by the authors of individual papers are marked with an asterisk to acknowledge their contributions and to aid the reader in assessing the completeness and reliability of the information. Methods on which no replies were obtained are included if they are essential and contained adequate, although not necessarily complete, information. Otherwise, they were deleted from the manuscript.

The conventions used throughout this book in tabulating conditions for chromatography are as follows:

Sample Compilation of Operating Parameters

Chromatograph	John Smith Inc., Model U-2 temperature-programmed instrument with gas sampling and backflush valves, and a 6×0.5-cm i.d. pre-column packed with Drierite.
Column dimensions	4×0.5 cm (i.d. or o.d. as given) copper U tube.
Solid support	Celite 545 (30/60 U. S. mesh) washed with aqua regia (Jones, 1960).
Stationary phase	Squalane (20:80).
Temperatures	Injection: 150°C. Detector: 125°C. Column: 30°C. → 125°C in 30 minutes, linear.

Carrier gas	Helium at 90 ml/min. Inlet pressure: 300 mm Hg. above atmospheric. Outlet pressure: atmospheric.
Detector	Brown Co. four-filament hot-wire (Pt) T/C cell operated at 300 ma.
Recorder	Green Instrument Co., 0 to 5 mv; 1 second; 2 cm/min.
Sample size	1 to 5 μl of 2% solution in CCl_4.
Analysis time	About 30 minutes to component of major interest.

a. *Comments on Individual Entries*

1. *Chromatograph.* If a commercial instrument was used, the name and model are included when given, since this may provide information on temperature control, detector characteristics, etc., if these factors are not discussed explicitly in the publication. Modifications of the instrument such as the use of drying columns and backflush valves are mentioned here.

2. *Column Dimensions.* Dimensions are given in units stated in the publication cited, or as corrected by the author. Originally, it was planned to convert all values to metric units, but this was abandoned at least temporarily in view of the confusion it might cause in fitting columns to commercial instruments of British or United States origin. Most authors give the outside diameter of the column. Inside diameter is much more important from a scientific point of view, but it must be conceded that outside diameter is also important if the column is to fit the chromatograph. Column shape and material of construction are included, since the former may influence efficiency, and the latter, if incorrectly chosen, can lead to breakdown of some labile compounds.

3. *Solid Support.* The solid support and its mesh size are given. There is some confusion regarding mesh size, since a number of different systems are used (see Appendix 3). Consequently, it is desirable to state the type of screen used for grading, as well as the size. If the solid support is treated chemically, details are given if these are brief. Otherwise, a reference is given to the original publication or to a detailed method included elsewhere in the book.

4. *Stationary Phase.* The chemical name of the liquid is given, followed by the parts of liquid to parts of solid on a weight basis in parentheses (liquid:solid). If the liquid is a commercial product of indefinite composition, the name of the manufacturer is included. Unfortunately, it was not feasible to include the total weight of the liquid used in a chromatographic column, since this information is rarely provided. If the stationary phase is a solid adsorbent, entries 3 and 4 are replaced by the entry "Active solid."

5. *Temperatures.* When provided, temperatures of the injection port, detector block, and column are given. If the temperature is adjusted stepwise during the run, this is stated as: Column: 50°C to *n*-decane; 100°C to *n*-octadecane. If the temperature is programmed linearly during the run, this

is stated as: Column: 35° → 150°C, 30 minutes, linear. Accuracy of column temperature control is not given, since this is not stated in most publications.

6. *Carrier Gas.* It is assumed that the flow rate of the carrier gas is measured at the outlet at atmospheric temperature and pressure unless otherwise stated. Pressures are given in millimeters of mercury or pounds per square inch above atmospheric. There is considerable confusion regarding this, and it is always best to state explicitly whether the pressure referred to is relative or absolute. It would be helpful if authors would use the term *psig* for gauge pressure, and *psia* for absolute pressure. The abbreviation *psi* is ambiguous.

7. *Detector.* Complete details of detector construction and geometry are not given, since most of them are available commercially, and usually all that is required is enough information to make the proper selection.

8. *Recorder.* The name of the manufacturer, the millivolt range, the response time, and the chart speed are given. These parameters are fairly standard now, so this information is of questionable value. However, information on supplementary equipment such as special amplifiers is included here.

9. *Sample Size.* This is included only as a practical guide to the analyst. It is recognized that sample size will vary with the composition of the material, the sensitivity of the detector, the attenuation setting of the instrument, and other factors. These variables will have to be taken into account when adapting an established method to a new instrument.

10. *Analysis Time.* This is the time required for chromatography, including backflushing the column, if necessary. It does not include the time required for isolation of the sample or preparation of derivatives. If the method is a tentative one, and complete information is unavailable, the time required to elute the component of major interest is given. This information is not intended as a replacement for accurately measured and adequately corrected retention values. It is included only to give the practical analyst information on how long it will take to obtain results by using the operating parameters stated.

b. Conventions for Multiple-Column Arrangements

1. *Single Columns with Serial Packings.* Sometimes several packings are included in series in the same column. When this is done, the components are separated by // marks, the component to the left being nearest the injection port. The length of column packed with each component and the ratio of liquid to solid support used in preparing it are given. *Example:* 100 cm squalane on firebrick (20:50) // 150 cm type 5-A molecular sieve.

2. *Separate Columns in Series.* When separate columns are used in series they are labeled A and B, and all other conditions pertaining to them are

labeled A and B, including column dimensions, solid supports, temperature, and detectors. If any operating parameter is the same or different for the two columns it will be so stated. For example, temperatures might be listed as follows: Injection: (A and B) 175°C. Detector: (A) 150°C; (B) 100°C. Columns: (A) 140°C, (B) 80°C.

3. *Columns in Parallel.* Columns in parallel and all operating parameters pertaining to them are designated by roman numerals I and II. Otherwise the same conventions are used that are employed for columns in series. No distinction is made between samples actually run at the same time on different columns, and samples that are run successively on different columns, as long as the same material is applied to each. In other words, the use of columns alternately or in parallel generally produces the same results, the only difference being one of instrumentation.

B. Chromatograph Design and Operation

I. INTRODUCTION

Gas chromatographs may be laboratory-built or purchased complete, including columns which are packed, conditioned, and ready for use. Inclusion of complete designs is beyond the scope of this book, since multitudinous variations are possible. However, some basic flow diagrams and operational details are given which may assist in the building of a homemade instrument or in the selection of a commercial one. The basic units are simple and inexpensive, yet prices may range up to $10,000 if a variety of accessories is desired, including alternative detecting systems, provision for both capillary and packed columns, and mechanical integrators. Nevertheless, a homemade instrument can be made for under $100, exclusive of the recorder (Casey, 1959), and several commercial instruments are available priced around $1000. A novel and potentially useful approach of one manufacturer is to supply packaged units which can be purchased individually and assembled to produce an instrument of any degree of complexity (Research Specialties Co.).

In most commercial chromatographs, the columns are contained within insulated metal cabinets, constant temperature being maintained by an electronically controlled air thermostat. Gas flow between component parts takes place through stainless-steel or aluminum tubing equipped with gas-tight fittings, designed so that connections can be made and broken easily. However, many laboratory-built chromatographs are made of glass, and the column is kept at constant temperature by vapors from refluxing solvents. A glass apparatus fitted with interchangeable ground joints is available from Gas Chromatography Ltd.

A list of European and American manufacturers supplying gas chromatographs and accessory equipment for their construction is contained in Appendix 1.

Gas chromatographs are inexpensive instruments compared to mass or infrared spectrometers and will yield information on the composition of complex mixtures out of all proportion to their cost. At the same time they are simple enough in construction to be built or modified in any laboratory serviced by a moderately well equipped machine shop. The gas chromatograph is one of the few remaining "black boxes" that the average biochemist is competent to open.

II. Basic Chromatograph

The design shown here for illustrative purposes is representative of any one of a number of commercial instruments (Fig. 6) employing a thermal

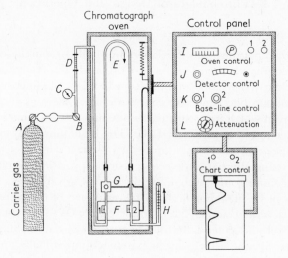

Fig. 6. Basic design of a gas chromatograph employing a thermal conductivity cell.

conductivity cell (T/C) as a detector. Some differences occur in the placement of flowmeters, the location of the reference side of the thermal conductivity cell, and the means by which temperatures of the various component parts are controlled. Upon this structure may be superimposed circuits for reversing the flow of carrier gas, for use of multiple-column arrangements, and for temperature programming. Nevertheless, all instruments, whether laboratory-built or commercial, contain the same essential components, arranged in approximately the same manner.

a. Component Parts

The standard chromatograph illustrated here consists of four major units: a source of carrier gas and valves for regulating the flow rate, a column-detector system, a control panel, and a recorder. The gas cylinder (A) equipped with a two-stage diaphragm reducing valve, supplies the mobile phase. It is connected to the chromatograph through a constant pressure regulator (B), which is standard equipment on most instruments. The back pressure of the column is read on gauge (C), and the flow rate of the gas on meter (D). The chromatographic column (E) and the detector (F) are housed in an oven that can be adjusted to any desired temperature which will remain constant to within 0.05°C. The sample injection port (G) is mounted on the outside of the instrument and is covered with a self-sealing diaphragm through which samples can be injected with a hypodermic needle. The line leading from the carrier gas cylinder to the column passes through a long section of the thermostat so that the mobile phase has time to warm up to operating temperature. Before the gas enters the injection port and chromatographic column, it passes through the reference side of the thermal detector (F_1) (see Section D.II for details). The chromatographic column (E) must be easy to replace. Therefore it is attached to the instrument by knurled thumbscrews sealed with O rings, Swagelok Quick-Connect fittings, or other devices. After the gas leaves the column, it passes through the sensing side of the detector (F_2) and out of the instrument. The flow rate at atmospheric temperature and pressure is read on a soap film meter (H). In this particular design, the detector measures the difference in response given by the carrier gas alone (reference side) and the carrier gas plus the sample (sensing side), since it is made to pass through the reference side of the T/C cell before the sample is injected.

The control panel (Fig. 6) contains read-out meters and variable resistances for regulating operating parameters. Line I contains a temperature read-out meter connected to a thermocouple located in the column oven, a knob regulating a variable voltage transformer used to control heater input, and coarse and fine controls to adjust the temperature of the oven. Line J contains a control to regulate the voltage supplied to the detector bridge, and a voltmeter. Line K contains fine and coarse controls to adjust the recorder pen to a zero base line on the recorder paper. Line L contains an attenuation switch which regulates the sensitivity of the instrument. It can be adjusted to preset positions so that the chromatograph can be operated at full sensitivity, ½ sensitivity, ¼, ⅛, etc. Usually, sensitivity is reduced in geometric steps, although this is not always the case. The last component is a standard 0- to 1-mv or a 0- to 10-mv recorder. This strip chart recorder contains switches to activate the pen and chart drive mechanism.

b. Hypothetical Operating Conditions

The hypothetical conditions tabulated below provide an example of the parameters that must be adjusted to make a simple analysis. It is assumed that previous experience has shown that all the peaks can be recorded on the chart at an attenuation setting of ¼. Actually, attenuation settings usually must be changed a number of times during a single recording to measure both major and minor peaks satisfactorily. Therefore no attempt has been made to provide attenuation settings along with other conditions of analysis. If fully automatic operation is desired, it is possible to install an attenuation changer. This device will lower the sensitivity of the instrument when the recorder pen passes a preset point on the ordinate of the chart—for example, 80% of total displacement.

In this example, helium is the mobile phase; consequently all the chromatographic peaks will be recorded in a "positive" direction, since helium has a higher thermal conductivity than all other gases or vapors except hydrogen. However, with nitrogen, both positive and negative pen deflections may be obtained, since some organic vapors are more, and others less, conductive than nitrogen. These "negative" peaks can be recorded by turning a switch which reverses the polarity of the instrument. This merely changes the direction of travel of the recorder pen with respect to a given stimulus. Nitrogen and similar gases are not used often with T/C cells, since sensitivity is poor relative to hydrogen and helium. However, if for some reason they must be used, it is worth while to install an automatic polarity reverser on the instrument, so that all peaks appear to be "positive," regardless of the direction of the signal.

1. Conditions for Chromatography

Chromatograph	John Smith & Co., Model U-2.
Column dimensions	4-meter × 0.5-cm i.d. stainless-steel U tube.
Solid support	C-22 firebrick (30/60 U. S. mesh).
Stationary phase	Squalane (20:80).
Temperature	110°C. throughout.
Carrier gas	Helium at 100 ml/min. Inlet pressure: 15 psig. Outlet pressure: atmospheric.
Detector	Matched 8000-ohm thermistors operated at 8 volts.
Recorder	Jones & Co., 0 to 5 mv; 1 second; 2 cm/sec.
Sample size	1 to 5 μl.
Analysis time	About 45 minutes.

c. Operation under Above Conditions

A column having the above specifications is prepared according to methods described in Section C and installed in the chromatograph. The valve of the gas cylinder, A, is opened, and the reducing valve is set to deliver 30 to 35 psig of helium. The pressure-regulating valve of the instrument is then opened cautiously, and the column back pressure is brought up to 15 psig. The flow rate of carrier gas as measured on the pre-column meter should be noted at this point to determine if it is abnormally high, indicating a leak. Normally it will be somewhat higher than at operating temperature because of the lower viscosity of cold gas. If, after this factor is accounted for, the flow rate still seems too high, the flow rate at the exit should be checked with a soap film meter and the pre-column meter reading corrected to atmospheric temperature and pressure according to the calibration chart provided for the purpose. If the inlet flow rate is higher than the outlet reading by a significant amount, the connections should be tested for leaks with an aqueous detergent solution.

When the apparatus is leaktight, the oven should be closed, the air circulation system turned on, and the powerstat (line I) set so that the oven will operate on a 50% on–off cycle at 110°C. This value is obtained from a chart supplied by the manufacturer. The coarse temperature control is set to give the approximate temperature, and the exact operating temperature of 110°C is stabilized with the fine adjustment.

While the oven is warming up, the switch to the detector should be turned on and the power supply adjusted to 8 volts as indicated on the meter in line J. Attenuation should be set at a low value (say, $\frac{1}{32}$ to $\frac{1}{128}$), and the recorder pen and chart drives turned on. The pen should then be brought to 50% displacement on the recorder chart by adjusting the controls in line K, so that the establishment of a steady base line can be observed.

When the oven temperature is stabilized at 110°C, the attenuation should be reduced stepwise, and the controls in line K adjusted to bring the pen near the base line. The sample should not be injected until a steady base line is obtained with the attenuation set at $\frac{1}{4}$ (in this particular example).

When the base line is steady, the flow rate of carrier gas at the exit should be measured with a soap film meter and, if necessary, the inlet pressure adjusted to give a rate of 100 ml/min. If the change in pressure is large, it may be necessary to wait a while for the base line to become re-established. When this occurs, all the operating parameters should be rechecked, and a 1- to 5-μl sample injected through the self-sealing diaphragm of the liquid injection port with a microsyringe equipped with a hypodermic needle.

After the chromatogram has been recorded, the flow rate should be rechecked with the soap film meter attached to the exit line of the chromatograph.

To shut down the chromatograph, gas flow should be cut off at A and B, and all the switches actuating the oven thermostat, detector, and recorder should be turned off.

III. Multiple Columns and Backflushing Systems

Chromatographic columns containing different stationary phases some-times are connected in series. Often this results in better peak resolution in the analysis of complex mixtures, since some components can be resolved best on polar packings, whereas others require nonpolar packings. Occasionally, series operation is necessary to avoid subtraction of peaks by irreversibly binding some of the components to one of the column packings.

Columns are used alternately or in parallel for similar reasons. Frequently members of homologous series of chemical compounds are identified by plotting logarithms of their retention volumes on polar and nonpolar packings against one another. Therefore it is convenient to be able to run a sample on two different stationary phases without cooling the oven between times to change columns. Results obtained on alternate and parallel columns are identical, and the terms are often used interchangeably in this text. The only differences are in instrumentation and analysis time.

Supplementary columns can be used also to dispose of high-boiling components that are of no interest analytically. These can be trapped on a pre-column and vented to the atmosphere while low-boiling components are being partitioned in the main column. This saves analysis time, since it becomes unnecessary to run the main column until the unwanted solutes are eluted before the next sample is injected. The same objective can be achieved by backflushing a single column. This consists in running the column in a forward direction until the components of interest are eluted, and then reversing the gas flow to dispose of slow-moving components. Obviously if such materials have moved only one-tenth the length of the column during the main part of the analysis, it will take much less time to get rid of them by backflushing than by continuing to run the column in a forward direction.

a. Columns in Series

1. *Simple Series Operation.* In this method, the columns are connected to one another directly, and the effluent is passed through a single detector (Fig. 7*A*). The same purpose can be achieved with multiply-packed columns. All chromatographs can be adapted to this type of operation. For example, two packings have been used in series to obtain better separations for the chromatography of pyridine derivatives (Chapter 4, method D.I.a.1), and for separation of low-molecular-weight hydrocarbons mixed with permanent gases (Chapter 2, method E.V.c.1).

2. *Series Operation with Bypass Line.* In this mode of operation two columns are connected in series so that the second column can be bypassed, when desired, by rotating a six-way valve (Fig. 7*B*). When thermal detectors are used, the alternate line must contain a flow restrictor so that the bypass has the same resistance to gas flow as column 2. Otherwise the change in flow

rate will shift the base line. This setup is used when components separated on column 1 are adsorbed irreversibly or are retarded for long periods of time on column 2, so that the latter can be bypassed at the time they emerge from column 1. Other components can be passed through both columns to achieve more complete separation.

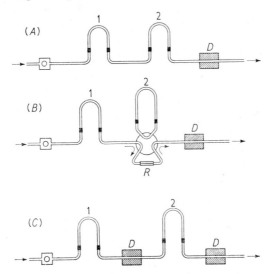

FIG. 7. Columns arranged in series: (A) columns 1 and 2 connected directly; (B) with bypass valve at column 2; (C) with detector; (D) at outlet of each column.

3. *Series Operation with Detector at Exit of Each Column.* This arrangement is shown in Fig. 7C. Separate detectors measure the components emerging from each column. This mode of operation is convenient when some sample components are not resolved in column 1, and others are adsorbed irreversibly on column 2. For example, column 1 can be packed with silica gel to separate carbon dioxide from air. However, oxygen and nitrogen are not separated, and therefore this must be accomplished on a second column packed with molecular sieve. The simple arrangement shown in Fig. 7A cannot be used, since the carbon dioxide will never emerge from column 2. Instead, a detector is interposed between the two columns to measure the carbon dioxide before it enters column 2.

b. Alternate and Parallel Columns

1. *Alternate Operation with Complete Shutdown of One Column.* This mode of operation is shown in Fig. 8A. With the valve in the position shown, the carrier gas flows from the injection block through column 2 and out of the detector. During this time, the gas in column 1 is stationary. By turning the six-way valve, the carrier gas can be directed through column 1. This makes

it possible to run an analysis on either column without opening the oven to change columns.

2. *Alternate Operation with Continuous Gas Flow in Both Columns.* In this method (Fig. 8B) two injection ports and two columns are used, the columns

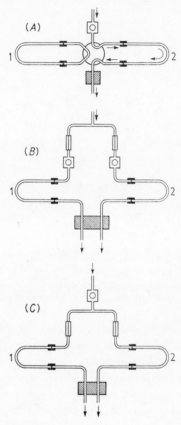

FIG. 8. Alternate and parallel arrangements of chromatographic columns: (A) column 2 in use with carrier gas motionless in column 1; (B) alternate use with continuous gas flow in both columns; (C) columns arranged in parallel.

being positioned so that the carrier gas stream is split and a portion of it passes through each leg of the system. Since the resistances of columns are variable, flow restrictors must be placed upstream from the injection ports to adjust rates. When a sample is injected into one of the ports, it is chromatographed on the corresponding column. Meanwhile carrier gas continues to sweep through the standby column. The two sides of the detector are used alternately for reference and sensing. If the flow rates in each leg of the system are equal, the net result is to cancel out background caused by bleeding of the packing. Of course all the components must be eluted from column 1 before a second sample is injected into column 2, unless advance knowledge is available on the positions of all the peaks on the chromatogram.

The same objective can be achieved by use of a chromatograph with a single injection port and a column-switching valve.

3. *Parallel Operation.* Two columns can be operated in parallel by means of a chromatograph equipped with a single injection port and a T tube placed downstream from it to divide the flow of carrier gas. The amount of mobile phase passing through each column is governed by flow restrictors, by the density of the column packings, by column length, or by some combination of these variables. After traveling through the column, the two gas streams emerge through opposite sides of a thermal detector, which are used alternately as reference and sensing cells. In arriving at operating conditions for such a system it is necessary to adjust retention volumes by changing the column length so that sample components do not pass through the two sides of the detector simultaneously. Therefore alternate-column methods are often preferable for multicomponent samples of unpredictable composition, even though analysis time is longer.

c. Multiple-Stage Chromatographs

1. *Two-Stage System* (Davis and Schreiber, 1957). This system consists of two complete chromatographs, including detectors and recorders, connected in series. It is intended primarily for the analysis of mixtures of permanent gases with light hydrocarbons. A GLC column is installed in unit 1, and a GSC column (molecular sieve) in unit 2. The sample is injected into unit 1. The permanent gases pass through the GLC column rapidly as an unresolved peak while the hydrocarbons are retained and partitioned. The fixed gases are retained on the GSC column in the second unit and separated. As soon as they enter the GSC column, the two units are disconnected to avoid contaminating the molecular sieve with hydrocarbons.

*2. *Triple-Stage System* (Brenner *et al.*, 1958). A chromatograph with three separate stages is available commercially (Perkin-Elmer Corp.) which may be operated in series or independently, at the option of the analyst. In analyzing complex mixtures containing components having wide boiling-point ranges, each stage may contain a different column, each operated at a temperature best suited for the components of one fraction of the sample. A schematic diagram of the apparatus is shown in Fig. 9. Mobile phase from a single source is passed through each of the units in sequence including the injection ports, columns, and detectors. Carrier gas for the reference sides of the detectors (thermal) is supplied by a parallel flow system. Coupling valves are provided to connect or disconnect adjacent stages. A single turn of the valve will direct effluent from the preceding unit through a restriction valve and flowmeter to the atmosphere instead of allowing it to pass on to

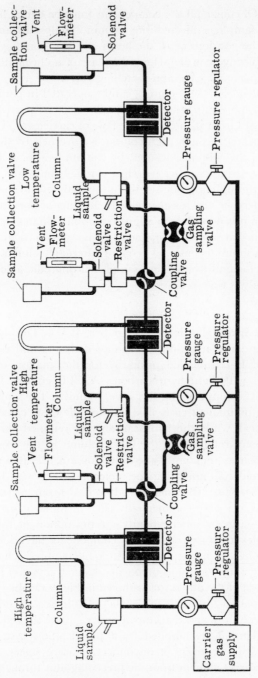

Fig. 9. Triple-stage gas chromatograph (Brenner *et al.*, 1958).

the next unit. This also rechannels the gas coming from the pressure-regulating system of the succeeding unit to the column itself instead of passing it to the vent line. Prior to analysis, the pressures and restrictors are matched so that each unit has the same input pressure and the same flow impedance in both coupled and uncoupled modes of operation. Once all flows have been matched, it is not necessary to make any further adjustments in switching from coupled to uncoupled operation.

The first two stages can be operated at temperatures up to 225°C. The third stage is operated at room temperature or lower by immersing the column in a coolant contained in a Dewar flask. This equipment is designed primarily for separating mixtures having wide boiling-point ranges. The same objectives usually can be achieved on a single column or columns in series by programming the temperature (see Section F.IV.e). Therefore, the use of multiple-stage instruments is declining rapidly.

d. Venting of High-Boiling Components

1. *Through a Stripper Column.* High-boiling components of no analytical interest can be disposed of by passing the sample through a stripper column and an analytical column connected in series (Fig. 10A). The sample is

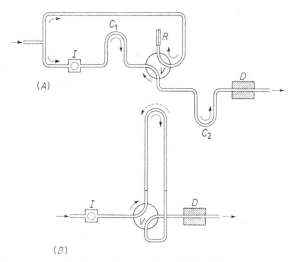

Fig. 10. Chromatograph designs for venting high-boiling components: (A) through splitter column; (B) through backflush valve.

injected at I and first passes through the stripper column (C_1), where the high-boiling components are retained. The low-boiling components of the sample pass on to column C_2, where they are separated. The valve (V) is then rotated a quarter of a turn so that the carrier gas passing through C_1 vents to the atmosphere. At the same time, this connects the alternate carrier gas stream, which is split at the T, to the analytical column, so that development of this column continues while the stripper column is being purged of unwanted components. This saves time that otherwise would be wasted in clearing the analytical column of slow-moving solutes. A flow impedance (R) must be attached to the vent line to balance the gas flow; otherwise almost all the carrier gas would vent to the atmosphere with the valve in the position shown.

2. *Through a Backflush Valve.* Unwanted high-boiling components can be disposed of by reversing the flow of gas in the chromatographic column after the low-boiling components have been eluted and the peaks arising from them recorded. This is accomplished with a reversing or backflush valve (Fig. 10B). With the valve in the position shown, gas moves from the injection block (I) through the column in the direction of the solid arrow. When the valve (V) is turned clockwise, flow through the column is reversed in the direction indicated by the broken arrow. It should be noted that with the valve in *either* position the carrier gas flows from the injection block through the detector (D), only the flow in the column and associated tubing being reversed. This permits measurement of the total amount of slow-moving components with the detector–recorder system, if this is desired.

IV. SUMMARY

The basic chromatograph consists of a carrier gas supply and regulatory valves, a column and a detector housed within a thermostat, electrically operated controls and meters for adjusting experimental conditions, and a strip chart recorder. Superimposed on this may be arrangements for multiple columns in series or in parallel or, for that matter, complete chromatographic units in consort for analyzing a single sample. The basic units are relatively inexpensive and will achieve results far out of proportion to their cost when compared to other methods of instrumental analysis.

C. Preparation and Properties of Chromatographic Columns

I. INTRODUCTION

The chromatographic column is the heart of the instrument, and therefore special care must be taken in its selection or preparation. Unlike detectors, most columns are prepared in the laboratory by the individual investigator; consequently the materials and procedures are described in some detail. However, the analyst who wishes to employ one of the more commonly used columns often can purchase it complete with packing from various instrument manufacturers. Sometimes packing ratios, diameters of tubing, and other information are not furnished. These should be ascertained in advance of accumulating data for publication.

Three types of columns are described here; the GLC column, the GSC column, and the capillary column. The first two can be employed interchangeably in any standard chromatograph. However, capillary columns require an instrument equipped with an ionization detector having small effective volume, and the injection system must be modified so that very small samples can be introduced.

II. The Stationary Liquid

Selection of the stationary liquid is the most important choice to be made in developing a gas chromatographic method, for it determines whether any given pair of solutes can be separated. A few general guides can be given to properties that are most desirable, but beyond this the selection must be governed by the nature of the individual problem. A systematic method for narrowing the choice to reduce random testing has been described by Ober (1958). Extremes in whatever solvent properties are considered desirable are evaluated first, and further testing is guided systematically by the results obtained. However, the initial selection must depend always on the polarities and volatilities of the compounds being separated; therefore specific details are included under individual subject headings.

The liquid selected as the stationary phase must be substantially nonvolatile and thermally stable at the operating temperature of the chromatograph. As a general rule, the partition liquid should boil at 250°C to 300°C higher than operating temperature; however, the maximum allowable vapor pressure in each individual case is governed by the sensitivity of the device used for detection. If the solvent bleeds from the column excessively, detector background will be high, the base line unsteady, column life short, and fractions collected from the effluent gas contaminated with liquid phase or its decomposition products. Therefore it is obvious that solvents such as dimethyl sulfoxide and dimethylsulfolane, which give excellent separations at room temperature, cannot be used for the separation of high-boiling liquids. As the operating temperature is increased, the choice of solvents becomes more and more restricted and finally becomes the limiting factor in setting the upper limit. Thus only irradiated asphaltenes, polyphenyl tars, and eutectic mixtures of inorganic salts can be used at temperatures above 350°C for any length of time. Mixtures of sodium, potassium, and lithium nitrates supported in conventional manner on crushed firebrick are the most heat-stable stationary liquids available currently and have been evaluated for the separation of a number of types of organic compound (Hanneman et al., 1960). Resolution is low compared to organic liquids, but retention volumes are also low, permitting the use of long columns.

Other physical properties that must be considered include melting point and viscosity. The stationary phase should be liquid at column temperature, and low viscosity is desirable. If the liquid phase is highly viscous at operating temperature, the time required for equilibration of the solute between the mobile and stationary phases will be increased, and column efficiency diminished correspondingly. However, viscosity is not so critical a factor in making the selection as vapor pressure.

Once the physical requirements the stationary liquid must meet are known, it is necessary to select one that will give good separation factors for the solutes being analyzed. Usually a value for α of about 1.1 or over will suffice, the degree of peak separation being dependent on the plate efficiency of the column. If compounds having the same polarity and different boiling points are to be separated, a nonpolar liquid phase will prove most satisfactory. The most commonly used liquids belonging to this class include squalane, the Apiezon greases, silicone oil, and esters of high-molecular-weight alcohols and dibasic acids. If compounds must be separated according to polarity—that is, by unsaturation or degree of aromaticity—a polar liquid should be used. Examples are polyethylene glycols, polyesters prepared from short-chain dibasic acids and dibasic alcohols, ethers and esters of carbohydrates, and derivatives of ethylenediamines. Sometimes superpolar liquids such as solutions of silver nitrate in ethylene glycol are used to resolve closely related olefins. Often, good separations can be obtained if the solvent can form secondary valence bonds with one or more of the solutes, charge-transfer complexes being an example. In some instances, better separations can be achieved on two columns in series containing different stationary phases than on either column alone. Comparable results are often attained by mixing the two liquids and using a single column.

Polarity is a relative term that is used all too frequently in an absolute sense. To call one liquid polar and another nonpolar can be true only in extreme cases. There are all types of intermediate gradation just as there are with solutes. Nevertheless, the terms have been used so extensively in the literature that there is little choice here other than to follow the convention. Perhaps standard solutes differing in boiling point and unsaturation could be used to define a relative polarity index for solvents, just as it is possible to use the latter to discriminate between solutes.

If anything, there is an oversupply of stationary liquids, and the list expands constantly. Along with this there is a tendency to use liquids of ill-defined composition including stopcock greases, lubricating oils, commercial detergents, and reaction products of natural and synthetic high polymers. A great deal of this may be necessary to achieve the separations required. However, if this is so, the source of the material and sufficient physicochemical data to characterize it should be included in the publication. To reduce confusion regarding the relative retention volumes of solutes, a number of standard stationary liquids have been suggested for comparing them (May and Baker Standardized Column Materials). These include benzyldiphenyl, dimethylformamide, dinonyl phthalate, silicone oil, squalane, diglycerol, and tritolyl phosphate. Each of these has a different polarity and/or temperature range where it is most useful. In describing separation factors attainable with new liquids, comparisons should be made with one of these standards to give the reader some means of assessing the value of the innovation.

Most stationary liquids are obtainable commercially; consequently extensive coverage of synthesis and purification is not worth while. There are, however, a few isolated cases where it might be desirable to carry out preparations in the laboratory.

a. Synthesis of Polyesters

*1. *Poly(1,4-butanediol Succinate)* (Craig and Murty, 1959; Bishop and Cooper, 1960). Succinic acid (50 gm), 1,4-butanediol (50 gm), and zinc chloride are mixed together in a flask fitted with an air condenser and a tube for bubbling nitrogen through the reaction mixture. The contents of the flask are stirred and heated for 3 hours at 160°C, and then for 2 hours at 190°C. Nitrogen is bubbled through the melt during the reaction to remove water of esterification. Heating is continued for another 2 hours under reduced pressure to remove unreacted butanediol. The polyester is cooled and dissolved in chloroform, and the solution is passed through a column containing Amberlite IR-120 ion-exchange resin to remove catalyst. The product is recovered by evaporation of the solvent.

*2. *Poly(ethyleneglycol Adipate)* (Farquhar et al., 1959). "Ethylene glycol (32.6 grams) and adipic acid (73.1 grams) are mixed in a 250 ml. double inlet round bottom flask. These amounts represent a molar ratio of 1.05/1.00; the 5% excess of glycol forces the reaction to completion, theoretically leaving no free carboxyl groups of adipic acid.

"The mixture is heated in a silicone bath to a temperature of 180° while passing a stream of nitrogen slowly over the surface of the reactants. When the materials have melted, 25 mg. of p-toluenesulfonic acid is added as a catalyst. Water evolved in the reaction is prevented by the nitrogen stream from condensing on the reaction vessel. The polymerization reaction is allowed to proceed for approximately 2 hours. For a third hour at 180°, the nitrogen stream is discontinued while the reaction vessel is subjected to about 15 mm. Hg pressure (water vacuum pump), in order to strip out water and excess glycol." Next, the polymer is dissolved in 10 ml. of chloroform per gram of polymer, and this solution is equilibrated with an equal volume of water. The water phase, which is discarded, removes the catalyst, any unreacted adipic acid or ethylene glycol, and some lower molecular weight polymer. The water purification step is performed 3 times. The chloroform is evaporated and the ethylene glycol adipate polyester stored in a wide-mouthed glass-stoppered jar.

b. Purification Method

*1. *Silicone Grease* (Nelson and Milun, 1960). Dow Corning High Vacuum Silicone Grease (50 gm) is dissolved in ethyl acetate (100 ml) and precipitated from solution by the addition of 95% ethanol (100 ml). The precipitate is filtered and washed with 2 × 50-ml portions of 95% ethanol. After drying under vacuum for 2 hours, the grease is applied to the solid support in the usual way.

III. Solid Support for GLC

The solid used to support the stationary liquid is usually porous in order to absorb large quantities of solvent and still remain dry to the touch and free-flowing. Diatomaceous earths are employed most often, although other materials having lower absorptivity have been used in special applications. The support should not be too soft, since the particles will fragment on grinding, and it should pack uniformly into a column for maximum efficiency.

The particle size of the support is very important, as this property will affect both column efficiency and flow rate of the mobile phase. Finely divided solid supports yield packings with highest plate efficiencies. However, they impede passage of gas through the column, thereby making a higher inlet pressure necessary to maintain the same flow obtainable with coarser packings. This leads to a higher ratio of inlet to outlet pressure, unless flow is impeded by placing a restriction on the end of the column. If the pressure ratio exceeds 1.5 to 2.0, part of the column will not be used efficiently, since the rate along its length will not be uniform owing to the compressibility of the carrier gas (see Section G.III.a for details). Therefore, a compromise must be sought between column efficiency and flow rate in selecting particle size. This is comparatively easy to do, for impedance to flow continues to increase with decreasing particle size, whereas column efficiency tends to level off. Therefore the best size distribution for most applications is around 50/60 U. S. mesh. If it is necessary to obtain higher plate efficiency, a finer support may be used, but this will decrease flow rate or else make a bigger pressure drop across the column necessary. A packing with a narrow particle size range will give better results than one with a wide range even though the average size is the same, because small particles will fill in voids between large ones and thus increase impedance. Fines should be removed for the same reason. This can be done by water elutriation (method C.III.a.1) or by wet-screening the support between two sieves of different mesh sizes.

The most commonly used solid supports are Celite 545, C-22 firebrick, and Sterchamol 22. Chromosorb is a red powder similar to C-22 firebrick, and Chromosorb W a white powder similar to Celite 545. In some publications, firebrick is referred to as Silocel. Standard and acid-washed grades of these are available commercially from many manufacturers of chromatographs and auxiliary equipment. Mesh ranges (U. S.) currently available include 40/60, 60/80, 80/120, 100/120, and others. There has been a marked tendency in recent publications to use narrow size ranges, and in fact this was the most frequent change made by authors in updating conditions for chromatography for publication in this book.

Celite 545 is a white diatomaceous earth. It is somewhat softer than firebrick and does not flow so freely. When crushed, it forms many fine particles which must be removed by wet screening or elutriation. C-22 firebrick and Sterchamol are harder than Celite and have better packing characteristics; however, their residual adsorptive capacities for solutes are somewhat higher, and consequently tailing may be more of a problem when they are used at low liquid/solid ratios. According to Dimbat et al. (1956), columns prepared with these materials are more permeable to gas flow and operate at higher plate efficiencies than when Celite is used. This conclusion was not confirmed by Desty et al. (1958), when fractions having narrow particle size ranges were compared.

Adsorption of solutes on the solid support results in asymmetric peaks due to tailing. This is particularly noticeable in the chromatography of polar compounds, or when the stationary liquid is nonpolar. Tailing is not so much of a problem with polar liquids, as the liquid tends to deactivate the "active" sites on the solid. Tailing can be reduced and sometimes eliminated by chemical treatment of the packing. Hydrochloric or sulfuric acid is used to remove iron, and the product is dried and finally treated with methanolic sodium hydroxide (method C.III.a.1). More elaborate methods are used to deactivate supports for the chromatography of polar materials (methods C.III.a.2, C.III.b.2). Alkali treatment of the support also reduces the tendency of labile compounds to dehydrate or isomerize during chromatography.

A number of papers have been published on the deactivation of supports by treatment with chemicals which form films over the solid particles. These include dimethyldichlorosilane (Horning et al., 1959), hexamethyldisilazane, (Bohemen et al., 1960), and metallic silver (Ormerod and Scott, 1959). Hornstein and Crowe (1961) found that Celite 545 fractions can be deactivated satisfactorily by passing nitrogen saturated with dimethyldichlorosilane through a 100-gm batch of the support for approximately 1 hour. Chromosorb R requires a much longer exposure time to the vapors of this compound for deactivation. Best results in this latter case were obtained by exposing the granules to dimethyldichlorosilane vapors in a closed container for 2 weeks and then washing with methanol. Another procedure for de-activating solid supports when nonpolar stationary phases are used is to include a small amount of a polar material in the liquid. Compounds used for this purpose include sodium caproate (Bayer, 1958) and synthetic deter-gents (Harva *et al.*, 1959).

Highly absorptive materials other than diatomaceous earths have been used as solid supports. Decora and Dinneen (1960) prepared a finely divided inorganic material by exhaustive extraction of Tide, a synthetic detergent. This material is friable and requires careful handling during application of the stationary phase. However, it will hold up to 70 gm of liquid per 100 gm of support and still remain free-flowing. Symmetrical peaks are obtained when it is used in the chromatography of pyridine derivatives (Chapter 4, method D.II.a.1). Crushed unglazed white tile has been used also (Lukes *et al.*, 1960). It has a specific surface of 2.2 m^2/gm and will hold up to 18% tricresyl phosphate. This support has no catalytic effects on terpene hydro-carbons, is hard, and can be used at relatively high flow rates. The fact that it is relatively inert toward terpenes is of considerable importance, since isomerization catalyzed by Celite and firebrick is a major cause of artifacts in the analysis of these substances by GLC (Naves, 1958).

There has been a recent trend toward the chromatography of high-boil-ing compounds at low temperatures through use of small sample sizes and low liquid-to-solid packing ratios. Of course, this requires an inactive sup-port, since the film of liquid coating the solid is very thin and opportunities for adsorption are magnified correspondingly. However, since the amount of stationary phase is small, supports with little or no sorptive capacity can be used. Small glass beads have been employed most extensively (Microbeads Inc., Minnesota Mining and Manufacturing Co.). Metal beads made from stainless steel, tungsten, aluminum, copper, nickel, and nichrome are avail-able (Linde Co.). It is worth pointing out that the same amount of stationary phase per foot of column will give different packing ratios depending on the density of the support. Thus 13 mg of liquid per column foot will require packing ratios of 0.05% on steel balls, 0.15% on glass balls, 0.5% on fire-brick, and 1.2% on Celite (Fredrick and Cooke, 1960). The lowest amount of packing that can be used without getting adsorption on glass beads is about 0.15%, and the upper practical limit about 3%. Adsorption appears to be about the same on glass beads, stainless-steel beads, or silvered beads.

Other nonadsorptive solid supports include powdered sodium chloride (Nelson and Milun, 1960), metal helices (Sørensen and Søltoft, 1956; Kwantes and Rijnders, 1958), and powdered polymers such as Fluoropak (Fluorocarbon Co.). Fluoropak circumvents tailing when used in the chromatography of aliphatic amines (see Chapter 3, method D.IV.a.1). However, column efficiency is only about 50 theoretical plates per foot.

a. Celite Supports

1. *Deactivation with Methanolic NaOH* (James and Martin, 1952). Celite 545 is size-graded by suspending it repeatedly in water in a beaker 18 cm high and discarding all the fine material that does not settle out in less than 3 minutes. The coarse-grade material is heated in a muffle for 3 hours at 300°C and then treated with concentrated sulfuric acid to remove iron and basic impurities. It is washed thoroughly with water to remove acid and oven-dried at 145°C. Before use, it is treated with 5% (w/v) sodium hydroxide in methanol, decanted, and oven-dried at 100°C. It is stored in a desiccator over sodium hydroxide.

*2. *Deactivation for Analysis of Fatty Amines* (Link et al., 1960). Chromosorb W (40/60 mesh) is treated in turn with concentrated hydrochloric acid, water, 10% sodium hydroxide, and water in that order. It is then heated at 200°C for 2 hours. After screening to 40/60 mesh, 15.5 gm of the support is added to a solution of 1.5 gm of potassium hydroxide in 80 ml of methanol. The solvent is removed, and the support is heated again for 2 hours at 100°C.

b. Firebrick Supports

*1. *Alkali Treatment* (Link et al., 1960). Chromosorb (30/60 mesh) is washed overnight with a 1:1 mixture of concentrated hydrochloric acid and water. It is washed free of acid with distilled water and dried at 150°C overnight. The support (40 gm) is treated with a 5% solution of sodium hydroxide in methanol (200 ml) for 2½ hours. It is then transferred to a sintered-glass funnel, and the solvent is removed by suction. The Chromosorb is rinsed with methanol (200 ml), then with chloroform (100 ml), and air-dried.

*2. *Silver-Plated Firebrick* (Ormerod and Scott, 1959). C-22 firebrick is ground to 120/160 B.S. mesh and degreased with chloroform. It is then silvered by the Rochelle salt procedure described in the *Handbook of Chemistry and Physics* (41st ed., p. 3294). The brick dust (10 gm) is treated with silvering solution (100 ml) and degassed under reduced pressure to ensure that the solution penetrates the pores of the brick. Reducing solution (100 ml) is then added, and the solution is stirred for approximately 10 minutes. Vigorous stirring is avoided to prevent possible comminution of the solid. The liquid is decanted from the support, and an additional portion (100 ml) of silvering solution is added. This process is repeated until the desired amount of silver is deposited (4 to 10 gm/per 10 gm of firebrick). The support is degassed, and the stationary liquid is applied in the usual way.

c. Other Solid Supports

*1. *Inorganic Salts from Detergents* (Decora and Dinneen, 1960). Tide (a commercial detergent) is crushed on a screen by using a porcelain pestle with a gentle rotary motion. The material is sieved, and the 40/60-mesh fraction is retained, spread in a thin layer, and dried in an oven at 185°C for 24 hours. The weight loss is about 14%. The dried material is sieved (40/60 mesh) and extracted with petroleum ether (b.p., 30° to 60°C) in a Soxhlet extractor. The loss in this step is about 14%. The porous material remaining in the thimble of the Soxhlet serves as the solid support. This material is more fragile than Chromosorb or Celite 545; therefore the column packing is resieved after addition of the liquid to remove the fines created in its preparation.

IV. Preparation of Packed Columns

After the stationary phase and solid support have been selected, a number of other variables must be considered in the preparation of packed columns. These include the ratio of stationary liquid to solid support, and the length, diameter, and material of construction of the column. Then, the stationary liquid must be coated on the solid support uniformly, and the powder introduced into the column so that it is packed densely and the mobile phase does not channel. The column is then bent to the required shape and installed in the chromatograph with gastight fittings. Often it must be conditioned prior to use for analysis.

a. Selection of Packing Ratio

In preparing the packing the ratio of liquid to solid is an important variable, since it influences retention volumes, column efficiencies, operating temperature, and degree of adsorption of solutes on the solid support. Furthermore, the permeability of the column to the mobile phase is lower at high packing ratios, because there is less free space in the column for the passage of the gas. Ideally, the liquid should be spread over the internal and external surfaces of the support in the form of a thin film, but in practice it is not. The liquid enters the smaller pores first, owing to capillarity, the larger pores becoming filled as the packing ratio is increased. As a result, molecules of solute in the gas phase must diffuse a distance, d_g, from inter-particle space through unfilled pores before they reach the surface of the liquid. The *average* distance that solute molecules must diffuse in the liquid phase is given by d_f, or the film thickness. The relative rates at which the solute diffuses in the two phases is determined by the ratio of its diffusion coefficients in them, D_{liq}/D_{gas}.

Since diffusion takes place much more rapidly in gases than in liquids, the former is of relatively little importance in influencing mass transfer. The influence of the thickness of the liquid film and the diffusion coefficient of the solute in it are given by the third term of the van Deemter equation, as shown in equation 21, where K is the partition coefficient of the solute

$$HETP = A + B/u + \frac{8}{\pi^2} \frac{KF_{liq}/F_{gas}}{(1 + KF_{liq}/F_{gas})^2} \cdot \frac{d_f^2}{D_{liq}} u \qquad (21)$$

between the liquid and gas phases, F_{liq} is the volume fraction of the column occupied by liquid, F_{gas} is the volume fraction of the column occupied by gas, d_f is the film thickness of the liquid, D_{liq} is the diffusion coefficient of the solute in the liquid phase, and u is the velocity of the carrier gas. When the solid support is porous, as is usually the case in gas chromatography, the thickness of the liquid film will be proportional to the packing ratio. Therefore column efficiency in terms of the height equivalent to a theoretical plate should decrease as the amount of liquid phase is increased. The change, however, will not be directly proportional to the square of the film thickness, d_f, since the ratio F_{liq}/F_{gas} will increase also, because of the change in the relative proportions of the column volume occupied by the two phases. The van Deemter equation does not provide a quantitative description of the variation in column efficiency with packing ratio because of the approximate nature of the assumptions made in its derivation. Nevertheless, it indicates clearly that $HETP$ will increase as the liquid layer becomes thicker, because of increased resistance to mass transfer.

In practice, most workers use packings containing 15 to 40% liquid. Keulemans (1959) found 20 to 25% to be optimal for the separation of lower alkanes on hexadecane. Other workers recommend lower figures, in the range of 8 to 20%. It is likely that the optimum varies with the solute–solvent combination under investigation, and also with other considerations. Thus, if it is necessary to collect fractions of eluted materials for chemical analysis, comparatively large samples must be applied to the chromatographic column. This necessitates high packing ratios to avoid overloading. If, on the other hand, rapid separation is required, a low packing ratio is indicated to reduce retention volumes. However, if the solid support is adsorptive, low ratios will result in tailing. In summary, high ratios result in somewhat lower plate efficiency and high retention volumes, and are needed for the chromatography of large samples. Low packing ratios give low retention volumes, require small samples, may result in tailing, and yield higher column efficiency.

The smaller retention volumes achieved with low packing ratios can be sacrificed in order to operate at lower column temperatures, often with very beneficial results. Thus fair peak resolution is obtained on chromatographing mixtures of mono-, di-, and triethylene glycols on Carbowax 1000 at a packing ratio of 40:100 and a temperature of 180°C (Ring, 1958). When the packing ratio is reduced to 12:100, the peaks are not resolved because of the rapid elution of the components from the column. However, when the temperature is reduced to 150°C, sharp peaks and good resolution are obtained with a 12:100 ratio. This principle has been used by Hishta *et al.* (1960) for the chromatography of solid organic compounds at several hundred degrees below their boiling points. Glass beads with low adsorptive capacity are used, and the packing ratio is reduced to a few tenths of a per cent. Of course it is necessary to use small samples and correspondingly more sensitive detectors.

b. Column Dimensions

Columns 1 to 2 meters long are satisfactory for most purposes. However, the number of theoretical plates obtainable increases with length. Consequently columns 10 to 20 meters long are not uncommon for the resolution of solutes with low separation factors. Some packed columns may have efficiencies as high as 3000 theoretical plates per meter, but in other cases this value may be as low as 200, particularly with solid supports having low specific surfaces. Scott (1958) has obtained between 18,000 and 30,000 theoretical plates with a 15.3-meter column operated at a high inlet pressure. Columns 0.2 to 2 cm in internal diameter are used for quantitative analysis, sizes of 0.4 to 0.6 cm being most common. GLC columns do not lose efficiency seriously when the diameter is increased. Dimbat *et al.* (1956) report a case where an increase in column length of less than 50% compensated for the loss in efficiency caused by a 600% increase in diameter.

Columns are made of glass, stainless steel, or copper. The choice of the material is important, for sensitive compounds may react or isomerize catalytically at the column walls. This often leads to artifacts especially in the analysis of terpenes. The shape of the column must be considered also. Columns are most efficient when packed straight and then bent to the desired shape. Consequently glass is not a good choice unless the chromatograph is designed for straight columns. Sometimes a number of lengths of glass tubing are packed separately and connected serially with U-shaped jumper tubes. However, if a spiral column is desired, metal construction should be chosen.

Generally, straight tubes or U tubes are preferred when the column oven will accommodate them. However, columns 5 meters long or more must be wound on a mandril to spiral form to fit most chromatograph ovens.

Copper tubing is softened before it is packed by heating it to 500° to 600°C in a flame (Keulemans, 1959). If it has been treated properly, it will be quite soft for winding but will harden after it has been shaped.

Coiled columns are slightly less efficient per unit length than straight ones, but this is not serious for 0.5-cm analytical columns if the diameter of the coil is 15 cm or more. However, if the inside diameter is 8 cm and the radius of curvature is about 40 cm, the loss in resolution will be serious (Giddings, 1960).

c. Coating the Solid Support

The stationary liquid is usually dissolved in an organic solvent such as dichloromethane, acetone, or ethyl acetate and mixed with the solid support in a large evaporating dish. The solution is heated with stirring to drive off the solvent. If the equipment is available, it is more convenient to mix the solid and solution of stationary phase in a round-bottomed flask and remove the solvent in a rotary vacuum evaporator. The powder should be dry to the touch and free-flowing before it is used to pack the column. Several typical methods for preparing packings are given below.

1. *Mixing by Hand, Stirring* (Benedict, personal communication, 1960). The stationary liquid (8 gm) is dissolved in chloroform (250 ml), and to this solution is added 30/60-U. S. mesh firebrick (40 gm) with stirring. The mixture is heated with stirring on a steam bath until a homogeneous suspension is obtained. The heating is continued to remove the solvent, but stirring is stopped before the mixture thickens, because the grinding action produces many particles less than 60 mesh in size. Instead, mixing is achieved by tilting and turning the beaker to tumble the contents. After the chloroform has been removed, the material is ready to be packed into the column.

*2. *Mixing in a Rotary Vacuum Evaporator* (Zubyk and Conner, 1960). Column packings are prepared by dissolving a weighed amount of liquid phase in a low-boiling solvent and slurrying the solution with a weighed amount of solid support in a 2-liter, creased, round-bottomed flask. The flask is then attached to a rotary evaporator, and the solvent is removed under vacuum during continuous rotating and mixing. This method is preferred over conventional hand stirring because it is rapid, requires less attention, minimizes liquid phase migration, and results in very uniformly coated packings. Microscopic examination of Chromosorb particles after coating by hand stirring sometimes reveals the presence of particles that appear to contain less coating than others. In addition, it has been the experience of the authors that some hand-stirred packings cause isomerization of labile compounds (terpenes), whereas those prepared in a rotary evaporator do not.

d. Filling the Column

Before being filled, the bottom of the column is stoppered with a 1-cm plug of glass wool. The column is supported in a vertical position, and a powder funnel is attached to the top with a short length of plastic tubing. For long columns, it is convenient to have a top man to feed in the packing, and a bottom man to take care of the vibrating. The packing is placed in the funnel and sifted into place by vibrating the column. This is best accomplished by holding the bottom portion of the column against the flattened drive shaft of a motor rotating in a vertical position. The tube is rotated and moved up and down against the shaft during filling. If a vibrator is not available, the packing can be settled into place by having the bottom man tap the tube sharply with a blunt instrument. However, a vibrator is recommended.

The column is filled to within 1 cm of the top and sealed with a plug of glass wool. It is then bent to the required shape or spiraled around a mandril. For the former, a tube bender is very convenient (The Imperial Brass Mfg. Co.). Connection to the chromatograph is usually made with thumbscrews sealed with silicone O rings or Swagelok fittings.

Columns are conditioned by passing the mobile phase through them at the maximum use temperature or above. The exact conditions depend on the thermal stability of the packing and the sensitivity of the detector. Usually treatment for 24 to 72 hours will suffice. If a variety of columns are to be used with an ionization detector, it is convenient to have substitutes being conditioned at all times in a special apparatus built for the purpose. Otherwise, a considerable waiting period may ensue before detector background is low enough for use.

V. COLUMNS FOR GAS–SOLID CHROMATOGRAPHY

The active solids employed most frequently in GSC include molecular sieve, silica gel, activated charcoal, and alumina. These are often activated, or sometimes deactivated, prior to use; details are given in Chapter 2. Molecular sieves are synthetic metal aluminosilicates having three-dimensional pores. Three grades are available, 13-X, 4-A, and 5-A, the numbers referring to the pore sizes. They are the most efficient materials known for separating oxygen from nitrogen, but carbon dioxide is adsorbed irreversibly by them except at elevated temperatures. Silica gel is used most often for the separation of carbon dioxide from air and light hydrocarbons. It does not resolve oxygen and nitrogen. Activated charcoal is good for separating hydrogen from air. It will also separate oxygen from nitrogen, but not so efficiently as molecular sieve. Three grades are available, differing in activity (Burrell Corp.). Deactivated alumina has been used for separating high-molecular-weight hydrocarbons (Scott and Rowell, 1960). Low-molecular-weight hydrocarbons can be separated on alumina and silica gel columns in series, or on alumina coated with a partition liquid (see Chapter 2, method E.V.a.7).

Peaks obtained on GSC columns usually tail badly, since adsorption isotherms of gases on them are nonlinear. This can be reduced by coating the active solid with a small amount of strongly adsorbed stationary liquid. For example, 1.5% squalane has been used to reduce tailing on furnace black (Eggertsen *et al.*, 1956).

GSC columns are packed and installed in the chromatograph in the same manner as GLC columns.

VI. Preparation and Use of Capillary Columns

In preparing capillary columns, the stationary liquid is coated on the internal surface of the tubing in a layer about 3 to 5 microns thick. Despite the thinness of the film, capillaries can be used for prolonged periods before the stationary phase is eluted. The bore of the tubing is generally 0.01 to 0.1 cm, and the length 15 to 45 meters. Nylon capillaries (Garlock Packing Co.) one mile long have been described. Generally 2 to 4 mg of liquid per 10 meters of tubing is applied. The liquid is dissolved in a nonpolar volatile organic solvent, and this solution is forced into the capillary by pressure or suction. Once the tube is filled, solvent can be removed in either of two ways. In the first of these, the capillary is raised through a heated oven to volatilize the solvent as the tubing passes through a heated zone. More commonly, the liquid is forced out of the column with carrier gas, and the coating is formed from what adheres to the walls. Gas pressures used in filling the column vary from 2 to 100 psig, and for blowing out the plug of liquid from 40 to 100 psig. So far, no absolutely reproducible method has been developed for preparing them. Consequently, variable results are obtained on commercial columns as well as on those made in the laboratory.

The thickness of the liquid layer and its uniformity must be controlled carefully for optimum results. The gas selected to introduce and sweep out the liquid must be clean and dry. Also, the interior of the column itself must be dry and free of organic matter. Materials of construction include glass, nylon, copper, and stainless steel, the latter being used most widely. Metal columns must be treated chemically before packing to destroy "acid centers" and so minimize catalytic breakdown of labile compounds (method C.VI.a.1). Copper columns may contain a film of oxide that causes tailing (James, 1960). This also can be removed by chemical treatment.

Mitzner and Jacobs (1960) have found copper capillaries 0.05 cm in diameter cleaned by the procedure described in method C.VI.a.1 useful for the separation of terpenes. They are comparatively easy to coat, particularly with polar liquids. Small bits of airborne dust mitigate against good packings; therefore the solutions containing the stationary liquids are filtered at least three times before being applied to the column.

Because of the small amount of stationary liquid used, sample sizes must be kept very small, of the order of 1 μg. To do this, a normal-sized sample is injected, and most of it is vented to the atmosphere in a ratio of 100:1 to

1000:1 by a stream splitter placed between the injection port and the column. This procedure is not very reproducible, particularly for high-boiling compounds, since the sample may be fractionated partly before it enters the column. Therefore, sample introduction and application of the stationary liquid to the column are major problems that are still incompletely solved.

The linear flow rate through capillary columns is quite high, but the volume flow rate is very low, being of the order of 1 ml/min or less. Therefore the dead volume in the sample injection port and the detector must be correspondingly small, or holdup of the sample will be too high. The effective volume of the detector should be of the order of 1 to 10 μl, since fast-moving components may emerge from the chromatograph in a few tenths of a microliter of carrier gas. If the actual volume of the chamber is large, a scavenger gas can be used to hasten the flow of column eluates through it. Lipsky *et al.* (1959) employ a scavenger gas flow of 25 to 50 ml of argon per minute with an ionization detector having a 1-ml chamber. Loss of sensitivity is avoided by leading the flow from the capillary into the chamber by a metal tube of small diameter which also serves as the anode (see Section D.IV.a). When this is done, the greater part of the electric field is close to the surface of the inlet tube, making this the only part of the chamber where the primary electrons are accelerated sufficiently to generate excited argon atoms. Thus when the column eluates enter this region, they are ionized by the metastable argon before they are diluted to an appreciable extent by the carrier gas flow. Flame ionization detectors also are suitable for use with capillary columns. Thermal detectors are insufficiently sensitive.

a. Column Preparation

*1. *Cleaning Metal Columns* (Mitzner and Jacobs, 1960). To clean stainless-steel capillaries, 50 ml of each of the following solutions is passed through them in the order stated: 2 to 3% aqueous detergent solution, 10% potassium hydroxide solution, distilled water, methanol, acetone, chloroform, and benzene. A dry gas, preferably argon, is then blown through for drying. All solutions and solvents must be filtered at least twice before use. Copper capillaries are cleaned by the same procedure, except for omission of the potassium hydroxide treatment.

*2. *Filling Glass Columns* (Corning Glass Works Technical Information Circular). The capillary tubing is supplied clean and dry and is filled with dry gas. A 2 to 10% solution of the stationary liquid in a volatile solvent is blown through the tube under low gas pressure or pulled through it with a vacuum at a rate of 15 cm/min. After the tube is filled, the liquid is blown out of it and gas is passed through it until it is dry. Silicone connecting tubing should not be used during filling, since some solvents may dissolve a small amount of it and deposit it in the capillary.

*3. *Filling Metal Columns* (Lipsky *et al.*, 1959). The columns are filled by forcing a 6 to 12% solution of the liquid phase in chloroform (10 to 20 ml) through them from a short thick glass tube connected to one end of the capillary. Dry cylinder gas at 40 psig or a hydraulic pump capable of delivering fluid at 20,000 psig can be used. Once the capillary is filled, the liquid is blown out of it carefully at room temperature with cylinder gas at 40 psig. Gas flow is continued for several hours after the solution emerges from the column to remove the last traces of solvent.

VII. SUMMARY

GLC columns are generally 1 to 15 meters long and about 0.5 cm in internal diameter. They are packed with stationary liquids sorbed on porous solids or sometimes coated on glass or metal beads. High ratios of liquid to solid support result in high retention volumes and low plate efficiencies, but comparatively large samples can be used. Low ratios result in higher plate efficiency and low retention volumes, and require smaller samples, but they may result in tailing, owing to adsorption of solutes on the solid support. Packings having very low liquid/solid ratios (below 1%) are useful for separating high-boiling compounds at comparatively low temperatures.

GSC columns are packed with active solids such as charcoal, molecular sieve, silica gel, and alumina. They are used primarily for the analysis of inorganic gases and low-molecular-weight hydrocarbons. Tailing is a more serious problem than with GLC columns, but this can be reduced sometimes by adding a small amount of stationary liquid. Columns prepared with larger amounts of liquid can function through both adsorption and partition effects.

Capillary columns are about 0.05 cm in diameter and may be anywhere from 15 to 45 meters long. The stationary liquid phase is supported by the internal wall of the capillary. Plate efficiency is very high, but these columns are difficult to coat reproducibly. Linear flow rates of the mobile phase are high, but volume rates are low, making it necessary to minimize dead space in auxiliary equipment. Very small samples must be used to prevent overloading them; therefore highly sensitive detectors are required for monitoring the effluent gases.

D. Detectors

I. INTRODUCTION

High detector sensitivity and versatility are a direct consequence of using a permanent gas as the mobile phase in chromatography. These properties make possible the measurement of differences in thermal conductivity, ionizability of organic molecules, heats of combustion, and other similar properties for the detection of solutes in column eluates. Use of these intrinsic qualities would be impractical if not impossible in the liquid phase. With them it is possible to measure the amounts of solutes present in column eluates automatically, and in almost unbelievably low amounts. Thermistor detectors will respond to 10^{-8} mole of solute, and ionization detectors will record the presence of as little as 10^{-15} mole of an organic compound in the mobile phase. Sensitivity will increase inevitably with future technological developments, as neither of the ionization detectors in most common use is engineered to respond to its ultimate capacity.

High detector sensitivity coupled with automation is invaluable for the detection of trace components and the analysis of minute amounts of biological fluids. In addition, there are other hidden values which are not at once apparent. The capacity to detect small amounts of organic compounds makes it possible to use very small sample sizes and therefore obtain high column efficiencies in terms of theoretical plates. Moreover, small sample sizes can be coupled with low liquid/solid packing ratios. This makes possible the chromatography of solid organic compounds at column temperatures several hundred degrees below their boiling points and thus enormously increases the versatility of the method. Of course, gas chromatography in capillary columns would be unfeasible from a practical point of view were it not for the extreme sensitivity of ionization detectors.

Despite the indisputable importance of detectors in the functioning of gas chromatographs, this topic will be condensed out of all proportion to other subjects discussed in this manual. The more useful types are now available commercially, and instructions for operation and maintenance are obtainable from the manufacturers. Similarly, it will be assumed that bridge circuits and attenuation systems are now standard equipment on all commercial instruments. Sometimes recorders are not provided. In this event, a 0- to 1-mv or 0- to 2-mv recorder with a 2-second pen response and a chart speed in the general range of 30 inches per hour will be satisfactory for most analyses. Often, a 0- to 10-mv recorder will be satisfactory if a more sensitive one is not available.

The present discussion, therefore, will be confined to describing some of the general principles on which a few of the more widely used detectors operate, with the view of providing the minimum amount of information required to make clear their individual limitations and advantages.

Detectors can be classified in several ways: according to the manner in which the chromatographic data are presented; according to principle of operation; or according to universality of response to a variety of chemical compounds. Data are presented as integral or differential curves, depending on the method. Integral detectors measure the accumulated effect of all the compounds which pass into them during the course of analysis. An example is the titration cell, in which the total amount of standard alkali required to neutralize a series of acids eluted from the chromatographic column is measured. The chromatogram appears as a series of steps plotted against time, the height of each step being proportional to the amount of component present in the sample. Differential recorders measure the instantaneous concentration of solute vapor in the sensing part of the cell. The solute vapor is spread out in a longitudinal direction, so that all of it does not enter the cell at once. The concentration of vapor in the leading and trailing ends of the plug is less than in the center. Consequently, the chromatogram appears as a series of peaks, the amount of each component of the sample being proportional to the area under the peak it generates.

A large number of properties have been used as the basis for detection. However, the overwhelming majority of detectors in actual use are based on measurement of the differences between the thermal conductivities of the solute and the mobile phase, or measurement of the electric currents produced by causing the solutes to ionize. Thermal detectors are rugged, easy to build, and moderately sensitive. However, they are susceptible to changes in temperature and to the flow rate of the mobile phase. Ionization detectors are much more sensitive and are more stable with respect to changes in operating parameters. In the past, thermal detectors have been used most extensively, but it can be anticipated that ionization detectors will be employed more and more as they continue to improve in design and function.

Thermal detectors are universal in that they respond in a greater or lesser degree to the presence of all the components of a sample unless one of them happens to be identical to the carrier gas. Ionization detectors are semi-universal in that they respond to most organic compounds but not in a marked degree to inorganic compounds. For most work, universality of response is very desirable. However, in some instances it is impossible or inconvenient to resolve all the components of complex mixtures on the column. When this occurs it is possible sometimes to use a selective detector which "sees" only a selected group of compounds possessing some specific property or component in common. For example, a coulometric detector has been developed which responds only to compounds containing halogen and sulfur. This makes extensive pretreatment of the sample or complete resolution of all its components on the column unnecessary in order to obtain useful analytical results. Consequently, selective detectors can be extremely valuable and should be considered along with ordinary detection methods during the development of new analytical procedures.

One of the most important properties of a detector is the speed with which it responds to changes in the composition of a gas passing through it. Although instantaneous response cannot be achieved, it is possible to approach this ideal closely enough for practical purposes by keeping internal passages small and, in the case of thermal conductivity cells, by choosing sensing elements with low heat capacities. Another property of great importance to the practical analyst is detector sensitivity, but this is difficult to state except in approximate terms, since it depends on other variables, such as the nature of the sample employed for measurement, the flow rate of the carrier gas, and the settings selected to supply current to the sensing elements. Dimbat *et al.* (1956) have proposed a sensitivity parameter, S, which is given in units of milliliters times millivolts per milligram, as in equation 22,

$$S = \frac{aC_1C_2F_c}{W} \tag{22}$$

where a is the peak area in square centimeters, C_1 is the recorder sensitivity in millivolts per centimeter of chart, C_2 is the chart speed in minutes per centimeter, F_c is the flow rate of the mobile phase in ml./min. at the exit corrected to column temperature at atmospheric pressure, and W is the weight of the sample in milligrams.

This value has not been included in the conditions for chromatography given in the chapters of this manual concerned with applications, since few authors report it or give sufficient information to make possible its calculation. However, the sample weight and the general characteristics of the detector–recorder system are supplied. This should be enough information on which to base choice of detector. However, adjustment of operating parameters such as attenuation setting and exact sample size must be decided in each individual case by the properties of the instrument and the composition of the material being chromatographed.

II. Thermal Detectors

Thermal detectors are standard equipment on most commercial chromatographs and in the past have been used more extensively than any other type in applications research. However, ionization detectors are supplanting them rapidly even for use with packed columns, since they are much more sensitive and stable with respect to changes in operating parameters. Thermal detectors respond to chemical compounds of all types and are moderately sensitive to organic vapors when the carrier gas is hydrogen or helium. As little as 10^{-8} to 10^{-5} mole of solute can be detected in the carrier gas, depending on type, cell geometry, and operating temperature. Thermal detectors are very sensitive to temperature changes and should be thermostatted to within $0.05°C$ below $100°C$, and to within $0.1°C$ above this temperature to secure a stable base line. Therefore a considerable wait often ensues if the oven is opened between runs to change columns or if the temperature must be changed. Similarly, detector response is influenced by the flow rate of the mobile phase, and therefore this also must be kept constant. Consequently it is not feasible to stop the flow of carrier gas to apply a sample, since the base line of the recorder would not become established quickly enough on restarting the flow. Therefore the sample must be injected through a self-sealing diaphragm against the back pressure of the column.

The basic component of the thermal detector is a small resistance element made of a semiconductor (thermistor type) or a platinum or tungsten wire (katharometer type). Two of these elements are used in each cell, one serving as the detector and the other as a reference unit. A typical circuit arrangement is shown in Fig. 11. The detector element (D_1) and the reference

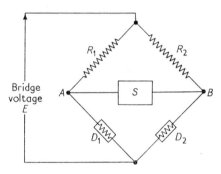

FIG. 11. Wheatstone bridge arrangement for thermal conductivity cell.

element (D_2), together with resistances R_1 and R_2, form a Wheatstone bridge across which a bridge voltage (E) is impressed. This serves to heat the resistance elements in the detector to a constant temperature. The variable resistances are then adjusted to zero the potential drop across AB, which feeds the recorder (S). This adjustment is made with pure carrier gas flowing through D_1 and D_2 so that the amount of heat carried away from the elements by conduction and convection remains constant. Under these conditions, the recorder pen will draw a straight line at the base of the chart. If a solute vapor passes through D_1, the resistance element will change in temperature because of the difference in thermal conductivity between the solute and pure carrier gas. If hydrogen or helium is used as the mobile phase, the temperature of the element in D_1 will increase, as all other gases have lower thermal conductivities and hence will conduct heat away from it less rapidly. This change in temperature will cause the resistance of the element in D_1 to increase, since a substance with a high temperature coefficient of resistance is chosen for construction. Meanwhile the resistance of the element in D_2 will remain the same, as the gas flow system is arranged so that pure mobile phase only flows through this side of the cell. As a result of the difference in resistance between the elements D_1 and D_2, a potential imbalance is created across AB which activates the recorder pen to draw a peak.

To operate properly, the resistance elements must be heated to a temperature above that of the cell block, in order to conduct heat away from the elements to the block at a rate which depends on the thermal conductivity of the surrounding gas and the difference in temperature between the element and the walls of the housing. In actual practice the sensing cell and the reference cell cannot be made to balance exactly with pure carrier flowing through them. Therefore the circuit is so designed that the signal arising from this inequality can be balanced with an opposing signal by means of an adjustable zero control.

When hydrogen or helium is the carrier gas, the peaks are always in the same direction, as all other materials have lower conductivities. However, with nitrogen, the temperature of the element in D_1 will become higher or lower depending on whether the solute passing through it has a higher or lower conductivity than nitrogen. Therefore negative peaks are obtained for some substances. To avoid this, a polarity switch is usually installed on the chromatograph to reverse the direction of the signal.

In many chromatographs, the reference cell is placed upstream from the injection port where the linear flow rate of carrier gas is slower than at the exit of the column. Any difference between the conductivities of the sensing elements are balanced out with a zero adjuster. Another arrangement is to split the carrier gas stream and send equal volumes of it through columns arranged in parallel, one of them being a dummy with the same impedance to gas flow as the analytical column. Both reference and sensing cells are then placed downstream from their respective columns. This reduces the amount of electrical compensation that must be made, since the flow rates through both cells of the detector now should be the same. However, it is difficult to construct two columns with exactly the same impedance to gas flow. A third alternative is to purge the reference cell thoroughly with carrier gas and seal it off hermetically. If this is done, care must be taken that light gases do not diffuse through the seal.

To be of value in gas chromatography, a thermal cell should have a large output for small changes in the conductivity of the gas flowing through it, so that a 0- to 5-mv recorder can be used directly. Also, the noise level should be low so that the signal can be amplified electronically if necessary. The materials for construction should be chemically inert, and the time constant should not be greater than 2 seconds. The voltage applied across the bridge should be varied with the nature of the carrier gas to obtain optimum results. Recommendations for adjusting this parameter are usually supplied by the manufacturer of the chromatograph. However, these should not always be followed blindly, since they may not yield maximum sensitivity. In case of doubt, detector responses for equal amounts of a standard compound should be measured at a number of different bridge voltages to determine the best value.

Thermal conductivity is a unique characteristic of each chemical compound which does not vary in an exact way with molecular weight or other characteristics. Therefore the T/C cell must be calibrated by measuring its response to known amounts of pure compounds if accurate results are required. But approximate results can be obtained on most organic compounds if hydrogen or helium is used as the mobile phase, since the spread between the conductivities of the carrier and solutes is great enough to minimize differences between the various solutes.

a. Katharometers

A katharometer is a thermal conductivity cell containing heated wires with high temperature coefficients of resistance, such as platinum or tungsten. Often four wires are used, two in the sensing side of the cell and two in the reference side. The wires may be straight or coiled, the former being more satisfactory, since they do not sag as much when heated. The wires can be placed directly in the gas stream, in a side chamber offset from it, or in a compromise position. Designs with the wire placed directly in the gas stream give the highest sensitivity and the fastest response, but they are very sensitive to changes in gas flow rates. If the sensing element is offset from the gas stream, the solute must diffuse into the side chamber. This reduces sensitivity and increases response time, but the detector base line is steadier, since the effects of random fluctuations in flow rate are smoothed out. The Pretzel design (Gow-Mac Instrument Co.) is a compromise arrangement in which the gas stream is divided evenly between parallel passages, and the sensing elements are placed in connecting tubes between these passages. This gives good stability coupled with fast response time.

Katharometers have been made that can be operated at temperatures up to 500°C. They are usually more sensitive than thermistors at high temperatures but considerably less sensitive below 100°C. A katharometer design has been described which is said to give a signal independent of flow rate (Scott and Han, 1961).

b. Thermistors

Thermistors are made of semiconductors such as oxides of manganese, nickel, and cobalt. The most common form is a glass-coated bead about 0.04 cm in diameter fitted with two platinum–iridium lead wires. The temperature coefficient of resistance of thermistors is about ten times as great as that of platinum or tungsten filaments. They are available with resistances of 2000, 8000, and 100,000 ohms. Operating currents are very low compared to those used with hot-wire T/C cells, sensitivity reaching a maximum and then decreasing as the current is increased. At room temperature, the thermistor is considerably more sensitive than the hot-wire T/C cell, but the temperature-sensitivity curves intersect around 150°C. However, a thermistor circuit has been designed that yields good sensitivity at elevated temperatures (American Instrument Co.). Flake thermistors are available that are useful from 30° to 325°C (Barnes Engineering Co.). Response speed is 0.25 second, and the instruments are sensitive to changes of 1 part in 10^7 in the thermal conductivity of the carrier gas. Miniature thermistors can be obtained for small-bore packed columns (Greenbrier Instruments Inc., Gow-Mac Instrument Co.). The detector block contains capillary passages and is equipped with small volume fittings.

III. Gas Density Balance

The Martin gas density balance is one of the first universal detectors to be described, but it has been used comparatively little, reportedly because it is difficult to construct. However, several new designs have appeared recently (Murray, 1959; Nerheim, 1960b), and commercial models are now available (Griffin and George Ltd., Gow-Mac Instrument Co.). Although the principle of operation is based on density differences between solute vapors and carrier gas, it is also in a secondary sense a thermal detector, since hot wires or thermistor beads are used to measure gas flow rates. However, it has several advantages not possessed by other thermal detectors. In the first place, nitrogen can be used in place of hydrogen or helium as the carrier gas, since differences in thermal conductivity are unimportant. This reduces costs and, with regard to hydrogen, eliminates a safety hazard. Moreover, peak resolution should be somewhat better, owing to lower diffusivity of the solute in the mobile phase. A second factor is that the sensing elements are never exposed to the solute vapors, which will eliminate fouling. Last, and most important, the need for calibration is reduced to the minimum, for detector response is directly proportional to the molecular weight of the solute. Hence if the identity of a compound (and therefore its molecular weight) is known, the weight per cent of it in the sample can be calculated directly from peak area.

This detector operates because vapors lighter than the mobile phase will move upward, and those heavier will move downward, on passing through it. These movements result in differences in gas flow rates which are measured by anemometers consisting of hot-wire or thermistor detectors. A schematic diagram of the apparatus is shown in Fig. 12. It must be positioned so that the center tube, designated by BCD, is vertical. Reference gas enters the detector at A, and the stream is split so that half of it takes the upper channel, ADE, and the other half takes the lower channel, ABE. Matched resistance elements (S_1 and S_2) are situated in the upper and lower reference gas channels and are balanced by a Wheatstone bridge circuit at a constant flow rate of the carrier gas, as described in Section D.II. The carrier gas issuing from the chromatographic column is introduced into the middle of the vertical channel *BCD* at *C*. In this case also, the stream splits, entering both the upper and lower arms of the detector. However, if a solute is present which is less dense than the carrier gas, it will rise and pass through the upper channel.

Since it is less dense, the flow rate through channel *ADE* will be faster than that through *ABE*. The net result will be that the thermal element S_2, which serves as an anemometer, will be cooled more than the element S_1, since gas is moving past it faster. Consequently their relative resistances will change, and the Wheatstone bridge will become unbalanced. This signal will be transmitted to a recorder in the usual way. If the solute vapor is denser than the mobile phase, the same effect is produced in an opposite way. The solute vapor takes the course *CBE*, thereby slowing the flow along *ABE*. This also unbalances the resistances of the thermal elements.

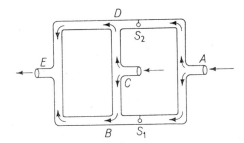

Fig. 12. Schematic diagram of gas density balance.

As can be seen from Fig. 12, the solute vapors enter their respective channels after the reference gas has passed the sensing elements. Therefore they do not come in contact with hot wires or thermistor beads, thus eliminating fouling of the detector.

Instrument response is linear for density differences up to 15% of the carrier gas density, and sensitivity is said to be considerably better than that of conventional thermal conductivity cells. Gas flow can be interrupted without upsetting the stability of the detector. A flow impedance equal in resistance to that of the analytical column is attached to the reference side to minimize random fluctuations in pressure which otherwise would result in displacements of the recorder pen.

In addition to its use as a detector, the gas density balance can be employed for determining the molecular weights of chemical compounds (Liberti *et al.*, 1956).

IV. IONIZATION DETECTORS

Ionization detectors are inherently more sensitive than thermal ones, responding to as little as 10^{-10} to 10^{-15} mole of solute in the carrier gas.

Basically, most of them operate on the same principle; an organic compound is ionized, and the ions (or electrons) formed are used to carry an electric current. The magnitude of the signal is then recorded with or without intermediate amplification. A number of ionization detectors have been described in the literature, but only three have found widespread use as yet and are available commercially. These are the argon detector, the flame detector, and the radiofrequency detector. Consequently, this discussion will be confined to them.

In general, ionization detectors are considerably less sensitive to temperature changes and fluctuations in the flow rate of the carrier gas than are thermal detectors. Furthermore, the signal-to-noise ratio is so high that reference cells are not needed. Because of their extreme sensitivity they are always used in capillary column chromatography. However, this should not obscure the fact that they can be exceedingly helpful in conjunction with packed columns, particularly for the detection of trace components or where the use of very small samples is desirable. Furthermore, they are usually insensitive, or relatively so, to water vapor and inorganic gases, so interference from these substances sometimes can be avoided. An ionization detector in series or parallel with a thermal detector often can yield valuable information, the ionization detector being used to measure trace components, and the thermal detector, major components of the mixture.

a. Argon Detector

In the apparatus developed by Lovelock (1958), argon is the carrier gas, and atoms of it are excited to a metastable state by ionizing radiation as they enter the detector. The excited argon atoms are stable until they collide with organic molecules, whereupon secondary electrons are produced, giving rise to an ionization current which is proportional to the concentration of solute in the carrier gas.

The detector used with packed columns consists of an ionization chamber with a volume of 3 to 10 ml, across which a high potential is applied. The chamber contains a source of ionizing radiation, usually Ra, Sr^{90}, or Pm^{147}, embedded in a metal foil. When argon atoms enter the chamber, some of them are ionized by α- or β-particles to yield positive argon ions and primary electrons. The electrons are accelerated by the applied potential to velocities high enough to excite large numbers of argon atoms to a metastable state having an energy of 11.6 ev. The activation process is described in the accompanying equations.

$$A + \alpha^{++} \text{ or } \beta^- \rightarrow A^+ + e^-$$
$$A + e^- + EMF \rightarrow A^*$$

When an organic vapor eluted from the chromatographic column enters the chamber containing excited argon atoms, collisions take place which release secondary electrons. These give rise to an increase in ionization current which is recorded in the usual way. The secondary electrons also generate more metastable argon atoms, replacing those deactivated in collisions with solute molecules. The response of the detector with respect to solute concentration is linear over a fairly wide range. If a radium source (50 μc) embedded in silver foil is used, the current in the chamber with pure argon flowing is about 2×10^{-8} amp, and the minimum detectable quantity of organic vapor is about 10^{-14} mole, for a signal-to-noise ratio of 2. With Sr^{90} as the radiation source, the noise level is only one-tenth as high, and the sensitivity is ten times as high, thus extending the limit of detectability to 10^{-15} mole (Lipsky et al., 1959).

The operation of this detector is based on the fact that atoms of noble gases can be excited to metastable states and will remain in this condition until they collide with atoms or molecules possessing ionization potentials lower than the excitation potential of the noble gas. Since the excitation potential of argon is 11.6 ev, it will ionize most organic compounds (C_1 and C_2 hydrocarbons being excepted), but not inorganic gases such as oxygen, nitrogen, and carbon dioxide, since their ionization potentials are too high. In practice, the argon detector does respond to the presence of solutes such as methane and hydrogen and has been used for their analysis (Galwey, 1960).[4] However, comparatively large samples are required, and the detector is not being used to optimum advantage. With metastable helium, the detector will respond to trace quantities of all substances but neon (Berry, 1960). However, the helium must be ultrapure, and the detector will lose its selectivity of response, which often can be used to advantage (see Chapter 2, Section E.III).

For use with capillary columns, the effective volume of the ionization chamber must be decreased to compensate for the small volumetric flow rate of the carrier gas. This can be done by running a scavenger gas through the ionization chamber (see Section C.VI) or by decreasing its size. A microversion of this detector has been devised which will ionize 1 to 5% of the solute vapor entering it. The dynamic range is about 10^6 (Lipsky, 1960). Chamber geometry and positioning of the collecting anode are critical. The detector is relatively insensitive to wide variations in flow rate, temperature, and pressure.

A modification of the argon detector, developed by Teranishi et al. (1960), enables one detector block to be used for either capillary or packed columns. It can be operated at temperatures up to 250°C. The sensitivity of the argon detector can be reduced at will by blending the carrier gas with nitrogen (Welti and Wilkens, 1960). Response can be varied continuously

---

[4] This mode of operation is termed "cross section detection." Sensitivity is comparable to that of a good katharometer (Clark).

between the limits obtained with pure argon and pure nitrogen. Therefore, the detector will give full-scale recorder readings without overloading for sample fractions ranging in size from a few micrograms to over 1 gm. This procedure might be worth consideration if it is necessary to use a chromatograph equipped with an argon detector for preparative scale work.

b. Flame Detector

Organic compounds yield ions when burned in a flame, and if two electrodes at a potential difference of about 150 volts are inserted in it, differences in the conductivity of the flame can be measured as the solutes elute from the chromatographic column and are burned. This is the principle on which the flame ionization detector is based. The degree of ionization which occurs in a flame is much greater than would be predicted from the ionization potentials of organic compounds. It has been suggested (McWilliam and Dewar, 1958) that this is caused by the formation of carbon aggregates and their subsequent ready ionization due to the low work function of solid carbon. This view is supported by the fact that response is roughly proportional to the carbon number of the molecule, and the fact that combustible inorganic compounds such as hydrogen sulfide do not give responses. The flame gas is usually hydrogen. A more favorable signal-to-noise ratio is obtained by diluting it with nitrogen. More recently (Baddiel and Cullis, 1960) flame detectors have been described which utilize carbon monoxide. This is said to reduce corrosion problems when compounds containing halogens are being measured.

In one version of the flame detector (Condon, 1959), designed for use with capillary columns, nitrogen is the carrier gas. The column effluent is mixed with hydrogen flowing at a rate of 5 ml/min. This mixture is fed into the flame jet of the detector. The jet is a thin-walled stainless-steel tube which also acts as an electrode. The other electrode is a fine platinum wire held about 5 mm above the jet. The hydrogen flame is lit initially by a glowing pilot wire located within the combustion chamber. The size of the flame is a few cubic millimeters, although this varies slightly with flow rate. The combustion chamber is supplied with filtered air, since dust particles create disturbances in the flame. Furthermore, the air current serves to remove water formed by combustion of the hydrogen. The volume of the detector is only a few microliters, and response is practically instantaneous.

The electrodes are connected across a high impedance in series with a 200-volt battery. The high-impedance side is fed to the grid of a conventional electrometer type of amplifier which drives a recording direct-current milliammeter. An impedance converter may also be used to drive a standard millivolt potentiometer recorder.

The background current is about 10^{-11} amp and is easily suppressed electrically. The detector is insensitive to temperature changes, vibrations, and small fluctuations in the flow rates of carrier and flame gases. For hydrocarbons, response is roughly a function of carbon number, but rather large deviations from this are encountered for low-molecular-weight compounds containing functional groups (see Chapter 2, Table II). The detector does not respond to inorganic vapors such as air, carbon dioxide, water, ammonia, or hydrogen sulfide. However, unlike the argon detector, it yields a high response to methane and ethane. According to Lipsky (1960), the ion yield of the flame detector is only 1 to 3 parts per 100,000, compared to 1 to 5% for the argon detector, making it intrinsically less sensitive than the latter. Nevertheless it has proved satisfactory for the detection of organic gases at the parts-per-billion level (Andreatch and Feinland, 1960).

c. Radiofrequency Detector

A schematic diagram of a radiofrequency detector is shown in Fig. 13. The radiofrequency cell (A) consists of a metal cylinder containing a central

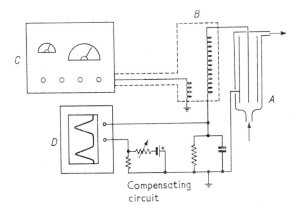

FIG. 13. Schematic diagram of radiofrequency detector (Karmen and Bowman, 1959).

wire (Karmen and Bowman, 1959). The cylinder is provided with entry and exit ports for the carrier gas and is electrically grounded. The central wire is supplied with power through the secondary winding of a tuned, radiofrequency step-up transformer (B). The primary winding of this transformer is connected by a low-impedance coaxial line to the antenna terminal of a 40-watt variable-frequency oscillator-stabilized, Viking Navigator radio transmitter (C). The secondary winding is grounded through a capacitor. The circuit through the discharge tube consists of the metal cylinder, the carrier gas (helium), the central wire, the secondary winding of the radiofrequency transformer, and the low-impedance pathway to the ground through the capacitor. A direct current flows between the metal cylinder and the central wire when a glow discharge is established in the gas. The potential drop across a resistor grounding the low side of the secondary transformer winding is used to operate a standard 5-mv recorder (D).

When radiofrequency power is supplied, a glow discharge is established in the helium, the maximum power being used that will not lead to arcing. When small quantities of organic vapors are passed through the cell, the direct current decreases in proportion to concentration. A 1.6-μg sample of methyl laurate produces a current change equal to 6% of the total direct-current signal.

A chromatograph equipped with a radiofrequency detector is now available commercially (American Instrument Co.). It is said to be sensitive to 10^{-12} to 10^{-15} mole of solute in the carrier gas. The effective cell volume is less than 0.1 ml.

V. Use of Selective Detectors for Fraction Identification

The trend in developing new detectors has been toward finding systems that will respond to all compounds in about the same way. Perhaps the gas density balance approaches this ideal most closely. The advantages of such a method are obvious. The same detector can be used for all samples, and calibration can be reduced to the minimum. Nevertheless, a need exists for detectors that will respond selectively, particularly to groups of related compounds having the same functional groups. This makes it possible to detect the presence of specific compounds in complex mixtures without resorting to the collection and analysis of fractions eluted from the chromatographic column. Furthermore, in such mixtures many components may be unresolved or incompletely resolved from substances having similar retention volumes. However, if the detector responds to only one component of a composite peak, the need for actually resolving the components is eliminated, provided that the column is not overloaded. This principle has been employed very effectively for the analysis of many pesticides in plant extracts, as these compounds often contain chlorine, whereas metabolites extracted with them usually do not (Coulson *et al.*, 1960).

Existing detectors probably have not been used to their full capacities for identifying sample components, and perhaps this is a way to employ one of their most troublesome attributes—that is, their failure to respond equally to various classes of chemical compounds and to individual compounds within classes. Detectors could be arranged in series or in parallel to monitor effluents from the same column, and tentative identification of some solutes could be made by computing relative peak areas. For example, if detector I gives the same response to compounds A and B, and detector II the same response as I to A, but only 0.2 of this response to B, the area ratios, $D_\mathrm{I}/D_\mathrm{II}$, would be 1 for compound A and 5 for B.

Systems for selective detection are based on differences in the chemical and physical properties of organic molecules. These include ionizability, the presence of a specific element such as chlorine or sulfur in the molecule, and ability to capture electrons. Several of the more valuable types used to date are discussed individually below.

a. Titration Cell

The titration cell was developed by James and Martin (1952) for the analysis of volatile fatty acids. Later it was used for the titration of aromatic and aliphatic amines. Theoretically, modifications of the titration cell could be developed for almost any compound that can be determined by a volumetric method of analysis. In the acid-base titration cell of James and Martin, the effluent from the column is led directly into a compartment containing an aqueous or a nonaqueous solvent and titrated automatically with standard acid or alkali. A color indicator, in combination with a photoelectric cell and relay, controls the addition of the titrant, the plunger of a syringe-type burette being coupled to a recorder. Integral curves are obtained by this method.

The temperature of operation is limited by the vapor pressure of the titration medium. The device is not sensitive to flow rate, but flow must be low enough to ensure that all the solutes dissolve in the liquid phase as the gases bubble through it. Sensitivity is of the order of 0.002 to 0.02 mg of acid or base.

b. Potentiometric Method

Thiols can be detected by bubbling the effluent gas into a solution containing iodine and potassium iodide and measuring the change in potential at a platinum electrode. Details are given in Chapter 3, method F.II.a.2.

c. Electrical Conductivity

Weak acids or weak bases can be detected by bubbling the effluent gas through a standard solution of a strong acid or strong base, respectively, and measuring the change in electrical conductivity.

d. Coulometric Detection

A coulometric method can be used for the detection of organic compounds containing halogens (Coulson et al., 1960). The effluent from the chromatographic column is mixed with oxygen, and the organic components are converted to water, carbon dioxide, and hydrogen halides in a combustion tube containing platinum gauze heated at 800°C. The products are absorbed in a titration cell, and the halogen ion is titrated continuously with silver ions generated electrically. The coulometer design incorporates a continuous balancing system, in which the titrating agent present in the cell is kept at a fixed concentration throughout the analysis. The electric current required to maintain a constant silver ion concentration in the cell is recorded on a strip chart recorder as a function of time. A chromatograph incorporating this type of detector is available commercially (Dohrmann Instruments Co.).

This method is also applicable to the selective detection of compounds containing sulfur if thermal decomposition is carried out in a hydrogen atmosphere. Alternatively, oxygen can be used and the sulfur dioxide evolved can be titrated in a redox cell employing a gold electrode. If the sample weight is known accurately, this detector can be used for determining the halogen and sulfur contents of organic compounds. Response to chlorine is essentially quantitative. However, response to bromine is only about one-half of that predicted by theory (Storrs and Burchfield, 1961). Presumably, elemental bromine rather than hydrogen bromide is produced in the gas stream. On dissolving in the electrolyte, this hydrolyzes to yield hypobromous acid and hydrobromic acid, and only the latter is titrated. When the oxygen content of the combustion gas is high, appreciable amounts of elemental chlorine or other oxidizing agents which yield a positive o-tolidine test can be detected.

e. Identification by Electron Capture

Compounds containing halogen atoms and polar functional groups can be identified by electron capture. This procedure is based on the fact that neutral molecules on passing through an ionization chamber can capture free electrons to form negative molecule-ions. The energy change accompanying the reaction is called the electron affinity of the compound. Electron affinity is determined primarily by the nature of the functional group in the molecule and is virtually independent of the size and shape of the hydrocarbon moiety. It is measured by placing the sample in an ionization chamber containing a radiation source and observing the current flow in the chamber at various applied voltages in the presence of an inert gas such as hydrogen, helium, or nitrogen (Lovelock and Lipsky, 1960). When current is plotted against applied voltage, the current increases sharply and soon reaches a limiting value in a chamber containing inert carrier gas only. When the carrier contains a solute capable of capturing free electrons, the curve is less steep, and the potential required to establish the saturation current is much higher than in the presence of carrier gas alone. This is because the negative molecule-ions formed through electron capture by the solute are much less mobile and more likely to react with positive ions than are free electrons. Consequently, a higher potential is required to establish the same current flow obtainable when the negative charges are unencumbered. When high voltages are applied to the ionization chamber, the molecule-ions may acquire enough energy to dissociate on collision with neutral molecules. This re-establishes the saturation current. The potential required to reach the saturation current should be characteristic of the electron affinity of the compound, other experimental conditions being held constant.

In practice, compounds containing various functional groups are passed through an ionization chamber operated at low applied voltage with helium as a carrier gas. Compounds containing polar functional groups give small negative peaks because of their high electron affinities, whereas hydrocarbons do not. This is explained as follows: At all voltages applied to the chamber, the rate of ion production is greater in the presence of polar organic molecules than when the chamber contains helium alone. However, at low voltages where electron capture can occur, the loss of ions by recombination exceeds the number formed. Thus, at sufficiently low voltages, all substances with a high affinity for free electrons cause a decrease in the current flowing through the chamber. This results in negative peaks. The applied voltage at which the transition from a negative to a positive peak occurs varies slightly with solute concentration and the nature of the carrier gas. Nevertheless, it is sufficiently constant to serve for the characterization of the major classes of organic compounds. Therefore, with a detection system of this type it is possible to chromatograph a complex mixture of polar and nonpolar compounds and to pick out the polar compounds, owing to the fact that they yield negative peaks.

In early designs of this detector, argon was not used as the carrier gas since ionization of the organic molecules by excited argon atoms largely offset the effects of electron capture. However, detectors are now available constructed so that the uncharged metastable atoms tend to be swept out of the chamber while the negatively charged electrons are accelerated towards the anode (Jarrell-Ash Co.). This separation insures to a large extent that only free electrons come into contact with organic molecules. When the applied potential is high enough to prevent capture, the metastable argon enhances detector sensitivity. However, anomalous responses are sometimes obtained when argon is used as the carrier gas.

This method has been used by Goodwin et al. (1960) in the analysis of crop extracts for pesticides. Its success in this application depends on the fact that most pesticides contain chlorine atoms or other polar groups with high electron affinity, while most naturally occuring metabolites extractible with nonpolar solvents do not. As a result, background interference from normal plant constituents is greatly reduced, thus minimizing the need for extensive sample clean-up prior to chromatography.

f. Mass Spectrometry

Conventional magnetic-field mass spectrometers can serve to identify peaks, to resolve the composition of peaks containing two or three components, and to identify components appearing as shoulders or lost in the background (Lindeman and Annis, 1960). The relative amounts of two or three components in multicomponent peaks can be determined accurately. Scanning is sufficiently rapid to give several mass spectra per gas chromatographic peak. The time-of-flight mass spectrometer has also been used in series with a conventional detector to identify components giving rise to chromatographic peaks (Gohlke, 1959).

g. Spectrophotometry

Ultraviolet methods can detect compounds that absorb radiation in that region of the electromagnetic spectrum (Johnstone and Douglas, 1959). This method is specific for aromatic and heterocyclic compounds, open-chain systems containing conjugated double bonds, and molecules containing chromophoric groups such as nitro, carbonyl, and nitroso. The degree of specificity can be increased by means of monochromatic radiation. Light intensities are measured by the usual photomultiplier system. Hydrocarbons can be measured in the infrared by using the C–H band at 3330 cm^{-1}.

h. Biological Detectors

Bayer and Anders (1959) have used males of the species Bombyx mori (L) to detect sexual attractants extracted from the abdomens of females. The crude extracts are partitioned on a chromatographic column, and the eluates are passed through containers holding the males. Marked stimulation occurs when the attracting substances are eluted. Of course this method is too highly specific for general use, but analogous applications will occur to the experienced biologist. The sense of smell stimulates a more general biological response, but unfortunately it is only qualitative and, at best, uncertain. However, the nose of an experienced flavor chemist applied to the outlet of a chromatographic column may often provide a clue to the identity of an unknown compound.

VI. Miscellaneous Nonspecific Detectors

Other physical methods that have been employed in detector systems include measurement of dielectric constants (Turner, 1958), measurement of changes in light intensity or direct-current signal produced in a glow discharge excited by a high-frequency Tesla coil (Sternberg and Poulson, 1960), determination of the heat of adsorption of sample components by the column packing (Dudenbostel and Priestly, 1956), measurement of flame emissivity when the carrier gas stream is mixed with coal gas and burned (Grant, 1958), measurement of the change in surface potential of vibrating plates (Griffiths et al., 1952), measurement of the breakdown potential of spark discharges at atmospheric pressure (Lovelock, 1958), use of a thermionic ionization gauge (Ryce and Bryce, 1957), measurement of the temperature changes produced by burning organic compounds in a hydrogen flame (Scott, 1955), measurement of the volume of residual gas after the carrier (carbon dioxide) is dissolved in alkali (Janák method), and measurement of differences of flow impedance through a capillary tube (Griffiths et al., 1952).

VII. Combustion and Hydrocracking of Column Eluates

Calibration is very much simplified, and the sensitivity of thermal detectors increased, if all organic materials issuing from the chromatographic column are converted to a single chemical compound before they enter the detector. Hydrocarbons and their derivatives can be converted to CO_2 and water by combustion, or to methane and water by catalytic reduction. These reactions are carried out directly in the carrier gas stream. If the water is absorbed in a drying tower, only carbon dioxide or methane pass through the detector and are measured. Chlorinated hydrocarbons can be burned over a platinum catalyst, and the hydrochloric acid that is formed can be measured coulometrically (see Section D.V.d). Thus the response of the detector to a single compound and the empirical formulas of the uncombusted eluates are the only information required for calibration. Sensitivity to thermal detection is improved somewhat, since a large number of molecules pass through the detector than were present in the original sample, owing to the lower molecular weights of the reaction products. Unfortunately, sensitivity does not increase in direct proportion to the number of new molecules created. Nevertheless, the change is appreciable and should be considered in deciding whether to use this method. Furthermore, carbon dioxide and methane are permanent gases, and consequently thermistor detectors can be used at low temperatures where they are most sensitive without fear of the column eluates condensing in them. The main disadvantage is that the sample is destroyed; therefore these methods are not suitable for the analysis of mixtures of unknown composition.

a. Experimental Methods

*1. *Combustion to Carbon Dioxide* (Hunter et al., 1960). The outlet of the chromatographic column is attached to a stainless-steel combustion tube 8 inches long and ¼ inch in diameter which is filled with 20-mesh copper oxide and heated in a combustion furnace to 600°C. To remove water of combustion and water introduced with the sample, the outlet of the combustion tube is in turn connected to a 12-inch length of ¼-inch-diameter glass tubing filled with magnesium perchlorate. The outlet of this tube is connected to the line leading to the detector.

2. *Reduction to Methane* (Zlatkis et al., 1960). In this method, the organic compounds are reduced catalytically to methane and water in a reactor

placed between the column and detector. Details are given in Chapter 8, Section A.IV.b.

VIII. Summary

Thermal detectors and ionization detectors are used most frequently in gas chromatography. Thermal detectors are universal in their response to compounds of various types, and ionization detectors are nearly so. However, both must be calibrated for accurate work. To minimize calibration requirements, a gas density balance should be used. Alternatively, organic compounds can be combusted to carbon dioxide or hydrocracked to methane, and these products measured with a thermal conductivity cell. Thermal detectors are useful for measuring the major components of samples; ionization detectors are recommended for trace analysis because of their higher sensitivity.

Sometimes it may be desirable to choose a selective detector that will respond only to compounds having narrowly defined characteristics. This eliminates some interferences arising from overlapping peaks and at the same time provides information on the qualitative composition of the sample.

E. Introduction of Liquid and Solid Samples

I. General Introduction

The introduction of accurately measured quantities of liquids and solids into a gas chromatograph often constitutes a major problem because of the small sample sizes that are used. Sometimes this difficulty can be avoided by inclusion of an internal standard or normalizing peak areas (see Section H.III), but situations still occur where the amounts of materials applied to the column must be known accurately. This problem is aggravated when capillary columns and ionization detectors are used, since as little as 1 μg of material may be chromatographed. This situation led one worker to suggest, perhaps not altogether seriously, that the best solution is to use a large sample and a correspondingly less-sensitive detector.

With ionization detectors, carrier gas flow can be stopped to introduce the sample without destabilizing the base line. In this case, the plug sealing the injection port is removed, and the sample is applied directly to the column. With most instruments, however, the sample must be introduced against the back pressure of the column with the carrier gas flowing. Therefore liquid samples are injected through self-sealing diaphragms with hypodermic syringes, or through specially designed injection ports with micropipettes. Both liquid and solid samples can be introduced by sealing them in glass or metal capillaries and releasing the contents by melting or crushing the capillaries in the carrier gas stream.

Often specialized methods of sample introduction are employed which are applicable only to specific groups of compounds. Thus permanent gases are introduced through specially designed gas sampling valves (Chapter 2, method A.IV.c), volatile amines by treating their hydrochlorides with alkali in the gas stream (Chapter 3, section D.II.b.2), and volatile carbonyl compounds by flash exchange of their 2,4-dinitrophenylhydrazones with α-ketoglutarate in a capillary attached to the injection port (Chapter 3, section E.II.a.1). These techniques are described under individual subject headings in the appropriate chapters of this book.

Sample volumes applied to packed columns with internal diameters between 0.25 and 0.75 cm usually vary between 0.1 and 10 μl when thermal conductivity cells are used. In most cases the upper limit should not exceed 20 μl. It is now generally accepted that small samples yield high column efficiencies, other operating parameters being optimum. Bernhard (1960), for example, has shown that the theoretical plate number for a polyester succinate column drops by 39.5% when the sample volume (D-limonene or α-terpinene) is increased from 0.1 to 0.5 μl.

Very small samples are needed with capillary columns. These cannot be measured accurately by syringe or pipette methods. Therefore, the usual procedure is to inject a much larger sample and vent the greater proportion of it to the atmosphere by means of a split stream system. This is accomplished by flash evaporating the sample and sweeping it though a Y tube. One arm of the Y leads to the column, and the other to the atmosphere. The impedance of the vent line to the gas flow can be varied at will by capillary tubes or a Venturi sampler. Gas flow can be adjusted so that any desired proportion of the sample is discharged to the atmosphere, the remainder of it entering the column. Generally, only 0.01 to 0.001% of the sample injected is used. Reproducibility is not very good, and partial fractionation of high-boiling liquids sometimes occurs before the sample enters the column.

The temperature of the injection block is also an important variable in sample introduction, since column efficiency is low unless the material vaporizes rapidly. This topic is discussed in more detail in Section F.II.a. It will suffice to say here that injection block temperatures are usually set 50° to 100° higher than column temperatures, *providing* it can be shown that artifacts are not produced by thermal decomposition of solutes.

II. Introduction by Syringe

The fastest and most popular way of introducing liquid samples is with a syringe fitted with a hypodermic needle. Almost all commercial and laboratory-built chromatographs contain liquid injection ports designed for this purpose. The openings of the injection ports of laboratory-built instruments are often closed with rubber or neoprene serum bottle caps. The needle is plunged through the cap, the contents of the syringe expelled, and the needle withdrawn. The puncture made by this procedure is self-sealing. However, it is advisable to select a needle with a Huber point to avoid coring of the diaphragm. Each cap can be used for about twenty to thirty injections before it must be replaced. At higher temperatures, and on most commercial instruments, silicone septa are used. They are more stable chemically and thermally than rubber and have good self-sealing properties. The septum is usually held in place against an opening somewhat smaller than itself by the pressure of a knurled thumbscrew with a center hole through which the hypodermic needle is thrust. These septa can withstand several hundred punctures before failure, but it is best not to use them too long, since slow leaks may develop that go unnoticed unless a careful check is kept of the flow rate of the carrier gas. They must be replaced more often when used at high temperatures than at low.

Sometimes, ordinary medical syringes serve for sample introduction, but these are inaccurate and tend to leak around the barrel when injections are made against the high back pressure of the column. This has led some workers to conclude that the syringe method of introducing samples is unsatisfactory. However, leakproof syringes have been developed and are available commercially. They are capable of surprising accuracy in delivering volumes of the order of 1 μl, particularly when they are equipped with a device for limiting the thrust of the plunger to a fixed distance.

Usually, the syringe is operated against the back pressure of the column, and therefore the liquid seal between barrel and plunger must be tight. However, a valve has been developed by Samsel and Aldrich (1959) that permits injection of volatile liquids into a sample chamber maintained momentarily at atmospheric pressure, while carrier gas flows continuously through the rest of the instrument. The valve has been used up to a temperature of 250°C. The chamber is large enough to prevent pressure being built up by vaporization of the sample. Reproducibility is within 0.25% with 50 μl-samples.

a. Microliter Syringe with Chaney Adaptor

Syringes are available commercially with capacities of 1, 10, 50, and 100 μl (Hamilton Co. Inc.). The two smaller sizes are available only with cemented-on needles; with the larger sizes the needle is optional. Syringes with separate needles are best for highly viscous liquids. The three larger sizes are made of precision-bore glass with stainless-steel plungers. The 10-μl syringe is subdivided into units of 0.2 μl. The plunger of the 1-μl model is a tungsten wire which bottoms at the needle point; therefore the syringe is without holdup or dead volume. It is graduated in units of 0.02 μl. A visual check on the liquid level in this syringe is not possible; therefore when it is filled it should be pumped a number of times, and adequate time should be allowed for the sample to suck up into the bore. Liquid levels in the larger sizes can be checked directly. These syringes are leaktight when tested with water at 150 psig but are not gastight when clean and dry. For syringes that can be used to inject gas samples, see Chapter 2, method A.IV.a.

1. *Maintenance.* The clearance between barrel and plunger is very small; hence liquids more viscous than water are not suitable for lubrication until after the barrel is worn by prolonged use. Otherwise it may split. The barrel also may split if the syringe is subjected to sudden temperature changes, owing to the difference in coefficients of thermal expansion between glass and metal. Thus the syringe should be heated or cooled slowly, or first the plunger should be removed from the barrel. Drying them assembled in an oven at 150°C or lower is permissible.

Cleaning is best accomplished with a soap solution followed by a water rinse, the plunger being used to flush the bore. If the needle becomes plugged, a wire (not supplied with the smaller sizes) should be fed through it to dislodge the obstruction. Attempts to force liquid through the needle with the plunger may split the barrel. Acids should not be used for cleaning syringes with cemented needles. However, the cement is resistant to most organic solvents.

2. *Sample Introduction without Adaptor.* The syringe is grasped by the flange and plunger, and the air is pumped out. Care should be taken not to touch the barrel, or errors may be caused by thermal expansion of the glass. Next, the needle is immersed in the liquid to be tested, and the plunger is pulled out to overfill the syringe. With the 1-μl model, adequate time must be allowed for filling, since the liquid level is not visible (see above). After it has been filled, the syringe is held in a vertical position against a white background, and the plunger is depressed just to the top of the marking representing the volume desired. The needle is blotted lightly, care being taken not to draw the liquid out of it by capillarity. The needle is then thrust through the closure of the injection port, and the plunger is depressed quickly to discharge the sample.

3. *Sample Injection with Chaney Adaptor.* The Chaney adaptor is a device for limiting the thrust of the syringe when it is filled, so that reproducible liquid volumes can be delivered (Fig. 14). It consists of a metal plate (A) attached to the plunger. The plate is equipped with an adjustable stop rod (B) which strikes the flange of the barrel (C) when the plunger is depressed. The length of the stop rod is adjusted so that the desired volume is delivered by loosening the setscrew which holds it in place, and by sliding it so that one end touches the barrel flange when the bottom of the plunger is just at the top of the appropriate marking on the barrel. The setscrew is then tightened.

If approximate but reproducible sample sizes are required, the markings on the syringe barrel can be used to estimate volume. Otherwise trial samples should be discharged and weighed, and the length of the stop rod adjusted as required to deliver the desired sample size.

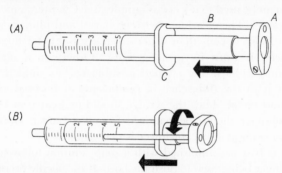

Fig. 14. Microsyringe equipped with Chaney adaptor for injection of liquid samples: (A) with stop rod rotated to strike flange for filling with a constant volume of liquid; (B) with stop rod rotated to pass flange for injection of sample.

To inject a sample, the syringe is overfilled, and the head is rotated so that the stop rod hits the barrel flange when the plunger is depressed. The needle is wiped and thrust through the septum closing the injection port. The plunger is rotated until the stop rod clears the flange and then is depressed rapidly to inject the sample.

The 1-μl syringe will deliver a volume of 0.25 μl with an accuracy of $\pm 3\%$ when used with an adaptor.

b. Micrometer Syringes

Several syringes driven by micrometers are available commercially. The Agla syringe (Burroughs Wellcome Ltd.) has been modified by Sweeting (1959) to permit more rapid discharge of samples, since he found that the slight delay in injecting sample volumes greater than 10 μl often caused spreading of peaks. A syringe with a capacity of 250 μl and a micrometer scale graduated in units of 0.1 μl is available from California Laboratory Equipment Co.

Lichtenfels et al. (1956) describe a micrometer syringe that was subsequently modified by Langer and Pantages (1958). The barrel is a 0.5-ml tuberculin syringe fitted with a Teflon plunger. The control is a micrometer screw seated in the upper end of the plunger. The chromatograph is depressurized before the sample is injected. A small amount of air is drawn into the syringe in advance of the sample to flush out the needle assembly and serve as a marker peak from which to measure zero time.

c. Syringes with Stepwise Volume Adjustment

Several syringe assemblies have been described in which the volume of sample delivered is adjustable in steps rather than continuously. This makes it easier to inject a series of different-sized samples reproducibly, and for many applications the loss in flexibility may not be important. Dal Nogare and Safranski (1960) have adapted a standard 250-μl syringe to this purpose by equipping the plunger and barrel with threaded fittings. A short pin fastened to the plunger fitting coincides with each of four holes drilled in the barrel fitting, the depth of the holes determining the volume displaced from the syringe. The volume can be adjusted as desired by rotating the plunger. For precise work the exact displacement at each position should be determined by calibration. Accuracy is of the order of 0.8% in the 5- to 50-μl range.

A microsyringe has been described by Carle (1958) in which plunger travel is set by means of slotted metal spacers which adjust the position of a collar stop. The latter is locked into position with a setscrew, and the spacer is removed before the syringe is used. Spacers are available calibrated directly in volume (Beckman Instruments Co.). The capacity of the syringe is 60 μl, and reproducibility is 0.1 to 0.5% in the 5- to 50-μl range. Samples can be injected against positive column pressures.

III. Introduction by Micropipettes

Several systems have been described for introducing samples into chromatographs with micropipettes. In the method of Tenney and Harris (1957), one end of the pipette is introduced into the instrument through a special attachment which replaces the self-sealing injection port standard on most instruments. Once the pipette is inside the instrument, the sample is blown from it with carrier gas. This apparatus is now available commercially (Fisher Scientific Co., Perkin-Elmer Corp.). Pipettes with volumes of 1 to 500 μl are supplied. A 5-μl sample can be introduced with an accuracy of 0.5 to 1.5%, depending on its volatility.

A modified mass spectrometer inlet system has also been used for liquids with low boiling points (Davis and McCrea, 1957). The introduction unit utilizes an evacuated chamber with a mercury-sealed orifice, and a means for bypassing and sweeping out the chamber with carrier gas. Mercury is used to force the sample from the pipette into the evacuated system. The method is said to be reproducible to within 1.2% with a 3.6-μl sample.

A method has been devised by Stanford (1959) for introducing 1- to 100-mg samples from a capillary tube equipped with a micro rubber squeeze bulb. The sample is drawn into the capillary and weighed by difference on a semimicrobalance. This method is suitable only when the chromatograph is operated at inlet pressures less than atmospheric. Accuracy is not given.

The first two methods described above were developed before leakproof syringes capable of withstanding the pressure of the carrier gas became available. They are less convenient than syringe injection, and now they are no more accurate. Consequently a complete description of the apparatus and techniques for injection will be omitted here, since these procedures are unlikely to be employed in the future to an extent comparable to the syringe method.

IV. Introduction in Sealed Capillary Tubes

When small samples are used, and it is necessary to know their sizes accurately, they can be sealed into glass capillary tubes. The tubes are then introduced into the gas stream, brought up to vaporization temperature, and crushed or broken *in situ* with a suitable mechanical device. Methods for doing this have been described by Dimbat *et al.* (1956), McCreadie and Williams (1957), Bowman and Karmen (1958), and Joklík and Bažant (1959). It has been reported that volumes of 0.004 to 0.5 μl can be introduced with a reproducibility of 10% (Bowman and Karmen, 1958).

A method for introducing solid samples in capillaries made of Wood's metal or other low-melting alloys has been developed by Dubský and Janák (1960). The capillary is placed in a cold inlet trap located between two metal stopcocks and then dropped into a heated declivity where it melts and the sample is released. Melting is sufficiently fast to give good chromatographic peaks at temperatures of 150°C and up. The apparatus does not contain heat-labile materials of construction and so can be used at 500°C. Therefore, it is particularly suitable for the high-temperature chromatography of solids. Accuracy is of the order of 2 to 4% for the introduction of 1- to 4-mg samples.

a. Experimental Methods

*1. *Introduction of Liquids in Glass Capillaries* (Bowman and Karmen, 1958). *Preparation of capillaries.* The internal diameters of about 0.1 × 10-mm sections of glass capillary tubing are measured accurately with a microscope. The end of a section is applied to the surface of a liquid sample and allowed to fill partially. The tube is shaken gently to move the liquid to the center part, and the ends are sealed in a flame. The length of the liquid column is measured under a microscope, and the sample volume is calculated.

Construction of capillary crusher. A diagram of the apparatus used to crush the capillary is shown in Fig. 15. *A* is a vertical section of brass tubing equipped with a side arm (*B*). The tube is connected to the inlet side of the chromatographic column with a brass fitting. Carrier gas enters the crusher through the side arm (*B*) and passes into the column. A slotted plate (*C*) is placed over the column to serve as an anvil on which to crush the capillary.

D is a stainless-steel piston with a groove (E) 1 cm long milled in its side in which to place the capillary. The piston is inserted in a sliding joint placed at the upper end of the vertical brass tube (A), the joint being made leak-tight by a polytetrafluoroethylene compression fitting somewhat longer than the groove.

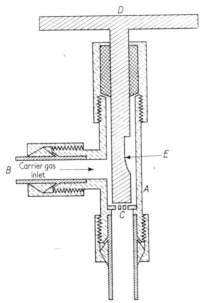

FIG. 15. Apparatus for crushing capillary tubes (Bowman and Karmen, 1958).

Operation. The piston (D) is moved upward so that the groove (E) is above the fitting. The capillary containing the sample is then placed within the groove, and the piston is pushed down to its original position so that the groove is in the gas stream. The capillary slides out of the groove and falls onto the slotted metal plate (C) below. The air contained in the groove is swept through the column with carrier gas, after which the capillary is crushed by depressing the piston, thus liberating the sample. The compression fitting is heat-resistant, making it possible to operate the crusher at temperatures high enough to cause rapid volatilization of liquids such as methyl laurate.

*2. *Introduction of Solids in Metal Capillaries* (Dubský and Janák, 1960). *Preparation of capillary.* The capillary is made of Wood's metal (m.p. 60.5°C), or a low-melting (47°C) alloy containing 10.6% Sn, 22.1% Pb, 41.0% Bi, 8.2% Cd, and 18.1% In. A thin sheet is prepared by permitting the melted metal to trickle onto a cold glass plate. A piece about 8×10 mm is cut out and rolled on a small metal core to form a capillary tube about 2 mm in diameter. The tube is sealed by touching one end and the side with a warm object. The sample is introduced into the capillary, and the other end is sealed in the same way.

Apparatus. The equipment for introducing the sample (Fig. 16) consists of a vertical metal tube connected to the chromatographic column. The

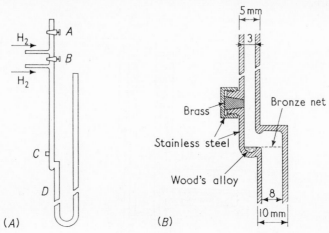

FIG. 16. Apparatus for introducing samples into chromatographs in metal capillaries: (*A*) general diagram of injection system; (*B*) details of vaporizing saddle (Dubsky and Janák, 1960).

tube is provided with two side arms to admit carrier gas, and two stopcocks (*A* and *B*) which can be closed off to form a cold inlet chamber. The upper part of the tube is offset from the lower part and terminates in a small heated declivity or saddle (*D*) in which the capillary is melted. An outlet is provided just above the declivity for removal of accumulated metal.

Procedure. Stopcock *B* is closed, and column operating conditions are established. Stopcock *A* is opened, and an auxiliary flow of carrier gas is permitted through the inlet chamber to sweep out air and prevent it from entering the sampling device. The capillary tube containing the weighed sample is dropped into the cold inlet chamber, and *A* is closed. Then stopcock *B* is opened, and the capillary drops into the declivity *D* (Fig. 16*B*) where the metal melts and the sample is released into the carrier gas stream. The small amount of air contained within the capillary serves as a marker. The quantity of metal introduced with each sample is very small, so that up to two hundred analyses can be performed before the declivity (saddle) must be emptied.

V. SUMMARY

Liquid samples with volumes of 0.2 to 50 µl are introduced most conveniently and accurately into gas chromatographs with leakproof syringes fitted with hypodermic needles. Introduction is through a rubber or silicone diaphragm closing the injection port. Best results are obtained when the syringe is equipped with a device that limits the travel of the plunger to a fixed distance. With syringes thus equipped, samples can be delivered with a reproducibility of 0.5 to 3%, depending on volume. Liquid samples also can be introduced with micropipettes, but these are more cumbersome and are no more accurate than the newer leakproof syringes.

Small liquid and solid samples in the 1- to 5-mg range can be introduced by sealing them in capillaries, which then are broken or melted in the carrier gas stream. Small samples can be applied to capillary columns by injecting larger samples and splitting the stream, but reproducibility is not entirely satisfactory.

Highest column efficiencies are obtained if the sample size is kept small and the injection port is heated to a temperature sufficiently high to cause flash evaporation of the materials introduced.

F. Regulation and Selection of Operating Temperatures

I. Introduction

Control of column and detector temperature is a vital factor in gas chromatography, for the temperature influences reproducibility of retention volumes, base-line stability, and constancy of peak areas. Moreover, inadequate heating of the injection block lowers column efficiency, and condensation of solutes in the exit lines prevents collection of fractions. Consequently, it is more important to consider the over-all effects of temperature rather than to focus attention on any one component part of the instrument. Once adequate means are available for adjusting temperatures with the requisite precision, optimum conditions must be selected for the particular separation being attempted. This requires studies of changes in retention volumes with respect to temperature, and studies of the influence of temperature on separation factors and column efficiencies. Finally, the thermal stabilities of the solutes and stationary phase must be considered. All these factors must be weighed in arriving at operating specifications.

If the mixture to be analyzed is complex and contains components that boil at temperatures as much as 100° to 200°C apart, no single temperature may be satisfactory. In this case it may be necessary to increase the temperature of the chromatographic column during the analysis, either stepwise or continuously, to achieve the separations desired. Alternatively, the sample can be prefractionated before chromatography by ancillary physical methods such as fractional or azeotropic distillation.

II. Regulation of Temperature

The temperature of all the component parts of a chromatograph must be controlled to obtain optimum performance. There are some exceptions to this, notably in the separation of permanent gases; but, in general, the better the temperature control, the better will be base-line stability, column efficiency, and reproducibility. There are two general methods of regulating temperature. The first method is to place all the component parts of the chromatograph in the same oven. This is inexpensive, simplifies instrumentation, and reduces repair and maintenance problems to the minimum. However, flexibility is lost, and analysis times may be lengthened. Some problems cannot be handled satisfactorily with this type of equipment. The other method is to thermostat the major components of the chromatograph separately. This increases the number of instrumental adjustments that must be made, but at the same time it greatly enhances the versatility of the method. Instruments of both types are available commercially, and, as would be expected, the greater the degree of temperature control, the greater is the cost. The choice is governed by the nature of the problem. Many routine analyses can be handled satisfactorily on an instrument equipped with a single control. However, on research instruments, the temperature of the injection block, the column, and the detector should be regulated separately.

a. Injection Block Temperature

To obtain optimum peak resolution the sample should be introduced into the carrier gas stream as a homogeneous plug of vapor, in so far as this is

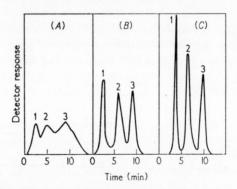

Fig. 17. Effect of injection temperature on shapes of peaks obtained on chromatographing (1) methanol, (2) ethanol, and (3) isopropanol: (*A*) injected at 21°C; (*B*) injected at 48°C; (*C*) injected at 105°C (Pollard and Hardy, 1955).

possible. For liquid samples, the temperature of the injection block governs the rate of vaporization, and therefore the extent of mixing of the vapor with carrier gas. This can have a profound effect on column efficiency (Fig. 17). Thus the peaks arising from methanol, ethanol, and isopropanol overlap badly at an injection temperature of 21°C, and are resolved completely at 105°C, operating conditions being otherwise the same (Pollard and Hardy, 1955). Similar effects have been reported for aromatic hydrocarbons and esters (Littlewood *et al.*, 1955). For best resolution, the injection block should be heated to a temperature close to the boiling point of the least-volatile sample component. As this is usually not the best column temperature, control and read-out should be independent of the temperature of the main oven of the chromatograph. The injection block can be heated by wrapping it with insulated resistance wire and regulating the current input with a variable transformer. Alternatively, the block can be fitted with a cartridge heater installed through a port equipped with a gastight seal. Samples injected into the chromatograph are vaporized when they strike the hot sheath of the heater. The heater used with the Perkin-Elmer Model D Vapor Fractometer has a rating of 22 watts at 117 volts, and its temperature at maximum power is about 100°C above that of the column oven.

In general, injection block temperatures are held at 50° to 100°C above column temperature, to ensure flash evaporation. However, care must be taken to make sure artifacts are not created through pyrolysis or isomerization of sample components, for, even though a compound may be stable at the column temperature, it could decompose or rearrange at the injection temperature. Therefore the injection temperature should be controlled entirely separately from the column temperature, and the block should be equipped with its own thermocouple connected to a read-out meter.

b. Temperature of the Column

Chromatographic columns are operated at temperatures varying from −200° to 1000°C and the range is expanding continually. Zero and subzero temperatures are achieved most conveniently by immersing the column in a liquid coolant. This may be a wet ice bath, an ice–salt bath, a solvent–dry ice bath, or a liquefied permanent gas such as nitrogen, depending on the requirements of the analysis. The columns are usually coiled and placed inside a Dewar flask containing coolant.

For operation above room temperature, the column can be heated in an oil bath, a vapor bath, or an air oven, or it can be wrapped with heating tape. Oil bath temperatures can be regulated accurately but cannot be changed rapidly because of the large volume and high specific heat of the oil. Vapors from refluxing solvents are convenient, since thermoregulators and relays are not required for control. However, they have the disadvantage that temperatures cannot be adjusted continuously. Pure solvents having various boiling points, and mixtures of these, must be used to increase temperature stepwise over the desired range. Moreover, boiling points vary with atmospheric pressure, and thus data obtained in this manner will not be reproducible at various altitudes.

Enclosure of the column in an air oven is the most widely adopted means of controlling column temperature. A detailed discussion of electronic circuits for regulation is outside the scope of this book. In one instrument (Perkin-Elmer), a thermistor bead located in the column oven is the sensing element. It serves as one leg of a Wheatstone bridge circuit which is balanced at the desired temperature by means of fine and coarse controls, so that the output of the bridge is zero. When the oven temperature exceeds the preset value, the bridge becomes unbalanced and an output voltage is produced which de-energizes a relay and thus turns off the oven heater. When the oven cools below the preset temperature, the bridge is unbalanced again, and the signal that is produced turns on the heater. The heater is a coiled resistance wire. Air is circulated around the wire and throughout the chamber with an electric fan.

If operating temperatures must be changed very rapidly, columns can be wrapped with heating tape and heated directly. In this way part of the lag associated with changing the temperature of a large body of fluid and its container is avoided.

Regardless of the method of regulation, accurate adjustment of temperature is necessary to secure reproducible retention volumes. Control within 0.1°C is desirable over the entire operating range.

c. Temperature of the Detector

In many chromatographs the detector is located within the column oven. This saves space and reduces costs, but it is inconvenient when columns must be changed often or when the temperature must be readjusted during a run, especially when thermal conductivity cells are used. The temperature change alters the resistance of the sensing elements, so that the base line must be re-established. Consequently, it is more convenient to have the detector thermostatted separately. For best results the temperature of a T/C cell should be controlled to within 0.05°C below 100°C and to within 0.1°C above that figure. The detector should be operated at or slightly above the highest column temperature employed to avoid condensation of solute vapors in it. The line leading from the column to the detector should be as short as possible and should be heated. If the line cannot be contained within the oven walls, it should be wrapped with insulated resistance wire or heating tape. When the detector block and column oven are operated at temperatures that differ greatly, they should be insulated from one another to minimize deviations caused by heat flow.

d. Temperature of the Outlet

Collection of fractions for rechromatography or identification is often impossible because solute vapors condense in the line leading from the detector. Consequently, the exit line should be wrapped with insulated resistance wire or with heating tape, and the temperature controlled either by the detector thermoregulator or independently. If the fractions are collected through a hypodermic needle attached to the exit line, this must be heated also, particularly if high-boiling compounds are being chromatographed. This can be accomplished by enclosing the needle in a short metal tube approximately its own length and about 1.5 cm in diameter. The metal tube is wound with resistance wire and insulated, and the temperature is adjusted by means of a variable transformer (see Section I.II.c.1).

III. SELECTION OF COLUMN TEMPERATURE

Column temperature is one of the most important operating parameters to be determined in developing a new gas chromatographic method. If the temperature is too low, the solutes may not be eluted from the column, or, if they are, the peaks will be very broad owing to longitudinal diffusion in the carrier gas during the long residence time within the column. If the temperature is too high, the solutes will emerge without resolution. Generally, there is some intermediate temperature at which separation factors are at the maximum, and the column operates with high plate efficiency. Location of this range and determination of whether solutes and stationary phases are stable under these conditions constitute one of the major tasks in arriving at optimum operating conditions.

a. Relation of Retention Volume to Temperature

The principal effect of increasing column temperature is to decrease the partition coefficient of the solute between the mobile and stationary phases. In other words, a greater proportion of the compound being chromatographed is present in the vapor phase; therefore, it travels through the column faster, if a constant flow rate of carrier gas is assumed. A secondary effect is reduction of the proportion of space within the column occupied by the mobile phase caused by thermal expansion of the stationary phase. The net effect is reduction of retention volumes by about 5% for each degree of temperature increase, the exact value depending on the temperature range and amount of interaction between the solute and the stationary phase. The quantitative dependence of retention volume on column temperature can be expressed by an Antoine equation having the form of equation 23,

$$\log V_g = L + \frac{!M}{T\rho_L} = \frac{\Delta H}{2.3RT} + k \tag{23}$$

where V_g is the specific retention volume of the solute, L, M, and k are empirical constants, ρ_L is the density of the liquid phase at column temperature, T is the absolute temperature of the column, R is the gas constant (1.987 cal deg^{-1} mole^{-1}), and ΔH is the partial molar heat of solution of the solute vapor in the stationary liquid.

Changes in the density of the stationary liquid, ρ_L, with respect to temperature are comparatively small. Therefore, it is possible to evaluate the experimental constants L and M with satisfactory accuracy by plotting log V_g against $1/T$. When this is done, straight lines are obtained, each with a slope (M) and intercept (L) characteristic of the compound being investigated (Fig. 18). This is an extremely valuable method for evaluating

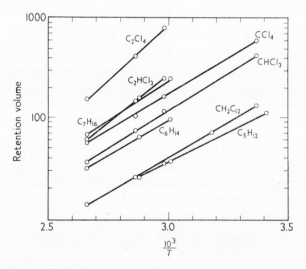

Fig. 18. Change in logarithm of retention volume with respect to reciprocal of absolute temperature for hydrocarbons and chlorinated hydrocarbons (Hoare and Purnell, 1956).

data, since a great deal of information can be obtained from readings taken at relatively few temperatures. From such plots, it is often possible to tell whether a separation is feasible at any given temperature. For example, the curve for C_7H_{16} (Fig. 18) has a different slope than the curve for C_2HCl_3, and the two intersect at a reciprocal temperature of 2.85. Consequently, it would be impossible to separate these compounds at a temperature corresponding to this value, since their retention volumes are identical.

In view of the usefulness of this relation, the change of retention volume with temperature should be determined, and the results reported for at least two temperatures, as far apart as is practicable.

b. Relation between Column Efficiency and Temperature

It is sometimes stated that column efficiency as measured by *HETP* increases with increasing column temperature. Peaks become narrower at higher temperatures because the solute does not remain in the column as long, and thus there is less time for longitudinal diffusion to take place. However, peak narrowness alone should not be taken as evidence of improved column performance. The theoretical plate number of a column is proportional to the square of the ratio of the retention volume to the peak width

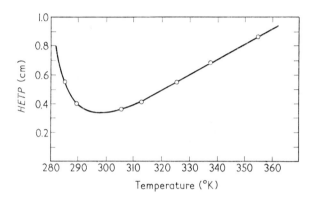

Fɪɢ. 19. Relation between absolute temperature and column efficiency for separation of *n*-pentane and *n*-hexane on liquid paraffin (de Wet and Pretorius, 1958).

(equation 14). Hence, as the retention volume becomes smaller, the number of plates decreases, and thus the two factors operate against one another. Consequently, it is the *ratio* of volume to width that must become larger; a reduction in width alone will not suffice. The peaks may be sharper, but they could also be closer together so that the per cent overlap is not reduced. Temperature does not appear as an explicit term in the van Deemter equation, (equation 2). However, the diffusivity of the solute in the mobile and stationary phases as well as its partition coefficient are temperature-dependent. The exact form of these relationships is unknown, but, by substituting approximate values in the van Deemter equation, de Wet and Pretorius (1958) arrived at the relation between efficiency and temperature given in equation 24, where *HETP* is the height equivalent to a theoretical plate, *T*

$$HETP = A + BT + C/T \tag{24}$$

is the absolute temperature, and *A*, *B*, and *C* are constants.

This equation represents a hyperbolic curve and is similar in form to the equation relating *HETP* to linear flow rate of the carrier gas (Section A.IV.b). Consequently, it should pass through a minimum, at which point column efficiency is optimum. De Wet and Pretorius found this value to be 24°C for the separation of n-pentane and n-hexane on a 120×0.4-cm column packed with liquid paraffin on Celite (30:70) at an average linear flow rate (hydrogen) of 2.5 cm/sec (Fig. 19).

Of course, this finding should not imply that 24°C, or in fact any temperature in this general range, is optimum in all cases. This will vary with the nature of the solutes, and between solutes when different solvents are used. In fact, as was pointed out earlier (Section A.IV.b), column efficiency as measured by *HETP* depends on the nature of the solute, even when all other parameters including temperature, flow rate, and the compositions of the mobile and stationary phases are held constant. However, it should be emphasized that column efficiency varies with temperature, and it often pays to find out what the optimum value is from the standpoint of making a practical separation.

c. Relation between Separation Factors and Temperature

Column efficiency is not the only criterion determining whether a separation is feasible. Separation factor is frequently more important, and this, too, is temperature-dependent. In general, separation factors for members of a homologous series diminish with increasing temperature, but this may not be universally true. It is often true because the velocity ratio for the movement of two solutes through the same column is an exponential function of their heats of solution in the stationary phase and the absolute temperature, as expressed in equation 25, where u_A is the linear velocity of

$$u_A/u_B \propto e^{-(H_A - H_B)/RT} \tag{25}$$

component A, u_B is the linear velocity of component B, T is the absolute temperature, and H_A and H_B are the heats of solution in the liquid phases of the two components, respectively. In general, the *difference* in heats of solution between two members of a homologous series of compounds does not change greatly with temperature. Hence if T increases while H_A and H_B remain the same, the ratio of the velocities, or in effect the separation factor, will diminish.

The importance of this in GLC is illustrated by the fact that the classically difficult separation of m-xylene from p-xylene can be achieved on a nonselective column packing (Wiseman, 1960). At room temperature these two isomers are easily separated on a 50-foot column containing dinonyl phthalate, the separation factor being 1.05 (Fig. 20). No separation is obtained at 80°C, although the column efficiency as measured by *HETP* remains the same. Low temperatures are advantageous in GSC also. Argon cannot be resolved from oxygen on a molecular sieve at room temperature.

However, by reducing the temperature to $-72°C$ good separation is obtained (Chapter 2, method B.II.a.5).

Low temperatures may not give the best separation factors in all cases. If the curves relating retention volume to reciprocal of the absolute tem-

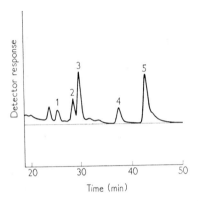

Fig. 20. Resolution of *m*-xylene and *p*-xylene on a nonselective stationary phase (dinonyl phthalate) at room temperature: (1) ethyl benzene; (2) *m*-xylene; (3) *p*-xylene; (4) *o*-xylene; (5) styrene; (Wiseman, 1960).

perature intersect, obviously better separation will be obtained both above and below this temperature, since the difference in V_g between the two compounds will be zero. See curves in Fig. 18, for example. However, in most practical examples described to date, lowering the temperature is beneficial.

d. Influence of Temperature on Solute Stability

Not least among the factors arguing for choice of the lowest operating temperatures consistent with practical retention volumes is the fact that many solutes are thermally unstable. This can lead to loss of components through chemical reaction with column packings, production of artifacts through pyrolysis, and isomerization of unsaturated compounds. Examples are treated in detail under specific headings and so will not be dealt with exhaustively here. It will suffice to say that interactions of fatty acid esters with polyester packings and isomerization of terpenes have been investigated most exhaustively. It is hoped that not too many of the wonderful discoveries made possible by gas chromatography are attributable to artifacts. Fortunately, such artifacts are comparatively easy to detect if the investigator thinks of the possibility in time. Several approaches that can be used are outlined below.

1. Run a pure sample of the compound to be analyzed through the

column and see if more than one peak is obtained. Collect the fractions, and confirm their identity by infrared or mass spectrometry.

2. Run the sample at a series of different column temperatures, keeping the flow rate and detector temperature constant. If peak areas become smaller with increasing temperature, it is likely that decomposition or interaction with the column packing has taken place. In this event, run the sample on a different (and less reactive) column packing to determine if thermal decomposition or interaction with the packing is the predominating cause of loss.

3. If a complex mixture of related compounds is being chromatographed, calculate the percentage composition of the mixture by the internal normalization method (see method H.III.c) on a series of runs made at different temperatures. If losses take place, the apparent composition of the mixture will vary with temperature. Under conditions where decomposition or interactions occur, the percentages of components having low retention volumes will increase while those of compounds with high retention volumes will decrease. This is because the fast-moving compounds do not remain in the column very long. Therefore, not as much material decomposes as when retention volumes are high. Since results are calculated on the basis of per cent of total peak area, discrepancies are accentuated.

4. Apply the sample to the column, and cut off the supply of carrier gas at about $\frac{1}{2}t_r$. Restart the gas flow, and complete the run. Repeat this with different shut-down times. If peak area diminishes with shut-down time, it is likely that attrition of the sample is taking place.

If loss of the solute is established, it is necessary to find a less-reactive column packing, reduce the temperature, or both. Generally, hydrocarbons such as the Apiezons and squalane are less reactive than polyesters. However, it may be necessary to use a polar packing to obtain the requisite separation factor. In this case it might be worth while to reduce the amount of partition liquid to less than 1% on the solid support and cut sample size proportionately. By this expedient, compounds can be chromatographed at as much as 200°C below their boiling points. Of course, it is necessary to select an inactive solid support and a highly sensitive detector. Glass beads and an ionization detector of the argon or flame type have been employed for this.

Separations by high-temperature chromatography will continue to be of interest, and there is no doubt that the ceiling will continue to be pushed upward. However, at the same time thought should be given to finding means of reducing the temperatures required. This not only reduces the risk of creating artifacts but also serves to increase the over-all range of compounds that ultimately can be chromatographed in the gas phase.

e. Influence of Temperature on Solvent Stability

Many of the more selective stationary liquids are volatile or decompose at high temperatures, and this places a ceiling on their usefulness. Common difficulties include unstable base lines on recorders arising from excessive elution of the stationary phase or its decomposition products through the detector, and contamination of solute fractions collected from the column effluent. Bleeding is particularly serious with ionization detectors, since background is often prohibitively high. Apiezon L, high-vacuum silicone grease, and polyethylene have been used at temperatures ranging from 150° to 350°C. Higher temperatures can be employed with conditioned silicone gum rubber, irradiated asphaltenes, and inorganic salts. However, none of the organic packings now available will survive prolonged use at 500°C.

Benzimidazole polymers recently developed by C. S. Marvel (Anon., 1960) warrant consideration as high-temperature packings. The polymer produced from diaminobenzidine and diphenyl isophthalate melts at temperatures above 770°C. There is very little weight loss in a nitrogen atmosphere at 500°C. Heating in air at 600°C for 5 hours results in a weight loss of 22%. If polymerization is carried out at temperatures below 500°C, the product is soluble in dimethyl sulfoxide, so there should be little difficulty in coating solid supports in the usual way.

f. Prediction of Optimum Column Temperature

It always is desirable to select optimum operating parameters with the minimum of experimental work, but so far no system that is applicable universally has been worked out to find the best column temperature for separating complex mixtures. If simple mixtures are being chromatographed, it often is expedient to determine retention volumes at several temperatures as far apart as practicable, and plot log V_g against $1/T$. From these curves, it is possible to select a temperature at which separation factors are at the maximum. If the solutes and stationary phase are stable under these conditions, the next step is to find the number of theoretical plates required to obtain the degree of separation needed, and adjust the column length accordingly. This can be done by the method of Glueckauf (1955).

A procedure for calculating the temperature required to separate two members of a homologous series is described by Grant and Vaughan (1956). First, it is necessary to assume that the two solutes have the same molecular weights and to know the difference between their boiling points. If this information is available, the temperature required to separate adjacent peaks by three standard deviations can be calculated from equation 26, where T

$$T = \Delta t n^{1/2}/0.283 \tag{26}$$

is the optimum temperature, Δt is the boiling-point difference (°C) between the two compounds, and n is the theoretical plate number of the column.

A more general relation is given by equation 27, where N is Trouton's

$$T = N \, \Delta t n^{1/2}/qR \tag{27}$$

constant (21 for nonassociated liquids), R is the gas constant (1.987), and q is the number of standard deviations desired between the peaks. Although useful, this method can be applied only to closely related compounds of known boiling points.

A procedure for establishing optimum column temperature, described by Hoare and Purnell (1956), is based on logarithms of retention volumes plotted against logarithms of the saturation vapor pressures of the solutes. This calculation is useful only when vapor pressures are known in advance, which is seldom the case for compounds of biochemical interest. More often, it is expedient to determine retention volumes at several temperatures and find the best conditions for separation by plotting log V_g against $1/T$.

IV. Temperature Programming

There is no optimum column temperature for chromatographing complex mixtures of compounds having widely separated boiling points. At high temperatures extremely volatile compounds are not resolved, and at low temperatures high-boiling components are not eluted. At intermediate temperatures peaks arising from low-boiling components are likely to be crowded, whereas those of high boilers may be inconveniently broad because of high residence times in the column. The only satisfactory way of resolving such mixtures on packed columns is to chromatograph each group of compounds at the temperature best suited for the separation of its components. This can be accomplished by using two columns heated to different temperatures, by applying two samples to the same column at different temperatures, by increasing the temperature stepwise while a run is in progress, or by increasing the temperature continuously during a run. Usually, more elaborate equipment is required than for isothermal runs. Regardless of the method, the flow rate of the carrier gas will decrease with increasing temperature at constant inlet pressure because of its higher viscosity. Therefore the inlet pressure must be adjusted manually or automatically, to obtain comparable retention volumes.

a. Columns in Series at Different Temperatures

This method requires two complete chromatographs connected in series so that the effluent from the first unit passes directly into the second unit. The column oven of the first unit is heated to a temperature sufficiently high to obtain good separation of the less-volatile components in a reasonable length of time. The oven of the second unit is maintained at a lower temperature to allow for better separation of the lower-boiling components. This is termed two-stage chromatography. The stationary phases in the two units may be the same, or they may be different. Often it may be advantageous to use a polar liquid in the first stage and a nonpolar liquid in the second stage, or vice versa. Analysis time is usually less than when one column is used and the temperature is increased continuously. However, the slower-moving components yield broader peaks (Harrison *et al.*, 1958).

b. Injection of Multiple Samples with Columns at Different Temperatures

In this procedure, the column temperature is adjusted for optimum separation of the low-boiling components. A sample is injected, and the chromatogram is recorded. Next, the column is backflushed to remove noneluted materials, after which the temperature is raised to a value suitable for the separation of high-boiling components. A duplicate sample is injected, and the analysis is repeated. On the second chromatogram, peaks arising from volatile constituents are unresolved or crowded, whereas those representing the higher-boiling materials should be well separated.

c. Stepwise Adjustment of Temperature

The sample is injected at a column temperature chosen to give good separation of volatile components, and partition is continued for a predetermined period of time. The temperature is then increased as rapidly as possible to a value suitable for the elution of the less-volatile components. At the same time, it is necessary to increase inlet pressure to maintain a constant flow rate of the carrier gas. To use this method effectively with a thermal detector, the detector must be thermostatted separately from the column at a temperature slightly above the highest one used for partition. Otherwise, the time required to re-establish a steady base-line between temperature changes would be too great.

d. Nonlinear Temperature Programming (Sullivan et al., 1959)

A standard chromatograph is modified by replacing the internally located T/C cell with a separately thermostatted hot-wire detector located about 8 inches from the exit end of the column. The connecting tubing is wrapped with heating tape, and its temperature and that of the detector are adjusted to the highest value to be used during the run. The variable voltage transformer which controls the oven temperature (Aerograph Model No. A-100) is turned up to full scale with the power switch off. The oven is adjusted to the desired starting temperature, and the sample is injected. The oven switch then is turned on. The temperature rises slowly during the first 10 minutes, and thereafter more rapidly. About 30 minutes elapsed time is required to reach 150°C with this particular instrument. Undoubtedly great variations in heating rate will be found among different makes of chromatographs. The flow rate of the carrier gas, initially 100 ml/min is not adjusted during the run. A total decrease of 10 ml/min is observed by the time the temperature reaches 150°C, but this does not appear to affect the separations obtained. Mixtures of thiols and thio ethers having boiling-point ranges of 200°C can be separated with satisfactory resolution of both high-boiling and low-boiling components. No data are given on reproducibility of peak areas.

e. Linear Temperature Programming (Dal Nogare and Harden, 1959)

A more elegant procedure than the above is to regulate the power supply to the column heater so that the temperature increases linearly with time. If the flow rate of the carrier gas is controlled also, peak areas are reproducible to within 3% over a sixfold change in heating rate. In the apparatus described by Dal Nogare and Langlois (1960) and Dal Nogare and Safranski (1960), the column is wrapped uniformly with insulated resistance wire (Fig. 21). Power is supplied from a Pyr-O-Vane temperature controller (Min-

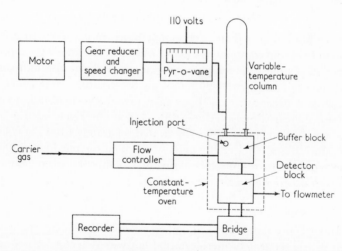

Fig. 21. Schematic diagram of temperature-programmed chromatograph (Dal Nogare and Safranski, 1960).

neapolis-Honeywell Regulator Co.), the set point of which is driven up-scale linearly by a constant-speed motor equipped with a gear reduction train having a ratio of 300,000:1. Heating rates between 3°C and 17°C per minute are obtained by means of a variable-ratio speed changer. Column temperature is measured by a thermopile consisting of six thermocouples placed between the windings and column at regular intervals along its length and indicated on a galvanometer attached to the Pyr-O-Vane recorder. A light source and photocell are installed on the set-point arm of the controller so that the metal vane of the galvanometer needle interrupts the light beam when the needle and the set-point arm coincide. This activates a relay which interrupts the power supply and permits the column to cool. A solenoid valve, actuated simultaneously, turns on an air blast to accelerate cooling. In a more advanced design, the recorder is equipped with a variable chart drive control which permits simultaneous changes of chart speed and heating rate so that all chromatograms covering a given temperature range are recorded on the same length of chart paper. Heating rates can be varied over a range of 1.7° to 56°C per minute by adjusting the chart speed control (Insco Co.).

The sensing elements in the thermal conductivity cell are matched 10^5-ohm thermistors. The temperature of the detector block is held constant (203°C was used), and a large buffer block heated to the same temperature is placed between it and the column to minimize drift caused by heat conduction through the connections between the column and detector. The mass flow rate of the carrier gas as measured at the exit of the instrument is maintained constant with a Moore constant-differential flow controller (see Section G.III.c).

Comparatively large samples can be applied to temperature-programmed columns without overloading them, and this is useful in trace analysis. Also, runs can be made quite rapidly, but considerable build-up of residues may occur. Furthermore, impurities in the carrier gas are sorbed at low temperature and may be desorbed as the temperature is increased, yielding a broad background peak. Therefore a drying tower should be placed between the cylinder containing the carrier gas and the injection port (see Section G.II.f).

Programming the temperature spreads out peaks which appear early in isothermal runs at high temperatures and sharpens up peaks which have long retention times at low temperatures, thereby resulting in more uniform presentation of the data. There has been considerable discussion over whether programming temperature actually increases column efficiency. This is an interesting point, but from a practical outlook perhaps irrelevant, since there is little doubt that it simplifies the analysis of complex mixtures with wide boiling-point ranges. However, it must be kept in mind that the formula for calculating the height equivalent to a theoretical plate in temperature-programmed chromatography is not the same as that used for isothermal conditions (Habgood and Harris, 1960b).

Other temperature-programmed instruments have been described by Harrison *et al.* (1958) and by Habgood and Harris (1960a). Commercial models are now available (F & M Scientific Corp.; Wilkens Instrument and Research, Inc.; Perkin-Elmer Corp., etc.). Examples in this book in which temperature programming has been used to good effect include the separation of high-molecular-weight hydrocarbons derived from lipids (Chapter 7, Section B.III.a.2), and resolution of atmospheric gases on a molecular sieve (Chapter 2, Section B.II.d.2).

f. Chromathermography

Improved separations in gas chromatography can be achieved by using a moving temperature gradient within the column to reduce spreading and tailing of zones. The gradient is produced by enclosing a portion of the column in a heated sleeve which is driven down the column during the run. Zones are compressed because the tailing edge is at a higher temperature than the leading edge and tends to overtake it. As a result, the last peak recorded is as sharp as the first one. However, overlap may occur, since peaks may overtake one another. Nerheim (1960a) has reported a modification of this procedure in which a heater is passed down a column several times in succession, each time at a temperature higher than that in the preceding pass. This method is said to improve separations as well as to yield narrower peaks.

V. Summary

The temperatures of the chromatographic column, detector block, and injection port can be regulated with a single control, or they can be adjusted separately to different values by incorporating several thermostats in the design. The former approach is simpler and reduces costs, but it lessens versatility greatly, particularly when the temperature must be changed during a run.

The selection of an optimum column temperature is a compromise between a number of variables including separation factors, column efficiencies, and thermal stabilities of solutes and stationary phases. In general, separation factors tend to be larger at lower temperatures, although this is not always the case. Column efficiencies appear to increase with temperature, since peaks become narrower, but this should always be considered in relation to the decrease in retention volume to determine whether the improvement is real. In arriving at a compromise, separation factors should take precedence over column efficiencies, as the latter are generally less sensitive to temperature changes, and deficiencies can be compensated for in part by increasing column length. Naturally any tentative choice is abrogated automatically if the solutes undergo thermally induced changes, or if the packing bleeds excessively.

In some cases, it may be impossible to select a single satisfactory operating temperature because of the wide boiling-point range of the sample components. In this event, it may be necessary to change the temperature during analysis. This may be done stepwise, or by a continuous increase through linear or nonlinear programming. Mixtures having wide boiling-point ranges can be separated more satisfactorily under isothermal conditions on capillary columns than on packed columns.

G. Selection and Regulation of the Carrier Gas

I. INTRODUCTION

Use of a permanent gas as the mobile phase is the salient feature distinguishing gas chromatography from other forms of chromatography. Yet comparatively little attention is given to factors influencing its selection, because the choice is limited, being confined at present to hydrogen, helium, nitrogen, air, argon, neon, and carbon dioxide. However, these gases, as well as others that might be used, possess individual chemical and physical characteristics that often determine whether a particular type of analysis is feasible or not. Therefore, careful attention should be given to properties that influence flow rate, detector sensitivity, selectivity of detector response, and chemical stability in the gas stream. Furthermore, the flow rate of the carrier gas should be selected to obtain optimum resolution of peaks, and variations in rate should be kept to the minimum to ensure reproducible retention volumes and good detector performance. Some of these factors are treated briefly in this section. Properties common to all gases that make them uniquely suitable as mobile phases in chromatography are described in Section A.

II. FACTORS INFLUENCING CHOICE OF CARRIER GAS

a. Viscosity and Diffusivity

Gases are much less viscous than liquids, this being the principal reason why gas chromatography is a rapid method of analysis compared to liquid–liquid or liquid–solid chromatography. Nevertheless, considerable differences in viscosity occur between them, so some leeway in the selection of this operating parameter is possible. According to elementary kinetic theory, the viscosity of an ideal gas is given by equation 28, where M is its

$$\eta = \tfrac{1}{3} M \bar{w} c \Lambda \qquad (28)$$

molecular weight, $\bar{w}$ the average molecular velocity, c the number of moles per milliliter, and Λ the mean free path.

For isotope molecules (H_2 and D_2, for example) which have approximately the same sizes and shapes, the only difference is the mass M, which occurs in equation 28 as an explicit factor, and which appears implicitly in the form $M^{-1/2}$ in the velocity term ($\bar{w}$). Consequently, the ratio of the viscosity of deuterium to that of protium is $\sqrt{4}/\sqrt{2}$, or 1.41. This has been confirmed by experiment. Gases possessing the same molecular dimensions have similar viscosities. Thus, nitrogen resembles carbon monoxide and nitrous oxide resembles carbon dioxide in this property, since each of the pairs has the same molecular weight and the same number of electrons as its isostere.

However, these relationships, though basic, are obscured when a wider variety of gases is considered (Table I). Hydrogen is the least viscous of all

TABLE I

PHYSICAL PROPERTIES OF GASES AT 0°C
(Data compiled from the literature)

Gas	Molecular (or atomic) weight	Diffusion coefficient (cm²/sec) Into H_2	Into CO_2	Viscosity (micropoises)	Thermal conductivity $\times 10^5$	Ionization potential (ev)
H_2	2	—	0.550	83.5	41.6	15.6
He	4	—	—	186.0	34.8	24.46
CH_4	16	0.625	0.153	102.6	7.21	14.5
NH_3	17	—	—	91.8	5.22	11.2
Ne	20.2	—	—	297.3	—	21.47
CO	28	0.651	0.137	166	—	14.1
N_2	28	0.674	0.144	156.3	5.81	15.51
Air	—	0.611	—	170.8	5.83	12.8
C_2H_6	30	0.459	—	—	4.36	—
O_2	32	—	—	189	—	12.5
H_2S	34	—	—	—	—	10.42
A	39.9	0.77	0.14[a]	209.6	—	15.68
CO_2	44	0.550	—	141	3.52	14.4
C_3H_8	44	—	—	—	3.58	—
SO_2	64	—	—	115.8	—	13.1

[a] At 20°C.

gases, as befits its low mass, but helium is more viscous than any other material listed except the other noble gases and oxygen. At the other extreme, sulfur dioxide, with a molecular weight of 64, has a lower viscosity than any members of the series except methane, ammonia, and hydrogen. This irregular behavior should make it possible to select a pure or mixed carrier with almost any combination of values for viscosity, diffusivity, and thermal conductivity desired, since these properties do not vary in a parallel manner.

Several factors implicit in equation 28 are important in gas chromatography. In the first place, it is apparent that the viscosity of a gas should be independent of its density, since the mean free path is inversely proportional to the number of moles per milliliter. Thus, when the gas is compressed, the number of molecules per unit volume is increased, but the contribution each makes to viscosity, as a carrier of momentum, is diminished. As a result, the viscosity of air increases by only 1% when the pressure is raised from 1 to 35 atmospheres, and this is caused only by deviations from ideal gas behavior. Consequently, increases in column inlet pressure are not important in so far as they influence gas viscosity. Temperature changes are much more important, since the average molecular velocity ($\bar{w}$ in equation 28), and the mean free path (Λ) increase with temperature. The resultant effect on viscosity is given by equation 29, where M and R are empirical constants.

$$\eta = M\frac{T^{1/2}}{1 + R/T} \qquad (29)$$

It is important to realize that the viscosities of all gases increase with temperature (Fig. 22). This is in sharp contrast to the behavior of liquids,

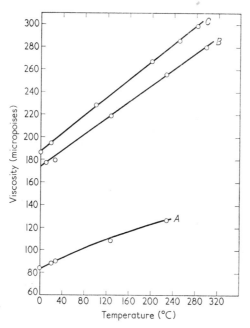

FIG. 22. Change in viscosity of gases with temperature: (A) hydrogen; (B) nitrogen; (C) helium. (Data from *Handbook of Chemistry and Physics.*)

which usually become more fluid when heated (molten sulfur is an interesting exception), owing to decreases in intermolecular bonding. However, intermolecular bonds between gas molecules are relatively unimportant. There-fore, heating merely increases thermal motion, and consequently viscosity. This factor is particularly important when the temperature of the chromato-graph must be changed during an analysis. The viscosity of the gas will change also, and so will the flow rate. If constant mass or linear flow is required by the characteristics of the detector, or for other reasons, a suitable regulating valve (Moore Products Co.) must be included upstream from the injection block.

Another inherent property of gases that must be considered is diffusivity. This is measured by the diffusion coefficient, which is a function of viscosity, density, and degree of molecular interaction. The diffusion coefficient is defined from a relation giving the number of molecules passing through a unit cross section in unit time and is obtained experimentally by measuring the flow of one gas species into another. Data for the diffusion of a number of gases into hydrogen and into carbon dioxide are shown in Table I. It can be seen that all gases diffuse into hydrogen at a relatively high rate, but the tendency becomes less as molecular weight increases. On the other hand, diffusion rates into carbon dioxide are low. This suggests that better resolu-tion of gas chromatographic peaks will be obtained by employing nitrogen, argon, and carbon dioxide as carriers rather than by choosing gases with high diffusivity such as hydrogen and helium, since there will be less longitudinal diffusion of the solute during transport through the system. To oversimplify the situation, carbon dioxide will tend to carry the sample through the col-umn as a compact plug, whereas in hydrogen the plug will spread out. Consequently, some workers believe the use of high-molecular-weight gases to be advantageous where other factors are not overriding.

However, there is reason to believe that gases having low viscosity and high diffusivity are advantageous when analyses must be obtained rapidly, and when high hold-up times in the column are undesirable (Loyd et al., 1960). Furthermore, if the sample can be run through the column rapidly, owing to the low viscosity of the carrier, there will be less time in transit during which the peaks can broaden, even though the rate of longitudinal diffusion may be relatively high. However, if the rate of gas flow is too high, additional broadening may take place as a result of resistance to mass trans-fer. Consequently these factors must be balanced against one another in arriving at a choice of carrier gases.

Loyd et al. (1960) present evidence suggesting that hydrogen may be preferable to nitrogen or helium as a carrier when both peak resolution and time of analysis must be taken into account. With a column packing con-taining 30% bis[2-(2-methoxyethoxy)ethyl] ether on Chromosorb, the num-ber of theoretical plates obtained on chromatographing 1,3-butadiene was slightly smaller when hydrogen replaced nitrogen as a carrier gas. However, the flow rate for optimum performance resulted in reduction of retention time by a factor of 2.3 when the hydrogen was used. When the packing ratio was reduced to 10%, results obtained with hydrogen were even more favorable. Equivalent resolution was obtained with either carrier, but the time required with hydrogen was only one-fourth that required for nitrogen

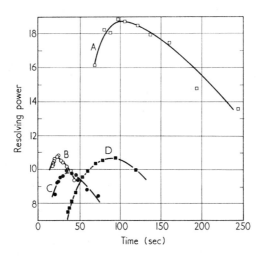

Fig. 23. Resolving power versus retention time for the chromatography of 1,3-butadiene on bis[2-(2-methoxyethoxy)ethyl] ether at 25°C with different carrier gases: (A) hydrogen with 12-foot column; (B) hydrogen with 4-foot column; (C) helium with 4-foot column; (D) nitrogen with 4-foot column (Loyd et al., 1960).

(Fig. 23). Performance with hydrogen was superior to that obtained with helium on both packings.

No experimental evidence is available at present, but it is interesting to speculate on whether the inferior performance of helium was caused by a combination of high viscosity with high diffusivity.

b. Thermal Conductivity

The thermal conductivity of a gas, or the amount of heat flowing per second through a unit area of it under a temperature gradient of 1° per centimeter, is given by equation 30, where η is its viscosity, C_v its molar heat

$$\lambda = \eta C_v / M \qquad (30)$$

capacity at constant volume, and M its molecular weight. Consequently, thermal conductivity decreases rapidly with increasing molecular weight, particularly for the first few elements of the periodic table. Since the intensity of the signal obtained from thermal detectors depends on the *difference* in conductivity between the carrier and the solute, it is obvious that this should be as great as possible. Much has been written concerning the relative merits of gases of high and low conductivity as carriers, but only a few salient facts need be considered to make a practical choice. These are: (1) Thermal conductivity differences between carrier and solute are important only when a thermistor or hot-wire detector is used to measure the composition of the gas. They are not important when ionization detectors are employed, or when a thermal conductivity cell is used indirectly as in the gas density balance. (2) Vapors of most organic compounds have conductivities far closer to those of nitrogen, argon, or carbon dioxide than to those of hydrogen or helium; consequently only the latter gases should be used for their detection with T/C cells unless other considerations are overriding. With nitrogen, sensitivity is diminished and peak inversions may occur, since it is less conductive than some organic vapors. (3) The change in thermal conductivity with respect to the mole fraction of solute in the carrier gas is much less dependent on the nature of the organic compound when hydrogen or helium is used. Consequently, the need for calibration is reduced (but not eliminated), particularly when compounds of a similar nature are being measured. (4) Higher sensitivity will be obtained with hydrogen than with helium. However, hydrogen may be dangerous in some situations, and thermal anomalies may occur if the solute can be reduced catalytically at the hot wire. (5) If hydrogen or another light gas is the component being measured, helium should not be chosen as the carrier gas, and vice versa. Instead, argon, carbon dioxide, or some other carrier should be chosen to make the difference in conductivity as large as possible. Alternatively, the hydrogen can be oxidized to water and detected in a helium carrier. See Chapter 2, Section C, for a further discussion of this point.

It should be remembered that thermal conductivities of mixtures of gases are not additive. Often it is possible to calculate the concentration of solute at high dilutions by interpolation. However, this should be verified by calibration in each individual case, since graphs of thermal conductivity versus the compositions of binary mixtures of gases sometimes pass through minima.

As mentioned above, the thermal conductivities of the carrier and the solute should differ considerably to obtain good detector sensitivity. There are, however, specific cases where some advantage may be gained by using a carrier gas identical to one of the sample components, and thereby canceling it from the chromatogram, owing to the fact that the detector does not respond to its presence. This expedient is suitable when two components are difficult to resolve, making it easier to analyze mixtures of them by conductivity differences than by partition. For example, argon cannot be separated from oxygen on molecular sieve except at low temperatures. However, the error in the oxygen analysis caused by the presence of argon can be avoided by using argon as the carrier gas and so eliminating its contribution to the area of the composite peak. Conversely, argon can be determined in air with oxygen as the carrier gas. The same expedient has been employed for ascertaining the deuterium content of hydrogen without actual resolution of protium and deuterium on the column (see Chapter 2, Section C, for details). Theoretically, this technique of masking the presence of an unwanted component by swamping it with carrier gas could be applied to many other situations. Thus methane and other light hydrocarbons present in air could be determined with pure air as the carrier gas. However, it must be remembered that thermal conductivity differences will usually be much lower than when hydrogen or helium is used. Therefore it may be necessary often to sacrifice sensitivity for selectivity.

It is also possible to utilize this swamping effect even when it is not feasible to employ the component to be eliminated as the carrier gas. Detector responses due to water, for example, can be canceled by passing the gas stream through a pre-column packed with calcium hydride and using hydrogen as the carrier gas (see Chapter 3, Section V, for details). The water is converted to hydrogen, and this, being identical to carrier, is not detected. Presumably most active hydrogen compounds could be subtracted from the gas stream in this way by the selection of a proper pre-column.

c. Excitation and Ionization Potentials

Excitation potentials are important only when a noble gas is used in conjunction with an ionization detector as a means of conserving radiation energy temporarily. In this case, the excitation potential of the gas must exceed the ionization potentials of the compounds to be measured (Table I). This observation may seem trivial, yet papers have appeared in the literature in which an argon detector (11.6 ev) has been used to measure hydrogen, nitrogen, methane, and carbon dioxide, which have ionization potentials ranging from 14.4 to 15.6 ev. Argon detectors exhibit small (and sometimes negative) responses to permanent gases when they are present in massive quantities, but they are not used to their fullest advantage in this application. Consequently, they should not be employed to detect materials having ionization potentials greater than 11.6 ev. This excludes most of the inorganic gases except ammonia and hydrogen sulfide, as well as C_1 and C_2 hydrocarbons. However, argon detectors are useful for most other organic compounds.

If trace quantities of the permanent gases must be detected, helium could be selected as the carrier, since it has an excitation potential sufficiently high to ionize all other gases but neon. However, the helium must be carefully purified. This is accomplished by means of the following adsorbents:

molecular sieve at $-20°C$ and $-196°C$, titanium at $1000°C$, and Hopcalite at $400°C$ (Berry, 1960). According to Lovelock (1961) formation of metastable atoms by electron bombardment is much more difficult to achieve in helium than in argon, and, if such a detector could be made, it would have to be of a different design.

d. Adsorptivity

One of the advantages of GLC, compared to methods in which the mobile phase is a liquid, is that most gases do not dissolve to an appreciable extent in the stationary phase. Of course this cannot be entirely true, since carbon dioxide and nitrous oxide are separable on dimethyl sulfoxide. Nevertheless, it is sufficiently true so that interactions between the moving and stationary phases can be considered for the most part to be nonexistent. This is not even approximately true for GSC, since most gases are separable on active solids. Consequently, the nature of the carrier gas can influence retention times by displacement of the solute on the active sites of the adsorbent. This is illustrated by the work of Greene (1957), who compared the retention times of methane on a charcoal column with five different carrier gases. With helium and argon, which themselves are bound only slightly, retention times were 34 and 22 minutes, respectively. However, acetylene eluted the methane in only 5 minutes, showing that it probably acted as a displacement as well as a partition agent.

Interactions of this type may be very important in gas analysis, since it is a fairly common practice to employ a carrier gas identical to one of the sample components to achieve a masking effect when thermal conductivity cells are used. It is legitimate to question what side effects this will have on the resolution of components with similar retention volumes. For example, Greene (1959) could not resolve protium, protium deuteride, and deuterium at liquid oxygen temperatures with a charcoal column and nitrogen or argon as carriers. He suggested that the mobile phase was adsorbed on the charcoal, and that this interfered with separation. However, when neon was substituted, partial resolution was obtained, thus illustrating some degree of specificity on the part of the carrier.

Sometimes the shapes of chromatographic peaks can be improved by modifying the polarity of the carrier gas through inclusion of a second component. Thus, tailing of the water peak on a column packed with β,β'-oxydipropionitrile can be reduced by using wet helium (Knight, 1958, 1959).

e. Chemical Reactivity of Carrier Gas

Generally, highly reactive carrier gases should be avoided. Hydrogen may reduce organic compounds in hot-wire detectors, and oxygen or air can cause breakdown of some column packings at high temperatures. Presumably gases such as hydrogen chloride, sulfur dioxide, ammonia, and hydrogen sulfide could find application because of unique physicochemical characteristics were it not for their noxious or corrosive properties.

However, in some instances special advantages may accrue through use of a reactive gas, and it should therefore always be considered as a means of augmenting the versatility of the method. The reducing power of hydrogen, for instance, can be utilized to simplify detection and calibration in the chromatographic analysis of aldehydes obtained by oxidation of amino acids (Zlatkis *et al.*, 1960). The aldehyde vapors in a hydrogen carrier are passed through a heated column packed with nickel–kieselguhr located between the column and detector. The aldehydes are hydrocracked to methane and water, and the latter compound is removed in a drying tower. Thus the only material to pass through the detector is methane. This simplifies calibration, since the carbon number of the aldehyde and the response of the detector to methane are the only data required to obtain quantitative results. Furthermore, the detector can be operated at room temperature without danger of condensing sample components.

Oxygen has been used as a carrier gas with the secondary purpose of converting organic compounds to carbon dioxide and water prior to detection. The principle involved is the same as in reduction to methane; it is necessary to know only the carbon number of the compound and the response of the detector to carbon dioxide to process the data. However, this technique is seldom employed, since organic compounds can be oxidized to carbon dioxide in a tube packed with CuO by using an inert carrier gas.

The reaction of carbon dioxide gas with aqueous alkali to form solutions of alkali metal carbonates forms the basis of a unique detection system originally developed by Janák. Low-molecular-weight hydrocarbons are eluted from a column with carbon dioxide, and the mixed gases are collected in a burette filled with sodium hydroxide solution. The carrier gas is absorbed quantitatively, but light hydrocarbons accumulate above the liquid and are measured volumetrically. Undoubtedly analogous results could be obtained with hydrogen chloride, ammonia, or sulfur dioxide, should special circumstances warrant their use.

f. Purity of Carrier Gas

Many industrial cylinder gases of commercial grade contain varying amounts of water and organic vapors which are introduced during cleaning and refilling of the tanks. It is often unnecessary to remove these when thermal detectors or detectors unresponsive to water and light hydrocarbons are used. However, steadier base lines can be obtained and column life prolonged by inserting a drying column containing silica gel or molecular sieve between the gas cylinder reducing valve and the chromatograph inlet valve. This is particularly important for polyester packings, since they are hydrolyzed readily by water at high temperatures. Drying towers that will do this are available commercially (Coast Engineering Laboratory). They consist of stainless-steel tubes $\frac{1}{2}$ to 1 inch in diameter and 36 to 60 inches long, equipped with high-pressure fittings and flexible hose connections for attachment to the reducing valve of the gas cylinder. The tubes are loaded with graded, fines-free, type 13-X molecular sieve. This reduces the residual water vapor content of the gas to 1.5 parts per million or less. One filling will decontaminate a cylinder containing 350 cubic feet of gas.

Guild *et al.* (1958) use a 25-ml drying tube filled with type 5-A molecular sieve for purifying helium. This is essential to obtain a steady base line in temperature-programmed runs, since the amounts of impurities bound by the analytical column will vary with temperature. Furthermore, the time required to reach a steady-state concentration of impurities in the carrier gas eluting from the analytical column may be extremely long, or for practical purposes it may not be attained at all at temperatures below 100°C. The gas purification tower is placed just before the partition column to avoid recontamination of the gas by vapors picked up in the connecting tubing. However, it should be noted that tubes of large volume, when placed in this position, give rise to fluctuations in flow rate engendered by temperature changes. Exhausted molecular sieve can be reactivated by heating it for 1 to 2 hours at 300°C.

The use of ionization detectors sometimes requires a much more elaborate clean-up of the carrier gas to avoid background readings, because of high sensitivity and the fact that they are not employed for differential detection. Fortunately, this is mitigated to some degree by the fact that many of the detectors respond weakly to trace quantities of water vapor and inorganic gases. However, it must be pointed out that the helium detector responds to all substances save neon, so that the carrier (helium) must be purified exhaustively. Furthermore, the flame ionization detector is sensitive to methane, which is present in laboratory air, compressed air, oxygen, and outside air in concentrations of several parts per million (Andreatch and Feinland, 1960).

Commercial helium for use with the thermionic ionization gauge is purified by passing it through a large column containing potassium hydroxide, Drierite ($CaSO_4$), Anhydrone ($MgClO_4$), and Ascarite to remove water and carbon dioxide. Residual traces of water are removed in a dry ice trap, and finally the gas is passed through titanium sponge heated to 800°C to remove nitrogen. This rigorous purification procedure is essential because of the high sensitivity of the detector and the resulting high noise level from impurities in the gas stream (Farrington *et al.*, 1959). Similar steps are required to purify helium to a degree that it can be used in its metastable state to ionize other gases (Berry, 1960).

III. RATE OF GAS FLOW AND ITS REGULATION

a. Selection of Optimum Inlet and Outlet Pressures

In liquid–liquid or liquid–solid chromatography both the volumetric flow rate and the linear flow rate are invariant across the length of the column, since, for all practical purposes, the mobile phase is incompressible. However, gases are highly compressible, and this salient fact must be taken into account in calculating retention volumes or in selecting operating conditions. In a gas chromatograph, the pressure at the inlet side of the partition column must be of necessity higher than the outlet pressure for flow to take place. Consequently, the pressure varies continuously from p_i (inlet pressure) to p_o (outlet pressure) along the length of the column. Since this is true, the linear velocity of an imaginary point carried along by the gas stream must increase as it approaches the outlet of the column. Hence the linear flow rate of the gas increases with distance from the inlet side of the column (x), even though the volumetric flow rate at the column exit (milliliters per minute) is constant. The linear flow rate at any point within the column is directly proportional to the pressure gradient (dp/dx), inversely proportional to the viscosity of the gas (η), and directly proportional to the permeability of the column packing (ϕ), as shown in equation 31. As noted in Section

$$u = -\frac{\phi}{\eta}\frac{dp}{dx} \tag{31}$$

G.II.a, the viscosity of the gas does not change with pressure.

On making suitable substitutions in equation 31, and integrating between limits, equation 32 results, where l is the length of the chromatographic col-

$$\frac{x}{l} = \frac{(p_i/p_o)^2 - (p/p_o)^2}{(p_i/p_o)^2 - 1} \tag{32}$$

umn, x is the distance of any arbitrary point from the inlet side of the column, p is the gas pressure at that point, p_i is the inlet pressure, and p_o is the outlet pressure. Since p_i, p_o, and l are constant under any given set of operating conditions, it is possible to calculate the pressure (p) at any point x within the column. Furthermore, since pressure within the column is inversely proportional to linear gas velocity, it is possible to compute the velocty relative to inlet velocity (u/u_o) at any relative distance (x/l) from the iinlet side of the column at various arbitrary ratios of inlet to outlet pressures (p_i/p_o). When this is done, and the results are plotted, a family of curves is obtained showing how the linear velocity of the gas changes along the length of the column at different inlet-to-outlet pressure ratios (Fig. 24).

From this graph it is evident that pressure ratios of 3 or more result in rapid increases in linear gas velocity toward the outlet side of the column. It will be shown below that an optimum flow rate exists for every chromatographic separation, on either side of which column efficiency as measured by *HETP* (height equivalent to a theoretical plate) diminishes. Therefore,

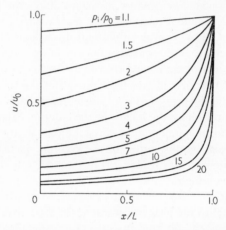

FIG. 24. Plot of u/u_o against x/L with p_i/p_o as parameter (Keulemans, 1959).

to operate a column at maximum efficiency, the linear flow rate should be constant, in so far as this is possible, and should be regulated at the optimum value along the entire length of the column. When this is not the case, part of the column is being operated inefficiently. Thus, high inlet-to-outlet pressure ratios result in suboptimum performance. When high inlet pressures are needed to force gases through long, densely packed columns, the outlet should be constricted to reduce the pressure differential. This technique has been employed by Scott (1958) to operate columns at an inlet pressure of 200 psig, and having efficiencies between 18,000 and 30,000 theoretical plates. Most chromatographs are not constructed to withstand such pressures and are better operated with the outlet at atmospheric pressure and the inlet pressure at 1.5 to 2.0 atmospheres. Under these conditions the linear gas velocity throughout the column is practically constant, and the packing performs with acceptable efficiency along its entire length.

However, many times it is necessary to decrease the time required for the elution of a particular component for practical reasons. This can be done by increasing the inlet pressure, or decreasing the outlet pressure, or both, and it is necessary to know which procedure is most satisfactory. Keulemans

(1959) has considered this problem for a hypothetical column operated at an inlet pressure of 1 atmosphere and an outlet pressure of 0.25 atmosphere, which has a ratio of outlet velocity to inlet velocity (u_o/u_i) of 4. When the outlet pressure is decreased by a factor of 2.5, the residence time of the gas is decreased by only 9%, whereas the velocity ratio is increased to 10. However, if the outlet pressure is held constant, and the inlet pressure is increased by 15%, residence time drops by 15%, while the velocity ratio increases to only 4.6. Therefore, increasing the inlet pressure is more effective than decreasing the outlet pressure for shortening residence times, and, moreover, it does not increase the velocity gradient within the column as much.

For this reason and others, it is best to operate chromatographs with the outlet at atmospheric pressure or higher and at a value for p_i/p_o between 1.1 and 2. Operation with the outlet under reduced pressure may result in inefficient utilization of part of the column. The sensitivities of thermal detectors are improved somewhat by operation under partial vacuum, but this is counterbalanced by the fact that it is more difficult to maintain a stable base line because of pressure fluctuations. Moreover, there is no basis for the commonly held belief that chromatography at low pressures is equivalent to vacuum distillation, since the retention time of any component is a function only of the flow rate of the carrier gas and the partition coefficient of the solute between the mobile phase and stationary phase.

b. Selection of Optimum Flow Rate

Selection of flow rate is based frequently on personal preference or expediency. Some chromatograms contain as many as 20 to 30 peaks, and it would be impossible to select a value optimum for all of them. If a column temperature has already been selected, a low flow rate will give the best presentation of data for compounds with low retention volumes, and a higher rate is preferable for compounds retarded to a greater extent by the column packing. If both groups are of interest, a compromise must be sought. Values reported in the literature generally range between 20 and 200 ml of gas per minute, measured at the column outlet. A rate of 100 ml/min is about average for a 2-meter column 0.5 cm in diameter and at least is a good starting point if no background of information is available on the column characteristics and partition coefficients of the sample components. Of course, the volumetric flow rate must be changed in proportion to the cross-sectional area if tubing of a different bore is used to keep the linear flow rate constant. To some extent, the flow rate should be adjusted according to the nature of the carrier gas. With a gas of high diffusivity, such as hydrogen, the rate should be higher than with nitrogen to hurry the sample through the column before the peaks spread too much. Since hydrogen also has a low viscosity (Table I), this can be done at comparatively low inlet pressures.

Even though flow rates often are selected arbitrarily, a value exists for each set of experimental conditions at which the column operates with maximum efficiency. An equation relating column efficiency in terms of *HETP* to linear gas velocity, diffusivity of the solute in the liquid and gas phases, and other column parameters has been derived on theoretical grounds by van Deemter *et al.* (1956). This equation has since been modified by Kieselbach (1961), but the simpler form of it will be sufficient for this discussion, since the first three terms of both equations are identical. The simplified van Deemter form is given in equation 33, where H is the height

$$H = A + \gamma D_g/u + Cu \tag{33}$$

equivalent to a theoretical plate, u is the linear gas velocity, A is a constant that represents the contribution of eddy diffusion,[5] γ is a correction for the tortuosity of the channels in the column packing, D_g is the diffusivity of the solute in the gas phase, and C is a collected constant representing the resistance of the column to mass transfer. This is a hyperbolic equation with a minimum at $u = (\gamma D_g/C)^{1/2}$, which represents the flow rate at which column efficiency is greatest. If the constants are evaluated, a curve can be plotted relating column efficiency to linear gas velocity (Fig. 25).

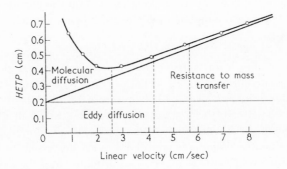

FIG. 25. Relation between average velocity of carrier gas and column efficiency as calculated from the van Deemter equation.

The area under the curve can be divided into three regions corresponding to the three terms of equation 33. At low rates, column efficiency decreases because of peak broadening caused by molecular diffusion. At high rates, efficiency decreases because of resistance of the solute to mass transfer. Eddy diffusion is independent of flow rate. As a result of these interacting factors, the curve passes through a minimum which is the optimum flow rate.

[5] "Eddy" diffusion arises from the movement of solute molecules along tortuous paths created by voids in the column packing. It is porportional to the particle size of the packing and is not considered to be true eddy diffusion.

The minimum in Fig. 25 is rather shallow; consequently there is a tendency to discount the importance of selecting an optimum rate except to warn about the dangers of excessively low (below 10 ml/min) or excessively high (above 400 ml/min) values. Actually, sizable differences in column performance can be obtained with only moderate variations in rate. This is particularly noticeable when sample size, temperature, and column parameters are also held at values close to optimum. Thus the optimum flow of helium for the separation of α-terpinene and D-limonene on a poly(diethylene glycol succinate) column is about 45 ml/min (Fig. 26). If the rate

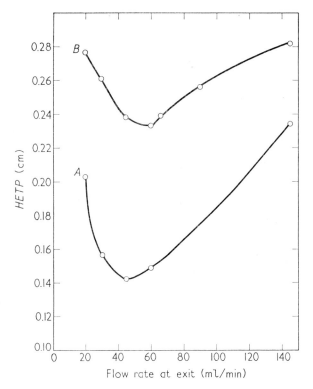

Fig. 26. Effect of flow rate on the efficiency of a 3.05-meter polyester column for the separation of α-terpinene and D-limonene at 100°C: (A) 0.1-μl sample; (B) 0.5-μl sample. [Plotted from the data of Bernhard (1960).]

is reduced to 20 ml/min or increased to 100 ml/min, the height equivalent to a theoretical plate as calculated from the experimental data is reduced seriously. This is most noticeable at small sample sizes. It is interesting that the minimum of the curve shifts in the direction of higher rates when the volume of sample applied to the column is increased by a factor of 5.

c. Maintenance of Constant Pressure and Flow Rates

The flow rate of the carrier gas influences both the retention times of compounds eluted from the chromatographic column and the magnitude of the signal obtained from thermal detectors. Therefore, the chromatograph must be equipped with controlling devices so that flow can be re-established reproducibly and pressure surges do not occur during a run. Furthermore, flow should be adjustable over a wide operating range.

Carrier gases are supplied in compressed form in cylinders. These are fitted with two-stage diaphragm reducing valves to regulate the pressure of the gas delivered to the chromatograph. The chromatograph itself may be equipped with an auxiliary regulating device such as a variable restrictor (Lockwood and McLorie, Inc.) or a pressure regulator coupled with a capillary orifice. The reducing valve connected to the gas tank is always set at a pressure higher than the auxiliary valve. To operate at a column pressure of 15 psig, the diaphragm valve may be set at 30 to 35 psig. A surge tank sometimes is placed between the gas cylinder and the injection port to minimize slight random fluctuations in flow, but this is largely unnecessary, since the back pressure of the gas on the column serves the same purpose. For optimum detector response, the flow rate should not vary by more than a few tenths of a milliliter per minute. When operated at highest sensitivity, thermal detectors are sometimes sensitive to pressure fluctuations such as those produced by opening or closing a door. These effects can be minimized by attaching a buffer column to the chromatograph outlet. A 10×0.5-cm tube filled with Chromosorb or a similar solid support usually will suffice.

Most commercial chromatographs have pressure regulators only at the inlet, although at least one model (Griffin and George Ltd.) is equipped for vacuum operation. A wider range of operating conditions can be obtained if a regulator is also placed at the outlet.

Satisfactory pressure regulation is not difficult to achieve during isothermal runs, but, if the temperature is programmed, the carrier gas flow rate will decrease with increasing temperature, if the gas is supplied to the column head at constant pressure. This results from the increased viscosity of the gas. Quantitative results can be obtained only if the volumetric flow rate of the gas through the detector is kept constant. A device for achieving this has been developed which works on the principle of maintaining a constant pressure difference across a constriction, so that the pressure difference and hence the flow through the constriction are independent of inlet pressure (Guild et al., 1958). A schematic diagram of the apparatus is shown in Fig. 27. It consists of a valve (A), operated by a diaphragm (B), and a needle valve (C). Spring D regulates the pressure drop across valve C. A constant pressure is supplied upstream at P_1, and the flow is regulated with the needle valve (C). The gas pressure operates against spring D and actuates the flexible diaphragm (B). This causes valve A to adjust automatically to maintain a constant pressure differential P_2 across C. The flow rate remains constant to within 1% when the column temperature is varied between 20°C and 200°C.

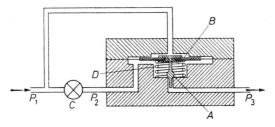

Fig. 27. Apparatus for the regulation of gas flow rates (Guild *et al.*, 1958).

A device working on the same principle can be constructed from a glass float valve similar to those used in manostats (Knox, 1959). A schematic diagram of the apparatus is shown in Fig. 28. Gas is supplied to the regulator

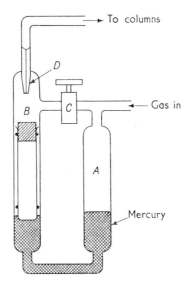

Fig. 28. Apparatus for regulation of the flow rate of the carrier gas (Knox, 1959).

at a constant pressure of 10 to 20 cm of Hg over the maximum required for operation of the column. When pressure is applied to chamber A, the float in B rises and closes outlet D when the rubber bung (B) makes contact with the ground tip of the capillary. However, gas leaks slowly through the needle valve (or capillary) at C, tending to equalize the pressures in reservoirs A and B. When this happens, the float descends, permitting gas to escape through D. This reduces the pressure in B, and the valve closes again. In theory, this operation cycle is repeated indefinitely, but when operating properly the float remains stationary in such a position that the flow through D is exactly the same as the controlling flow through the constriction at C. The flow rate is independent of the back pressure of the column, provided the area of the float is large compared to the area of the capillary. It may be varied by changing the resistance at C or the height between the capillary and valve. The ground end of the capillary should be made slightly off-horizontal, and the top of the float should be dusted with chalk to prevent oscillation of the float and consequent surging of gas. Flow rate is constant to within 1% at 100 ml of gas per minute when the temperature is programmed between 20°C and 120°C.

A controller for maintaining constant flow rate is available commercially (Moore Products Co.). It has been used in the construction of a temperature-programmed chromatograph (Dal Nogare and Bennett, 1958).

d. Measurement of Flow Rates

Flow rates must be measured accurately for the computation of retention volumes, and continuously to determine if fluctuations occur during a run. Usually two types of indicator are used: a soap film flowmeter for precise work, and a rotameter (float meter) or Venturi (orifice) meter for constant observation. The rotameter and orifice meter respond to changes in temperature and should be located within the column oven. The soap film meter is attached to the exit and gives the flow rate at atmospheric temperature and pressure, under which conditions it should be reported in publications. The soap film meter is accurate to within 1% and gives virtually no back pressure. These meters can be obtained from many laboratory supply houses and manufacturers of chromatographs.

1. *Soap Film Meter.* A schematic diagram of a soap film meter is shown in Fig. 29. It consists of a graduated tube (A) fitted with an inlet (B). A small rubber bulb (C) containing a solution of detergent is attached to the bottom of A. To take a reading, the meter is attached to the exit line of the chromatograph at B, and a film of soap is introduced into A by squeezing the bulb. The time required for the soap film to pass between two calibrated marks (usually 10 ml) on the burette is measured with a stop watch.

2. *Venturi (Orifice) Meter.* The apparatus is shown in Fig. 30. A is a piece of capillary tubing of predetermined length and bore attached to the outlet of the chromatograph. B is a manometer containing colored water (Warburg

FIG. 29. Soap film meter.

fluid will do) which subtends the capillary. The impedance of the carrier gas flow by the capillary results in back pressure which is registered on the manometer. The instrument is calibrated by running gas through it at

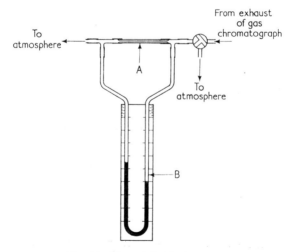

FIG. 30. Venturi (orifice) meter.

various constant rates as measured with a wet test meter. Manometer readings are plotted against rate in milliliters per minute, and carrier gas readings are interpolated from this graph. A calibration curve must be made for each carrier gas, since viscosities vary considerably. Usually it is necessary to have available a number of capillaries of various lengths and internal diameters to achieve the range and sensitivity required for gas chromatography measurements. Commercial models are available having several orifices contained within a hollow standard-taper stopper (Fisher Model 11-162, for example). Any one of the orifices can be used by adjusting the position of the stopcock.

3. *Float Meter* (*rotameter*). The float meter consists of a glass tube mounted in a vertical position. It has a precision bore which tapers and becomes larger toward the top. The tube contains an aluminum or glass float which rises or falls in proportion to the flow rate of the gas. The distance of the float from the bottom of the tube is measured with a centimeter scale. Calibration curves must be constructed for different conditions of temperature and pressure, and for different gases. Metal floats are more satisfactory than glass, since the latter tend to chip during continual use.

IV. SUMMARY

The number of elements and compounds that can be used as the mobile phase in gas chromatography is much more limited than when liquids are used to elute the solutes. Moreover, interactions between the two phases are minimum, so the choice is often not critical. Nevertheless, gases possess a number of intrinsic chemical and physical properties that should be considered in selecting the mobile phase. Among these are viscosity, diffusivity, thermal conductivity, excitation and ionization potentials, adsorptivity on active solids, and chemical reactivity with solutes or the stationary phase. Sometimes the proper selection of the carrier gas makes possible analyses that would not be feasible otherwise.

The flow rate of the carrier gas should be adjusted to give optimum column efficiency. Very low flow rates are undesirable because the solute zones will spread by molecular diffusion during the long residence time in the column. Very high flow rates are undesirable because of resistance to mass transfer. There is generally some intermediate rate that is optimum for each separation. Best results are obtained when the linear flow rate of the gas is constant along the length of the column in so far as this is possible. This situation can be approached most closely by keeping the ratio of inlet to outlet pressure as low as possible consistent with satisfactory retention times. If faster flow rates are required, it is better to increase the inlet pressure than to reduce the outlet pressure. In general, operation of a gas chromatograph under reduced pressure is not conducive to better separations.

H. Quantitative Analysis

I. INTRODUCTION

Gas chromatographs are suitable for quantitative analysis as well as for the separation of chemical compounds. When operating conditions are adjusted satisfactorily and peak parameters are measured carefully, accuracy should be within 1% (Oster, 1959). Results obtained on instruments equipped with integral detectors are easy to interpret, since the height of each step in the chromatogram is directly proportional to the amount of solute present (see Fig. 3A). Furthermore, the response of the detector is frequently related to some accurately known or easily predictable property of the molecule such as acid value or molecular weight. Consequently, extensive calibration is unnecessary.

However, most chromatographs are equipped with differential detectors, and with these the fundamental analytical parameter is the area of the peak rather than its height. This must be measured indirectly. Furthermore, the responses of many thermal detectors vary with the nature of the compound being measured in a way that is often unpredictable. Therefore special attention must be given to calibration and computation of areas under curves. Discussion of these topics will occupy the major part of this section.

II. PARAMETERS INFLUENCING PEAK DIMENSIONS

a. Peak Height

Measurement of peak height is useful in quantitative analysis only when all operating parameters can be reproduced exactly from experiment to experiment. Careful adjustment of flow rate is particularly important, since peaks broaden and become lower with increasing residence time in the column, owing to longitudinal diffusion of the solute in the mobile phase. Consequently, peak heights will vary with the retention volumes of the compound even when the detector response is approximately the same. Furthermore, peak height is not directly proportional to reciprocal flow rate, so that it is inconvenient to correct values mathematically if this parameter differs from experiment to experiment. Both relative and absolute peak heights increase with temperature even when the flow rate is kept constant; thus it is necessary to construct a calibration curve under the same conditions used for analysis. Other variables that must be controlled include filament current when katharometers are used, and secondary factors such as the column length and porosity of the packing, since these factors influence flow rate when the pressure differential is constant. Consequently, peak height is not a very satisfactory measurement for many purposes.

However, peak height is easy to measure and is useful for routine analysis when operating conditions can be reproduced exactly. It has been employed mostly for the analysis of compounds with short retention times such as permanent gases, since peaks are very narrow and high, and large responses are obtained for comparatively minor changes in sample composition. One method for detecting very small changes in gas composition is to use a zero suppresser attachment so that only the tips of the peaks are recorded, the base line being shifted to an imaginary position off the chart paper. By this means small differences can be observed that would probably pass unnoticed in area measurements.

Obviously peak height measurements are most sensitive at low retention volumes where ratios of width to height are very small, and they become progressively less useful with increasing residence times of the solutes in the column.

b. Peak Area

Peak area increases with decreasing flow rate; however, the relation between area and the reciprocal of the rate is linear, so arithmetic corrections for variations in this parameter are made easily. Furthermore, peak areas produced by different chemical compounds do not change relative to one another when the rate is changed. Temperature variations have very little effect on absolute areas and no observable effect on relative areas. If the detector is a katharometer, increasing the filament temperature will increase absolute but not relative areas. Consequently, absolute area is more independent of operating conditions than height, but not so much so as relative area. The vast majority of chromatograms are quantitated by area measurements.

III. CALIBRATION METHODS

Calibration is required to ascertain the response of the detector–recorder system to the presence of a known amount of solute passing through the sensing cell. Detector sensitivities will vary by many orders of magnitude, depending on the principle on which they operate, and cell geometry. The need for calibrating each instrument is therefore obvious. This would be comparatively simple were it not for one unfortunate fact; the detectors in most common use do not respond to the presence of different chemical compounds in a uniform way either on a molar or on a weight basis. There are, however, differences between detectors that must be considered before deciding whether calibration is necessary.

The responses of thermal conductivity cells vary considerably with the nature of the solute, particularly when the carrier gas is nitrogen. With hydrogen or helium, differences are smaller because of the greater conductivity spread between mobile phase and solutes. Therefore, for rough work, calibration can be based on a single component of a mixture. This is particularly advantageous if the components are members of a homologous series, since a correlation exists between detector response and molecular weight, making it possible to predict values for given compounds when related information is available. Thus the response of a katharometer or a thermistor to a variety of alkanes, alkenes, alkylbenzenes, and oxygenated compounds can be calculated from equation 34, where r is the response

$$r = A + BM \qquad (34)$$

relative to benzene (100 units per mole), M is the molecular weight of the homologue, and A and B are empirical constants. Values for A and B for a number of homologous series are given in Table II.

TABLE II

CONSTANTS FOR CALCULATION OF RELATIVE KATHAROMETER RESPONSE
FROM MOLECULAR WEIGHT BY USING EQUATION 34[a]

Series	Range of compound	Slope	Intercept	Correlation[b]
n-Paraffins	C_1–C_3	1.04	20.6	0.982
	C_3–C_{10}	1.35	6.7	0.992
Methyl paraffins	C_4–C_7	1.25	10.8	0.999
Dimethyl paraffins	C_5–C_7	1.20	13.0	0.998
1-Olefins	C_2–C_4	1.20	13.0	0.998
Trimethyl paraffins	C_7–C_8	1.16	13.9	0.999
Methylbenzenes	C_7–C_9	1.16	9.7	0.999
Mono-n-alkyl benzenes	C_7–C_9	1.06	17.9	0.999
Mono-sec-alkyl benzenes	C_9–C_{10}	1.04	18.1	0.999
n-Ketones	C_3–C_8	0.861	35.9	0.999
Primary alcohols	C_2–C_7	0.808	34.9	0.999
Tertiary alcohols	C_4–C_5	0.808	34.9	0.999
Secondary alcohols	C_3–C_5	0.857	33.6	0.997
n-Alkyl acetates	C_2–C_7	0.841	37.1	0.997
n-Alkyl ethers	C_4–C_{10}	0.886	43.3	0.994

[a] From Messner et al., 1959.
[b] Fraction of variation in relative response due to variation in molecular weight.

The procedure is applicable when the variety of compounds being measured is limited. For heterogeneous mixtures, calibration curves must be determined for individual components for optimum results.

More uniform response is obtained with other detector types. The flame ionization method yields moderately consistent results for hydrocarbons when computations are made on a weight basis (Chapter 2, Table II), the response per mole increasing roughly with carbon number. However, much lower responses per unit weight are obtained from alcohols and chlorinated hydrocarbons, so that once more rather extensive calibration is required to obtain quantitative data. The performance of the argon ionization detector is somewhat more predictable for compounds with high molecular weight, but it must be calibrated to obtain accurate results with a number of compounds having molecular weights under 150. Thus the response per mole and the response per unit mass obtained on alkanoic acids increases markedly with increasing carbon number (Table III). Conversely, the response of this de-

TABLE III

PEAK AREAS OF FATTY ACIDS PER MOLE AND PER UNIT MASS[a]
(Relative to those of pelargonic acid)

Compound	Relative peak area per mole	Relative peak area per unit mass
Butyric acid (C_4)	0.09	0.16
Valeric acid (C_5)	0.35	0.54
Caproic acid (C_6)	0.53	0.72
Enanthic acid (C_7)	0.74	0.90
Caprylic acid (C_8)	0.86	0.94
Pelargonic acid (C_9)	1.00	1.00
Capric acid (C_{10})	1.09	1.00

[a] From Böttcher et al. (1960).

tector to other compounds has been found to decrease strongly with rising molecular weight up to a value of 100 (Lovelock, 1958). Thus the argon detector gives consistent results when the molecular weight is above 150 to 200 but should be calibrated otherwise.

The Martin gas density balance is the most reliable nondestructive detector from the standpoint of uniformity of results. Response is related directly to the molecular weight of the solute, and quantitative results can be obtained with very simple calibrations. This device has not been used as much as its versatility would seem to warrant, reportedly because it is difficult to construct. However, new designs have been reported recently, and several manufacturers (Gow-Mac Instrument Co.; Griffin and George Ltd.) now supply these instruments.

If the sample need not be conserved, the solutes can be combusted and measured as CO_2, or reduced catalytically and measured as methane. Thus all the components of the mixture are converted to the same substance and can be quantitated from a single curve relating detector response to amount of CO_2 or methane. The only additional information required is a knowledge of the carbon numbers of the individual sample components. The reaction products are usually measured with thermal conductivity cells, so the method is not highly sensitive. Neither flame nor argon ionization detectors respond to carbon dioxide, but the former is extremely sensitive to methane. Therefore catalytic reduction of the sample, coupled with use of a flame detector, might be a satisfactory method for quantitative analysis of traces of low-molecular-weight organic compounds without resorting to individual calibration.

Aside from variability of detector response, the other major problem in constructing a calibration curve is introduction of an accurately measured sample into the chromatograph. This can be done now with fair reproducibility in the 0.5- to 10-μl range with some of the newer syringes that have been developed. Direct calibration on medium- and large-sized samples is therefore possible. However, alternative methods are available that do not require an accurate knowledge of the size of the sample introduced into the chromatograph. These are the internal standard method and the internal normalization method. In the internal standard method a known amount of standard, for which the detector response has been determined, is added to the sample. The mixture is chromatographed, and the concentration of the unknown is computed from its peak area relative to that of the standard. In the internal normalization method the areas of all the peaks on the chromatogram are measured, and the *total* area is divided into the area of the peak generated by the component of interest.

a. Direct Calibration

Calibration curves can be based on weight per cent, volume per cent, or mole per cent. With pure liquids, the density must be known to compute weight per cent, since injection is usually by volume. To prepare a calibration curve from pure liquids, a number of samples of different size are injected, and peak area is plotted against volume or weight. If different attenuation settings are used, the readings must be corrected to a common value, usually highest sensitivity. A more convenient procedure is to weigh out accurately known amounts of all the components of the sample, mix them, and dilute the mixture to standard volume with a volatile solvent that does not interfere with any of the sample peaks. A series of dilutions is made from the stock solution, and aliquots of each are injected into the chromatograph. Peak area, corrected for attenuation, is plotted against amount of component for each solute. The amount of each component in unknown samples then can be interpolated from the curves. Extrapolation should not be used indiscriminately, since detector response may depart from linearity.

The relation between sample weight and detector response can be expressed algebraically by equation 35, where w_s is the weight of solute, θ is

$$w_s = s\theta a \qquad (35)$$

the calibration constant, s is the attenuation setting, and a is the peak area.

b. Internal Standard Added Before Sample Injection

An internal standard should be selected with a retention volume as close as possible to the peak being measured, without overlapping it. If several widely spaced peaks are being quantitated, a separate standard is needed for each peak. If the retention volumes of two sample components are relatively close, a single standard can be chosen that peaks between them. The peak heights of the standards should not differ too much from those of the components being measured. Generally, it is impractical to use internal standards when a large number of components are being measured because of excessive dilution of the sample and difficulty in finding materials with the requisite retention volumes. In such cases, internal normalization or combustion of the sample to CO_2 should be considered as a possible alternative. Internal standards are valuable in that they compensate for minor variations in operating parameters. This is particularly important when peak height is the basis for quantitation.

*1. *Example of Use of Internal Standard* (Brealey *et al.* 1959). *n*-Propanol is used as an internal standard in the analysis of aqueous chloroform preparations, since it peaks between chloroform and water. Standards containing 0.1%, 0.2%, and 0.4% of chloroform and 1% of *n*-propanol are prepared, and suitable aliquots are chromatographed. Samples of unknowns are diluted as necessary to adjust the chloroform content to within the standard range, and then 1% of *n*-propanol is added. The samples are chromatographed under the same conditions as the standards. Calibration curves are obtained from the chromatograms of the standards by measuring the ratio of the peak heights of chloroform and *n*-propanol and plotting this ratio against percentage of chloroform. It is possible to use peak heights rather than peak areas in this example, since standard operating conditions can be reproduced exactly, and the peaks are sharp and symmetrical. The concentrations of chloroform in the unknown are determined by computing the chloroform–propanol height ratios from the chromatograms and interpolating on the calibration curve.

The peak height ratios are insensitive to changes in sample size over a threefold range, illustrating that exact reproduction of sample volume is unnecessary for quantitative results with this technique (Table IV). Recovery values obtained on samples fortified with chloroform at the 0.1% level vary from 96 to 104%. This calibration curve could not be reproduced exactly

TABLE IV

Effect of Sample Size on the Ratio of Peak Heights of Chloroform and n-Propanol at Different Concentrations of Chloroform[a]

Size of sample (μl)	Concentration of chloroform (%)	Ratio of peak heights
12	0.1	0.66
25	0.1	0.62
36	0.1	0.68
12	0.2	1.10
25	0.2	1.13
36	0.2	1.16
12	0.4	2.33
25	0.4	2.34
36	0.4	2.34

[a] Brealey et al. (1959).

from day to day but was subject to slight changes in slope. However, it was necessary to check only two points on the curve each day.

c. Internal Standard Added during Tissue Extraction

Usually, the only requirement for an internal standard is that it be stable chemically, and have a retention volume close to that of the compound being analyzed for. However, errors introduced by losses of material during extraction of tissue and sample clean-up also can be by-passed by adding a known amount of standard to the tissue at the extraction step (Storrs and Burchfield, 1961). For this application, the standard should have physicochemical properties almost identical to those of the compound being analyzed for, except that there is a difference in retention volume great enough to permit good peak resolution. Ideally, quantitative results could be calculated from the amount of standard added to the tissue and the ratio of peak areas, regardless of losses incurred during sample preparation. In practice, it is always necessary to establish an empirical correction factor experimentally.

A number of ways exist through which compounds of biological interest can be modified to obtain useful internal standards. One of these is to replace a single atom in a compound with the element next above (or below) it in the periodic system, *providing* it can be shown that the substitution does not produce a fundamental modification in physicochemical properties. For example, 2-chloro-4-bromophenoxyacetic acid is a suitable internal standard in the analysis of 2,4-dichlorophenoxyacetic acid. The properties of these two compounds are quite similar, but their retention volumes are sufficiently different to permit good peak resolution. Similarly, bromopentachloro-benzene is a satisfactory standard in the analysis of hexachlorobenzene, while dimethyl monobromotrichloroterephthalate is readily resolved from the pre-emergence herbicide, dimethyl tetrachloroterephthalate. Substitution of atoms other than halogen might prove effective. For example, replacement of sulfur with selenium might provide a suitable internal standard for use in the analysis of the psychoactive drug Chlorpromazine.

In some instances, substitution of one atom for another might not be suitable, owing to profound changes in chemical reactivity. Thus silicon would not be a satisfactory replacement for carbon since the C—Si bond is easily hydrolyzed. In such cases it might be possible to procure suitable standards by multiple labeling with heavy isotopes. Thus the molecular weight of heavy benzene ($C_6{}^{13}D_6$) is 15% greater than that of ordinary benzene. n-Hexane can be separated from n-heptane with great ease by GLC, and the molecular weight difference is about the same. Therefore, it is possible that ordinary and heavy modifications of many compounds could be resolved by replacing only one of the elements with a heavy isotope. Such a procedure would be similar in principle to isotope dilution employing radioactive compounds, but ease of sample handling would be improved, and requirements for clean-up reduced.

d. Internal Normalization

In the internal normalization method, the per cent of each component in the mixture is computed without regard for the absolute amount of material present. Therefore results obtained by this method are independent of sample size, within reasonable limits. The procedure is to sum the areas of all the peaks and divide this value into area of the individual peak. Thus the percentage of the ith component in the mixture is given by equation 36,

$$\text{Per cent} = 100a_i \bigg/ \sum_{j=1}^{j=n} a_j \tag{36}$$

where a is the peak area, and n is the total number of peaks.

The data may be treated by several methods which differ in accuracy. Good results are obtained only if certain conditions are fulfilled. Firstly, all the components of the sample must be volatile enough to pass through the chromatographic column, for, if some components do not give rise to peaks, misleading results will be obtained on others. Thus if a solute comprises only 10% of a mixture, and half the sample is not vaporized, a result of 20% will be obtained, conditions being ideal otherwise. Secondly, if some solutes undergo partial degradation on the chromatographic column, all the results will be affected, even though many components come through intact. This is particularly noticeable in the analysis of members of homologous series having the same chemical properties and differing only in retention volume. The more-volatile components will be least affected, since they will remain in the column for a comparatively short time, and so have less opportunity to interact with the packing. Much larger amounts of the slower moving components will be lost. Consequently, results obtained on them will be low, and those on the faster components disproportionately high, since they constitute a greater proportion of the eluate than they do of the original sample. Therefore internal normalization is satisfactory only if all the components of the mixture are known to be volatile and are not altered chemically during passage through the chromatographic column.

1. *Use of Uncorrected Peak Areas.* Approximate results can be obtained by internal normalization by using peak areas that are read directly from the chromatogram without correction for variations in detector response. Of course this method is satisfactory only when detector response does not vary much from compound to compound. Thermal detectors are unsatisfactory, but measurements made with argon detectors are fairly good if the sample does not contain components having molecular weights under 150.

2. *Successive Approximation Method.* This procedure, sometimes called the bracketing method, is of value when only a few samples must be analyzed and extensive calibration is not worth while. A chromatogram is run, and the results are calculated from uncorrected peak areas by equation 36. Next, a synthetic mixture having this exact composition is prepared and chromatographed. Peak areas for each component are compared with those obtained in the original run, and appropriate corrections are made. If the corrections are large, a second synthetic mixture is prepared and chromatographed, and the results are compared with those of the first, etc.

3. *Use of Corrected Peak Areas.* The best results are obtained with a wide variety of detectors if each peak area is multiplied by a factor to correct it for variations in detector response to different compounds. These factors are obtained by chromatographing synthetic mixtures of accurately known composition and determining the peak area per unit mass for each component. When this procedure is used, the percentage of the ith component of the mixture is given by equation 37, where a is the peak area of the ith compo-

$$\text{Per cent} = 100\delta_i a_i \bigg/ \sum_{j=1}^{j=n} \delta_j a_j \qquad (37)$$

nent, δ_i is the corresponding correction factor, and n is the total number of components.

Calibration factors can be regarded as constants only if operational parameters and sample composition are not varied over a wide range.

IV. Measurement of Peak Area

Peak area is used most often for the quantitation of gas chromatographic data. If mechanical integrators are not available, computation can be very tedious when large numbers of chromatograms, each containing many peaks, must be evaluated. Consequently short-cut methods have been developed to simplify the procedure. These vary in accuracy and so must be selected in accordance with the requirements of the analysis.

a. Calculation from Peak Parameters

1. *Height × Width at Half-Height* (Cremer and Müller, 1951). This is probably the most widely used method for estimating peak area. The area is obtained by multiplying peak height (*BE* in Fig. 3*A*) by the width at half-height (*HJ*). When the curves are nearly Gaussian, this procedure gives results that correspond to 0.84 times the area found by integration. The technique is fast and reproducible. Results are not satisfactory on very narrow peaks because the percentage error in measuring width is large. The error can be reduced by employing a slower chart speed.

2. *Triangulation.* Straight lines are drawn along the inflection points of the peak so that they intersect the base line. The area of the triangle formed by this procedure is given by the product of its height and one-half the base. The triangle will have an area about 4% less than that of the peak, provided the latter is symmetrical.

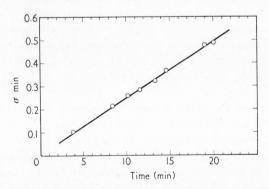

Fig. 31. Relationship between standard deviation (σ) and retention time (Bartlet and Smith, 1960).

*3. *Height × Standard Deviation* (Bartlet and Smith, 1960). Peaks obtained in GLC closely approximate a normal or Gaussian distribution curve. The area of such a curve is given by equation 38, where h is the peak height, and σ

$$a = 2.507h\sigma \qquad (38)$$

is the standard deviation. The standard deviation equals the width of the peak at 0.882 of peak height. Values for 2σ can be measured at $0.607h$, for 3σ at $0.324h$, and for 4σ at $0.134h$. These should give concordant results for area when substituted in equation 38. For highest accuracy, peak width measurements should be made with a magnifying viewer equipped with a reticle (Bausch and Lomb No. 81-34-97-20). *Unresolved peaks.* Values for σ increase linearly with retention time (or volume) owing to longitudinal diffusion of the solutes in the mobile phase (Fig. 31). Therefore they can be obtained by interpolating from graphs of σ versus t_R for a given column under the same conditions when peaks are insufficiently resolved for accurate measurement. These values can be substituted in equation 38 to calculate peak areas. However, heights (h) measured directly are often too large, owing to the contribution of the adjacent peak. Values for correcting h can be obtained from a graph relating the per cent correction to the distance separating the apices of the two peaks in units of standard deviation (Fig. 32). If

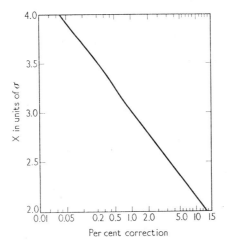

Fig. 32. Peak height corrections for given separations measured in units of the interfering peak (Bartlet and Smith, 1960).

the distance separating the peaks is more than 4σ, the correction is usually negligible, even though the valley between them does not return to the base line. When a peak appears only as a shoulder, it is necessary to obtain retention volumes of the two compounds from other data so that the distance between the peak apices is known accurately. *Isolated asymmetrical peaks.* The areas of symmetrical and asymmetrical peaks having the same heights and retention volumes are almost identical. Therefore the areas of the latter can be calculated from equation 38. Calculation of areas of overlapping asymmetrical peaks is more complicated and requires a series of successive approximations.

b. Semimechanical Integration

1. *Weighing Method.* The peaks are cut out with scissors, and the paper is weighed on an analytical balance. Squares of paper from adjacent areas are weighed to determine weight per unit area. This method is accurate but tedious. Errors may arise from variations in the thickness and moisture content of the paper. This procedure is not very satisfactory for estimating the areas of overlapping peaks. Furthermore, the chromatogram is destroyed in making the measurement, unless a tracing is employed.

2. *Planimeter.* Peak areas can be measured with a polar planimeter. The method is time-consuming and no more reliable for overlapping peaks than the weighing method.

c. Mechanical Integration

1. *Printing Integrator.* Equipment is available commercially that will automatically print cumulative integrals of peak areas (Perkin-Elmer Corp.). It can be used in conjunction with an attenuation changer so that peak areas and positions are recorded entirely automatically after the sample is injected. It has been reported that nonlinearities in this integrator as well as the recorder lead to significant errors in peak area measurements (Orr, 1961). A formula has been derived that permits calculation of the true area from the recorded integral.

2. *Disc Integrator.* This is a ball and disc integrator that is adaptable to most strip chart recorders (Disc Instrument Co.). The integrator operates an auxiliary pen that moves in continuous back-and-forth motions at a speed proportional to the displacement of the recorder pen from the base line. The integrated area is proportional to the number of strokes made by the pen.

I. Fraction Collection for Qualitative Analysis and Measurement of Radioactivity

I. INTRODUCTION

Gas chromatography is by itself an excellent method of qualitative analysis. Retention volumes (V_g) of chemical compounds on specified liquid phases are independent of all operating parameters except temperature. They are characteristic and reproducible and so can be used for tentative identification. Further confirmation can be obtained by running unknowns, together with standards, on several liquids differing in polarity to make certain that peaks do not overlap fortuitously (Brown, 1960). Moreover, it is possible to assign some unknown compounds to certain homologous series and determine their molecular weights by means of retention volumes obtained on polar and nonpolar liquids (see Chapter 7, Section G.VII, for example). Nevertheless, final confirmation of identity must be sought through chemical tests or instrumental methods of analysis.

To do this, samples must be collected in pure form, uncontaminated with column packing or fractions which precede them through the chromatograph. Samples for analytical columns are ordinarily small, so special methods are needed for their collection. If larger samples are required, specially constructed preparatory columns can be used for separation. Unfortunately, none of the chemical or instrumental methods currently in practice are sensitive enough to analyze the minute amounts of materials eluted from capillary columns. Consequently this section will be concerned with collection of fractions from packed columns having ordinary dimensions.

Methods for identifying compounds trapped from the effluents of chromatographs include chemical tests for functional groups (see Chapter 3, Section A.II), ultraviolet spectrophotometry, infrared spectrophotometry, mass spectrometry, and nuclear magnetic resonance spectrometry. In a book of this limited scope, details on the theory, techniques, and results obtained with these methods cannot be given. Yet there is one ancillary technique to gas chromatography that demands limited discussion, since this is a book on biochemistry. The technique is, of course, radiochemistry. Modern biochemistry would not exist today without it. Even such a versatile method as gas chromatography would have limited horizons if a way could not be found to combine the virtues of the two methods into a unified technique of instrumental analysis.

II. General Methods

A number of methods can be used for sample collection. The vapors eluted from the chromatograph can be condensed in a chilled U tube, absorbed by cotton wool moistened with a solvent, or trapped in a solvent. Regardless of the method, it is essential that the sample be free of contaminants, particularly with optical methods of analysis. The two principal sources of contaminants are the carrier gas and the column packing. Volatile impurities in the carrier gas usually can be removed by passing the gas through a cold trap situated between the cylinder and the pressure regulator of the chromatograph. The trap can consist of a coiled metal tube immersed in coolant. It will operate more efficiently if filled with finely divided metal shot to increase the surface and act as a heat-transfer agent.

Contamination from the column usually results from bleeding caused by insufficient conditioning, or from operation at a temperature too high for the particular packing. Interference from this source will be recognized immediately if the spectra of all the samples collected resemble one another and that of the stationary liquid or its decomposition products. The only remedies are to increase conditioning time, reduce operating temperature, or change the liquid phases. Insertion of a cold trap between the column and the collector will be of value only for compounds with very low boiling points. Reasonably pure fractions can be obtained from columns packed with Apiezon L or silicone grease at temperatures of 240° to 260°C and below.

Loss of samples through condensation in lines leading from the column to the collector is another potential source of difficulty in the analysis of high-boiling materials. The exit lines in some chromatographs are not heated, and in others heating is insufficient. If samples are to be collected, the exit lines should be wrapped with heating tape or insulated resistance wire and heated to column temperature or slightly above. Heating should be continuous from the column exit to the point of collection, since a cold spot anywhere along the route can cause trouble in the collection of high-boiling sample components (method I.II.c.1).

Samples also may be lost through failure to condense them in the trap. For the collection of volatile components, the trap should be cooled in an ice bath, a dry ice bath, or a liquid nitrogen bath, depending on the boiling points of the compounds. Efficiency can be increased by filling the trap with an inert particulate solid, such as very pure quartz sand or finely divided glass beads, to increase the surface available for condensation. Of course, the compounds must be extracted from the packing, and this entails an extra step. Active solids such as silica gel or charcoal can be used in traps, but if possible this should be avoided, since some sample components may not be desorbed quantitatively when the trap is warmed.

High-boiling compounds also may be lost through incomplete condensation, since they may form fogs consisting of a cloud of charged particles when the carrier gas is cooled suddenly. The particles are extremely small and will not condense in ordinary cold traps. If the hot vapors are allowed to condense in a trap at room temperature, fogging is reduced considerably, particularly if a thermal gradient is established between the chromatograph and the trap, so that cooling is slow. However, fogging is eliminated entirely and sample recovery is practically quantitative if the carrier gas is passed through a tube containing a plug of cotton wool moistened with solvent (method I.II.a.1). This sorbs the sample, so that an aerosol does not form. Other methods for sample collection involving auxiliary solvents include bubbling the carrier gas through a small quantity of solvent contained in a micro test tube (method I.II.a.2) or mixing the carrier gas with heated solvent vapors which are then condensed (method I.II.a.3). The latter method results in considerable dilution of the sample but may be a useful means of avoiding premature condensation in the lines.

Losses due to aerosol formation can be overcome without dilution of the sample with solvent by imposing a high voltage generated by an induction coil across the exit end of the cold trap (method I.II.c.2). This acts on the same principle as a Cottrell precipitator and results in condensation of the fog in the tube, thus reducing loss of sample (Kratz *et al.*, 1959). Recovery of essential oils was increased from about 10% to over 90% by this device, the trap not being cooled in either case. None of the compounds tested formed a fog that could not be precipitated.

Regardless of how samples are collected, they must be recovered from the trap in some form suitable for optical or chemical analysis. If a solvent is used, it is often expedient to choose one that is also a suitable medium for the type of analysis contemplated. For example, hexane and methanol are good choices when the solutes will be analyzed by ultraviolet spectrophotometry, and carbon disulfide and carbon tetrachloride are best for infrared work, since they transmit electromagnetic radiation in these regions. If optical properties are not a paramount consideration, and the solutes must be recovered by evaporation, a solvent with a low boiling point should be chosen.

Sometimes it is possible to recover liquid samples without a solvent and so eliminate one step in the analysis. To make this possible, the trap should be designed so that the sample accumulates in a declivity or capillary tip from which it can be withdrawn by a hypodermic needle equipped with a syringe. A U tube (method I.II.b.1) or a straight glass tube (method I.II.b.2) can be modified for this purpose. When samples are collected in straight glass tubes (Lesser, 1959) or U tubes without narrow declivities, it is usually necessary to wash them out with solvents because of the small volume of the condensed liquid.

Most of the procedures discussed in this section are intended for the collection of single fractions. However, multiple-fraction collectors have been described in the literature (Weinstein, 1957; Napier and Rodda, 1958) and are available commercially from many manufacturers of chromatographs and auxiliary equipment. It seems safe to say at this time that techniques for fraction collection have not advanced to the same level of automation reached by other operations essential to gas chromatography.

a. Collection of Fractions by Means of Solvents

1. *On Moistened Cotton Wool* (James, 1960). Defatted cotton wool is wetted with methanol or petroleum ether and packed loosely into the bulb of a small drying tube, of the same type ordinarily used to contain calcium chloride. To take a sample, the tube is attached to the outlet of the chromatograph with silicone rubber tubing. This procedure is useful for trapping high-boiling compounds which otherwise tend to fog when the carrier gas is cooled suddenly. It has been used for the collection of methyl esters of fatty acids.

*2. *In a Solvent* (Zubyk and Conner, 1960). The effluent line of the gas chromatograph is fitted with a 20-gauge hypodermic needle. The solvent (0.5 to 1.0 ml) is placed in a 103 × 9-mm o.d. test tube. When the peak appears on the chromatogram, the needle is immersed beneath the surface of the liquid, and the sample is collected. For collection periods of over 2 to 3 minutes the tube is immersed in an ice bath to reduce evaporation of solvent. This method has been used for the collection of liquids boiling between 140° and 220°C.

*3. *Condensation with Solvent Vapor* (Jones and Ritchie, 1958). The apparatus is shown in Fig. 33. *A* is a flask equipped with an electric heater for

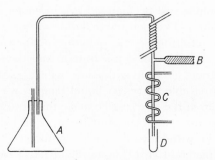

FIG. 33. Apparatus for collecting fractions by entrapment in solvent vapor (Jones and Ritchie, 1958).

generating solvent vapors. It is connected to the outlet of the chromatograph at *B* with ¼-inch o.d. copper tubing fitted with a T joint. The tubing between the vapor-generating flask and the connection to the chromatograph is wrapped with heating tape to warm the solvent vapors to column temperature. The section of tubing below the connection to the chromatograph is fitted with a condenser (*C*) made from ⅛-inch copper tubing wrapped in a spiral and soldered in place. *D* is a tube to collect the condensed vapors. A number of these tubes can be placed in a fraction collector operated by a time switch, so that fractions can be collected for optical analysis at preset intervals. The rate of distillation of the trapping solvent is adjusted so that 5 ml of solution per fraction is collected at ½-minute intervals. This system has been used for trapping vapors of aromatic amines.

b. Collection without Solvents

*1. *In a Modified U Tube* (Frisone, 1959). This apparatus (Fig. 34) consists of a U tube with a well sealed into it at the bottom of the bend. Access to the well is through a ground-glass stopper. The tube is immersed in a suitable coolant and attached to the outlet of the chromatograph. When the fraction of interest has collected, the trap is warmed, and the condensate, if liquid, is removed from the well with a microsyringe.

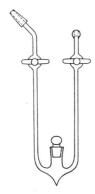

Fig. 34. Modified U tube for collection of fractions (Frisone, 1959).

*2. *In a Straight Tube with Capillary Tip* (Feinland, personal communication, 1960). The apparatus for collection is shown in Fig. 35. The main

Fig. 35. Sample collection tube (Feinland, personal communication, 1960).

tube (*A*) is constructed of 0.6-cm i.d. Pyrex tubing. It is about 12 cm long and is drawn to a capillary tip just wide enough to admit the point of a hypodermic needle. The tube contains a 0.6-cm i.d. side arm (*B*) located about 2 cm from the open end. Both the main tube and the side arm are closed with $\frac{5}{16}$-inch silicone rubber plugs (Kirkhill Rubber Co.). A 13-cm hypodermic needle with a Huber point is pushed through the plug closing

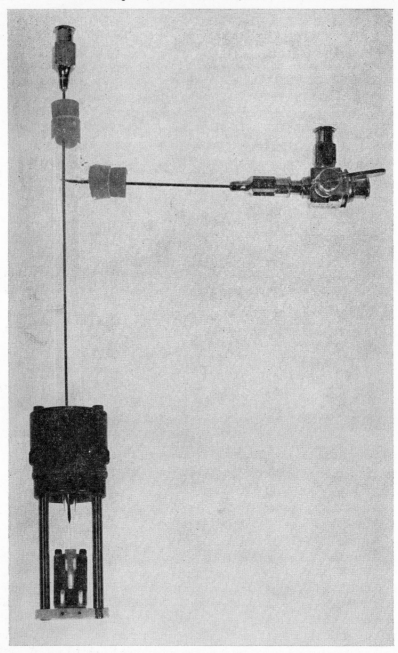

FIG. 36. Apparatus for collecting fractions in an infrared microcell (Wilks and Warren, Connecticut Instrument Co., Wilton, Conn., 1960).

the main tube to serve as an outlet for the carrier gas. To take, for instance, a low-boiling sample, the collector is immersed in a suitable coolant, and the plug closing the outlet to the side arm is pressed against a hypodermic needle connected to the chromatograph so that the point pierces the silicone plug and enters tube *A*. The sample then condenses on the walls of the tube. If the sample is liquid, the collector is placed in an adaptor and centrifuged until the liquid collects in the capillary tip. If the sample is solid, it is necessary to wash down the walls of the collector with a suitable solvent before centrifugation. The sample is then withdrawn from the capillary tip with a syringe for chemical or instrumental analysis.

*3. *In an Infrared Microcell* (Wilks and Warren, 1960). A modification of procedure I.II.b.2 above has been described in which the sample is transferred directly to an infrared ultramicrocell (Fig. 36). The tip of the condenser is cut off, permitting the capillary opening to be inserted into the orifice of the infrared cell. The assembly consists of the condenser, a metal frame which holds the infrared cell to the bottom of the condenser, and the cell itself. A cylindrical metal can is provided which slips over the lower part of the assembly and fits snugly around the frame to protect the cell from moisture. To take a sample, the assembly is immersed in coolant, and a sample is admitted to the condenser as described in method I.II.b.2. The apparatus is warmed to room temperature, and the protective can is removed. If more than a microliter of liquid is collected, enough of it may run down into the cell to fill it. If not, the sample can often be shaken down into the cell. If less than a microliter has been collected, it may be necessary to centrifuge the assembly to drive the sample down from the side walls of the condenser. A small-volume cavity-type cell is used for sample collection and infrared measurement (Jones and Nadeau, 1958). This equipment is available commercially (Connecticut Instrument Corp.). The spectrophotometer should be equipped with a beam condenser when used with cells of this size.

c. Auxiliary Methods

*1. *Heated Exit Line* (Feinland, personal communication). The equipment for preventing sample condensation in exit lines during fraction collection is shown in Fig. 37. *A* is a heated exit line leading from the chromato-

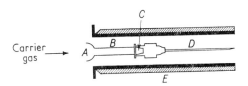

Fig. 37. Heated outlet tube for fraction collection (Feinland, personal communication, 1960).

graph, and *B* is a short length of 1- to 2-mm i.d. stainless-steel tubing. *C* is a metal adaptor for a hypodermic syringe sealed onto the end of *B* with silver solder. *D* is a hypodermic needle with a Huber point. The stainless-steel tubing and hypodermic needle are enclosed in a copper jacket wrapped with insulated resistance wire. Heat input to the jacket is controlled with a variable voltage transformer. Fractions are collected in tubes equipped with side arms closed with silicone stoppers. To take a sample, the stopper is pressed against the needle until the point pierces it and enters the collection chamber.

*2. *Electrostatic Precipitation of Fog* (Kratz *et al.*, 1959). The equipment is illustrated in Fig. 38. The exit tube of the sample collector is wrapped with a

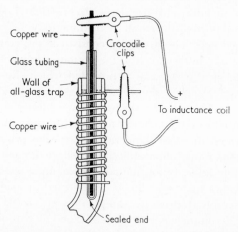

FIG. 38. Apparatus for eliminating fog from chromatograph effluents by electrostatic precipitation (Kratz *et al.*, 1959).

tightly coiled spiral of copper wire which serves as the outer electrode. The inner electrode consists of a copper wire contained in a 8 × 0.3-cm length of glass tubing. The electrodes are connected to an induction coil (FTC-40 ignition coil, F. & B. Mfg. Co.) powered by a 6-volt battery. During operation, a silent discharge between the two electrodes produces a purplish glow. This apparatus prevents smoke formation, so recovery of fractions is practically quantitative. The device should not be used when hydrogen is employed as the carrier gas or under other conditions where sparking might be dangerous. Care must be taken also to avoid electric shocks.

III. RADIOCHEMICAL ANALYSIS

The recorder tracing of the gas chromatograph gives a qualitative and quantitative measure of the mass distribution of metabolites in samples of biological origin. However, this information is often insufficient to provide an answer to the problem under investigation, since it may be necessary to determine the extent to which various compounds participate in metabolism by feeding tissues or organisms radioactive substrates and measuring distribution of label. Therefore, gas chromatography often must be used in conjunction with radiochemical analysis to yield the maximum amount of usable information. The development of techniques and instrumentation for this is proceeding rapidly.

The type of detector employed to measure radioactivity must be governed to a considerable extent by sensitivity requirements coupled with the energies of the particles produced by atomic disintegrations. The earliest method was to pass the effluent from the chromatograph through a gas cell containing a thin-walled Geiger counter connected to a ratemeter. This is satisfactory for many elements, but C^{14} and H^3, two isotopes used very frequently in biochemical research, are weak β-particle emitters. Tritium would not register at all, and C^{14} only weakly. An alternative is to pass the carrier gas containing the radioactive solutes through the Geiger tube and so avoid adsorption by the walls. However, helium and nitrogen, which are used quite often as mobile phases, are poor counter gases. This difficulty has been overcome by injecting methane into the gas stream after it leaves the chromatograph, thereby producing a mixture that will give adequate response to radioactive disintegrations when passed through a proportional counter (Wolfgang and Rowland, 1958). The apparatus has been used to count C^{14}- and H^3-labeled compounds at temperatures up to 200°C, with a differential method for recording results.

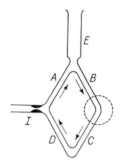

Fig. 39. Apparatus for collection and measurement of radioactive fractions by scintillation counting (Popják *et al.*, 1959).

C^{14} can be detected in minute amounts with a scintillation counter. The usual procedure is to collect eluted samples on a cotton wool plug moistened with toluene, or to bubble the carrier gas through toluene to absorb the vapors. A suitable phosphor is added to the toluene solution containing the radioactive sample, and the scintillations are counted with a photomultiplier. This method can be for counting the activity in individual peaks separately or for continuous integral counting, and it is probably the best procedure presently available for measuring C^{14}, since it is sensitive, and problems arising from condensation of solute vapors are avoided. In the continuous integral method (Popják *et al.*, 1959), the effluent carrier gas is passed into a vapor trap filled with a solution of a phosphor (diphenyloxazole) in toluene. This apparatus is shown in Fig. 39. The gas enters the trap at *I*, and its pressure prevents the liquid in the trap from flowing backward into the chromatograph. The gas bubbles (40 to 160 ml/min) pass through arm *A* of the trap and leave the apparatus through the chimney (*E*), the solutes being extracted into the phosphor solution during transit. The gas flow sets the liquid in the trap in circular motion along the direction indicated by the arrows, thereby causing thorough mixing of the solutes with the scintillation liquid. A photomultiplier tube is positioned between *B* and *C* (indicated by the dotted circle). The output from it is amplified, measured with a rate

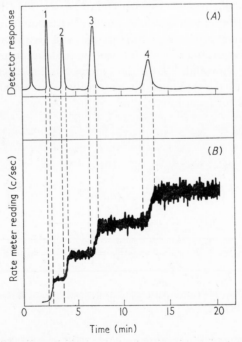

Fig. 40. (*A*) Chromatogram obtained on methyl esters of C^{14}-labeled fatty acids: (1) 10:0; (2) 12:0; (3) 14:0; (4) 16:0. (*B*) Measurement of radioactivity of same sample by means of scintillation counter (Popják *et al.*, 1959).

meter, and the level of activity recorded continuously. Since radioactive substances accumulate continuously in the phosphor solution, the record obtained is an integral one, the height of each step being proportional to the amount of radioactivity found in each chromatographic peak (Fig. 40).

A discontinuous method is described by Karmen and Tritch (1960) for measuring C^{14} with a scintillation counter. The same technique can be applied also for integral measurements. The eluates from the chromatograph are collected in short (2½-inch × 9-mm o.d.) tubes connected to the exit of the chromatograph. The tubes are packed with D.C. 550 silicone oil coated on anthracene. The anthracene serves both as a support for the stationary phase and as a phosphor. The trapping columns are maintained at room temperature so that the stationary phase retains the substances eluted from the analytical column in the shortest possible length. The trap is then detached from the chromatograph and counted in a liquid scintillation spectrometer. Stationary phases other than silicone grease can be used, but counting efficiency is not so high. These traps, together with a fraction collector, are available commercially (Packard Instrument Co. Inc.).

Scintillation counters are satisfactory for C^{14}, but with tritium the efficiency is low and the background high. Therefore proportional counters or ionization chambers are usually used for measuring it. Cacace and Inam-ul-Haq (1960) describe a method in which the carrier gas is passed through an ionization chamber after it leaves the thermal conductivity cell of the chromatograph, thereby supplying differential records of both mass distribution and label distribution in the sample. The unique feature of this method is that the gas flow rate through the ionization chamber is kept constant and independent of the operating conditions of the chromatograph. This makes it possible to calibrate the ionization chamber under a constant set of conditions that need not be changed. This is accomplished by carrying out the calibrations at a flow rate higher than any used for chromatography. Gas is then metered into the carrier gas stream at a point between the exit of the chromatograph and the entrance to the ionization chamber so that the total flow rate of the gas entering the latter will be constant. A rate of 10 liters per hour and a chamber volume of 100 ml were found to be satisfactory. Vapors of moderately high boiling compounds (about 155°C) do not condense in the chamber, even when operated at room temperature, because of the high degree of dilution with auxiliary gas. However, an ionization chamber can be constructed from readily available materials which can be operated at 240°C (Mason *et al.*, 1959).

After the method for measuring radioactivity is selected, it is necessary to decide whether counting should be done on fractions collected intermittently or whether the results should be recorded continuously by differential or integral methods. Intermittent fraction collection is advantageous in that the samples can be handled individually and can be counted as long as necessary to obtain results with any degree of statistical significance desired. However, it is tedious and at times may lead to error. For example, suppose a trace component having high specific activity has a retention value only slightly less than that of a cold major component. If the entire peak is sampled and counted, the radioactivity probably would be ascribed to the major component. However, with continuous recording the differences in positions of the mass distribution peaks and the label distribution peaks might be evident. Nevertheless, collection of peaks individually is convenient, accurate, and probably sufficiently reliable when known systems are employed.

Differential records are obtained when the carrier gas is passed continuously through a proportional counter or ionization chamber without depositing the sample. This method is advantageous in that small peaks can be seen easily, and the presentation of data is parallel to that obtained on mass distribution curves obtained on most chromatographs. However, this method is sensitive to changes in operating parameters and the dimensions of the sensing chamber, just as these quantities also affect the performance of conventional chromatograph detectors.

Either of two situations may exist when a plug of radioactive gas is passed through a sensing chamber, depending on the size of the chamber and the length of the plug. If the chamber is large compared to the length of the plug, all the radioactive material will be within the confines of the sensing chamber at the same time, and consequently the *height* of the peak as measured with a rate meter will be directly proportional to the amount of radioactivity. In other words, the ionization chamber or proportional counter will behave like an integral detector. If the chamber is small compared to the length of the plug of vapor, only a small fraction of the total radioactivity will register at any one time, the amount of radioactivity will be proportional to the area under the curve, and the rate meter will function as a differential detector. Of course intermediate situations exist; if the specific activity of a component is desired, calibration with a sample of that component having known specific activity must be made. Furthermore, if the operating parameters of the column are changed so that the width of the peak changes, the old calibration is no longer valid. In measuring a large number of radioactive compounds, the task of calibration becomes a major one. Furthermore, standard samples of *all* the radioactive compounds of interest must be available, since they will have different retention volumes and consequently different peak widths. Consequently, it is often expedient to use an integral detector, particularly when it is not disadvantageous to remix the components separated on the analytical column. This can be accomplished by dissolving the fractions in a scintillation liquid as they emerge from the chromatograph (Popják *et al.*, 1959) or by condensing them on a cold trap placed within the counting chamber (Blyholder, 1960). Each of these methods for measuring the radioactivity of eluted fractions has specific advantages, but none of them is ideal for all purposes. Therefore they must be selected to fit the needs of the specific problem to which they are applied.

IV. Summary

Fractions eluted from chromatographic columns can be dissolved in solvents or condensed in cold traps. In some of these methods, the sample is collected in a form that can be used directly for further analysis by infrared spectrophotometry or mass spectrometry. The main sources of experimental difficulty are contamination from carrier gas and column packings, loss of vapors through condensation in cold spots, and losses through formation o aerosols during cooling. All of these can be avoided if adequate precautions are taken.

The radioactivity of eluted fractions can be measured with Geiger counters, proportional counters, scintillation counters, or ionization chambers. Fractions can be collected and measured batchwise, or the effluent from the column can be monitored continuously by differential or integral methods. Measurement of C^{14} with a scintillation counter is very sensitive and convenient, whereas with H^3 an ionization chamber or proportional counter is preferable. Probably the most sensitive method for C^{14} is to combust the sample to $C^{14}O_2$ and pass the gas through a Geiger tube.

References

Ambrose, D., A. T. James, A. I. M. Keulemans, E. Kovats, R. Rock, C. Rouit, and F. H. Stross. 1960. Preliminary recommendations on nomenclature and presentation of data in gas chromatography. *Pure and Appl. Chem.* **1:** 177–186.

Andreatch, A. J. and R. Feinland. 1960. Continuous trace hydrocarbon analysis by flame ionization. *Anal. Chem.* **32:** 1021–1024.

Anon. 1960. Polymer resists heat. *Chem. Eng. News.* **38:** 41.

Baddiel, C. B. and C. F. Cullis. 1960. The use of a carbon monoxide flame detector in gas chromatography. *Chem. & Ind. (London)* pp. 1154–1155.

Bartlet, J. C. and D. M. Smith. 1960. The determination of the areas of resolved and partially resolved chromatography peaks. *Can. J. Chem.* **38:** 2057–2065.

Bayer, E. 1958. Separation of derivatives of amino acids using gas-liquid chromatography. *In* "Gas Chromatography" (D. H. Desty, ed.), pp. 333–339. New York, Academic Press.

Bayer, E. and F. Anders. 1959. Biologische Objekte als Detektoren zur Gaschromatographie. *Naturwissenschaften* **46:** 380.

Benedict, N. 1960. Preparation of the column used for the chromatographic separation of Dacthal (DAC 893). Personal communication.

Bernhard, R. A. 1960. Effect of flow-rate and sample-size on column efficiency in gas-liquid chromatography. *Nature* **185:** 311–312.

Berry, R. 1960. An ultra-sensitive ionization detector for permanent gas analysis. *Nature* **188**: 578–579.

Bishop, C. T. and F. P. Cooper. 1960. Separation of carbohydrate derivatives by gas-liquid partition chromatography. *Can. J. Chem.* **38**: 388–395.

Blyholder, G. 1960. Integrating counter cell for use with vapor phase chromatography. *Anal. Chem.* **32**: 572.

Bohemen, J., S. H. Langer, R. H. Perrett, and J. H. Purnell. 1960. A study of the adsorptive properties of firebrick in relation to its use as a solid support in gas-liquid chromatography. *J. Chem. Soc.*: pp. 2444–2451.

Böttcher, C. J. F., G. F. G. Clemens, and C. M. van Gent. 1960. Response of the β-ray ionization detector to unesterified lower fatty acids in gas-liquid chromatography. *J. Chromatog.* **3**: 582.

Bowman, R. L. and A. Karmen. 1958. A micro sample introduction system for gas chromatography. *Nature* **182**: 1233–1234.

Brealey, L., D. A. Elvidge, and K. A. Proctor. 1959. The determination of chloroform in aqueous pharmaceutical preparations. *Analyst* **84**: 221–225.

Brenner, N., L. O'Brien, and V. J. Coates. 1958. Analytical applications of a triple stage gas chromatographic instrument. Pittsburgh Conference on Analytical Chemistry and Applied Spectroscopy.

Brown, I. 1960. Identification of organic compounds by gas chromatography.

Cacace, F. and Inam-ul-Haq. 1960. Radiometric analysis of tritiated organic compounds by means of vapor phase chromatography. *Science* **131**: 732–733.

Carle, D. W. 1958. Precise liquid sampling in gas chromatography. *In* "Gas Chromatography" (V. J. Coates, H. J. Noebels, and I. S. Fagerson, eds.), pp. 67–72. New York, Academic Press.

Casey, P. J. 1959. Construction of a gas chromatographic apparatus. *Proc. Penna. Acad. Sci.* **33**: 97–101.

Clark, S. J. (undated). Ionization detectors. Technical Information Bulletin. Jarrell-Ash Co., Newtonville, Massachusetts.

Condon, R. D. 1959. Design considerations of a gas chromatography system employing high efficiency Golay columns. *Anal. Chem.* **31**: 1717–1722.

Corning Glass Works, Special Apparatus Section. Corning, New York. Technical Information Circular.

Coulson, D. M., L. A. Cavanagh, J. E. de Vries, and B. Walther. 1960. Microcoulometric gas chromatography of pesticides. *J. Agr. Food Chem.* **8**: 399–402.

Craig, B. M. and N. L. Murty. 1959. Quantitative fatty acid analysis of vegetable oils by gas-liquid chromatography. *J. Am. Oil Chemists' Soc.* **36**: 549–552.

Cremer, E. and R. Müller. 1951a. [Separation and determination of gases by chromatography.] *Microkhim. Acta* **36/37**: 553–560; *Chem. Abstr.* **45**: 5057h, 1951.

Cremer, E. and R. Müller. 1951b. [Separation of substances by chromatography in the gas phase.] *Z. Elektrochem.* **55**: 217–220; *Chem. Abstr.* **45**: 9335a, 1951.

Cremer, E. and F. Prior. 1951. [Application of chromatographic methods to the separation of gases and determination of adsorption energies.] *Z. Elektrochem.* **55**: 66–70; *Chem. Abstr.* **45**: 9334h, 1951.

Dal Nogare, S. and C. E. Bennett. 1958. Programmed temperature gas chromatography. *Anal. Chem.* **30**: 1157–1158.

Dal Nogare, S. and J. C. Harden. 1959. Programmed temperature gas chromatography apparatus. *Anal. Chem.* **31**: 1829–1832.

Dal Nogare, S. and W. E. Langlois. 1960. Programmed temperature gas chromatography. *Anal. Chem.* **32**: 767–770.

Dal Nogare, S. and L. W. Safranski. 1960. Gas chromatography. *Org. Anal.* **IV:** 91–227.

Davis, R. E. and J. M. McCrea. 1957. Liquid sample inlet system for gas chromatographs. *Anal. Chem.* **29:** 1114–1115.

Davis, R. E. and R. A. Schreiber. 1957. Double-column gas chromatography. Analysis of noncondensable and light hydrocarbon gases by a combined gas-liquid, gas-solid chromatograph. Symposium Preprints: Advances in gas chromatography, Div. Petrol. Chem. Am. Chem. Soc. Col. 2(4), Papers D-91 to D-95.

Decora, A. W. and G. U. Dinneen. 1960. Gas-liquid chromatography of pyridines using a new solid support. *Anal. Chem.* **32:** 164–169.

Desty, D. H., F. M. Godfrey, and C. L. A. Harbourn. 1958. Operating data on two stationary phase supports. *In* "Gas Chromatography" (D. H. Desty, ed.), 200–211, New York, Academic Press.

de Wet, W. J. and V. Pretorius. 1958. Some factors influencing the efficiency of gas-liquid partition chromatography columns. *Anal. Chem.* **30:** 325–329.

Dimbat, M., P. E. Porter, and F. H. Stross. 1956. Gas chromatography. Apparatus requirements for quantitative application of gas-liquid partition chromatography. *Anal. Chem.* **28:** 290–297.

Dubský, H. E. and J. Janák. 1960. A sampling method for solid substances in high-temperature gas chromatography up to 500°. *J. Chromatog.* **4:** 1–5.

Dudenbostel, B. F., Jr. and W. Priestly, Jr. 1956. Gas chromatography for process control. *Ind. Eng. Chem.* **48** (9): 55A–56A.

Eggertsen, F. T., H. S. Knight, and S. Groennings. 1956. Use of liquid-modified solid adsorbent to resolve C_5 and C_6 saturates. *Anal. Chem.* **28:** 303–306.

Farquhar, J. W., W. Insull, Jr., P. Rosen, W. Stoffel, and E. H. Ahrens, Jr. 1959. The analysis of fatty acid mixtures by gas liquid chromatography: construction and operation of an ionization chamber instrument. *Nutrition Rev.* **17:** Suppl. 1–30.

Farrington, P. S., R. L. Pecsok, R. L. Meeker, and T. J. Olson. 1959. Detection of trace constituents by gas chromatography. Analysis of polluted atmosphere. *Anal. Chem.* **31:** 1512–1516.

Feinland, R. 1960. Personal communication.

Frederick, D. H. and W. D. Cooke. 1960. The use of glass microbeads as support for the separation of high molecular weight compounds at lowered temperatures. Eastern Analytical Symposium, New York, New York. November, 1960.

Frisone, G. J. 1959. Trap for liquid fractions separated by gas chromatography. *Chemist Analyst* **48:** 47.

Galwey, A. K. 1960. Gas chromatographic analysis of hydrogen-methane mixtures using the radioactive ionization detector. *Chem. & Ind. (London)* pp. 1417–1418.

Giddings, J. C. 1960. Coiled columns and resolution in gas chromatography. *J. Chromatog.* **3:** 520–523.

Glueckauf, E. 1955. Theory of chromatography. Part 9. The "Theoretical plate" concept in column separations. *Trans. Faraday Soc.* **51:** 34–44.

Gohlke, R. S. 1959. Time-of-flight mass spectrometry and gas-liquid partition chromatography. *Anal. Chem.* **31:** 535–541.

Golay, M. J. E. 1958. Theory of chromatography in open and coated tubular columns with round and rectangular cross sections. *In* "Gas Chromatography" (D. H. Desty, ed.), pp. 36–53. New York, Academic Press.

Goodwin, E. S., R. Goulden, A. Richardson, and J. G. Reynolds. 1960. The analysis of crop extracts for traces of chlorinated pesticides by gas-liquid partition chromatography. *Chem. & Ind. (London):* pp. 1220–1221.

Grant, D. W. 1958. Emissivity detector for gas chromatography. *Gas Chromatog., Proc. Symposium, Amsterdam,* pp. 153–163; *Chem. Abstr.* **53:** 16609; 1959.

Grant, D. W. and G. A. Vaughan. 1956. A consideration of factors governing the separation of substances by gas-liquid partition chromatography. *J. Appl. Chem.* **6:** 145–153.

Greene, S. A. 1957. The calculation of the limiting retention volume in gas-liquid partition chromatography. *J. Phys. Chem.* **61:** 702.

Greene, S. A. 1959. Gas-solid chromatographic analysis of fractions from air rectification columns. *Anal. Chem.* **31:** 480.

Griffiths, J., D. James, and C. Phillips. 1952. Gas chromatography. *Analyst* **77:** 897–903.

Guild, L., S. Bingham and F. Aul. 1958. Base line control in gas-liquid chromatography. *In* "Gas Chromatography" (D. H. Desty, ed.), pp. 226–241. New York, Academic Press.

Habgood, H. W. and W. E. Harris. 1960a. Retention temperature and column efficiency in programmed temperature gas chromatography. *Anal. Chem.* **23:** 450–453.

Habgood, H. W. and W. E. Harris. 1960b. Plate height in programmed temperature gas chromatography. *Anal. Chem.* **32:** 1206.

Hanneman, W. W., C. F. Spencer, and J. F. Johnson. 1960. Molten salt mixtures as liquid phases in gas chromatography. *Anal. Chem.* **32:** 1386–1388.

Harrison, G. F., P. Knight, R. P. Kelley, and M. T. Heath. 1958. The use of multiple columns and programmed column heating in the analysis of wide boiling range halogenated hydrocarbon samples. *In* "Gas Chromatography" (D. H. Desty, ed.), pp. 216–225. New York, Academic Press.

Harva, O., P. Kivalo, and A. Keltakallio. 1959. Determination of the hydrophilic-lipophilic character of polyhydric alcohol esters by gas chromatography. *Suomen Kemistilehti* **B32:** 52–54.

Hishta, C., J. P. Messerly, R. F. Reschke, D. H. Fredericks, and W. D. Cooke. 1960. Gas chromatography of solid organic compounds. *Anal. Chem.* **32:** 880.

Hoare, M. R. and J. H. Purnell. 1956. Temperature effects in gas-liquid partition chromatography. *Trans. Faraday Soc.* **52:** 222–229.

Hodgman, C. D., ed. 1960. "Handbook of Chemistry and Physics," 41st ed. Chemical Rubber Publ., Cleveland, Ohio.

Horning, E. C., E. A. Moscatelli, and C. C. Sweeley. 1959. Polyester liquid phases in gas-liquid chromatography. *Chem. & Ind.* (*London*) pp. 751–752.

Hornstein, I. and P. F. Crowe. 1961. Influence of column support on separation of fatty acid methyl esters by gas chromatography. *Anal. Chem.* **33:** 310–311.

Hunter, I. R., V. H. Ortegren, and J. W. Pence. 1960. Gas chromatographic separation of volatile organic acids in the presence of water. *Anal. Chem.* **32:** 682–684.

James, A. T. 1960. Qualitative and quantitative determination of the fatty acids by gas-liquid chromatography. *In* "Methods of Biochemical Analysis" (David Glick, ed.), Vol. 8, pp. 1–59. New York, Interscience.

James, A. T. and A. J. P. Martin. 1952. Gas-liquid partition chromatography. The separation and microestimation of volatile fatty acids from formic acid to dodecanoic acid. *Biochem. J.* **50:** 679–690.

Johnstone, R. A. W. and A. G. Douglas. 1959. A detector for gas-liquid chromatography. *Chem. & Ind.* (*London*) p. 154.

Joklík, J. and V. Bažant. 1959. Drtič kapilár pro použití v plynové chromatografii. *Chem. listy* **53:** 277–278.

Jones, R. N. and A. Nadeau. 1958. Cavity type microcells for infrared spectrometry. *Spectrochim. Acta* **12:** 183–191.

Jones, J. H. and C. D. Ritchie. 1958. A new procedure for the collection of fractions in gas chromatography. *J. Assoc. Offic. Agr. Chemists* **41:** 753–756.

Karmen, A. and R. L. Bowman. 1959. A radio frequency glow detector for gas chromatography. *Ann. N. Y. Acad. Sci.* **72:** 714–719.

Karmen, A. and H. R. Tritch. 1960. Radioassay by gas chromatography of compounds labeled with carbon-14. *Nature* **186:** 150–151.

Keulemans, A. I. M. 1959. "Gas Chromatography," 234 pp. New York, Reinhold.

Kieselbach, R. 1961. Gas chromatography. The effect of gaseous diffusion on mass transfer in packed columns. *Anal. Chem.* **33:** 23–28.

Knight, H. S. 1958. Gas chromatography of olefins. Determination of pentenes and hexenes in gasoline. *Anal. Chem.* **30:** 9–15.

Knight, H. S. 1959. Correction of Anal. Chem. 30: 9–15 (1958). 2,2'-oxydipropionitrile should be 3,3'-oxydipropionitrile. *Anal. Chem.* **31:** 1159.

Knox, J. H. 1959. Constant flow device for temperature programmed gas chromatography. *Chem. & Ind. (London)* p. 1085.

Kratz, P., M. H. Jacobs, and B. M. Mitzner. 1959. A smoke-eliminating device for a vapour- phase chromatographic fraction collector. *Analyst* **84:** 671–672.

Kwantes, A. and G. W. A. Rijnders. 1958. The determination of activity coefficients at infinite dilution by gas-liquid chromatography. In "Gas Chromatography" (D. H. Desty, ed.), pp. 125–135. New York, Academic Press.

Langer, S. H. and P. Pantages. 1958. Microsyringe for small liquid volumes. *Anal. Chem.* **30:** 1889–1890.

Lesser, J. M. 1959. Device for isolation of components separated by gas chromatography. *Anal. Chem.* **31:** 484.

Liberti, A., L. Conti, and V. Crescenzi. 1956. Molecular weight determination of components by gas-phase chromatography. *Nature* **178:** 1067–1069.

Lichtenfels, D. H., S. A. Fleck, F. H. Burow, and N. D. Coggeshall. 1956. Gas partition analysis of light ends in gasolines. *Anal. Chem.* **28:** 1376–1379.

Lindeman, L. P. and J. L. Annis. 1960. Use of a conventional mass spectrometer as a gas chromatography detector. Abstr. of Papers, 137th Am. Chem. Soc. meeting, April: No. 25B.

Link, W. E., R. A. Morrissette, A. D. Cooper, and C. F. Smullin. 1960. Gas-liquid chromatography of fatty derivatives. III. Analysis of fatty amines. *J. Am. Oil Chemists' Soc.* **37:** 364–366.

Lipsky, S. R. 1960. Comments on the theory and practice of ionization techniques in gas chromatography. Eastern Analytical Symposium, New York, November, 1960.

Lipsky, S. R., R. A. Landowne, and J. E. Lovelock. 1959. Separation of lipides by gas-liquid chromatography. *Anal. Chem.* **31:** 852–856.

Littlewood, A. B., C. S. G. Phillips, and D. T. Price. 1955. The chromatography of gases and vapours. Part V. Partition analyses with columns of Silicone 702 and of tritolyl phosphate. *J. Chem. Soc.*, pp. 1480–1489.

Lovelock, J. E. 1958. A sensitive detector for gas chromatography. *J. Chromatog.* **1:** 35–46.

Lovelock, J. E. 1961. Ionization methods for the analysis of gases and vapors. *Anal. Chem.* **33:** 162–178.

Lovelock, J. E. and S. R. Lipsky. 1960. Electron affinity spectroscopy—A new method for the identification of functional groups in chemical compounds separated by gas chromatography. *J. Am. Chem. Soc.* **82:** 431–433.

Loyd, R. J., B. O. Ayers, and F. W. Karasek. 1960. Optimization of resolution-time ratio with packed chromatographic columns. *Anal. Chem.* **32:** 698–701.

Lukeš, V., R. Komers, and V. Herout. 1960. Ground unglazed tile—A new support for gas-liquid chromatography. *J. Chromatog.* **3:** 303–307.

McCreadie, S. W. S. and A. F. Williams. 1957. The quantitative measurement and transfer of samples in gas chromatography. *J. Appl. Chem.* **7:** 47–48.

McWilliam, I. G. and R. A. Dewar. 1958. Flame ionization detector for gas chromatography. *In* "Gas Chromatography" (D. H. Desty, ed.), pp. 142–147. New York, Academic Press.

Martin, A. J. P. and R. L. M. Synge. 1941. A new form of chromatogram employing two liquid phases. 1. A theory of chromatography. 2. Application of the micro-determination of the higher monoamino-acids in proteins. *Biochem. J.* **35:** 1358–1368.

Mason, L. H., H. J. Dutton, and L. R. Blair. 1959. Ionization chamber for high temperature gas chromatography. *J. Chromatog.* **2:** 322–323.

Messner, A. E., D. M. Rosie, and P. A. Argabright. 1959. Correlation of thermal conductivity cell response with molecular weight and structure. Quantitative gas chromatographic analysis. *Anal. Chem.* **31:** 230–232.

Mitzner, B. M. and M. H. Jacobs. 1960. The application of capillary column gas chromatography to the essential oil industry. 137th Am. Chem. Soc. meeting, April.

Murray, K. E. 1959. A new design of the Martin and James gas density meter. *Australian J. Appl. Sci.* **10:** 156–168.

Napier, I. M. and H. J. Rodda. 1958. A multiple fraction collector for gas chromatography. *Chem. & Ind. (London)*, p. 1319.

Naves, Y. R. 1958. Some remarks on the nature of the fixed phase or of the carrier in gas-liquid partition chromatography of essential oils and aromatics. *J. Soc. Cosmetic Chemists* **9:** 101–103.

Nelson, J. and A. Milun. 1960. Gas chromatography of high molecular weight fatty primary amines. *Chem. & Ind. (London)*. pp. 663–664.

Nerheim, A. G. 1960a. Gas-liquid chromathermography. *Anal. Chem.* **32:** 436–437.

Nerheim, A. G. 1960b. A new gas-density detector for gas chromatography. Abstr. of Papers, 137th Am. Chem. Soc. meeting, April: No. 24B-25B.

Ober, S. S. 1958. The interrelationship of column efficiency and resolving power in gas chromatography. *In* "Gas Chromatography" (V. J. Coates, H. J. Noebels, and I. S. Fagerson, eds.), pp. 41–50. New York, Academic Press.

Orr, C. H. 1961. Recorder-integrator errors in gas chromatography area measurements. *Anal. Chem.* **33:** 158–159.

Ormerod, E. C. and R. P. W. Scott. 1959. Gas chromatography of polar solutions with a non-polar liquid base. *J. Chromatog.* **2:** 65–68.

Oster, H. 1959. Bedingungen zur Erzielung hoher Messgenauigkeit bei der chromatographischen Gasanalyse. *Z. anal. Chem.* **170:** 264–271.

Phillips, C. 1956. "Gas Chromatography," 105 pp. New York, Academic Press.

Pollard, F. H. and C. J. Hardy. 1955. The effect of temperature of injection upon the separation of liquid mixtures by gas-phase chromatography. *Chem. & Ind. (London)*, pp. 1145–1146.

Popják, G., A. E. Lowe, D. Moore, L. Brown, and F. A. Smith. 1959. Scintillation counter for the measurement of radioactivity of vapors in conjunction with gas-liquid chromatography. *J. Lipid Res.* **1:** 29–39.

Ring, R. D. 1958. The effect of the ratio of partition liquid to inert support on the separation of (1) mono-, di- and triethylene glycols and (2) *cis-* and *trans*-2,5-dimethylpiperazine. *In* "Gas Chromatography" (V. J. Coates, H. J. Noebels, and I. S. Fagerson, eds.), pp. 195–201. New York, Academic Press.

Ryce, S. A. and W. A. Bryce. 1957. An ionization gauge detector for gas chromatography. *Can. J. Chem.* **35:** 1293–1297.

Samsel, E. P. and J. C. Aldrich. 1959. Sample injection valve for gas chromatography. *Anal. Chem.* **31:** 1288.

Scott, C. G. and D. A. Rowell. 1960. Gas-solid chromatographic separation of hydrocarbons of high molecular weight. *Nature* **187**: 143–144.

Scott, D. S. and A. Han. 1961. A modified thermal conductivity cell independent of flow rate. *Anal. Chem.* **33**: 160.

Scott, R. P. W. 1955. A new detector for vapour-phase partition chromatography. *Nature* **176**: 793.

Scott, R. P. W. 1958. The construction of high efficiency columns for the separation of hydrocarbons. *In* "Gas Chromatography" (D. H. Desty, ed.), pp. 189–196. New York, Academic Press.

Sørensen, I. and P. Søltoft. 1956. A low resistance vapour-phase chromatograph column. *Acta Chem. Scand.* **10**: 1673–1674.

Stanford, F. G. 1959. A sample injection method for gas-liquid chromatography. *Analyst* **84**: 321–322.

Sternberg, J. C. and R. E. Poulson. 1960. A Telsa discharge detector for gas chromatography. *J. Chromatog.* **3**: 406–410.

Storrs, E. E. and H. P. Burchfield. 1961. Internal standards in the analysis of phenoxyacetic, benzoic, and terephthalic herbicides by gas chromatography. American Chemical Society, Chicago, Illinois, September, 1961.

Sullivan, J. H., J. T. Walsh, and C. Merritt, Jr. 1959. Improved separation in gas chromatography by temperature programming. Application to mercaptans and sulfides. *Anal. Chem.* **31**: 1826–1828.

Sweeting, J. W. 1959. Modification of "Agla" micrometer hypodermic syringe for use in vapour-phase chromatography. *Chem. & Ind. (London)*, p. 1150.

Tenney, H. M. and R. J. Harris. 1957. Sample introduction system for gas chromatography. *Anal. Chem.* **29**: 317–318.

Teranishi, R., C. C. Nimmo, and J. Corse. 1960. Versatile ionization detector for gas chromatography. *Anal. Chem.* **32**: 896.

Turner, D. W. 1958. A robust but sensitive detector for gas-liquid chromatography. *Nature* **181**: 1265–1266.

van Deemter, J. J., F. J. Zuiderweg, and A. Klinkenberg. 1956. Longitudinal diffusion and resistance to mass transfer as a cause of non-ideality in chromatography. *Chem. Eng. Sci.* **5**: 271.

Weinstein, A. 1957. Fraction cutter for gas chromatography. *Anal. Chem.* **29**: 1899–1900.

Welti, D. and T. Wilkins. 1960. Effect of an argon-nitrogen carrier gas mixture on the sensitivity of a gas chromatographic ionization detector. *J. Chromatog.*, **3**: 589–591.

Wilks, P. A., Jr. and C. W. Warren. 1960. Personal communication.

Wiseman, W. A. 1960. Separation factors in gas chromatography. *Nature* **185**: 841–842.

Wolfgang, R. and F. S. Rowland. 1958. Radioassay by gas chromatography of tritium and carbon-14-labeled compounds. *Anal. Chem.* **30**: 903–906.

Zlatkis, A. and H. R. Kaufman. 1959. Use of coated tubing as columns for gas chromatography. *Nature* **184**: 2010.

Zlatkis, A., J. F. Oró, and A. P. Kimball. 1960. Direct amino acid analysis by gas chromatography. *Anal. Chem.* **32**: 162–164.

Zubyk, W. J. and A. Z. Conner. 1960. Analysis of terpene hydrocarbons and related compounds by gas chromatography. *Anal. Chem.* **32**: 912–917.

Chapter 2

Permanent Gases and Condensable Organic Vapors

General Introduction

Permanent gases and condensable organic vapors are treated together because they coexist in nature or in man-contrived situations. Biochemically, they are of interest because of their functions in photosynthesis, respiration, and the nitrogen and carbon cycles in soil, and because as respiratory poisons or air pollutants they at times present health hazards.

Gases and vapors differ basically from liquids in the manner in which they are collected in the field and introduced into the gas stream of the chromatograph. Liquids are injected in volumes of a few microliters or less and expand suddenly by flash evaporation within the confines of the instrument. Gases, on the other hand, are introduced in volumes ranging from 0.25 to 25 ml through valves specially designed for the purpose. The larger samples are used when trace elements are being analyzed: if the sample exceeds 2% of the retention volume of the component of interest, poor peak resolution will be obtained. Consequently it may be necessary to concentrate trace components by specialized techniques useful exclusively for samples of this type.

Also, liquid samples rarely contain inorganic compounds other than water, whereas gas samples may contain oxygen, nitrogen, and carbon dioxide, as well as organic vapors. This means that separation of the sample by both gas–solid chromatography and gas–liquid chromatography may be necessary for complete analysis. At the same time, advantage can be taken of the fact that selective ionization detectors are available that will respond to one class of compounds and not to the other, and this can often be used to simplify the process.

Finally, gases and vapors will flow through complex circuits at room temperatures without condensing. This has resulted in the development of more advanced circuitry than is generally used in the chromatography of high-boiling liquids, where keeping the sample in the vapor phase is a paramount concern.

A. General Techniques for Sample Collection, Sample Introduction, and Calibration

I. Introduction

Some of the techniques for sample collection and introduction are applicable to all gas samples and have little in common with methods for handling liquids. Consequently, they are included here rather than in Chapter 1, since they have specific rather than general utility. However, treatment of specialized methods for the concentration of trace amounts of organic vapors present in air samples is deferred until Section E.II, since such methods are not applicable to atmospheric gases other than carbon dioxide.

II. Collection of Free Gases

The simplest way to deliver gas samples to a chromatograph is to connect the source of supply to a gas sampling valve installed on the instrument (see Section A.IV.c). If the source is under positive pressure (city gas or cylinder gas, for example), it can be made to flow continuously through a bypass line in the instrument, and samples of predetermined size can be applied to the analytical column at any time by merely turning the knob of the sampling valve. It should be remembered that the weight of the gas introduced is proportional to the pressure within the sample loop.

If the gas is at atmospheric pressure, it must be drawn through the sample line by suction. Hand-operated bicycle tire pumps or rubber aspirator bulbs can be used to take small intermittent samples, but for continuous operation a house vacuum, a water aspirator, or a small electrically driven blower or pump is better. A Gast pump (Gast Manufacturing Co.) will deliver air at rates up to 25 liters/min, and rotary air pumps (Leiman Bros. No. 26, for example) will move 2 to 3 cubic feet of air per minute. If gas is being recycled in a closed system from a chamber containing experimental material, it is important that the pumping device does not contaminate the atmosphere. Also, it should be remembered that each gas sample applied to the column is replaced by an equal volume of carrier gas. Since the pressure of the carrier gas is generally greater than atmospheric (about 5 to 60 psig), it is evident that the pressure within the chamber will increase with each sample taken, or the chamber will leak. If the volume of the chamber is great compared to the size of the samples, these effects will be negligible. However, if the volume of the chamber is small, dilution of the atmosphere with carrier gas will have to be taken into account.

When the source of the gas is situated some distance away from the chromatograph, samples must be taken in sealed containers and brought to the instrument for introduction. This may be done in vacuum tubes, vacuum bottles, gas or liquid displacement collectors, or plastic bags.

a. General Methods

1. *Vacuum Containers.* Vacuum tubes for gas sampling (Fig. 1A) are glass bulbs with strong walls having a capacity of 250 to 300 ml. They must be able to withstand pressures of at least 15 psig without collapsing. Most

of the air (99.9%) is removed from them with a vacuum pump. The necks are heated, drawn, and sealed during the final period of evacuation. They are taken to the place the air is to be sampled, and the drawn-out end is scratched with a file and broken. Air rushes in to fill the vacuum, and the broken end of the tube is sealed with a wax-filled cartridge. They are then taken to the laboratory for analysis of the gas. Since these tubes have only one outlet, gases cannot be forced out of them by displacement with a liquid. Consequently, the sample must be withdrawn by means of a vacuum

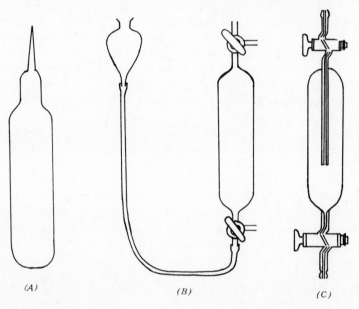

(A)   (B)   (C)

Fig. 1. Gas sampling apparatus. *A*, vacuum tube. *B*, displacement collector with three-way stopcocks and leveling bulb. *C*, U. S. Bureau of Mines sampling tube with internal glass tube.

pump or water aspirator and is therefore taken at reduced pressure. Vacuum bottles accomplish the same purpose as vacuum tubes, except that they are evacuated just before sampling. They are strong-walled bottles equipped with a two-hole rubber stopper, one hole of which contains a thermometer, and the other a T tube. The T tube contains stopcocks at both ends, and one end is connected to a manometer. The other end is attached to a vacuum pump, and the bottle is evacuated. The stopcock nearest the pump is turned off, and the manometer stopcock is opened. The pressure and temperature are read and recorded. The pump is disconnected, and a tube leading to the sample reservoir is installed in its place. The tube should be purged of air with at least 10 volumes of the gas to be collected. The stopcock nearest the sample line is then opened, and the bottle is filled.

2. *Displacement Collectors.* Displacement collectors are long narrow tubes with stopcocks at each end (Fig. 1*B*). They may be made of copper or glass. Copper tubes are rugged but should not be used for sampling corrosive gases. Glass tubes may be equipped with either two-way or three-way stopcocks. Three-way stopcocks are most convenient, since the line leading to the sample reservoir can be purged and the tube filled in one operation. The tube is connected to the sample source with the three-way stopcock venting to the atmosphere. The line is cleared of air with at least 10 to 15 volumes of the gas, after which the stopcock is turned to admit the sample. In sampling a large reservoir of gas held at pressures greater than atmospheric, air can be swept from the tube with the sample (10 to 15 volumes). However, if the sample supply is more limited, the tube should be filled with liquid and the liquid displaced. Mercury or water saturated with sodium chloride should be used. Salt solutions are more convenient and easier to use, but some gases dissolve in them. The U. S. Bureau of Mines gas sampling tube is equipped with a small glass tube which extends inside the larger main tube (Fig. 1*C*). This makes it possible to collect samples at constant rates and prevents sucking back or backward diffusion of the gas being sampled.

b. Special Methods

1. *Respiratory Gases.* Samples of tidal air can be collected by having the subject exhale into a collapsed bag that has been previously purged of air with carrier gas. Alveolar air can be obtained by having the subject expel air from his lungs with extreme suddenness and force into a cylinder 5 feet long and about 1 inch in diameter. The cylinder is purged with air from the respiratory passages and deeper parts of the lungs. The portion of the tube next to the mouth contains alveolar air. The tube is closed rapidly with the tongue, and the air in the upper part of the cylinder is sampled by one of the methods described above.

*2. *Gases in Flexible Food Packages* (Stahl *et al.*, 1960). A 1-inch-square inner-tube patch is glued to the food package with rubber cement. When the cement is dry, a syringe is inserted through the patch, care being taken not to tear the package or otherwise cause it to leak. The syringe is filled with gas to the desired volume, withdrawn from the package, and its contents injected into the chromatograph. The rubber patch reseals the hole made by the needle so that the package can be resampled.

*3. *Gases in Head Spaces of Cans* (Stahl *et al.*, 1960). The apparatus for piercing the can is a Zahm air tester (Zahm and Nagel Co., Inc.). It is modified by replacing the pressure gauge with a metal socket 8 mm long and 6 mm in diameter into which a rubber seal is inserted (Burrell Corp., No. 274–276). The modified apparatus is shown in Fig. 2. The gas is sampled with a Vim No. 200 1-ml syringe having a stainless-steel plunger (Mac-Gregor Instrument Co.) and fitted with a No. 22⅝-inch hypodermic needle. For sampling vacuum-packed cans, a small metal stopcock (Becton Dickinson and Co.) must be attached to the syringe. The joints connecting

Fig. 2. Modified Zahm air tester for sampling head space gases in cans. (Stahl *et al.*, 1960).

syringe, stopcock, and needle are coated with a resin or heavy grease to minimize gas leakage. *Cans at atmospheric pressure or greater:* The can-piercing device (Fig. 2) is centered over the can, and a thin layer of grease is smeared on the can at the spot where the rubber seal will make contact. The device is lowered until a good seal is made between the rubber and the can (*A*), but the can is not pierced. The needle valve (*B*) is connected to a water aspirator, the chamber evacuated to 20 mm Hg, and the needle valve closed. The can is then pierced, a sample of gas removed with a syringe through the rubber seal (*C*), and the sample injected into a chromatograph. *Vacuum-packed containers:* These are sampled in somewhat the same way, except that it is necessary to have a stopcock attached to the end of the syringe. The can is pierced as described above, and the syringe is filled. Before it is withdrawn from the container, the stopcock is closed, and the plunger is permitted to slide down the barrel until the pressure is equalized. The syringe is withdrawn from the container, and the plunger is pushed down until a slight positive pressure is attained within it. The stopcock is opened, and a small amount of sample is ejected to replace the air which has collected in the needle. The remainder of the sample is injected into the chromatograph.

III. Sampling of Dissolved and Bound Gases

Inorganic gases of biological interest may be found dissolved in liquids such as plasma, nutrient solutions, and malt beverages, or they may be chemically bound as are oxygen and carbon monoxide by the hemoglobin of the blood. If a gas is merely dissolved and participates only in hydration equilibria with the solvent, its concentration in the liquid phase can be determined by analyzing the gas phase in equilibrium with it (Bovijn, Pirotte, and Berger, 1958; Hissel, 1958; Massart and Missa, 1960). The relation between the partial pressure of a gas (*p*) and the mole fraction of the gas in the liquid phase (*N*) is given by Henry's law, equation 1,

$$p = kN \qquad (1)$$

where *k* is constant. Bovijn, Pirotte, and Berger (1958) have shown that this equation takes the form of equation 2,

$$C = 10^5 \, qp \qquad (2)$$

where *C* is the concentration of gas in micrograms per kilogram of solvent, *p* is the partial pressure of the gas in volume per cent at a total pressure of 1 atmosphere, and *q* is the weight in grams of the dissolved gas in 100 gm of pure solvent under a total pressure of 760 mm Hg at the temperature considered. Solubility data for individual gases at various temperatures are given by Seidell (1958). This equation holds exactly only for ideal gases, or for real gases at infinite dilution; however, the corrections are negligible (see Section A.V.b). Moreover, it is not necessary to distinguish between molarity and molality in this application, and for the same reasons molarity can be considered proportional to mole fraction. Therefore, it is possible to calculate the concentration of a gas in a liquid phase by knowing its concentration in the vapor phase in equilibrium with it.

Bovijn, Pirotte, and Berger (1958) describe a method for equilibrating water containing dissolved hydrogen with an inert carrier gas (see Section A.III.a.1) and then measuring the concentration of hydrogen in the gas phase by GSC on 5-A molecular sieve (see Section C.III.a.1). The concentration of hydrogen in the liquid phase is calculated from equation 2. To establish equilibrium, the water is run through diffusers contained within glass bulbs filled with the inert gas at a rate of 1 to 2 liters/min (Fig. 3).

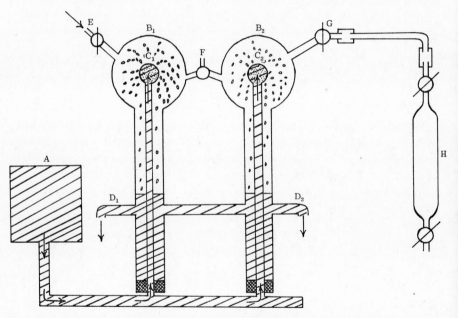

Fig. 3. Diagram of apparatus for sampling carrier gas in equilibrium with water. Shaded areas indicate portions of apparatus containing water, and unshaded areas those portions containing gas. (Bovijn, Pirotte, and Berger, 1958)

In about 2 hours the gas phases within the bulbs are in equilibrium with the liquid phase and can be sampled and analyzed. Equilibrium is re-established in another hour. This technique obviously requires large volumes of water such as would be available during studies of the gas content of streams and ponds, and possibly of nutrient culture solutions.

Gases dissolved in small amounts of biological fluids can be freed by vacuum extraction in a Van Slyke gas analysis apparatus (see Section A.III.a.2). About 1 ml of plasma is introduced into a gas pipette, and a Torricellian vacuum is created by lowering the mercury-filled leveling bulb (Fig. 4). The apparatus is shaken mechanically for a few minutes, after which the liberated gases are introduced into the gas stream of a chromatograph through a capillary tube by raising the leveling bulb. This method has been

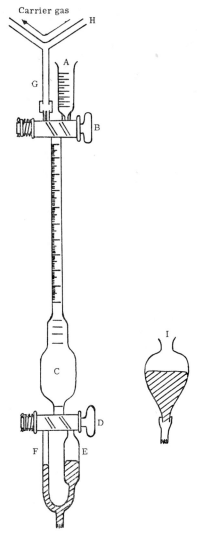

Fig. 4. Vacuum extraction apparatus (Van Slyke type) for removing gases from biological fluids.

used for measuring the oxygen tension of water and plasma by means of a column packed with molecular sieve for chromatography (see Section B.II.a.1). The time required to extract the gases from the sample is less than 5 minutes, and the time required for elution from the column is less than 2 minutes. During this latter interval another sample can be extracted (Ramsey, 1959). Many determinations previously made by the Van Slyke, Haldane, Scholander, and Warburg methods can now be made by gas chromatography with equal or better accuracy and simplicity and in less time.

Some gases occur in blood in bound form, and chemical treatment is necessary to liberate them. Carbon dioxide exists as bicarbonate ion and is freed by treatment with 0.1 N hydrochloric acid. Oxygen and carbon monoxide are combined with hemoglobin, and treatment of the blood with a hemolyzing agent such as saponin and potassium ferricyanide together with an antifoaming agent is required for their release. Methods for doing this are included in standard texts on blood chemistry (Peters and Van Slyke, 1956). Once the gases are liberated, they can be transferred from the Van Slyke apparatus to a chromatograph as described below in Section A.III.a.2.

Dominguez et al. (1959) describe a method by which carbon monoxide is released from carboxyhemoglobin by treatment with potassium ferricyanide reagent, and the gas is extracted from the liquid phase with helium contained in a hypodermic syringe (see Section A.III.b.1). An aliquot of the helium is then injected into a chromatograph, and the carbon monoxide is separated on a molecular sieve column (see Section D.II.a.1). Analyses are made on the sample as received and on an equivalent sample saturated with carbon monoxide in the laboratory. The per cent carboxyhemoglobin in the sample is computed from the ratio of the peak height obtained on the unsaturated specimen (carbon monoxide content) to the peak height of the saturated specimen (carbon monoxide capacity), with appropriate corrections for differences in sample volumes. Excellent agreement is obtained between the gas chromatography method and the Roughton-Scholander microgasometric method when blood samples containing various amounts of carbon monoxide are analyzed (Table I). Measurable peaks are found with gas samples containing 5×10^{-4} ml of carbon monoxide in 25 ml of helium; a thermistor and a 1-mv recorder are used for detection. This method gives good results even though the technique for introducing the sample into the chromatograph is not ideal. The carbon monoxide is applied to the column diluted with about 50,000 volumes of carrier gas, whereas, as noted in Section A.IV.a, injection as a plug of carbon monoxide would be preferable.

Bound gases in blood can be released by chemical treatment, and simultaneously entrained by carrier gas, in a reactor attached directly to a

TABLE I

REPRODUCIBILITY OF GSC METHOD FOR ANALYSIS
OF CARBOXYHEMOGLOBIN IN BLOOD[a]

Per cent saturated		Standard deviation (16 replicates)
Actual	Found (average)	
1.0	1.05	0.095
7.5	7.8	0.433
15	15.1	0.296
25	25.5	1.260
30	32.5	1.687
50	49.3	1.704

[a] From Dominguez et al. (1959).

chromatograph (Taylor and Presseau, 1959). The diagram in Fig. 5 shows how this chamber is constructed. The carrier gas enters the bottom section

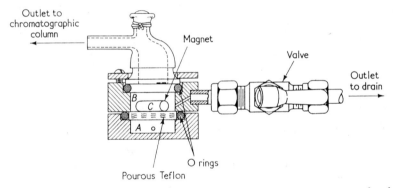

FIG. 5. Chamber for liberating bound gases from blood in the gas stream of a chromatograph. (Taylor and Presseau, 1959)

of the chamber (*A*), and passes through a porous Teflon disk into section *B*, which contains the blood sample and reagent. The Teflon disk disperses the carrier gas through the liquid mixture, and uniform agitation is provided by a small stirring magnet (*C*). The evolved gases are passed through a short drying tube to remove moisture and then onto the column. To run a sample, the hemolyzing reagent is injected into the reaction chamber and purged of air with carrier gas. An accurately measured blood sample (about 0.1 ml) is then injected. In 10 seconds or less, the blood gases are freed, dried, and swept onto the column with carrier gas. This system will separate and measure oxygen, nitrogen, and carbon dioxide in 5 to 6 minutes. Two columns, one packed with type 950 silica gel (28/200 mesh) and the other with type 13-X molecular sieve, are used in series to separate the gases (see Section B.II.c.2). The reproducibility of the method is better than 1%, and results obtained for carbon dioxide and oxygen agree with the Van Slyke method to within ±1 volume %. At the time of writing, details were not available on the composition of the hemolyzing reagent, so the extraction procedure is not included in the experimental part of this chapter.

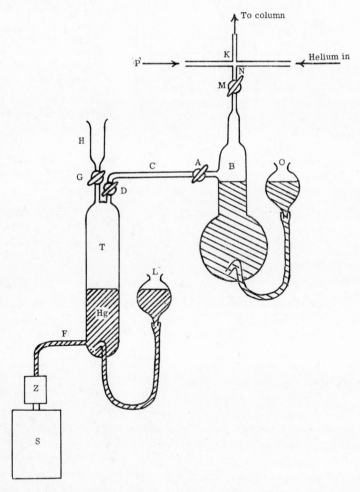

FIG. 6. Apparatus for isolating air dissolved in bottled beer. (Bethune and Rigby, 1958)

Gases in beer, soft drinks, and other carbonated beverages can also be analyzed by gas chromatography. Since the gases are dissolved under pressure, it is only necessary to pierce the top of the container with a Zahm air tester (Zahm and Nagel Co., Inc.) or similar device. The gas and foam froth over into a receiver when the container is shaken.

Of course, the main constituent of the gas is carbon dioxide, so it is necessary to absorb this in alkali before analyzing for oxygen and nitrogen on molecular sieve to avoid deactivating the column. Bethune and Rigby (1958) found that a mixture of beer and alkali absorbs oxygen. Therefore, they developed a sampling apparatus in which the gas and some beer are collected over mercury in a reservoir (Fig. 6). The gas, without the liquid, is then transferred to a pipette containing alkali, and the carbon dioxide is absorbed. The residual gas is then introduced into the carrier gas stream of a chromatograph attached directly to the sampling apparatus. This technique avoids mixing the beer and alkali and so eliminates losses of oxygen caused by absorption.

a. Dissolved Gases

*1. *Gases in Equilibrium with a Liquid Phase* (Bovijn, Pirotte, and Berger, 1958). *Apparatus:* Component A in Fig. 3 is a cooler which condenses steam into water. The water is fed into B_1 and B_2 at a constant rate; B_1 and B_2 are vessels in which the gas and liquid phases are equilibrated. Each is equipped with a rubber or plastic diffuser (C_1 and C_2) and an overflow (D_1 and D_2) for keeping the water level constant. E is a capillary stopcock for admitting inert gas, F a stopcock connecting the two equilibration vessels, G a stopcock for sampling the gas in C_2, and H a standard gas sampling tube. *Procedure:* The air in C_1, C_2, and the connecting tubing is displaced with an inert gas, and a reservoir of this gas at atmospheric pressure is connected to stopcock E. Helium is satisfactory for the analysis of dissolved atmospheric gases, but argon would be better for the determination of hydrogen with a T/C cell. Stopcock E is left open, stopcock G is closed, and stopcock F is turned so that vessels B_1 and B_2 are connected. Water, adjusted to a temperature close to room temperature, is then injected through the diffusers and out of the apparatus via overflows D_1 and D_2 at a rate of 1 to 2 liters/min. Slight amounts of inert gas in bulb B_1 dissolve in the water and are carried out of the system at overflow D_1. Therefore, a slight current of gas moves through stopcock E into vessel B_1, and a smaller amount of gas moves from B_1 to B_2. Gases dissolved in the water tend to escape into the inert atmosphere in B_1 in accordance with Henry's law, but equilibrium is not established. However, equilibrium of the gas phase with the water is established in receiver B_2 in about 2 hours, since the gas is already partially equilibrated, and there is very little displacement of it. After this initial time lapse, a

50-ml sample can be withdrawn from B_2 every hour for analysis, by means of gas sampling tube H. To do this, receiver B_2 is isolated from the rest of the system by closing stopcock F. The gas sampling tube (H) is filled with mercury and connected to the apparatus at G. The mercury is allowed to drain out of H and is replaced by the equilibrated atmosphere in B_2. Stopcock G is then closed, and stopcock F is opened to connect the two receivers. The gas in C_2 reaches equilibrium with the water again in 2 hours and can be resampled. The gas in tube H is then transferred to a chromatograph and analyzed by the appropriate method. The concentration of gas dissolved in the water is then calculated from equation 2, p. 149.

*2. *Vacuum Extraction* (Ramsey, 1959). *Apparatus:* A modified Van Slyke apparatus is used to extract the gases from the fluid (Fig. 4), but the analysis could be carried out with any vacuum extraction apparatus having a double outlet and mercury flow path. Component C is a 50-ml volumetric gas burette, with three-way stopcocks (B and D) sealed onto the upper and lower ends. E is a reservoir for holding the fluid *after* gases have been extracted from it, and F is a bypass line for filling the burette (C) with mercury from the leveling bulb (I) when the holding vessel (E) contains spent fluid. A is a small funnel sealed onto stopcock B which is used for introducing the sample. G is a capillary tube, also sealed onto B, which is normally used for ejecting spent fluids from the apparatus. In this present modification of the Van Slyke apparatus, capillary G is cut off 0.5 inch from its connection to stopcock B and a glass Y tube is connected to it. The Y tube is connected into the carrier gas line of a chromatograph upstream from the column. All stopcocks and connections must be leakproof and clamped in place so that they cannot be blown out by pressure from the leveling bulb or carrier gas stream. To test the apparatus for leaks, it is filled completely with mercury from the leveling bulb (I), including the capillary connections above the upper stopcock (B). The bulb is then lowered, so the liquid level falls to the middle of E. When the apparatus is refilled by lifting the bulb, the mercury should strike the upper stopcock with a sharp click. However, the chromatographic method is so sensitive that this cannot be accepted as evidence that the system is free of air. Therefore, an initial blank analysis must be made. This is done by withdrawing a sample of the carrier gas into the chamber through G and running an analysis as if a sample were present. Blank runs are repeated until no peaks are observed when the carrier gas sample is passed through the column and detector. *Procedure:* Before beginning an analysis, the carrier gas stream is started, and stopcock B is turned to connect reservoir A with the volumetric pipette (C). The leveling bulb containing mercury is lifted to force air out of the system through A. The stopcock is then turned to connect G with the pipette, leaving the bore and tubing connecting A to it filled with mercury. Air is displaced from capillary tube G by adjusting the level of bulb I so that the mercury meniscus reaches the intersection of G with the carrier gas tube (H). The bulb is then lowered until the mercury is level with the top of the pipette. The method chosen for introducing the sample will depend on whether dissolved gases only are to be measured, or whether chemically bound gases are to be released by addition of reagents. For these latter applications the reader is referred to any of the standard texts on blood analysis. To liberate dissolved oxygen from blood plasma, a 1-ml sample is introduced into the pipette (C) from reservoir A, after which a drop of mercury is placed in A and permitted to run down into the capillary as far as stopcock B in order to seal it. With the upper stopcock closed, the lower stopcock is opened to the mercury reservoir, and a vacuum is produced by lowering the leveling bulb until the mercury meniscus falls to the 50-ml mark on the pipette. The apparatus is then shaken gently for 2 to 3 minutes to liberate dissolved gases from the plasma. Then the leveling bulb is lowered still further so that the fluid is drawn into chamber E. Bubbles caused by foaming of the fluid are broken when the liquid passes through the bore of the lower stopcock. Next, stopcock D is turned so that mercury is readmitted to the pipette through bypass line F. When the mercury level reaches the 0.2-ml mark in the gas pipette, stopcock B is turned to connect with side arm G, and the extracted gases are injected into the carrier gas stream of the chromatograph by moving the mercury level to the junction of the side arm and the carrier gas tubing (H). After a 5-second interval, the mercury and small amount of plasma remaining above it are returned to the pipette by lowering bulb I. The apparatus is then closed off from the carrier gas, and the pipette is shaken again to release any gas that may have redissolved in the small amount of fluid remaining above the mercury. Capillary gas rather than mercury is left in capillary G and its portion of the stopcock after introduction of the main sample. Similarly, a small amount of carrier gas is returned to the extraction chamber with the fluid and mercury in preparation for re-extraction, since the carrier is always flowing through the detector and therefore is not recognized by it. After this residual gas has been introduced into the chromatograph as described above, stopcocks D and B are turned to connect chambers E and A to the pipette. The spent liquid in E is then forced out of the apparatus through A by filling the pipette with mercury from the reservoir.

*3. *Gases in Carbonated Beverages* (Bethune and Rigby, 1958). *Apparatus:* The equipment for sampling gases from beer cans and freeing them of carbon dioxide is illustrated diagrammatically in Fig. 6. S is the can containing the beer, and Z is a Zahm air tester for piercing the can and liberating the beer and gases (see Section A.II.b.3). T is a tube 40 mm in diameter, with a volume of 150 ml, for collecting the sample. L is a leveling bulb containing mercury attached to the bottom of the sample collector. The portion of the tube connecting L to T that extends inside T is bent to prevent escape of gas or beer through the leveling bulb. H is a 30-ml funnel connected to the sample collector through the capillary stopcock, G. It contains 1 ml of hexyl alcohol and 0.5 ml of a solution prepared by combining 3 liters of water, 750 ml of 50% sulfuric acid, and 120 gm of potassium sulfate. D is a capillary stopcock attached to stopcock A with Tygon tubing (C). B is a burette used to absorb carbon dioxide and measure the volume of the gas sample (Roberts *et al.*, 1947). O is a leveling bulb containing alkali which is attached to an outlet at the bottom of the burette. M is a stopcock, and K is a four-way connecting tube through which carrier gas flows and which provides the port of entry of the sample into the chromatograph. *Procedure:* At the outset of each run, T is filled with mercury from the leveling bulb (L), and B is filled with 15% aqueous sodium hydroxide. All air is expelled from the collector (T) by forcing mercury through stopcock D to stopcock A, and through stopcock G into funnel H. The mercury is then drawn back into the collector, allowing a little alkali from burette (B) to enter the bore of stopcock D. The acid–sulfate solution (0.5 ml) and a few drops of the hexyl alcohol in funnel H are then drawn into the collector. Only a few drops of the alcohol are allowed to enter, the excess being present to prevent entry of air. The sample bottle (or can) top is pierced, and the gas is collected. It is necessary to transfer the gas from the collector to the burette once or twice before all of it is collected to prevent overfilling T. This is done by opening stopcocks A and D and allowing the beer to rise to within 1 cm of the top of the collector (T). Stopcock D is then closed, and the collection is continued. After the last collection, beer is allowed to rise to within 1 cm of the top of the collector. The collector is then tilted to shake out any gas bubbles caught in the entrance to the funnel. The remaining gas is forced into the burette until only a bubble is left in the outlet to D. Next, the collector is tilted so that the beer runs out into funnel H, where it is discarded. The remaining gas is forced over into the burette. If beer enters connecting tube C during this transfer, it must be backflushed with alkali, and the washings discarded through H. When this is done, the volume of gas in connecting line C is reduced through absorption of the carbon dioxide by the alkali. The residual gas remaining in C is then transferred to the burette by forcing mercury over to stopcock A. Mercury is then drawn back to stopcock D, and the connecting tube is left filled with sodium hydroxide solution. The stopcocks are closed, and the burette inverted and shaken one hundred times. The volume of gas is read, and the burette is inverted and shaken another hundred times. This is continued until successive readings differ by no more than 0.02 ml.

To introduce the gas samples into the chromatograph, the flow of carrier gas is stopped, and the four-way connecting tube, K, is connected momentarily to a vacuum pump through P to evacuate the head of the column. The vacuum is then shut off, and the sample drawn into the head of the column by opening stopcock M. To keep the sample volume as small as possible, alkali is drawn into K up to the point N. Stopcock M is then closed, and the helium flow is restarted. To remove the gas from the beer the container is shaken nine times, the gas being released after each shaking. After the ninth time, the container is shaken again and inverted for a few seconds to fill the connecting tube with beer.

b. Chemically Bound Gases

1. *Carbon Monoxide in Blood* (Dominguez *et al.*, 1959). *Sample preparation:* blood is diluted 1:10 with distilled water. This yields a more uniform sample and permits identical aliquots to be used for carbon monoxide content and carbon monoxide capacity. The external surfaces of tissues, including liver, kidney, spleen, lungs, bone marrow, and muscle, are removed and dis-

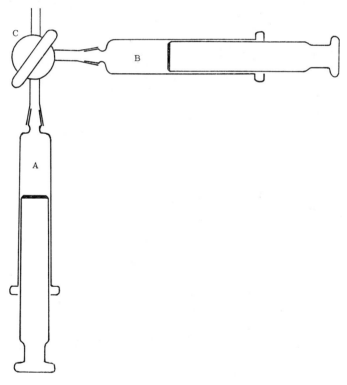

FIG. 7. Arrangement for transferring carbon monoxide in helium from syringe A to syringe B via a three-way surgical stopcock, C. (Dominguez *et al.*, 1959)

carded to preclude contamination. The remaining tissue is diced, and distilled water is added to extract the blood. *Liberation of carbon monoxide:* potassium ferricyanide reagent is used to liberate carbon monoxide from carboxyhemoglobin. It is prepared fresh daily and consists of potassium ferricyanide (48 gm) and saponin (1 gm) dissolved in distilled water (100 ml) and enough sodium acetate reagent to yield a final volume of 200 ml. Sodium acetate reagent is prepared by dissolving the salt (70 gm) in 15% (v/v) aqueous acetic acid (100 ml). *Procedure:* Diluted blood or tissue extract (5 to 20 ml) is transferred with a pipette through a three-way surgical stopcock into a 100-ml hypodermic syringe containing 3 ml of light liquid petroleum to lubricate the syringe and render it airtight. Air is expelled, and potassium ferricyanide reagent (10 ml) is drawn into the syringe from a pipette, care being taken not to reintroduce air. A second 100-ml syringe is made airtight with a minimum amount of mineral oil and filled with helium. The stopcocks from the two syringes are connected, and exactly 40 ml of helium is transferred to the syringe containing the sample and the reagent. The syringe containing the sample is then shaken for 1 minute to liberate the carbon monoxide. It is then allowed to stand in an upright position for a few minutes to allow foam to settle. A 30-ml syringe lubricated with liquid petroleum is attached to it as illustrated in Fig. 7. A sample of gas (30 ml) is then removed for injection into the chromatograph (see Section D.II.a.1). *Measurement of carbon monoxide capacity:* To measure the maximum amount of carbon monoxide the sample can bind, an aliquot (5 to 20 ml) is taken up in a 30-ml syringe, and the remainder of the space is filled with carbon monoxide. The mixture is shaken mechanically for 10 minutes, after which the unbound gas is expelled from the syringe completely. The sample is freed of dissolved carbon monoxide by shaking it in the syringe with helium. This is repeated twice. Finally, the carbon monoxide-saturated sample is transferred to a 100-ml syringe, and chemically bound gas is liberated as described above. *Calculations:* The carbon monoxide levels in the unsaturated and in the saturated specimen are measured by the method described in Section D.II.a.1. Results are calculated by equation 3,

$$\text{Per cent carboxyhemoglobin} = \frac{h \times v_s \times 100}{h_s \times v} \tag{3}$$

where h is the peak height obtained on the unsaturated specimen (carbon monoxide content), h_s the peak height obtained on the saturated specimen (carbon monoxide capacity), v the volume of unsaturated specimen, and v_s the volume of the saturated specimen.

2. *Chemically Bound Hydrogen in Water.* See Section C.II.a.2.

IV. Sample Introduction

a. By Syringe

Small gas samples can be injected into any standard gas chromatograph with a syringe fitted with a hypodermic needle. Often medical syringes are used, but they tend to leak around the barrel. Escape of gas can be reduced here by greasing the plunger lightly with mineral oil. However, in some instances this may change the composition of the gas mixture by dissolving one of the components selectively. This is likely to be particularly important in the analysis of respiratory gases containing anesthetics. Loss of gas without lubrication can be minimized by using a gastight syringe (Hamilton Co., Inc.). Such syringes are made with a stainless-steel plunger coated with Teflon resin and have a Teflon tip. The plunger movement is smooth, but stiff. The leak rate is said to be less than 3 μl/hour under a partial vacuum of 20 mm Hg, and there is no apparent leakage at pressures up to 3 atmospheres. Sizes currently available range from 0.1 to 10 ml. They can be bought with or without cemented needles, and with or without Chaney adaptors. The barrels are calibrated in milliliters at 20°C, accuracy being of the order of 1%.

Instructions given by the manufacturer to avoid damage and to prolong the life of the syringe are as follows: (1) "Be exceedingly careful when assembling. Insert the plunger into the barrel at an angle. Rotate slightly when inserting. When the Teflon tip is completely in the barrel, straighten the plunger and carefully insert it into the barrel. (2) After use, pull the plunger back at least $\frac{1}{2}$ inch. The tip may be constricted, and prolonged contact with the base of the barrel may deform the Teflon tip. (3) Do not lubricate the plunger. (4) To maintain the sealing contact of the Teflon tip, spin out the leading and trailing seal edges slightly with your fingernail. Doing this occasionally during cleaning will insure a constant seal. (5) Be exceedingly careful not to mar the Teflon tip. Scratches on the sealing surface may cause leaks."

In addition to being gastight, these syringes are also corrosion-resistant. They have been used in the authors' laboratory to transfer and inject hydrogen chloride, hydrogen, and atmospheric gases. Reproducibility has been better than with lubricated medical syringes.

In studying changes in the composition of gases or vapors, the sample of material generating them is often stored in an airtight container equipped with a port closed by a rubber or silicone septum. To take a sample for analysis, air is expelled from the barrel of the syringe by depressing the plunger, and the needle is forced through the septum. The plunger is withdrawn to take in the volume of gas desired, the needle is pulled out of the sample bottle, and the sample is injected rapidly into the chromatograph. A Huber point needle with a side opening is recommended, since it will not core the septum of the sample bottle or the injection port.

Small gas samples can be injected through the port provided for liquids on all standard chromatographs. However, the volumes are usually large compared to liquid samples. Hence, the plunger of the syringe should be depressed rapidly to ensure, as far as possible, that the gas enters the instrument as a plug rather than being mixed with carrier gas. Otherwise, the gas will be spread out over a long length of tubing when it enters the analytical column. As a result, peaks will be broad, and maxima will be displaced from their true values. This factor becomes most important when it is necessary to separate pairs of substances having similar retention times, for example oxygen and argon.

*b. From Sample Loop Operated with Stopcocks

Ideally, the sample should enter the instrument as a homogeneous plug of gas. This situation can be approached most closely by injecting it into

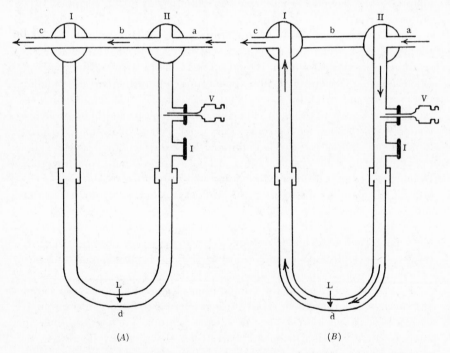

Fig. 8. Apparatus for introducing gas into a sample loop with a syringe. A, with carrier gas bypassing sample loop. B, with loop in carrier gas stream. (Smith and Clark, 1960)

an evacuated chamber which is temporarily bypassed by the carrier gas stream. After introduction, valves are turned which divert the carrier gas through the sample chamber and carry the sample with it onto the separation column. Apparatus for accomplishing this is shown in Fig. 8. L is a sample loop of predetermined volume, and I and II are three-way stopcocks connected to each other through a short length of glass tubing (b) and the sample loop to form a complete circuit. V is a port for evacuating the sample loop and is closed with a serum bottle cap pierced by a hypodermic needle. I is the injection port. It is also closed by a serum bottle cap or similar self-sealing diaphragm. The entire apparatus is mounted in the carrier gas stream of the chromatograph upstream from the liquid injection port. Stopcocks I and II are turned so that the carrier gas stream takes route abc, bypassing the sample loop (Fig. 8A). A vacuum pump is attached at V, and the system is evacuated. Next, a sample of gas commensurate in volume with the size of the sample loop is injected through port I by means of a gastight syringe. Stopcocks I and II are turned simultaneously so that the route of the carrier gas becomes adc, carrying the sample with it. The operation of this equipment could be simplified by replacing the three-way stopcocks and the connecting tubing (b) with a four-way, twin-V bore stopcock (see Fig. 11). With this modification, the sample can be introduced into the gas stream by a 180° turn of a single stopcock.

c. Through Commercial Gas Sampling Valves

The most widely used method for introducing reproducible plugs of gas into a chromatograph is through gas sampling valves specially designed for this purpose. These may be manually or electrically operated. Manual valves are supplied as standard or optional equipment with most commercial instruments. A typical six-way rotary valve is shown schematically in Fig. 9. Component R is a Teflon valve rotor enclosed by a stainless-steel body (B). The bearing surfaces between rotor and body are polished to give a dry seal with minimum leakage. It is usually preferable to avoid lubrication to prevent absorption of gases. However, if a very tight seal is required, a trace of high-vacuum stopcock grease can be used. The instruction manual supplied by the manufacturer should be consulted for information on how to apply the grease.

Component L is a metal loop, usually copper or stainless steel, that defines the size of the gas sample and serves as a reservoir for it just before it is introduced into the carrier gas stream. Loops can be interchanged to adjust sample size. Tubes with volumes of 0.25 to 25 ml are available commercially. Other sizes can be easily made and calibrated by the user. The loops are connected to the gas sampling valve at Q_1 and Q_2 with leakproof connections that can be easily made and broken to allow for rapid interchanges. Swagelok Quick-Connect fittings (Crawford Fitting Co.) are useful for this purpose.

With the valve in the position shown in Fig. 9A, the path of the sample gas entering and leaving the valve is *abcdefg*. At this point it is routed through the valve and sample loop without entering the main stream of the instrument. Meanwhile, the carrier gas passes through another section of the

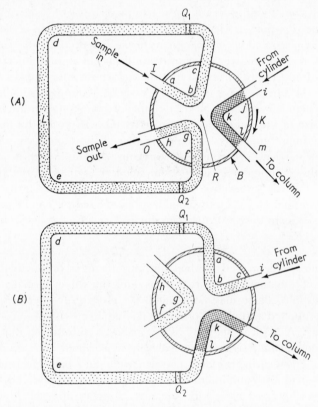

FIG. 9. Flow diagram of manually operated rotary gas sampling valve. A, with sample loop open to air. B, with sample loop in carrier gas stream.

valve independently, following route *ijklm*. With the valve in this position, the bottle containing the gas is attached to the inlet tube. Gas is permitted to flow from the sample bottle through the valve to purge the dead air space and fill the sample loop. A volume of 10 to 15 ml is usually enough to clear the lines and provide a 1-ml sample. The sample is transferred from the loop into the carrier gas stream by turning the knob of the valve in the direction indicated by K in Fig. 9A. The path of the carrier gas stream is now *icbadelkj* (Fig. 9*B*). The plug of gas in the loop and part of the valve, extending from *c* to *l*, is thus swept onto the column. During the same time the sample is being chromatographed, the valve can be rotated to its original position, and the next sample introduced into the loop. If a continuous stream of gas is being monitored, as for example when air from an incubation chamber is pumped continuously through the valve, plugs of gas can be introduced into the instrument in rapid succession, the only restriction being that the last component of the preceding sample must leave the detector before the first component of the new sample. Since it is usually possible to separate atmospheric gases by gas chromatography in 5 minutes or less, it is obvious that a large number of samples can be handled in this way.

Valves of different design are available that will accomplish the same purpose equally well. For example, a six-way valve that is sold commercially (Wilkens Instrument and Research, Inc.) is operated linearly, the plug of gas in the sample loop being introduced into the chromatograph by depressing a plunger for a few seconds. This valve employs rubber to metal O-ring seals and is said to be leakproof. Sample size is reproducible to within 0.2%.

d. By Solenoid Valve System

When a large number of samples must be introduced consecutively from a gas stream flowing continuously through the apparatus, and the system must be made leakproof without stopcock grease, an electrically operated introduction system may be advantageous. Such apparatus can be constructed in the laboratory by using two two-way and two three-way solenoid valves actuated by alternating current (Palmer *et al.*, 1960). Valves are available that will withstand pressures up to 1000 psi and vacuums down to 5 μ without serious leakage (Skinner Chuck Co.). Operation with a DC power supply is preferred, since AC-operated valves frequently chatter. Figure 10 shows diagrams of the system with the valves in nonenergized (sample loop open to air) and energized (sample loop in carrier gas stream) positions.

When the solenoids are not energized, the carrier gas enters the chromatographic column along route *abc*, passing through valve I in transit. Valves III and IV are closed to the carrier gas but allow the sample gas stream to pass through the sample loop along *defi*. The path designated by *dghi* is a bypass line. It is closed off by a two-way valve (II) from the rest of the system when the electric current is off. When the system is energized, valve I closes to shut off the flow of carrier gas along route *abc*. Simultaneously, valves III and IV open so that the carrier gas takes the new route *aefc*, carrying the plug of sample gas in the loop with it onto the chromatographic column. Valve II also opens so that the stream of sample gas is recycled or

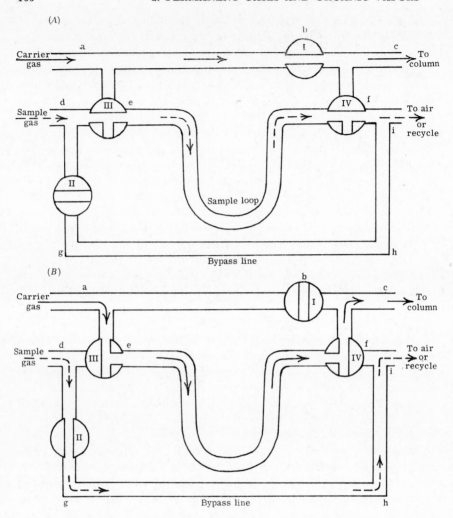

FIG. 10. Flow diagram of gas sampling apparatus operated by solenoid valves. *A*, with valves not energized. *B*, with valves energized.

vented to the atmosphere. This prevents pressure build-up in the external gas circuit. A valve with an orifice size of $\frac{3}{32}$ inch has an internal volume of 1.5 ml. The volume of two three-way solenoids plus the volume of the sample loop give the total amount of gas injected.

Although no data have been reported in the literature, there seems to be no reason why such an apparatus could not be used to study gas exchange in photosynthesis and similar problems. The atmosphere from a sealed chamber containing the experimental material could be cycled through the valve continuously, and samples taken and analyzed at preset times as determined by an interval timer. The operation could be made completely automatic and would give results for oxygen as well as for carbon dioxide, if a split-stream system or automatic attenuator were used to compensate for the disparate amounts of the two gases present in most atmospheres.

e. By Combined Sample Collection and Introduction Unit

Small samples can be collected and introduced with an all-glass apparatus in which flow is controlled with a single stopcock (Fig. 11). This apparatus is best suited for use with a laboratory-built chromatograph,

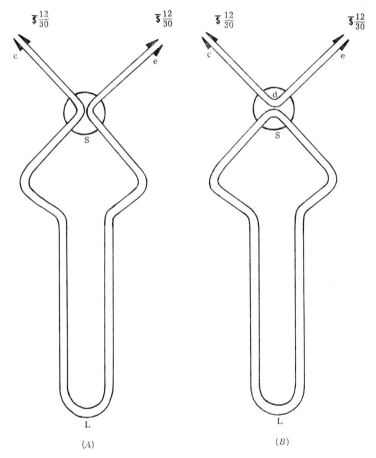

FIG. 11. Apparatus for sample collection and introduction. A, with sample loop in gas stream. B, with sample loop closed. (Bazinet and Walsh, 1960.)

but commercial models could be adapted for it by inserting a little additional plumbing in the carrier gas line. This combined sampling and injection tube is an 8 × ¼-inch o.d. loop made of Pyrex tubing sealed to a four-way, twin-V bore, 2-mm stopcock (Martin Glass Co.). Gas inlet and outlet tubes are also provided which terminate in male $\bar{\mathbb{S}}$ $\frac{12}{30}$ joints. A glass blind with a female $\bar{\mathbb{S}}$ $\frac{12}{30}$ joint is provided to seal off either the inlet or the outlet arm when this device is used as a sample tube for mass spectrometry, or when a sample is being transferred to the U tube from a vacuum chamber. If desired, the sample loop can be made of capillary tubing to reduce sample volume.

When the apparatus is operating as a sampling device, a glass blind is placed on one side arm, and the other side arm is attached to a vacuum pump. The stopcock (S) is turned to the position of Fig. 11A, and the entire apparatus, including the sample loop, is evacuated. The stopcock is then rotated to seal off the sample loop, and the apparatus is disconnected from the vacuum pump. A gas sample is introduced into the U tube by free expansion, by cooling it, or by both. To introduce the sample into the chromatograph, the side arms c and e are tied into the carrier gas stream with plastic tubing. Provision for doing this is not made on most commercial chromatographs, but suitable fittings can be made easily or purchased. With the stopcock in the position shown in Fig. 11B, carrier gas is swept through cde to purge the sample lines. The stopcock is then turned to the position shown in Fig. 11A, and the plug of gas in the sample loop (L) is swept onto the chromatographic column.

f. Transfer of Gas from Container to Sample Loop

If the sample is contained in a metal or glass tube at a pressure above atmospheric, there is no problem in introducing it into the chromatograph. The stopcock of the container is attached to the inlet arm of the gas sampling valve with the shortest piece of Tygon tubing possible. The stopcock is then opened slightly, with the knob of the sampling valve in the position shown in Fig. 9A, and gas is allowed to bleed through the sample loop to flush out the air. Finally, the stopcock is closed, and the sample is allowed to equilibrate with the vent line open to the air for 5 to 10 seconds to equalize pressure. The sample is then introduced into the carrier gas stream by turning the knob of the gas valve to the position shown in Fig. 9B. About 10 to 15 ml of gas at STP is enough to flush out the lines and fill a 1-ml sample loop.

If the sample is at or below atmospheric pressure, several alternative procedures can be followed to fill the sample loop. In working with respiratory gases the sample is often exhaled into a large plastic bag. This can be attached to the inlet side of the sample loop, and a small vacuum pump attached to the outlet through a three-way stopcock. The pump is turned on, and gas from the bag is drawn through the valve to purge the lines and fill the loop. The sample is equilibrated with the atmosphere for a few seconds by turning the stopcock between the vent line and the pump and then switched into the carrier gas stream. If the sample is in a rigid container, it can be forced through the gas sampling valve by displacement with mercury or a saturated salt solution. This is introduced through a second (lower) stopcock on the container by means of a leveling bulb (see Fig. 1*B*). If the concentration of gas to be analyzed is sufficiently high to allow dilution, the pressure in the container can be increased to above atmospheric by introducing carrier gas from a cylinder. The pressure is measured with a manometer before and after addition of the carrier, and the dilution factor is calculated from the gas law (see Section A.V.b.1).

Gases in containers closed with silicone septa or rubber serum caps can be introduced into the sample loop through a hypodermic needle attached to the inlet arm of the sampling valve. Apparatus for doing this is shown in Fig. 12. Prior to introducing the sample, the stopcock (*S*) is turned to shut

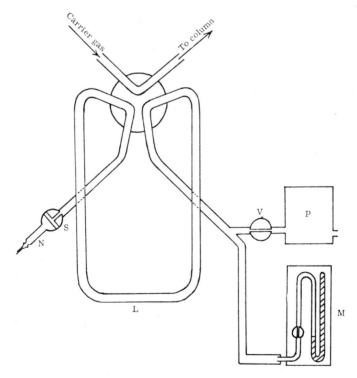

Fig. 12. Apparatus for introducing samples from a container sealed with a silicone or rubber septum.

off the inlet line from the atmosphere, and the sample loop (L) and connecting tubing are evacuated by turning on pump P. When the manometer reading (M) is constant, the pump is turned off, valve V is closed, the seal of the sample bottle is pierced by the needle (N), and stopcock S is turned so the gas flows into loop L. The pressure on the manometer is read, and the sample in L is introduced into the chromatograph in the usual way. This procedure has a disadvantage in that air in the hypodermic needle and connecting tubing up to the stopcock enters the chromatograph along with the sample. Therefore, the connecting tubing should be kept as short and narrow as possible. If the sample is contained in a plastic bottle, it is possible to purge this part of the line just prior to introduction of the sample by turning the stopcock to the atmosphere and squeezing the bottle. However plastic bottles should be used with caution in work of this type, since gases, particularly light ones, diffuse through them readily.

V. CALIBRATION AND CALCULATIONS

For precise results, calibration curves must be used when gas concentrations are measured with thermal conductivity cells, since different compounds do not elicit equivalent detector responses on either a weight or a molar basis. With flame or argon ionization detectors, response is more nearly equal on a weight basis for homologous series of hydrocarbons (Table II), but even with the flame detector sizable differences occur. Moreover, as the flame detectors are not suited for the measurement of inorganic gases, in many cases thermal detectors must be used and these always require calibration. Usually detector response is computed as the area under a peak after the appropriate correction for attenuation, and this method has almost universal acceptance. Nevertheless, peak height is sometimes used, particularly in the analysis of respiratory gases. These materials have short residence times in columns and consequently are recorded as sharp, narrow peaks. If operating parameters are reproduced exactly from experiment to experiment, heights can be read easily and accurately and are proportional to the concentration of the component in the sample. Otherwise, peak areas should be used for calibration.

Calibration by use of synthetic mixtures of known composition is not so accurate as for liquids, since gases cannot be weighed easily, and volumes may change during handling, owing to thermal expansion, compressibility, diffusion through permeable containers, etc. Nevertheless, several methods are available by which gas mixtures can be prepared with reasonable accuracy. They can be prepared at constant pressure by introducing the components, one after the other, into a plastic bag and measuring the volume of each with a wet test meter (see Section A.V.a.1). They can be prepared at constant volume by introducing the components serially into an

TABLE II

RELATIVE RESPONSE OF FLAME IONIZATION DETECTOR
TO VARIOUS ORGANIC COMPOUNDS[a]

Compound	Carbon number	Relative response (butane = 4.0)	
		Per unit weight	Per mole
Methane	1	3.4	0.95
Methanol	1	1.49	0.83
Carbon tetrachloride	1	0.24	0.64
Chloroform	1	0.40	0.85
Ethane	2	3.9	2.0
Ethylene	2	4.1	2.0
Acetylene	2	4.9	2.2
Ethanol	2	2.6	2.0
Propane	3	3.9	3.0
Propylene	3	4.0	2.9
Cyclopropane	3	4.3	3.1
Butane	4	4.0	4.0
Hexane	6	4.2	6.3
Cyclohexane	6	4.3	6.3
Benzene	6	4.3	5.8
Heptane	7	4.3	7.4

[a] From Andreatch and Feinland (1960).

evacuated flask and measuring the pressure inside the container with a manometer after each addition (see Section A.V.a.2). Finally, highly dilute mixtures for calibration at the parts-per-million level can be prepared by injecting pure gases into large sealed containers filled with carrier gas (see Section A.V.a.3). Mixtures prepared by any of these methods and containing the desired components at known concentrations are introduced into the chromatograph, and the detector response for each component is measured. Peak area (corrected for attenuation) is then plotted against volume per cent for each component.

It is possible also to introduce the components of a mixture into a chromatograph individually in order to obtain calibration curves (see Section A.V.a.4). This can be done with great accuracy, since gas volumes used in chromatography are relatively large and can be measured precisely. If the loop that confines and measures the sample is thermostated at the same temperature for calibration and analysis, the influence of temperature on the results is eliminated automatically. Moreover, if the sample is intro-duced into the sample loop at atmospheric pressure, and if the detector is also at atmospheric pressure, variations in barometer readings will not influence the results. It is customary to calibrate gases by passing them through the detector via the partition column. However, a simpler method can be employed if a peak integrator is available (van de Craats, 1958). In this method, the pure component is blended with carrier gas in a bypass line to a concentration of less than 10 mole %. The sample is then introduced directly into the detector.

Errors may be incurred through using pure gas samples for calibration, particularly when sample sizes are large (Weinstein, 1960). Such errors arise from pressure and flow rate changes which take place on introduction of the sample. These changes have been ascribed variously to difference in viscosity of the carrier gas and sample, and to sudden adsorption of sample compounds by the packing when they enter the column. Weinstein (1960) states that these effects may invalidate the calibration curve and gives the following explanation: "Consider, for example, the analysis of 10 per cent hydrogen in carbon monoxide, using the argon (*carrier gas*) Molecular Sieve (*column packing*) system. During calibration with hydrogen alone, a small flow rate increase takes place down the column. However, during analysis of the mixture, an initial flow rate decrease takes place as a result of adsorption of carbon monoxide. The normal gas peak obtained for hydrogen in the mixture will be different from that obtained for hydrogen in the calibration, as the column conditions are completely different."

TABLE III

CORRECTIONS FOR DEVIATIONS FROM IDEALITY
OF PERMANENT GASES AND ORGANIC VAPORS[a]

Component	Correction (%) at:		
	20°C	30°C	40°C
H_2, O_2, N_2, CO	<0.1	<0.1	<0.1
CH_4	0.2	0.2	0.2
CO_2	0.6	0.5	0.4
C_2H_4	0.7	0.6	0.5
C_2H_6	0.9	0.8	0.7
C_3H_6	1.6	1.4	1.3
C_3H_8	1.8	1.6	1.4
iso-C_4H_{10} and C_4H_6	2.8	2.5	2.3
iso-C_4H_8 and 1-C_4H_8	2.9	2.7	2.4
norm. C_4H_{10}	3.1	2.8	2.6
cis- and trans-C_4H_8	3.3	3.0	2.7
iso-C_5H_{12}	4.4[b]	4.0	3.6
norm. C_5H_{12}	4.9[b]	4.4[b]	4.0

[a] Compiled by van de Craats (1958).
[b] Theoretical values for 100% vapor.

Interference of this type has already been reported for another system (Smith *et al.*, 1958), and it occurs regardless of whether peak height or peak area is used for measurement, since both are affected by carrier gas velocity. Errors can be minimized with small samples and can be eliminated completely with an integral detector, or one that is insensitive to changes in the flow rate of the carrier gas.

Regardless of the method for calibration, gas volume must be adjusted to standard conditions of temperature and pressure for precise results. This can be usually done by employing the gas law in its simplest form, since hydrogen, oxygen, nitrogen, and carbon monoxide behave as ideal gases under the conditions usually used for sample collection and intro-duction (see Section A.V.b.1). However, carbon dioxide and the C_2 to C_5 hydrocarbons exhibit deviations ranging from 0.5 to 5% (Table III), and for precise results it is necessary to correct for these. Van de Craats (1958) describes a nomographic method for doing this for complex mixtures which is accurate enough for most applications (see Section A.V.b.2). Corrections of this order of magnitude are meaningless in trace analysis, but they may be desirable when carbon dioxide or an organic gas is a major component of a mixture.

a. Calibration Methods

1. *Gas Mixtures Prepared at Constant Pressure.* A large plastic bag equipped with an outlet tube and valve is purged thoroughly with carrier gas, and as much of the gas is forced out of it as possible. The bag is connected to a gas reservoir through a three-way stopcock and flowmeter, and the dead air space in the lines is swept out with at least 10 to 15 volumes of gas. The desired sample volume is then introduced into the bag and measured with the flowmeter. A reservoir containing the second component of the mixture is attached to the sample line, and a measured volume of the second gas is introduced in the same way. This is repeated until all the components of the mixture have been added. A known volume of gas is then introduced into the chromatograph by the method described in Section A.IV.f. Light gases diffuse through plastics very rapidly, so the composition of mixtures prepared in this way will change with time, particularly if hydrogen or helium is a component.

2. *Gas Mixtures Prepared at Constant Volume.* A round-bottomed flask is fitted with a three-way stopcock with one arm connected to a gas reservoir and the other to a vacuum pump and manometer. The flask and lines are evacuated until a constant reading is obtained on the manometer, and the pump is turned off. The needle valve of the reservoir is then cracked, and gas is allowed to bleed into the flask until the desired partial pressure is obtained as indicated by the manometer. The needle valve is closed, the

stopcock turned to cut off the reservoir, and the pressure reading taken. The first reservoir is replaced by a container holding the second component, and the sample line is evacuated; care should be taken not to turn the three-way stopcock so that the flask holding the sample is evacuated at the same time. The second gas is then admitted to a predetermined partial pressure, and the manometer reading is made as before. This is repeated until all the components have been added, and the total pressure is close to atmospheric.

*3. *Calibration in Parts-per-Million Range by Serial Dilution* (Andreatch and Feinland, 1960.) An injection port is sealed into the side of a 1-liter flask and closed by means of a serum bottle cap or silicone rubber septum. The flask is evacuated and filled with carrier gas at atmospheric pressure. A standard mixture containing 1000 ppm of the gas being analyzed is prepared by injecting a 1-ml sample of the pure gas into the flask with a gas-tight syringe. The gases are mixed by shaking the flask with 5-mm glass beads (total volume 10 ml) which are introduced before evacuation of the flask. Two samples are taken at different times and analyzed by gas chromatography to determine if mixing is complete as indicated by equivalent peak areas. A second 1-liter flask containing an injection port and 10 ml of glass beads is evacuated and filled with carrier gas. A 1-ml sample taken from the 1000-ppm flask is injected into the second flask to obtain a 1-ppm standard. Mixing is again checked by analyzing duplicate samples. For vapor samples, the liquid is brought to constant temperature in a bottle equipped with an injection port. The concentration of vapor in the gas phase is then calculated from the known vapor pressure of the compound at the temperature chosen for sampling. A syringe is inserted into the bottle, and a sample of appropriate size is withdrawn and injected into a mixing flask filled with carrier gas. Samples containing various known concentrations of the gas being analyzed are run through the chromatograph, and a calibration curve is constructed in the usual way.

For liquid samples where the vapor pressure–temperature relationship is unknown, standards may be made by injecting a known volume of the liquid into the mixing flask. The concentration can be calculated from the gas law and the density of the liquid. If the density of the liquid is not known, it should be obtained by weighing a known volume of it.

4. *Calibration with Pure Gases.* The gas reservoir is attached to the gas sampling valve of the chromatograph, and the line is purged with a minimum of 10 to 15 volumes of the pure gas. The gas source is turned off, and about 5 seconds is allowed for the system to reach equilibrium. The sample is then introduced by turning the knob of the valve. This is repeated with sample loops having volumes of 0.25, 0.5, 1.0 ml, etc., and attenuation settings appropriate to the nature of the sample and the detector–recorder

combination. Detector response (after correction for attenuation) is plotted against gas volume.

b. Calculations

1. *Ideal Gas Law for Use with Inorganic Gases and Methane, Excluding Carbon Dioxide.* If gas samples are taken at temperatures and pressures greatly different than 25°C and 760 mm of mercury, they should be corrected to standard volume as in equation 4,

$$v_o = v\frac{298(p - p_w)}{760K} \tag{4}$$

where v_o is the corrected volume, p the total absolute pressure in millimeters of Hg, p_w the vapor pressure of water under the sampling conditions, and K the absolute temperature. If dry gases are sampled, $p_w = 0$.

2. *Approximate Correction for Complex Mixtures of Organic Gases for Departure from Ideality* (van de Craats, 1958). The mean carbon index of the gas is computed as in equation 5 (values for inorganic gases and methane being omitted),

$$I = \frac{2M_2 + 3M_3 + \cdots nM_n}{M_2 + M_3 + \cdots M_n} \tag{5}$$

where I is the mean carbon index, M_2 is the mole per cent of gases in the mixture with 2 carbon atoms, M_3 the mole per cent with 3 carbon atoms,

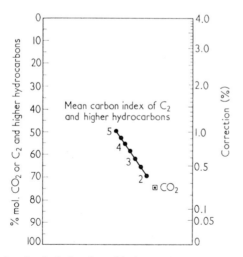

FIG. 13. Correction for deviation from ideal state for mixtures of gases with carbon dioxide or C_2 and higher hydrocarbons at 30°C and 760 mm Hg. (van de Craats, 1958)

etc. The total mole per cent of gases in the mixture having 2 or more carbon atoms is also computed. This latter value is located on the left-hand scale of the nomogram shown in Fig. 13, and a straight edge is aligned between it and the value for I on the middle diagonal scale. The correction factor is the point at which the straight edge crosses the vertical scale on the right.

VI. Summary

Free gases can be collected in vacuum containers or displacement collectors of the same type used in general gas analysis. Dissolved gases can be measured by analyzing the air in equilibrium with the liquid phase and calculating the amount dissolved from Henry's law. Alternatively, the gases can be removed from the liquid by vacuum extraction with the van Slyke or similar apparatus. If the gas is chemically bound as are carbon monoxide and oxygen by the hemoglobin of the blood, treatment with reagents is required to liberate it. Once the gas sample has been obtained, it can be introduced into the chromatograph by a syringe, or through a special gas sampling chamber equipped with stopcocks or valves for directing the flow into the carrier gas stream. The latter procedure is more accurate. To obtain precise analyses, especially with a thermal detector, it is necessary to calibrate the instrument for each component by using mixtures of known composition, or accurately measured volumes of pure gases.

B. Atmospheric Gases

I. Introduction

The constituents of air important in nitrogen fixation, photosynthesis, and respiration include nitrogen, oxygen, carbon dioxide, and water vapor. Argon is also normally present in amounts just under 1%. Ordinarily, its presence would be of little interest biochemically, since it is unreactive. However, it has a retention time just under that of oxygen on the best column packing presently known for the resolution of oxygen and nitrogen (molecular sieve); hence, it must be reckoned with as an interference.

Methods are provided for the chromatographic separation of all these materials except water vapor, which is measured more easily with a hygrometer. In fact, water vapor is usually subtracted on a pre-column filled with Drierite before it enters the analytical column so that it does not deactivate the packing. However, if for any reason it should be necessary to determine water by gas chromatography, it should be possible to do so on a polyethylene glycol packing.

Organic gases and vapors present sporadically in air, such as pollutants, odoriferous compounds, and anesthetics, are discussed in Section E.

II. Conditions for Chromatography

Oxygen can be separated from nitrogen with blood as a stationary phase (Gil-Av and Herzberg-Minzly, 1959). The hemoglobin of the blood is the agent of separation owing to its capacity for combining reversibly with oxygen to form oxyhemoglobin. To prepare the stationary phase, human or animal blood is added slowly to C-22 firebrick (120/170 or 170/200 mesh) in the proportion of 0.5 ml/gm of support. Mixing is continued until the mass becomes homogeneous; then the free-flowing powder is packed into a glass U tube. The column is conditioned with helium to deoxygenate the blood and stored under helium in a refrigerator when not in use. With a column length of 2 meters and a temperature of 30° to 40°C, excellent separation of oxygen from nitrogen is obtained, the oxygen peak being nearly symmetrical. At 20° to 25°C, results are not so good, and at 10°C no separation at all occurs. However, if the whole blood is replaced with hemoglobin solutions prepared according to the method of Drabkin (1946), separation is observed even at −8°C. If the flow rate of the carrier gas is less than 8 ml/min, some of the oxygen appears to be bound irreversibly. This separation can be made on much less esoteric column packings than blood, but the procedure is mentioned here because it may have useful clinical applications aside from any merit it may have for analyzing air. Thus, the retention volume of oxygen will change with the properties of the blood, since the partition coefficient will vary with such factors as per cent hemoglobin, the affinity of the hemoglobin for oxygen, and pH. It has been noted that patients having various blood diseases, and in particular different hemoglobin percentages and erythrocyte counts, yield column packings that give different retention volumes for oxygen under chromatographic conditions that are identical otherwise. Therefore, the procedure may have potential as a diagnostic method.

Oxygen and nitrogen can also be separated on activated charcoal. Oxygen is eluted first, its retention time being about 13 to 15 minutes on a 25-foot column packed with 20/48 mesh Columbia Grade L activated charcoal at 20°C, and a helium flow rate of 100 ml/min (Madison, 1958). Nitrogen comes off the column 2 to 3 minutes later. There is slight tailing, but the peaks are well resolved. With shorter columns and at higher temperatures the two gases are not completely separated (Greene et al., 1956).

Better resolution is obtained with shorter columns in less time by using molecular sieves as stationary phases, and these are now employed almost exclusively for this separation. Molecular sieves (Linde Co.) are prepared by outgassing finely divided synthetic zeolites (sodium aluminum silicates) at temperatures within the range of thermal stability of the crystals. The conditions for preparing them may be varied to produce sieves with different properties. The particles contain a network of channels having diameters of molecular size. Therefore, they can act as "sieves" by occluding small molecules while not taking up larger molecules, or molecules whose shapes will not permit them to diffuse into the channels. Furthermore, they retard the passage of some small molecules more than others, thus bringing about separations. They are not regarded as true adsorbents, since they retard gases by entrapment in a maze of interior channels rather than by surface phenomena.

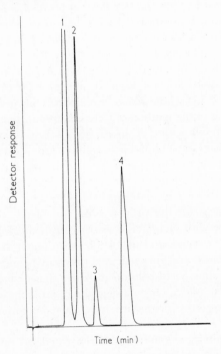

Fig. 14. Separation of atmospheric gases on hexamethylphosphoramide and molecular sieve columns operated in series. Hexamethylphosphoramide separates CO_2 while molecular sieve separates O_2 and N_2. (1) Composite oxygen and nitrogen peak at 4-mv sensitivity. (2) Carbon dioxide at 4-mv sensitivity. (3) Oxygen at 50-mv sensitivity. (4) Nitrogen at 50-mv sensitivity. (Taylor and Presseau, 1959)

Molecular sieves designated as types 13-X and 5-A have been used for the separation of nitrogen and oxygen by GSC, at temperatures ranging from 30° to 100°C, and with helium, hydrogen, and argon as carrier gases. Oxygen emerges from the column first, followed in a few minutes by nitrogen. The two peaks are completely resolved, tailing is negligible, and the analysis is completed in less than 5 minutes (Fig. 14). Adsorption of water vapor and carbon dioxide by molecular sieves is irreversible at room temperature, and, if large quantities of these compounds are taken up, the columns lose their capacities for separating atmospheric gases. Therefore, when carbon dioxide is the major component of a gas sample, and its concentration is of no analytical interest, it is best to absorb it in aqueous alkali contained in a gas pipette, and use only the residual gas for chromatography. This will prolong the life of the column. Many samples, expired air in particular, are saturated with water vapor, and this too is deleterious. To remove water vapor, a glass or plastic tube about 15 cm long and 0.4 cm in diameter should be installed in the chromatograph between the injection port and the separation column. This is filled with anhydrous calcium sulfate in granular form, which will absorb water but not the permanent gases. Preferably, the calcium sulfate should contain a moisture indicator so that it can be renewed when exhausted, as indicated by a color change. If desired, the drying tube can be placed outside the instrument between the sample container and gas sampling valve, although in this position it would have to be purged with 10 to 15 volumes of the gas being analyzed. Molecular sieve columns give good results for 2 or 3 months if the samples are dried prior to chromatography; otherwise, they may become useless in a few days.

Molecular sieve pellets as received from the manufacturer must be ground and screened to about 30/60 U. S. mesh size and activated by heating before use as a column packing. Bethune and Rigby (1958) dry type 5-A sieve in a vacuum oven at 180°C for 24 hours. After the material has cooled in a desiccator, the column is packed and conditioned in a current of helium for 20 hours at 200°C. The chromatograph is operated at 103°C. Efficiency decreases slowly during use, but this decrease can be offset by reducing column temperature. After 3 months, the operating temperature may be as low as 60°C, but separation factors and retention times remain essentially constant. Hamilton and Kory (1960) state that the length of a molecular sieve column necessary for optimum resolution of nitrogen and oxygen depends on the conditions for activation. They find that heating type 13-X material at 300°C for 24 hours produces a packing that requires a 250-cm column for optimum separation of oxygen and nitrogen. Jay and Wilson (1960) use a 12-foot $\times$ ¼-inch i.d. column packed with type 5-A molecular sieve (20/30 U. S. mesh) for the analysis of respiratory gases. The sieve is activated at 350°C, and the packing can be regenerated by heating it at 350° for 2 hours. Smith and Clark (1960) state that when a type 5-A column is no longer performing satisfactorily the packing can be removed and reactivated at 500° to 600°C.

This method for analyzing oxygen and nitrogen is rapid and precise, but, like the conventional Orsat procedure, accuracy is impaired by the presence of 0.94% argon always found in natural air, unless special steps are taken to circumvent this. In contradistinction to the Orsat method, the value for argon is added onto the oxygen result rather than the nitrogen. Argon has a slightly lower retention volume than oxygen on molecular sieve, but under the conditions generally employed the two peaks are not resolved. Thermal conductivity cells are usually employed to detect these gases, and responses are not additive algebraically. Consequently, a correction factor based only on the known argon/nitrogen ratio of air is not practical. Hamilton and Kory (1960) propose two methods for minimizing the error arising from the presence of argon. The first of these is based on comparing the observed height of the oxygen peak with the height of the nitrogen peak, and the true oxygen content of the sample as determined with a Scholander micrometer gas analyzer. This leads to equation 6,

$$h_c = h_o - 0.15h_n \qquad\qquad (6)$$

where h_c is the corrected height of the oxygen peak, h_o the observed height of the oxygen peak, and h_n the height of the nitrogen peak. The actual oxygen content of the sample is then computed from h_c and peak heights obtained with a known amount of pure oxygen. A somewhat simpler correction factor is proposed for calculating results obtained on the analysis of room air. It takes the form of equation 7,

$$P_c = P_o - 0.80 \qquad\qquad (7)$$

where P_o is the observed value for per cent oxygen in the air, and P_c is the corrected value. The correction factor is based on correlating results obtained on the analysis of thirty-eight air samples by both the GSC and the Scholander methods. It eliminates the necessity of measuring the height of the nitrogen peak, and it has the same order of accuracy as equation 4 for computing results obtained on room air.

Both methods rely on the assumption that the argon content of air as well as the argon/nitrogen ratio are constant. This is true in most cases, but it is possible that synthetic atmosphere may be required in some experiments where this is not true. For example, the production of nitrogen by soil microorganisms might be studied in an atmosphere containing 20% oxygen and 80% helium. Of course, the experimentalist would know this in advance and not apply the argon correction factor, but even so the synthetic atmosphere might be mixed with variable amounts of natural air. If the actual argon content is of no particular interest, and all that is required is a reliable value for oxygen, the simplest expedient is to use argon as the carrier gas (see Section B.II.a.2). The two gases differ in thermal conductivity sufficiently so that good peaks will be obtained. However, the thermal detector will respond only to the oxygen in the composite peak, and not to the small amount of argon. Hence, the error in the oxygen measurement will disappear automatically because of the selectivity of this carrier gas–detector combination.

If measurement of the amount of argon and oxygen in the sample is required, the analysis can be made on type 5-A molecular sieve at $-72°C$ (Lard and Horn, 1960) with a 4-foot $\times$ ¼-inch column immersed in an acetone–dry ice bath (see method B.II.a.5). Rigid adherence to the method of column preparation is required for good results. Type 5-A molecular sieve (30/70 U. S. mesh) is activated by drying in an oven at 300°C for 1 hour, and the column is filled as soon as the material is removed from the oven. Immediately after filling, the column is connected to the chromatograph, and helium is passed through it at a low flow rate until operating temperature is reached. This procedure preserves the activity of the packing during the cooling period. Under these conditions, argon present in the air appears as a small peak just before oxygen, the two gases having retention times of about 6 minutes and 8 minutes, respectively. Evidently nitrogen is irreversibly bound or at least eluted very slowly from molecular sieve at this temperature, since a peak for it is not obtained until the column is warmed up. The method is sensitive to 20 ppm with a thermistor operated at 25 ma and a 10-ml sample.

This procedure is useful when argon and oxygen must be measured on the same sample during the same run. When the argon content alone of the gas is desired, the same expedient can be employed as for the analysis of oxygen without a correction factor. Oxygen is the carrier gas, thereby canceling the oxygen peak from the chromatogram when a T/C cell serves as the detector. If both gases must be determined, and sample size is not a factor, dual analyses, with oxygen and argon alternately as the carrier gas, should solve the problem.

Molecular sieve is satisfactory for the separation of nitrogen and oxygen and also for the separation of oxygen from argon under carefully controlled conditions. However, it adsorbs carbon dioxide irreversibly at room temperature and hence cannot be used for the complete analysis of respiratory and photosynthetic gases under ordinary operating conditions. Silica gel columns at any degree of hydration will retard the passage of carbon dioxide enough so that it can be separated from other atmospheric gases (see method B.II.a.4). Davison type 15 silica gel screened to 35/60 U. S. mesh size is suitable for this purpose, but other grades will do as well. Columns of this type are useful for the analysis of carbon dioxide, but the other atmospheric gases emerge from them as a single peak. Carbon dioxide also can be separated from other components of air on short columns containing activated charcoal, or on partition liquids, but again nitrogen and oxygen are not resolved.

The stationary phases for separating carbon dioxide by GLC include di-*n*-butyl maleate, di-2-ethylhexyl sebacate, and hexamethylphosphoramide. Of these, hexamethylphosphoramide appears to be the most efficient.

So far, a single packing has not been found that will resolve carbon dioxide, nitrogen, and oxygen at room temperature. Therefore, most procedures for doing this have two columns which are used alternately, in parallel, or in series. All methods which are based on alternate columns employ molecular sieve for the separation of oxygen from nitrogen, coupled with a GSC or GLC column for separation of carbon dioxide from the composite air peak. Jay and Wilson (1960) employ a 12-foot column packed with type 5-A molecular sieve, alternated with an 18-inch column packed with 9 inches of 40/60 U. S. mesh activated charcoal, and about 9 inches of 20/30 U. S. mesh acid-washed firebrick, separated by a plug of glass wool (see method B.II.b.1). The column is connected with the firebrick section nearest the injection port. The firebrick increases the column length so that it will fit into the instrument more easily, and also decreases the flow rate, making better resolution possible. A longer charcoal column retards flow too much and causes tailing. However, it should be noted that several grades of activated charcoal are available commercially, with high, low, and medium activity. Therefore, it might be possible to select a material that will give optimum separations without the use of an inert solid phase. Also, the possibility of treating the charcoal with a material known to reduce tailing should be considered. Eggertsen *et al.* (1956), for example, find that 1.5% (w/w) of squalene practically eliminates tailing of C_6 and C_7 hydrocarbons on furnace black. Most workers, however, pack the alternate column with silica gel. As noted above, a partition liquid coated on an inert solid support may be substituted for the second GSC column. Dressler *et al.* (1960) use a 4-foot molecular sieve column alternated with a 12-foot column containing di-*n*-butyl maleate for the analysis of respiratory gases (see method B.II.b.2). It is likely that the same result could be obtained with a shorter GLC column packed with hexamethylphosphoramide.

The use of two columns for the analysis of air is inconvenient experimentally if only standard basic equipment is available. Either two chromatographs are needed, or the columns must be interchanged between runs. This difficulty can be overcome by installing the columns in the same oven, positioned so that the effluent gases of both pass through a single detector, and the sample can be diverted to either column at will by merely turning a valve (see Chapter 1, Section B). With this arrangement, it is possible to switch from one column to the other in a matter of seconds, so that the analysis becomes semiautomatic. The analysis can be made fully automatic by arranging the columns in parallel; the sample thus is divided, and fractions of it enter each of the two columns simultaneously (Brenner and

Cieplinski, 1959). An arrangement for accomplishing this is shown in Fig. 15: *A* is a 2-meter molecular sieve column, and *B* a 1-meter silica gel column. A sample injected at *C* will enter each of the two columns in amounts proportional to the resistance they offer to the flow of gas. Therefore, the columns function as a stream splitter, as well as for separating the sample components. The effluents from the two columns rejoin at *D* and pass

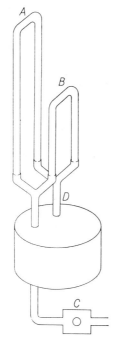

Fig. 15. Apparatus for splitting gas sample between molecular sieve and silica gel columns for N_2–O_2–CO_2 analysis. (Brenner and Cieplinski, 1959)

through a single detector. A needle valve is necessary to balance the flow of gas through the two parallel columns so that the peaks do not coincide. The entire analysis can be carried out easily in 5 minutes. During operation, the silica gel and the molecular sieve take up water. This gradually diminishes their separating power, and finally the columns may become plugged altogether. Therefore it is very important that the sample gas as well as the carrier gas be dried before entering the instrument. If the columns are stored for any length of time, their ends should be connected by a short piece of rubber tubing to protect the packings from the atmosphere. Flow rates may change with use, but these are easily restandardized. Equipment for analyzing respiratory gases with columns in parallel is available commercially (Perkin-Elmer Corp.). Gases also may be analyzed on columns connected in parallel by means of a valve that will deliver a predetermined volume of the sample to each column (Adlard and Hill, 1960).

Respiratory gases can be analyzed by means of two columns connected in series with a detector located at the exit end of each. The Fisher Model 25 gas partitioner is designed for this purpose, and any Aerograph instrument can be adapted to it after installation of a special detector block available from the manufacturer. A schematic diagram of the operation is shown in Fig. 16. The sample is introduced at A and passes through a GSC or GLC

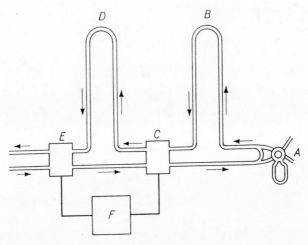

Fig. 16. Apparatus for chromatographing mixtures of oxygen, nitrogen, and carbon dioxide with two columns connected in series and a detector at the exit of each column.

column (B) which separates carbon dioxide from air. The first detector (C) picks up a carbon dioxide peak and a composite air peak. The air plug then enters the second column (D) and is separated into oxygen and nitrogen, which are measured by the second detector (E). Carbon dioxide enters the second column and is adsorbed irreversibly. There is a single recorder (F), so four peaks are inscribed on the same sheet of recorder paper. The composite air peak, oxygen, and nitrogen always appear in the order stated, but carbon dioxide may appear between air and oxygen, or after nitrogen, depending on the properties of the columns. Molecular sieve is always used for the second column (D), but any of the solid or liquid stationary phases used for analysis by the alternate- or parallel-column methods can be employed for the first column (B). The most important consideration is to choose the column length and packing so that the carbon dioxide peak is not coincident with the oxygen or nitrogen peaks. A 2-foot silica gel column connected in series with a 6-foot molecular sieve column is recommended with the Aerograph instrument (method B.II.c.1). This combination also causes the carbon dioxide peak to register before the oxygen peak. The carbon dioxide peak can be caused to appear after the nitrogen peak by using a more active adsorbent in the first column (*B*), increasing the length, or both.

The methods most commonly used to date for the complete analysis of air depend on two columns: alternately, in parallel, or in series. However,

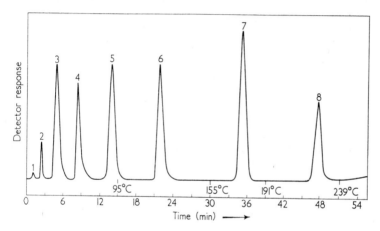

Fig. 17. Separation of inorganic gases and lower hydrocarbons on molecular sieve by programming the temperature (method B.II.d.2). (1) Hydrogen. (2) Oxygen. (3) Nitrogen. (4) Methane. (5) Carbon monoxide. (6) Ethane. (7) Carbon dioxide. (8) Ethylene. (Courtesy of the F. & M. Scientific Co.)

single-column methods are possible and may become practical in the future. Thus, Greene *et al.* (1956) are able to separate oxygen, nitrogen, and carbon dioxide on a 9-foot column packed with activated charcoal at a temperature of 170°C (see method B.II.d.1). Oxygen and nitrogen are not completely resolved, and the peaks tail badly. Carbon dioxide is not eluted until 30 minutes, indicating that the method is comparatively slow. Graven (1959) has shown that oxygen, nitrogen, and carbon dioxide can be resolved on molecular sieve by programming the temperature. More recently, excellent resolution of these compounds has been obtained by programming a molecular sieve column between 35° and 239°C [1] (see method B.II.d.2). Peak symmetry is good, and carbon dioxide is eluted in 36 minutes (Fig. 17). The method is reproducible to within ±5% for the analysis of carbon dioxide. Methane,

[1] Personal communication. F & M Scientific Co.

ethane, and ethylene can be separated from the inorganic gases and from one another by this method.

a. Analysis of Single Components

*1. Determination of Oxygen without Correction for Argon (Ramsey, 1959)

Chromatograph	Beckman Model GC-2 equipped with dual-column valve.
Column dimensions	122 × 0.635-cm o.d. coiled stainless-steel tubing.
Active solid	Type 5-A molecular sieve.
Temperatures	Injection and column: room temperature. Detector: 70°C.
Carrier gas	Helium at 80 ml/min. Outlet pressure: Atmospheric.
Detector	Four-filament hot-wire (Pt) T/C cell at 360 ma.
Recorder	1 mv; 1 second; 1.27 cm/min.
Sample size	Gas in 1 ml of plasma (see method A.III.a.2).
Analysis time	2 minutes.

*2. Oxygen Determination with Argon as the Carrier Gas (Bethune and Rigby, 1958)

Chromatograph	Laboratory-built.
Column dimensions	10-foot × 0.6-cm i.d. Pyrex U tube.
Active solid	Type 5-A molecular sieve (30/60 mesh) activated in vacuum oven for 24 hours at 180°C and conditioned in column with carrier gas at 10 to 20 ml/min at 200°C for 20 hours.
Temperature	Column: 103°C (lowered as column efficiency decreases with use). Detector: room temperature.
Carrier gas	Argon at 28 ml/min.
Detector	Thermistor.
Recorder	Brown, 0 to 1 mv, 0 to 50 mv, variable span; 1 second; 1 inch/min.
Sample size	0.25 ml of air.
Analysis time	Not given.

*3. Separation of Oxygen with Blood as the Stationary Phase (Gil-Av and Herzberg-Minzly, 1959)

Chromatograph	Perkin-Elmer Model 154-A fractometer.
Column dimensions	200 × 0.40-cm i.d. glass tubing.
Solid support	Johns Manville C-22 firebrick (120/170 U. S. mesh), washed with 4% HNO_3 and dried at 150°C.
Stationary phase	Hemoglobin solution (15%) (50:100).
Temperature	Injection, detector, and column: 25° to 35°C.
Carrier gas	Helium at 20 ml/min. Inlet pressure: 1280 mm Hg. Outlet pressure: atmospheric.
Detector	Thermistors, 2000 ohms at 25°C, at 4.0 volts.
Recorder	0 to 10 mv; 1 second; 1.27 cm/min.
Sample size	0.25 to 1 ml of gas.
Analysis time	8 to 15 minutes.

*4. *Separation of Carbon Dioxide on Silica Gel* (Brenner and Cieplinski, 1959)

Chromatograph	Perkin-Elmer Model 154-C.
Column dimensions	1-meter × ¼-inch o.d. copper U tube.
Active solid	Davison type 15 silica gel.
Temperature	22°C.
Carrier gas	Helium at 5 psig.
Detector	Thermistor operated at 8 volts.
Recorder	5 mv; 1 second; 30 inches/hour.
Sample size	0.25 ml.
Analysis time	2 to 3 minutes.

*5. *Separation of Argon and Oxygen* (Lard and Horn, 1960)

Chromatograph	Fisher-Gulf Model 300.
Column dimensions	4-foot × ¼-inch copper tubing.
Active solid	Type 5-A molecular sieve (30/70 U. S. mesh) activated at 300°C for 1 hour, packed into column immediately, and conditioned with helium during cooling.
Temperatures	Detector: 58°C. Column: −72°C (dry ice–acetone bath).
Carrier gas	Helium at 70 ml/min.
Detector	Thermistor operated at 25 ma.
Recorder	Bristol, 2 mv.
Sample size	0.5 ml of dry air.
Analysis time	About 10 minutes.

b. Separation of Oxygen, Nitrogen, and Carbon Dioxide with Columns in Parallel

*1. *With Two GSC Columns* (Jay and Wilson, 1960)

Chromatograph	Beckman CG-2 with gas sampling valve, drying tube, dual-column valve, and two columns in parallel.
Column dimensions	(I) 366 × 0.635-cm o.d. coiled copper tubing. (II) 45.7 × 0.635-cm o.d. stainless-steel tubing.
Active solids	(I) 20/30 U. S. mesh molecular sieve, type 5-A. (II) 20/30 U. S. mesh acid-washed firebrick (22 cm)–glass wool plug (1 cm)–40/60 U. S. mesh activated charcoal (23 cm).
Temperatures	Injection: 25°C. Detector: 40°C. (I) 40°C. (II) 40°C.
Carrier gas	(I) Helium at 95 ml/min. (II) Helium at 115 ml/min. Inlet pressure: 1300 mm Hg. Outlet pressure: atmospheric.
Detector	Four-filament hot-wire (Pt) T/C cell at 300 ma.
Recorder	1 mv; 1 second; 1.27 cm/min.
Sample size	2 ml.
Analysis time	About 2 minutes.

2. *With a GLC and GSC Column* (Dressler *et al.*, 1960)

Chromatograph	Beckman Model 178 with two columns in parallel.
Column dimensions	(I) 4 feet. (II) 12 feet.
Solid support	Not given.

Active solid and stationary phase	(I) Type 13-X molecular sieve. (II) Di-n-butyl maleate (Beckman column No. 17329).
Temperature	35°C.
Carrier gas	(I) Helium at 90 ml/min and 32 psi. (II) Helium at 48 ml/min and 25 psi.
Detector	T/C cell operated at 250 ma.
Recorder	0.5 inch/min.
Sample size	1.2 ml for each run.
Analysis time	(I) 1 minute. (II) 2½ minutes.

c. Separation of Oxygen, Nitrogen, and Carbon Dioxide with Two Columns in Series

*1. With Two GSC Columns (Anon., 1960a)

Chromatograph	Aerograph Model A-110-C.
Column dimensions	(A) 61 × 0.32-cm o.d. coiled stainless-steel tubing. (B) 183 × 0.63-cm o.d. coiled stainless-steel tubing.
Active solids	(A) Silica gel (30/60 U S. mesh). (B) 95% by weight molecular sieve, type 13-X; 5% by weight molecular sieve type 5-A.
Temperature	30°C throughout.
Carrier gas	Helium at 60 ml/min.
Detector	Four-filament hot-wire (Pt) T/C cell at 250 ma. Special flow design.
Recorder	0 to 1 mv; 1 second; 0.85 cm/min.
Sample size	0.25 ml.
Analysis time	7 minutes.

*2. With a GLC and a GSC Column (Hamilton and Kory, 1960)

Chromatograph	Fisher Model 25 with zero-suppression selector, drying tube, Wilkens Model A-202 gas sampling valve, two columns in series, and detector at the end of each column.
Column dimensions	(A) 300 cm. (B) 250 cm.
Solid support	(A) Chromosorb (30/60 mesh).
Stationary phase and active solid	(A) Hexamethylphosphoramide (30 : 70). (B) Type 13-X molecular sieve.
Temperature	25°C.
Carrier gas	Helium at 100 ml/min.
Detector	Two detectors with four matched thermistors operated at 5 ma.
Recorder	1 mv.
Sample size	1 ml.
Analysis time	Less than 2 minutes.

d. Separation of Oxygen, Nitrogen, and Carbon Dioxide on a Single Column

1. On Charcoal with Incomplete Resolution of Oxygen and Nitrogen (Greene et al., 1956)

| Chromatograph | Laboratory-built. |
| Column dimensions | 9-foot × ¼-inch o.d. copper coil. |

Active solid	Activated charcoal (40/60 mesh).
Temperature	170°C.
Carrier gas	Helium at 100 ml/min.
Detector	Gow-Mac T/C cell.
Recorder	5, 10, or 25 mv.
Sample size	10 ml.
Analysis time	About 30 minutes to carbon dioxide.

*2. *On Molecular Sieve with Programmed Temperature* (Anon., 1960b)

Chromatograph	F & M Model 500 linear-programmed high-temperature gas chromatograph equipped with a gas sampling valve.
Column dimensions	122-cm (4-foot) × 0.63-cm (¼-inch) o.d. stainless-steel tubing.
Active solid	Linde molecular sieve, type 5-A (30/60 U. S. mesh).
Temperatures	Injection port: 300°C. Detector: 300°C. Column: programmed 35°→239°C (linear, 4°C per minute).
Carrier gas	Helium at 60 ml/min at outlet. Inlet pressure: 36 psi (18,600 mm/sq. in.). Outlet pressure: atmospheric.
Recorder	Minneapolis-Honeywell, 1 mv; 1 second; 20 inches/hour.
Detector	Four-filament hot wire (tungsten) T/C cells at 100 ma.
Sample size	1 ml.
Analysis time	39 minutes to CO_2.

III. SUMMARY

Oxygen can be separated from nitrogen on activated charcoal or molecular sieve, but the latter packing is preferred, since the separation factor is better and shorter columns and briefer analysis times can be used. Argon has a retention volume slightly lower than that of oxygen, but under ordinary conditions elutes with it; however, the two gases can be resolved at low temperatures. Interference of argon with the oxygen determination can be corrected for mathematically, or it can be eliminated altogether by using argon as a carrier gas.

Carbon dioxide is bound irreversibly by molecular sieves at room temperature and thus cannot be analyzed on the same packing used for separation of oxygen from nitrogen. However, it can be resolved from air on silica gel or various GLC packings. With molecular sieve columns in combination with silica gel (or GLC) columns connected in series or in parallel, it is possible to obtain analyses for all three gases in a relatively short time. They can also be separated on molecular sieve by programming the temperature, and at least partially on activated charcoal at high temperatures.

C. Hydrogen Isotopes and Isomers

I. INTRODUCTION

The chromatographic separation of hydrogen and hydrogen isotopes is of biochemical interest because these substances have been used extensively as tracers. Deuterium is determined easily and rapidly by mass spectrometry, but the equipment is expensive, difficult to maintain, and not available in many laboratories. By contrast, this analysis can be made with equal accuracy by GSC with equipment costing in the neighborhood of $1000 and requiring no special skills to operate. Generally, the sample is combusted to water which is converted in turn to molecular hydrogen either electrolytically or chemically. The gas is then analyzed by GSC with a thermal detector. The time required for chromatography is only a few minutes. Tritium can be separated from protium at low temperatures. This technique may be valuable for concentrating it in radiochemical studies.

II. ISOLATION PROCEDURES

Hydrogen dissolved in water can be sampled by equilibrating the liquid phase with carrier gas (see Section A.III.a.1). Chemically bound hydrogen is liberated from water by electrolysis, or more easily by reaction with calcium hydride. The latter reaction is not highly reproducible from an analytical standpoint (Linde and Rogers, 1958). When moist gas is passed over calcium hydride at room temperature, somewhat more than the calculated amount of hydrogen is released, and the results are erratic. Little improvement is noted at 100°C and 150°C, but at 235°C there is less variability in the results. Temperatures much higher than this cannot be used, since nitrogen may begin to react, and the hydride itself begins to decompose with the liberation of hydrogen. Nevertheless, reaction with calcium hydride is a practical way to liberate hydrogen from water for the determination of protium/deuterium ratios because both isotopes react at the same rate. Therefore, the isotope ratio in the gas is the same as in the liquid. The water is added dropwise to pellets of calcium hydride contained within an evacuated chamber. The gas which is liberated is adjusted to atmospheric pressure by means of mercury-filled leveling bulbs, and an aliquot is introduced into the chromatograph through a gas sampling valve attached directly to the generator.

a. Sample Collection

*1. *Hydrogen Dissolved in Water.* See Section A.III.a.1.

*2. *Chemically Bound Hydrogen in Water* (Arnett et al., 1960). *Apparatus:* A diagram of the apparatus is shown in Fig. 18. *B* is a chamber for holding the water sample, and C is a cartridge containing granules of calcium hydride (Metal Hydrides, Inc.). The surface of the reagent must be fresh to ensure complete reaction. A is a tube 80 cm in length connected to a mercury-filled leveling bulb. It is used for holding the generated gas. E is a manometer connected to the gas generator (A) and the gas sampling valve of the chromatograph (F) through the three-way stopcock, D. G is a stopcock that connects the system to a vacuum pump. *Procedure:* With stopcock J closed,

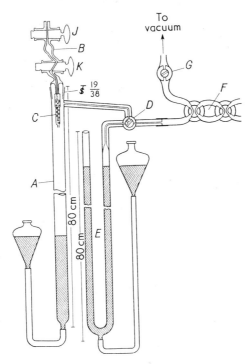

Fig. 18. Apparatus to generate hydrogen isotopes. (Arnett *et al.*, 1960)

and stopcocks K and D open, the gas-generating system is evacuated. Stopcocks D and K are then closed, and J is opened. A sample of water (about 0.1 ml) is introduced into chamber B and allowed to drop slowly into the calcium hydride contained in C. This liberates H_2 and HD into chamber A. The gas sampling valve, the manometer, and the connecting tubing are now evacuated, and the gas is introduced into the sample loop (see Section A.IV.c) through stopcock D. The pressure throughout the system is adjusted to atmospheric by means of the leveling bulbs. The gas in the sample loop is then introduced into the chromatograph by turning the knob of the gas sampling valve.

III. Separation from Atmospheric Gases

Hydrogen is readily separated from the components of air on activated charcoal or on molecular sieve at ordinary temperatures. Hydrogen emerges first, followed by oxygen and nitrogen in that order. Isotopes of hydrogen and nuclear spin isomers are not resolved under these conditions. Argon or nitrogen is generally preferred as carrier gas, but when atmospheric gases and/or hydrocarbons must be determined simultaneously, helium is often used to obtain greater sensitivity and to avoid peak inversions with these latter compounds. This renders quantitative determination of hydrogen difficult for several reasons (Madison, 1958). Sensitivity is comparatively low because of the small difference in thermal conductivity between the two gases. Furthermore, hydrogen–helium mixtures elicit anomalous responses from thermal conductivity cells in some concentration ranges. When the percentage of hydrogen in helium is high, the detector responds as would be expected for a component having a greater conductivity than the carrier gas. However, at low hydrogen concentrations the response is opposite to the one anticipated; that is, the detector behaves as though hydrogen has a lower rather than a higher thermal conductivity than helium. The effect of sample volume on peak size and shape as measured with a Gow-Mac four-filament T/C cell is shown in Fig. 19. For sample volumes

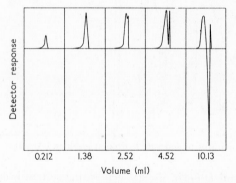

Fig. 19. Effect of sample volume on shape of hydrogen peak. (Madison, 1958)

of 0.212 and 1.38 ml, the peaks are similar to hydrocarbon peaks except for low sensitivity. However, at 2.52 ml a slight inversion occurs near the apex of the peak. This becomes more pronounced as the sample volume is increased, until at 10.13 ml the inversion extends far below the base line. This anomalous behavior can be attributed to a minimum in the thermal conductivity curve for hydrogen–helium mixtures. In other words, as noted in Chapter 1, the thermal conductivities of gases in mixtures are not necessarily additive. This same inversion has been observed when the measurement is made with a thermistor. The magnitude of this effect depends on operating parameters that influence hydrogen concentration. These include flow rate of carrier gas, column temperature, nature of the stationary phase, and column length.

With nitrogen as the carrier gas, complete inversion of the hydrogen peak is obtained, and sensitivity is many times as great. However, the use of nitrogen decreases sensitivity for all gases other than hydrogen and in some cases results in peak inversions. Helium gives superior results for all gases other than hydrogen and is satisfactory for samples containing up to 1 ml of hydrogen. Below this volume, the calibration factor for hydrogen is fairly constant, and it can be measured with reasonable accuracy with helium as the carrier gas.

However, if possible, helium should not be used as a carrier gas for hydrogen analysis unless the sample is modified chemically before it enters the detector, since sensitivity is sacrificed and anomalies may result. Furthermore, the higher sensitivity obtainable with argon, neon, or nitrogen should make it possible to reduce sample size, and concomitantly to increase resolution, suppress pressure surges, and reduce calibration errors arising from interactions between sample components. However, if helium must be used, it is possible to increase sensitivity by combusting the hydrogen to water in a short tube containing CuO placed between the column and the detector (Moore and Ward, 1958). This technique is based on the fact that the thermal conductivity difference between helium and water is much greater than that between helium and hydrogen.

a. Conditions for Chromatography

*1. *Separation from Atmospheric Gases on Molecular Sieve* (Bovijn, Pirotte, and Berger, 1958)

Chromatograph	Beckman CG-2 equipped with gas sampling valve.
Column dimensions	4-foot $\times$ $\frac{1}{4}$-inch copper tubing.
Active solid	15 gm of Linde molecular sieve (14/30 mesh).
Temperature	40°C throughout.
Carrier gas	Argon at 40 to 60 ml/min. Inlet pressure: 30 psig. Outlet pressure: atmospheric.
Detector	Four-filament T/C cell (W) operated at 150 ma.
Recorder	Honeywell Electronic, 1 mv; 1 second; 30 inches/hour.
Sample size	1 to 2 ml.
Analysis time	2 to 5 minutes.

IV. Separation of Isotopes and Isomers

The analysis of mixtures of protium and deuterium is very important from a biochemical standpoint, since the latter isotope is frequently used in tracer studies. Currently, most determinations are made with the mass spectrograph, or by falling-drop procedures, but the apparatus for gas chromatography is relatively cheap, and accuracy and speed of analysis are comparable.

Chromatography of mixtures of hydrogen isotopes is complicated by two equilibrium reactions that may be triggered by catalysts. These are given by equations 8 and 9.

$$para\text{-}H_2 \rightleftharpoons ortho\text{-}H_2 \qquad\qquad (8)$$

$$H_2 + D_2 \rightleftharpoons 2HD \qquad\qquad (9)$$

The first reaction (equation 8) involves the interconversion of the *ortho* and *para* nuclear spin isomers of protium (or deuterium). Normally, protium consists of three parts of *ortho* isomer to one of *para*, and the rate of isomerization is low. However, interchange is subject to catalysis, notably by oxides of iron. Since the two molecules differ appreciably in thermal conductivity, it is important that the ratio of them in the sample does not change through interaction with the column packing. If changes in composition occur at all, they should do so rapidly so that protium can be chromatographed as an equilibrium mixture yielding a single peak. An application of this principle will be described later.

Equation 9 represents the equilibrium reaction between protium and deuterium to yield protium deuteride. This can be catalyzed by column packings or heat. Palladium black, for example, dissolves the isotopes interstitially in atomic form and converts all the protium deuteride to protium and deuterium (Glueckauf and Kitt, 1957). Palladium can also be used as a partition material, but complete separation of the isotopes is not obtained (Thomas and Smith, 1959).

From the biochemist's point of view, the simplest way to analyze for total deuterium in the presence of protium is to use ordinary hydrogen as a carrier gas and measure the height of the unresolved peak due to HD and D_2 with a thermal conductivity cell (Ohkoshi *et al.*, 1958a, 1958b, 1958c; Riedel and Uhlmann, 1959; Arnett *et al.*, 1960). This can be done on an activated charcoal or molecular sieve column at ordinary temperatures (see Section C.IV.a.1). The only purpose of this column is to separate the hydrogen isotopes from other gases. The thermal detector does not respond to the protium in the sample, since this is the main constituent of the carrier gas. Deuterium and protium deuteride are swept through the column as an unresolved plug of gas that yields a peak on the chromatogram because their thermal conductivities are appreciably different from that of protium. The thermal conductivity of protium deuteride is intermediate between that of protium and deuterium. Consequently, detector response is proportional to the total amount of deuterium in the sample, regardless of whether it is present as HD or D_2. In any case, it would be possible to convert all the HD to D_2 by including a palladium black column in the system. From 0 to 10 mole % deuterium, the relation of peak height to deuterium content is linear (Arnett *et al.*, 1960), peak heights being more reproducible than peak areas measured with a planimeter. The coefficient of variation of replicate samples analyzed on the same day is 0.3%, and on samples analyzed on different days it is 0.5 to 1.0%, depending on deuterium content. The calibration line relating deuterium content of the gas to detector response is constant over the life of a cylinder of carrier gas, if the flow of hydrogen is left undisturbed, and if corrections are made for changes in atmospheric pressure. However, precision can be improved by running standards along with the unknown. Optimum sample size is governed by deuterium content. Twenty milliliters of gas is satisfactory for samples containing less than 2% of the heavier isotope, but smaller samples are better at higher concentrations. To achieve reproducible results, the flow rate of the carrier gas and the voltage on the thermal conductivity cell must be kept constant.

If desired, the analysis can be run on a column capable of resolving the mixture into three peaks representing protium, protium deuteride, and the deuterium (see Section C.IV.a.2).

Helium or neon is used as the carrier gas, so all three components are recorded on the chromatograph. The stationary phase is activated alumina coated with ferric oxide (Moore and Ward, 1960) or chromia–alumina (Smith and Hunt, 1960), and the column temperature is 77°K. The iron–alumina packing is prepared by treating 150/200 mesh alumina successively with 1.8 M ferric chloride solution and 3 M ammonium hydroxide solution. The material is then heated at 120°C for 24 hours. Tailing is virtually eliminated, and essentially symmetrical peaks are obtained if the packing is partially deactivated prior to use by adsorbing a small amount of carbon dioxide on it. Protium, protium deuteride, and deuterium are separated completely by a 365-cm column at 77°K and a flow rate of 112 ml of helium per minute (Fig. 20). The surface of the alumina is coated with iron oxide to prevent the nuclear spin isomers of protium and deuterium from emerging from the column separately and so complicating the chromatogram (Moore and Ward, 1958). The iron catalyzes *ortho-para* interconversions so that the transformations take place rapidly relative to rate of movement of the gas along the separation column. This causes the *ortho* and *para* isomers to appear as single peaks with retention times intermediate (weighted average) between those of the individual isomers in the absence of equilibration. Since this packing does not catalyze reaction shown in equation 9, the separation of the mixed isotopes into H_2, HD, and D_2 results. Columns packed with alumina activated for 8 hours at 480°C also catalyze equilibration of the spin isomers, apparently in the absence of iron. Partial deactivation with carbon dioxide restores their capacity for separating the *ortho* and *para* compounds. The accuracy of the procedure is within 0.2%. The limit of detection of HD in H_2 or D_2 is less than 0.01%. Hence deuterium can be detected in natural hydrogen.

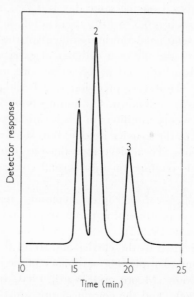

FIG. 20. Chromatogram of a mixture of hydrogen isotopes separated on alumina modified with ferric chloride. (1) Protium. (2) Protium deuteride. (3) Deuterium. (Moore and Ward, 1960)

The nuclear spin isomers of protium can be separated, and those of deuterium partly separated, by GSC (Moore and Ward, 1958). Up to the present, attempts to separate all four isomers as well as protium deuteride on a single stationary phase have been unsuccessful (Van Hook and Emmett, 1960). On chromatographing such a mixture on activated alumina cooled with liquid nitrogen, three peaks are obtained (see method C.IV.a.3) with retention times between 5 and 7 minutes. The first of these represents *para*-protium, the second an unresolved mixture of *ortho*-protium and protium deuteride, and the third an unresolved mixture of the nuclear spin isomers of deuterium (Fig. 21). It is possible to obtain a complete analysis, except for the latter pair, by combining results obtained by method C.IV.a.3 with results obtained by method C.IV.a.2. The area of the middle peak in Fig. 21 gives the sum of *ortho*-protium plus protium deuteride, and the area of the middle peak in Fig. 20 gives the amount of protium deuteride alone. Consequently, their difference will give the amount of *ortho*-protium.

The method is not exact because of incomplete resolution of the peaks in Fig. 21, and it can be used only when the HD concentration is greater than 10%.

Mixtures of para-H_2, ortho-H_2, HD, and D_2 can be separated in a single operation with two columns in series (Furuyama and Kwan, 1961). The first column contains alumina or molecular sieve, and the second column contains

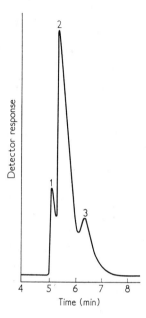

FIG. 21. Separation of hydrogen isotopes on activated alumina. (1) para-Protium. (2) ortho-Protium plus protium deuteride. (3) Deuterium. (Van Hook and Emmett, 1960)

alumina coated with ferric oxide prepared according to the method of Moore and Ward (1960). The spin isomers of protium are separated on the first column. They undergo rapid ortho-para interconversion during transit through the second column and are eluted as separate peaks. The isotopes are separated also, so that four peaks are obtained with retention times ranging between 6 and 10 minutes. At first glance such separations would seem of little interest to the biochemist. However, organisms are known that can use hydrogen in enzyme-mediated reductions, and it is possible that these might respond differently to different spin isomers as well as isotopes.

Mixtures of tritium and protium can be resolved on a 6.1-meter molecular sieve column at −160°C (Gant and Yang, 1959). The optimum linear flow rate for maximum column efficiency for HT and T_2 is about 10 cm of helium per second. The order of elution is *para*-H_2, *ortho*-H_2, HT, and T_2, the last compound coming off the column in about 20 minutes. Insufficient data are given to assess the practicability of the method. It would appear, however, to have considerable potential for concentrating tritium in radiochemical studies, particularly those concerned with chronological dating of specimens by isotope decay.

a. Conditions for Chromatography

*1. *Deuterium Analysis by Masking Protium in Unresolved Peak with Carrier Gas* (Riedel and Uhlmann, 1959)

Chromatograph	Perkin-Elmer Model 154-B with gas sampling valve.
Column dimensions	4-meter × ¼-inch o.d. U tube.
Active solid	Type 5-A molecular sieve (Perkin-Elmer "I" column).
Temperature	30°C.
Carrier gas	Helium at 75 ml/min and 7.4 psig. inlet pressure. Outlet pressure: atmospheric.
Detector	Thermistor operated at 7.0 volts with an electronically stabilized voltage-supply unit.
Recorder	Philips Model 2200A/21B, 5 mv.
Sample size	1, 10, or 25 ml.
Analysis time	2 to 3 minutes.

*2. *Column Resolution* of H_2, HD, *and* D_2 *by Equilibrating Spin Isomers* (Moore and Ward, 1960)

Chromatograph	Laboratory design.
Column dimensions	365 × 0.5 cm.
Active solid	Merck reagent alumina, 150/200 mesh, U. S. series equivalent 140/200, i.e., 0.104- to 0.074-mm opening. Treated successively with 1.8 M ferric chloride and 3 M ammonium hydroxide, heated at 120°C for 24 hours, and partly deactivated with CO_2.
Temperatures	Injection: room temperature. Column: −195.8°C. Detector: 100°C. Combustion tube: 750°C.
Carrier gas	Purified helium prepared by passage through cold trap immersed in liquid nitrogen (to remove water), then through a column of activated alumina followed by a column of activated charcoal, both immersed in liquid nitrogen. Flow rate (exit): 112 ml/min. Inlet pressure: 1630 mm Hg. Outlet pressure: atmospheric.
Detector	Two thermistors. Gases measured as water after combustion in tube filled with 35/48 mesh CuO.
Recorder	Leeds and Northrup Speedomax, Model 6, 10 mv; 1 second; 24 inches/hour.
Sample size	1 ml.
Analysis time	25 minutes.

*3. *Separation of para*-H_2, *ortho*-H_2, *plus* HD *and* D_2 (Van Hook and Emmett, 1960)

Chromatograph	Laboratory-built.
Column dimensions	12-foot × ¼-inch coiled copper tubing.
Active solid	Activated alumina (20/40 mesh).
Temperatures	Column: −195°C (liquid nitrogen). Detector: room temperature. Combustion tube: 750°C.
Carrier gas	Helium at 100 to 150 ml/min.
Detector	Gow-Mac TE 1997 T/C cell. Gases converted to water by CuO (35/48 mesh) tube between column and detector.
Recorder	Leeds and Northrup Speedomax, type G.
Sample size	1 to 2 ml.
Analysis time	5 to 7 minutes.

*4. *Separation of Spin Isomers and Mass Isotopes with Two Columns in Series* (Furuyama and Kwan, 1961)

Chromatograph	Shimadzu GC-1A, No. 58035.
Column dimensions	(A) 200 × 0.4 cm. (B) 50 × 0.4 cm. Coiled copper tubing.
Active solids	(A) Activated alumina. (B) Activated alumina coated with ferric oxide as described in method C.IV.a.2 (Moore and Ward, 1960).
Temperature	Column: −195°C.
Carrier gas	Helium at 65 to 69 ml/min. Inlet pressure: 500 mm Hg. Outlet pressure: atmospheric.
Detector	Hot-wire (W) T/C cell. Sample burned to water at 750°C before entering detector (see method C.IV.a.2).
Recorder	Shimadzu Type 21, −0.2 to 2.0 mv, 3 seconds, 1 cm/min.
Sample size	0.3 to 0.9 ml.
Analysis time	10 minutes.

V. SUMMARY

Hydrogen can be separated from atmospheric gases by GSC on molecular sieve or activated charcoal at room temperature. Isotopes and spin isomers are not resolved under these conditions. With helium as the carrier gas, sensitivity will be low and anomalies may result unless the sample is combusted to water before it enters the detector. The deuterium content of hydrogen can be determined without resolution on the column by masking the protium through the use of ordinary hydrogen as a carrier gas. Alternatively, protium, protium deuteride, and deuterium can be resolved at −195.6°C on alumina coated with ferric oxide. The nuclear spin isomers of hydrogen also can be resolved by low-temperature chromatography on aluminum, and tritium can be separated from protium on molecular sieve at −160°C.

D. Other Inorganic Gases

I. INTRODUCTION

Miscellaneous inorganic gases discussed under this heading include carbon monoxide, oxides of nitrogen, and ammonia. Carbon monoxide is a respiratory poison, and nitrous oxide is an anesthetic (see Section E). The other nitrogenous gases are important in nitrogen turnover and soil fertility studies.

Sulfur dioxide, hydrogen sulfide, and hydrogen fluoride also warrant attention, since they are frequently encountered as air pollutants. Although some work has been done on the separation of these compounds by gas chromatography, it is not far enough advanced yet to warrant inclusion.

II. CARBON MONOXIDE

Carbon monoxide is eluted after nitrogen on molecular sieve and gives a well-resolved peak, so there is no problem in determining it in atmospheric gases. Dominguez *et al.* (1959) employ GSC for the analysis of gases liberated from blood and find that carbon monoxide is eluted in about 5 minutes at 75°C from a 2-meter column packed with type 5-A molecular sieve at a flow rate of 135 ml of helium per minute (see method D.II.a.1). The extraction of the sample is described in method A.III.b.1. Methane, ethane, acetylene, hydrogen sulfide, carbon dioxide, hydrogen, and argon do not interfere. It has been reported that anomalous results are obtained in measuring carbon monoxide eluted from molecular sieve columns (Weinstein, 1959). When detector response (in millivolts) is plotted against gas pressure (in millimeters of Hg), a curve is obtained that does not pass through the origin. At pressures of 5 mm and less of carbon monoxide, no peaks are obtained, probably owing to the presence of a small number of highly active adsorbing sites on the zeolite. Others have observed that retention time increases with decreasing water content of the packing.

The simultaneous determination of carbon monoxide and carbon dioxide in mixtures of gases requires special methods, since, as noted in the preceding section, the latter compound is bound irreversibly by molecular sieve at room temperature. Furthermore, carbon monoxide moves with air on silica gel; although it is possible to analyze binary mixtures of the gases on this substrate, more complex mixtures containing oxygen and nitrogen cannot be resolved. Since simultaneous analysis of the two oxides may be important in air pollution and toxicology studies, the need for a simple procedure is evident. Separation can be accomplished by any of the dual-column methods described in Section BII. Carbon dioxide is retarded on a silica gel or liquid partition column, and carbon monoxide, oxygen, and nitrogen emerge as a single peak. The latter three gases are then separated on molecular sieve, carbon dioxide being bound irreversibly. Carbon monoxide and carbon dioxide can be separated from one another as well as from oxygen and nitrogen on activated carbon at 170°C, but the peaks tail badly and retention times are long (see method B.II.d.1). These two gases can also be separated on molecular sieve by programming the temperature (see method B.II.d.2).

Smith *et al.* (1958) have developed a simple single-column method that is ingenious as well as practical for separation of these compounds. A flow diagram is shown in Fig. 22. *A* is the gas sample valve of a chromatograph,

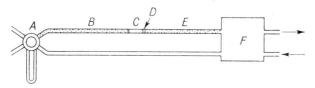

Fig. 22. Apparatus for separation of CO_2 and CO on silica gel by in-stream oxidation of CO with iodine pentoxide. (Smith *et al.*, 1958)

B a section of a chromatographic column packed with silica gel, *C* a section packed with iodine pentoxide, *D* a section packed with silver metal powder, *E* another section of the column packed with silica gel, and *F* a detector. The gas mixture is introduced into the instrument at *A*, and a preliminary separation is made on the silica gel section of the column (*B*). The passage of carbon dioxide is retarded by the adsorbent, while carbon monoxide and air pass through as an unresolved plug of gas. When this plug reaches the section of the column packed with iodine pentoxide (*C*), the carbon monoxide is oxidized to carbon dioxide, oxygen and nitrogen being unaffected. Iodine liberated during the reaction is bound by the silver metal (*D*). As the plug of unresolved gas passes through the second silica gel section (*E*), the carbon dioxide formed by oxidation is retarded and lags behind the air; the original carbon dioxide peak reaches this section later and is also retarded. Thus, three peaks are registered in turn by the recorder: first, the air peak; second, a carbon dioxide peak proportional in area to the amount of carbon monoxide present in the sample; and third, the original carbon dioxide peak. Therefore, it is possible to analyze for both oxides even though they pass through the detector as the same substance.

a. Conditions for Chromatography

1. *Separation on Molecular Sieve* (Dominguez *et al.*, 1959)

Chromatograph	Perkin-Elmer Model 154-C with gas sampling valve and 25-ml loop.
Column dimensions	2 meters × ¼-inch o.d.

Active solid	Type 5-A molecular sieve ($\frac{1}{16}$-inch pellets).
Temperature	75°C.
Carrier gas	Helium at 135 ml/min.
Detector	Thermistor operated at 8 volts.
Recorder	Leeds and Northrup Speedomax, 1 mv.
Sample size	30 ml of helium containing about 10^{-4} ml of CO.
Analysis time	5 minutes to carbon monoxide.

*2. *Analysis of* CO–CO$_2$ *Mixtures by In-Stream Oxidation of* CO (Smith *et al.*, 1958)

Chromatograph	Laboratory-built.
Column dimensions	10-foot × ¼-inch coiled copper tubing.
Column packing	Davison 28/200 mesh silica gel (5 feet)–iodine pentoxide powder (8 inches)–powdered Ag (½ inch)–silica gel (balance of column).
Temperature	115°C.
Carrier gas	Helium at 30 ml/min.
Detector	Gow-Mac Model 9193 cell with TE-II geometry.
Recorder	Varian Model G-10, 10 mv.
Sample size	1 to 2 ml at STP.
Analysis time	About 10 to 12 minutes to CO$_2$.

III. Compounds Containing Nitrogen (Gases in Soils)

The normal atmospheric gases—namely oxygen, nitrogen, argon, and carbon dioxide—are found in soils. Along with them may occur smaller amounts of nitrogenous gases produced from fertilizers or by microbiological degradation of plant and animal debris. These gases include nitrous oxide, nitric oxide, nitrogen dioxide, and ammonia.

The nitrogen, oxygen, and carbon dioxide content of soil gases can be determined by methods described in Section B, which will not be repeated here. However, it must be pointed out that silica gel columns are not useful for the separation of mixtures of carbon dioxide and nitrous oxide. The retention times of the two gases differ slightly on this substrate, but not enough to afford resolution. If the nitrous oxide content of the gas must be measured, and the carbon dioxide it contains is unimportant, the latter can be removed by including a section of Ascarite at either end of a silica gel column. This binds the carbon dioxide irreversibly and makes resolution of the two gases on the column packing proper unnecessary. If both gases must be analyzed, charcoal can be used as the stationary phase (see method D.III.b.2). Coconut charcoal (Fisher No. 5-690) screened to 60/200 U. S. mesh is satisfactory. It is washed with 0.1 N sulfuric acid, rinsed with water, and dried at 115°C. The retention volume of carbon dioxide on a 9-inch column packed with this material is 456 ml compared to 312 ml for nitrous oxide (Smith and Clark, 1960). These two gases can be separated by GLC on a 20-foot column packed with dimethyl sulfoxide coated on Sil-O-Cel (see method E.VI.a.1).

The separation of nitrogen dioxide from other soil gases is more complicated. When attempts are made to chromatograph it on a GLC column with fluorinated hydrocarbons or silicone oils as stationary liquids, sharp peaks with long tails result, and retention times are not reproducible. Evidently some type of interaction with the column packing occurs. In the absence of oxygen, satisfactory results can be obtained by chromatographing nitrogen dioxide on a column loaded with molecular sieve having the end nearest the injection port wet with water. The water converts NO_2 to NO and HNO_3 through reactions 10 and 11,

$$6NO_2 + 3H_2O \rightarrow 3HNO_2 + 3HNO_3 \tag{10}$$

$$3HNO_2 \rightleftharpoons HNO_3 + H_2O + 2NO \tag{11}$$

so that 1 mole of NO is produced for each 3 moles of NO_2. Nitric acid is strongly adsorbed by the packing and is not eluted. However, nitric oxide formed in the reaction passes through the column and gives a peak on the chromatogram. Its retention volume relative to nitrogen is about 1.5 on a 10-foot column packed with type 5-A molecular sieve and operated at 23°C. Consequently, it is readily separable from the usual atmospheric gases, and the amount present is directly proportional to the concentration of nitrogen dioxide in the original sample. However, low results are obtained in the presence of oxygen. Presumably the nitric oxide formed in the reaction combines with oxygen in the column to produce nitrogen dioxide. This in turn reacts with water, so that most of the nitrogen ultimately becomes immobilized as nitric acid. Losses incurred in this way can be prevented by removing oxygen from the sample before it enters the chromatographic column. This can be accomplished by condensing the nitrogen dioxide in an aluminum tube cooled in a dry ice bath. The tube is then purged of oxygen (and nitrogen) with carrier gas, after which the sample is vaporized and swept onto the analytical column.

Introduction of accurately known amounts of NO_2 into the chromatograph for calibration is complicated by reaction 12.

$$2NO_2 \rightleftharpoons N_2O_4 \tag{12}$$

The position of the equilibrium is a function of the total pressure in the sample tube. Therefore, the degree of association must be taken into account in computing sample weight. Consequently, it is more convenient to use nitric oxide for calibration and compute the equivalent amount of dioxide from equations 10 and 11. Greene and Pust (1958) have shown that good agreement is obtained between the two methods.

Nitrogen also occurs in soils in the form of ammonia. This compound can be chromatographed on polyethylene glycol 600 coated on C-22 fire-brick. The firebrick is washed with 1 N NaOH but not rinsed before the packing is prepared. The retention volume of ammonia on a 40 × ¼-inch o.d. column packed with this material is 298 ml at room temperature. Sensitivity obtainable with a hot-wire T/C cell is rather low, about 20 μg of gas being required to give a 0.01-mv peak. A method for separating ammonia from methylamines and detecting it with a titration cell is described in Section D.II.c.1 of Chapter 3.

a. Isolation Procedure

*1. *Separation of Nitrogen Dioxide from Oxygen* (Smith et al., 1960). *Apparatus:* A gas sampling valve similar to the one described in Fig. 8 is used. The sample loop (L) is made from 24 inches of ¼-inch o.d. aluminum tubing which is crimped with pliers at ⅛-inch intervals to increase the contact surface. The tubing is coiled to fit into a 400-ml beaker; V and I are outlets on the glass section of the loop, capped with sleeve-type serum bottle stoppers; V is pierced by a hypodermic needle to which a pump is attached to evacuate the system; I is the port through which the sample is injected; I and II are three-way stopcocks of 2-mm bore. A more efficient arrangement would be to replace these by a single twin-V bore stopcock (Fig. 11). *Procedure:* The coiled portion of the sample loop is immersed in an acetone–dry ice bath, and the stopcocks are turned to the position shown in Fig. 8A, so that the carrier gas stream bypasses the sample loop. The system is then evacuated through port V. Next, the gas sample is injected into the sample loop through port I with a hypodermic syringe. After 2 minutes, stopcocks I and II are turned simultaneously to the positions shown in Fig. 8B, so the sample loop is purged of noncondensible gases by the carrier gas stream. After an additional 30 seconds, the valves are turned to position A, and the dry ice bath is replaced with a beaker of water at 50° to 60°C to vaporize the nitrogen dioxide. The stopcocks are then turned simultaneously to the position shown in Fig. 8B to sweep the sample onto the chromatographic column.

b. Conditions for Chromatography

1. *Separation of* N_2, O_2, *plus* N_2O. See Section B.II.c.1.
*2. *Separation of* CO_2 *and* N_2O *by GSC* (Smith and C'ark, 1960)

Chromatograph	Beckman GC-1 equipped with gas sampling valve shown in Fig. 8.
Column dimensions	9 × ¼-inch o.d. copper tubing.
Active solid	Fisher No. 5-690 coconut charcoal, washed with 0.1 N H_2SO_4, rinsed with water, and dried at 115°C.
Temperature	Room temperature.

Carrier gas	Helium at 104 ml/min and 35 psi inlet pressure. Outlet pressure: atmospheric.
Detector	T/C cell.
Recorder	Brown, ½ inch/min.
Sample size	13 μg of CO_2 and 9.7 μg of N_2O for 0.01-mv peak.
Analysis time	About 5 minutes.

3. *Separation of* CO_2 *and* N_2O *by* GLC. See Section E.VI.a.1.

*4. *Analysis of* NO_2 *in Air after Conversion to* NO *in Carrier Gas Stream* (Smith and Clark, 1960)

Chromatograph	Beckman GC-1 equipped with gas sampling valve.
Column dimensions	48 × ¼-inch aluminum tubing.
Adsorbent	Type 5-A molecular sieve 32/100 U. S. mesh wet with 2 ml of water (12 inches)–dry type 5-A molecular sieve 32/100 U .S. mesh (36 inches).
Temperature	Room temperature.
Carrier gas	Helium at 70 ml/min.
Detector	T/C cell.
Recorder	Brown, ½ inch/min.
Sample size	8 μg for 0.01-mv peak.
Analysis time	8 minutes.

*5. *Chromatography of Ammonia* (Smith and Clark, 1960)

Chromatograph	Beckman GC-1 with gas sampling valve.
Column dimensions	40 × ¼-inch o.d. aluminum tubing.
Solid support	C-22 firebrick, washed with N NaOH and not rinsed.
Stationary phase	Polyethylene glycol 600 (33:67).
Temperature	Room temperature.
Carrier gas	Helium at 112 ml/min and 35 psi inlet pressure. Outlet pressure: atmospheric.
Detector	T/C cell.
Recorder	Brown, ½ inch/min.
Sample size	20 μg for 0.01-mv peak.
Analysis time	2½ minutes.

6. *Separation of Ammonia from Methylamines.* See Chapter 3, Section D.II.c.1.

IV. SUMMARY

Carbon monoxide can be resolved from oxygen and nitrogen on molecular sieve, but it elutes with the air peak on silica gel. However, it can be separated from carbon dioxide as well as from air by including a reactor unit midway between two sections of a silica gel column. CO and CO_2 are separated in the first section, and the CO is converted to CO_2 in the reactor. The CO_2 produced from the CO is then separated from the air peak on the second section of the column.

Nitrous oxide can be separated from carbon dioxide on activated charcoal, but resolution by GLC is also possible with dimethyl sulfoxide as the partition liquid.

The analysis of nitrogen dioxide on molecular sieve is complicated by the fact that it is converted *in situ* to nitric oxide and nitric acid by water contained in the packing. This is remedied by adding enough water to the column packing to make conversion quantitative, and calculating the amount of dioxide present in the original sample from the amount of oxide eluted. Low results are obtained when oxygen is present, so it must be removed before analysis.

E. Organic Gases and Vapors in Air

I. INTRODUCTION

Organic gases and vapors found in air include pollutants from factories and engine exhausts, methane evolved by bacteria, ethylene generated by fungi and higher plants, odoriferous compounds emanating from foods and fragrances, and anesthetics in expired air. All these are related directly to biochemistry, or indirectly because they represent health hazards.

Some organic compounds found in air are permanent gases; others are condensable vapors. The criterion for deciding whether material should be included in this chapter or discussed under volatile components of tissues (Chapter 3) has been determined solely by the method of sample collection and introduction. If a sample is introduced into the chromatograph as a gas, or is sorbed from free air in a trap filled with column packing, the method is included here, even though the sorbate may contain components that are ordinarily liquids. The analysis of tobacco smoke is included in Chapter 3, since the sample is burned and the vapors are condensed within an enclosed system.

Up to the present, most of the compounds that have been identified in air samples are hydrocarbons containing 1 to 7 carbon atoms; consequently, general principles governing the chromatography of these substances are discussed here. Unquestionably, many volatile oxygenated compounds will be isolated from air in the future, particularly from food and flavor emanations. However, to avoid duplication, conditions for separating them are mentioned only in Chapter 3. With a few exceptions, organic compounds are found in air in trace quantities. Consequently, special methods are needed for collecting and detecting them that are not generally applicable to the analysis of inorganic gas. In general, three procedures are followed. In the first of these, the trace constituents are concentrated by absorption in solution or on a pre-column, and then chromatographed with an ordinary thermal detector. In the second method, the sample is analyzed without concentration on an instrument equipped with an ionization detector. The third procedure is a combination of the first two. The trace constituents are concentrated and then measured with an ionization detector. This is the most sensitive method of all and can determine individual organic compounds present in air at concentrations of 1.0 ppb or less.

II. Concentration Methods

Organic gases and vapors can be separated from air by selective chemical reactions, by condensation in cold traps, or by sorption on GSC or GLC packings contained in pre-columns. The collection unit can be connected directly to the chromatograph, or sampling can be done in the field and the tube containing the sample taken to the laboratory for analysis.

Trapping methods based on selective chemical reactivity are useful when the gas or vapor can be released quantitatively and rapidly from the complex that is formed. An example of this technique is the isolation of ethylene produced by ripening fruit (Young *et al.*, 1952). The fruit is placed in a sealed chamber, and a current of air is passed through it to remove the gas as it is formed (method E.II.a.1). The effluent air is then bubbled through a solution containing mercuric perchlorate. This compound forms a nonvolatile complex with the ethylene, while permitting atmospheric constituents to escape. This solution is then transferred to a gas pipette, and the bound ethylene is released by addition of lithium chloride. Recovery of ethylene from air is of the order of 98 to 100%. Propylene and 1-hexene can be isolated by this technique also, but recoveries are lower (Huelin and Kennett, 1959). This is the only example of a selective trapping method for gases that has been disclosed thus far, but other possibilities are obvious and in fact have been explored for isolating and prefractionating volatile components of tissues (Chapter 3). Gaseous thiols can be trapped by complexing them with mercuric acetate, carbonyls by bubbling the air sample through 2,4-dinitrophenylhydrazine reagent, alcohols by reaction with 3,5-dinitrobenzoyl chloride, etc. Probably many of the trace materials found in the atmosphere could be absorbed selectively by one or the other of these reagents.

It is also possible to condense organic vapors by passing the air through cold traps, and in fact this has been done in the analysis of tobacco smoke by GLC (Chapter 3, Section B.II.a.1). However, this is not a very practical method for trace analysis, since the condensing surface would have to be very large and the tubing narrow to retain low-boiling components. Furthermore, the dead air space in such a trap would be very large. This would have to be purged with carrier gas, with possible loss of highly volatile compounds. Otherwise, large air peaks would be obtained on chromatograms when thermal detectors are used. Of course, this latter objection is not too much of a problem with ionization detectors. Nevertheless, it is much better to fill the trap with GSC or GLC packings to sorb trace components. In this case, the trap becomes a portable extension of the analytical column proper, which can be transported separately to the site of sampling.

After the sample is taken, the trap is connected to the main column by the shortest length of tubing possible, and the carrier gas stream is turned on to begin partitioning. An alternative procedure is to remove the packing and place it in the upstream end of the separation column, a section of which has been left void for this purpose. Of course this expedient cannot be used if the packing contains volatile materials that would be lost during transfer. In fact, in some cases, the trap must be maintained at liquid air temperatures until the sample is desorbed to avoid losses.

The pre-column is usually filled with the same packing as in the analytical column, but sometimes important advantages are gained by choosing a different one. Water, for example, is retained much longer than hydrocarbons by polyethylene glycol. Therefore, it should be possible to elute hydrocarbons from a glycol-packed pre-column onto a main column filled with a nonpolar stationary phase well ahead of the water peak and so reduce interference. Such expedients may be important in view of the statement by MacKay et al. (1959) that changes in apparent composition of trace components of air samples may occur when pretrapping devices for removing water are used.

The pre-column may be either short or long, but in general short columns are preferable. If the sample is collected by passing a large air sample through the packing at room temperature, partial fractionation of the sample along the length of the pre-column may result, the air functioning as a carrier gas. This can be compensated for in part by reversing the position of the column when it is connected to the chromatograph so that the direction of the carrier gas flow is opposite to that of the sample gas flow. This allows the more-mobile components to catch up with the slower-moving ones before the sample enters the main column. Premature fractionation can often be minimized by collecting the sample at a lower temperature than is used for chromatography. MacKay et al. (1959) suggest that the pre-column should be operated at a temperature 75° to 100°C lower than the partition column, assuming that the latter temperature is chosen logically with some specific application in mind. Most of their work is done with 25°C and 100°C oven temperatures, in combination with −80°C and 25°C collection temperatures. It should be noted that the low temperatures for sample collection do not imply that the pre-column is being employed as a cold trap. Concentrations of trace components in the air are usually so low that it is doubtful if actual condensation can occur even at dry ice temperatures. It is probable that the organic compounds dissolve in the partition liquid, and that the low temperature merely serves to retard their passage through the column and so avoid premature development.

Another expedient to avoid premature fractionation is to desorb the sample from the packing by the sudden application of heat. The pre-column is connected to the chromatograph but isolated from it by stopcocks. It is then evacuated, and the sample is desorbed from the packing by exchanging the vessel containing the coolant for a hot-water bath. The liberated vapors are then swept onto the main column by the carrier gas stream when the stopcocks are opened.

It is important that the length and temperature of the trapping column be chosen with due regard for the type of material being sampled. For example, West *et al.* (1958) recommend a trap containing 0.2 gm of activated charcoal and cooled to 0°C for the collection of air pollutants. They state that the efficiency of the combined operations of sampling, handling, and analysis is of the order of 80% when benzene vapor is the test material. However, recovery of methyl chloride (b.p. $-24°C$) is only 2 to 3% at 0°C. It is necessary to reduce the temperature to $-65°C$ to assure 70 to 80% recovery of this compound. Even at $-65°C$ the recovery of ethylene is only 25%. Therefore, it is obvious that a more efficient packing, a lower temperature, or both would be needed to concentrate ethylene and similar gases.

Hydrocarbons in polluted air have been concentrated in pre-columns containing dimethylsulfolane (Eggertsen and Nelsen, 1958) or di-*n*-butyl phthalate (Farrington *et al.*, 1959) coated on firebrick, with liquid oxygen as the coolant in both cases. In the procedure described by Eggertsen and Nelsen, carbon dioxide and water are removed from the air by passing the sample through a $8 \times \frac{1}{4}$-inch drying tube containing Ascarite before it enters the trap. Farrington *et al.* use a drying agent contained within the

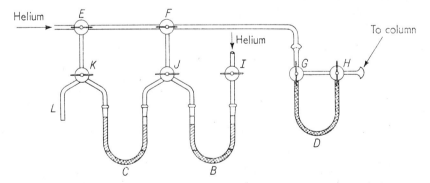

Fig. 23. Apparatus for drying organic compounds isolated from polluted air before introducing them into a chromatograph. (Farrington *et al.*, 1959)

trap placed before and after the column packing (see method E.II.b.3). Complete removal of moisture is accomplished by transferring the sample through two auxiliary traps containing column packing and drying agent before it enters the chromatograph (Fig. 23). Recovery of hydrocarbons is 100% regardless of whether the drying agent is molecular sieve, calcium sulfate, magnesium perchlorate, or potassium carbonate. However, substantial losses of oxygenated compounds are encountered with all these compounds except potassium carbonate.

In the procedures described above, the trap is taken to the sampling location for collection. However, if the gas sample can be brought to the laboratory, it can be concentrated in a pre-column attached to the chromatograph by the method described in Section E.II.b.4. The gas sampling valves of the Perkin-Elmer Vapor Fractometer and the Wilkens Aerograph have been adapted to this purpose by replacing the sample loop with tubing containing column packing. The gas sample is passed through this tube to sorb the trace constituents, and the volume is measured with a flowmeter. The trap is evacuated and heated to liberate the bound materials. These are swept onto the analytical column by turning the gas sampling valve.

a. Isolation through Chemical Reaction

*1. *Isolation of Ethylene by Formation of Mercury Complex* (Young *et al.*, 1952). *Apparatus:* The system for collection of the ethylene sample is shown in Fig. 24. Air is passed through the flowmeter (*A*), through a container of ethylene-producing material (*B*), through a bulb (*C*) which contains 2 ml of water saturated with *n*-butanol, and finally through an absorber (*D*), which is maintained at 0°C in an ice bath. The flowmeter (*A*) is used for measuring the velocity of air flow and may be a capillary flowmeter or a rotameter. Chamber *B* is any gastight container of suitable size with a gas inlet and outlet. The container shown in Fig. 24 is a 4¼-gallon cylindrical

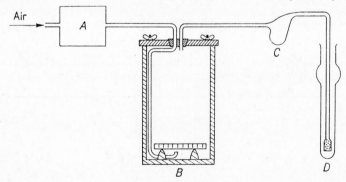

Fig. 24. Apparatus for collecting ethylene from fruit emanations. (Young *et al.*, 1952)

glass jar. Four brass rods screwed into a metal base provide a framework for the jar. A rubber gasket is placed over the top edge of the jar, which is closed by a ½-inch glass plate. Wing nuts and rubber-covered washers affixed to the threaded rods provide a means of tightly securing the glass plate to the jar. A hole in the glass plate accommodates a No. 6 two-hole rubber stopper to provide inlet and outlet tubes. The sample (fruit) is supported on a desiccator plate placed on three inverted beakers. The inlet tube extends below the plate so that the entire chamber can be swept with air. The absorber (D) is a 2.5-cm tube, 40 cm long, with a 4-cm bulb near the top. Taylor or Nessler tubes provide the material to fabricate the absorbers. A gas dispersion tube with a coarse-porosity fritted cylinder is inserted in the absorber.

Reagents: Mercuric perchlorate absorbing reagent: 172 ml of 70% redistilled perchloric acid is diluted to approximately 250 ml, and 54.2 gm of red mercuric oxide is added, with grinding in a glass mortar to dissolve without caking. The reagent is filtered with suction through asbestos and made up to 1 liter with water. *Caution: Perchloric acid should be stored by itself in a fireproof location. All surfaces contaminated with it should be washed immediately with copious amounts of water.* Sodium chloride (4 M) is used to decompose the ethylene–mercury complex. n-Butanol added to the absorber should be redistilled.

Procedure: The material which produces ethylene is placed in gastight container (B). Perchlorate reagent (25 ml) is placed in the absorber (D) together with 1 drop of n-butanol, and the mixture is cooled to 0°C in an ice bath. Water saturated with n-butanol (1 to 2 ml) is placed in the bulb (C) to replace evaporative loss of n-butanol from the absorber as air is passed through it. The purpose of the alcohol is to improve foaming action in the absorber. When the reagent is cooled, clean air is passed through the system at the rate of 300 ml/min as measured by the flowmeter (A). If blank runs show any contaminants in the air, it may be purified by passing through a combustion furnace, a molecular sieve, or brominated charcoal. During the absorption period, the solution in D should be in the form of fine bubbles filling the absorber almost to the bulb. At the end of the absorption period, the fritted tube is lifted out of the absorber and washed with 2 to 3 ml of water. The solution is made up to the 35-ml mark in the absorber or to some other suitable volume, and an aliquot is taken for the release and measurement of ethylene. Equal volumes of 4 N sodium chloride and the solution containing the ethylene–mercury complex are mixed to effect the release of the ethylene. The reaction can be carried out with any suitable gas collection equipment. One procedure would be to mix the two solutions in the Van Slyke apparatus used for liberating bound gases from blood (see Method A.III.a.2). The solutions containing the ethylene complex should be held at 0° to 5°C until analyzed. When emanations are absorbed from tissues which produce large amounts of volatiles other than ethylene, care must be taken not to prolong the sample collection period so long that the capacity of the mercury reagent for binding ethylene is exhausted.

b. Collection of Organic Compounds in Air on Pre-columns

*1. *Sampling Odorous Compounds above Crushed Fruit—Collection at Room Temperature* (MacKay *et al.*, 1959). Column packing (10% didecyl phthalate on 80/100 mesh firebrick) is conditioned by heating to drive off all volatile materials, and about 2 inches of it is placed in a small U tube. The tube is sealed at one end with a rubber septum. The air above crushed fruit contained in a flask is sampled by injecting 5 × 5-ml portions of it through the rubber septum closing the U tube with a hypodermic syringe, so that the odoriferous components are sorbed by the packing. The contents of the syringe are expelled gently each time, and the open end of the tube is smelled to determine if any aromatic materials pass through the pre-column. The open end of the U tube is then connected in series with an analytical column which may contain the same or a different packing. The tube is positioned so that the carrier gas flow will be in an opposite direction to the flow of air that was obtained when the sample was injected. This is done to reverse any partitioning of the components that may have taken place during sampling. The U tube and column are heated to operating temperature (50°C), and the flow of carrier gas is re-established. An ionization detector is required to register signals at this low concentration range.

*2. *Sampling Human Breath—Collection at Dry Ice Temperature* (MacKay *et al.*, 1959). A small U tube is filled with 1 inch of column packing that has been conditioned to drive off volatile impurities. One end of the tube is connected to a short length of flexible tubing and the other to an inverted cylinder containing water. The sample tube is then cooled with dry ice, and air is expired through it until about 400 ml of breath has been sampled as measured by displacement of water in the cylinder. The U tube is then disconnected from the sampling equipment, and its contents are emptied into a previously prepared analytical column, one end of which was left partly empty. The column is then installed in the chromatograph with the U tube packing upstream with respect to packing used for partition. An ionization detector is needed at this concentration range. *Caution: The use of volatile solvents in the cooling mixture or elsewhere in the laboratory must be avoided to minimize the possibility of recording contaminants.*

*3. *Sampling Air Pollutants—Collection at Liquid Oxygen Temperature* (Farrington *et al.*, 1959). *Equipment for sample collection:* The equipment for collecting the sample is shown in Fig. 25. Component *A* is a 16.4-liter metal

tank equipped with a needle valve. *B* is a glass U tube 15 cm high made of
0.7-cm o.d. glass tubing. It is filled to a height of 5 cm with di-*n*-butyl
phthalate coated on 20 mesh C-22 firebrick (25:75). The remaining space
in both arms is filled with anhydrous potassium carbonate. The U tube is
equipped with ⊤ 10/30 joints which connect it to the metal tank (*A*) and a
20-cm drying tube (*C*) through two sections of L-shaped glass tubing, each
of which is fitted with a two-way stopcock. The drying tube contains anhydrous potassium carbonate. *Procedure:* The metal tank is evacuated and attached to the sample collection system as shown in Fig. 25. The trap is

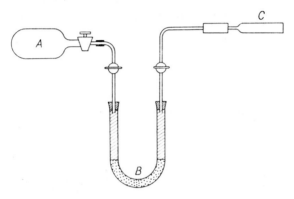

Fig. 25. Sample collection system for isolating organic compounds from polluted air.
(Farrington *et al.*, 1959)

immersed in liquid oxygen, and the needle valve of the tank is opened to
allow air to pass through the trap at a rate of about 0.5 liter/min. When
the flow of air ceases, the stopcocks are closed, and the trap is taken to the
laboratory while still immersed in liquid oxygen.

Equipment for sample introduction: The equipment for introducing the
sample into the chromatograph is shown in Fig. 23. *B* is the trap which
contains the sample dissolved in column packing. *C* is a trap of similar
construction which is filled with column packing (di-*n*-butyl phthalate on
firebrick) to a depth of 5 cm, the remaining space containing potassium
carbonate. The third trap (*D*) is made of 0.5-cm o.d. glass tubing 6 cm high
and attached to two three-way stopcocks. Traps *B* and *C* are attached to a
manifold by means of ⊤ 10/30 joints. *E, F, I, J,* and *K* are stopcocks for controlling the flow of gas through the system. Section *L* of the manifold leads
to a bubble trap. *Procedure:* The stopcocks are positioned so that the flow of
carrier gas to the chromatograph takes the route *EFGH*. An auxiliary source
of helium is attached to the system, and stopcocks *I, J,* and *K* are positioned
so that the direction of gas flow is *IBJCKL*. Traps *C* and *B* and the con-

necting tubing are flushed briefly with the stopcocks in this position to replace the air with helium. During this operation trap B is immersed in liquid oxygen. Next, the auxiliary carrier gas is turned off, stopcocks I and J are closed, and the coolant is removed from B. The trap is allowed to remain at room temperature for 1.5 hours to give the drying agent time to absorb some of the moisture. The remaining moisture is removed by transferring the sample to trap C. This is accomplished by immersing C in liquid oxygen and adjusting the stopcocks so that the auxiliary gas flow is again along route $IBJCKL$. Trap C is then closed off and allowed to remain at room temperature for 1 hour. The sample is transferred to trap D in a similar manner. Trap D is actually an extension of the chromatographic column which can be cooled to allow collection of the sample in a narrow zone, thus sharpening peaks and increasing sensitivity. Partition of the sample begins when D is warmed up to operating temperature (about 25°C).

*4. *Collection of Trace Components in Trap Attached to Gas Sampling Valve of the Chromatograph* (Brenner and Ettre, 1959). *Apparatus:* The equipment for collecting trace components is shown in Fig. 26. The container (A) holding the gas sample is attached to the inlet arm of a gas sampling valve (C) through a flow regulator (B).[3] For details on the construction of the gas sampling valve see Fig. 9. A three-way stopcock (E) is attached to the outlet arm of the valve which in turn is connected to a vacuum line and a flowmeter (F). The sample loop of the gas sampling valve is replaced by a 50-cm $\times$ $\frac{1}{4}$-inch copper U tube filled with the appropriate column packing. This may often be the same material as in the partition column. *Procedure:* The sample loop (D) is immersed in a vacuum flask containing a coolant such as acetone–dry ice. The gas sampling valve (C) is turned so that the path of sample flow will be $ABCDEF$. The flow regulator (B) is then adjusted, and sample gas is allowed to pass through the cooled column and out of the system through F. Impurities in the gas are bound by the packing in column D, and the volume of the sample is measured by the flowmeter (F). After the desired amount of sample has passed through D, the valve of tank A is closed, and stopcock E is turned to connect the system to a vacuum line to remove nonadsorbed gases. The trap must be cooled during this operation, and the time it is connected to the vacuum line should never exceed 2 seconds. Otherwise condensed gases also may be removed. If the retention volumes of the main component and the condensed impurities

---

[3] This procedure is designed for sampling gases contained under pressure. Gases at atmospheric pressure can be sampled in a polyethylene bag equipped with an inlet tube and valve. Gas is drawn from the bag through the flowmeter (F) along route $ABCDEF$ with a $\frac{1}{20}$-horsepower diaphragm vacuum-pressure pump. If the gas contains moisture, a drying tube containing anhydrous potassium carbonate should be included between sample container and trap.

are close to one another, it may be necessary to purge the trap with carrier gas. This is done by turning the gas sampling valve (C) so that carrier gas sweeps through the trap and into the chromatograph. This carries the remaining amounts of noncondensed gases out of the system. The recorder and detector should be turned on at this time to observe if any components

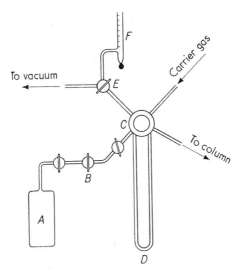

FIG. 26. Apparatus for concentrating impurities in permanent gases by absorbing them in a column substituted from the sample loop of a gas sampling valve. (Brenner and Ettre, 1959)

of analytical interest are lost during purging. When the trap has been purged sufficiently, the gas sampling valve is turned to connect it to the vacuum line in order to remove carrier gas. Again this must be done briefly to avoid losses of sample components. The trap is then closed off from the rest of the system, and the bound gases are liberated by replacing the coolant with a water bath heated at 50° to 60°C. When the column reaches this temperature, the gas sampling valve is turned to admit the vaporized materials into the gas stream of the chromatograph.

III. Detector Sensitivity and Selectivity

Analysis of traces of organic compounds present in air can be aided materially by selecting a detector that will give the required sensitivity coupled with some measure of selectivity. Thermal conductivity cells containing thermistor beads or hot metal filaments are used most often for measuring permanent gases, since they respond to inorganic as well as to organic compounds. They have their limitation for measuring traces of hydrocarbons in air samples, since they are often not sensitive enough and give high responses to the normal constituents of the atmosphere. They can, however, be used for the analysis of light gases at intermediate concentration levels. Methane in air can be detected in amounts as low as 5 ppm by a Gow-Mac thermal conductivity cell with TE-III geometry in combination with a high-gain D. C. voltage amplifier (Lawrey and Cerato, 1959). To measure amounts lower than this, a concentration step must be included. This is time-consuming and, for a gas boiling as low as methane, probably inefficient. Furthermore, the methane peak appears on the tail of a huge air peak (Fig. 27). The value of the thermal conductivity cell can be ex-

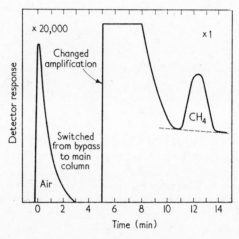

FIG. 27. Chromatogram of methane in air. (Lawrey and Cerato, 1959)

tended by concentration methods and improvements in design (Burg and Stolwijk, 1959). Nevertheless, they seem destined to be replaced by ionization detectors for the analysis of trace components, since the latter are inherently more sensitive, and at the same time selective. In particular, they do not give high responses to the normal constituents of air, namely oxygen, nitrogen, carbon dioxide, and water vapor. Flame ionization and β-ray argon detectors have been used most extensively. Each has its proponents. Both detectors are very sensitive, and no doubt sensitivity will be increased by improvements in design. Nevertheless, the flame ionization detector has one important advantage from the standpoint of trace analysis. It can measure the C_1 and C_2 hydrocarbons, whereas the β-ray ionization detector with argon as the carrier gas is insensitive to these compounds unless they are present in gross amounts. If highly purified helium is the carrier gas, the β-ray detector will respond to less than 10^{-13} mole of methane, but it will also detect equally small amounts of oxygen, nitrogen, carbon dioxide, and water vapor (Berry, 1960). Hence, selectivity is lost. Another factor that must be considered is whether the presence of an unresolved inorganic gas in the peak being recorded will influence sensitivity. Thus, traces of acetylene in nitrogen can be measured with an argon detector (Kent, 1960). The nitrogen peak is small and negative, so there is no obvious interference with the measurement of the area of the acetylene peak through tailing. Nevertheless, nitrogen in amounts greater than 0.1% must pass the detector before the acetylene peak registers, or its area is diminished.

A portable chromatograph equipped with a flame detector has been developed by Andreatch and Feinland (1960) for the measurement of hydrocarbons in air. Relative response per unit weight of hydrocarbon varies from 3.4 units for methane (butane = 4.0) to 4.9 for acetylene (see Table II). Maximum sensitivity to n-hexane is of the order of 0.001 ppm. Meigh et $al.$ (1960) use a flame detector for the analysis of fruit emanations that is sensitive to 0.03 ppm of ethylene in a 1-ml air sample. The flame detector is also valuable for continuous monitoring of the total hydrocarbons in air without separation of the individual components on columns (MacKay et $al.$, 1959). A portable instrument for this purpose with a built-in hydrogen generator is available commercially (Well Logging Equipment Manufacturing Co.).

For compounds containing 3 and more carbon atoms the argon detector is just as versatile and inherently more sensitive. For precise measurements, calibration is required for some substances having molecular weights under 150 (Lipsky, 1960). The flame detector is considerably more variable in its response to different compounds, the signal produced by methanol, for example, being only one-third that arising from an equal weight of acetylene. Therefore, the argon detector is better suited for semiquantitative work when the presence of polar compounds is suspected, and individual calibration of components is not feasible. Argon detectors can detect hydrocarbons in air at concentrations as low as 0.015 ppm. Sensitivity is improved by using a 1-curie tritium source instead of a radium source to provide the ionizing radiation. Whether or not this expedient will work depends on the design of the individual detector (MacKay et $al.$, 1959).

Other detectors for measuring hydrocarbons in air include the thermionic ionization gauge (Farrington et $al.$, 1959) and a nondispersive infrared analyzer. The ionization gauge can detect organic compounds in air in the range of a few parts per 100 million, but this sensitivity was reached when it was used in conjunction with a preliminary concentration step. The infrared method can detect compounds at the 1-ppm level if sensitivity is increased by combusting the compounds to carbon dioxide before they enter the analyzer. As would be anticipated, carbon monoxide and carbon dioxide give large peaks, making it difficult if not impossible to obtain quantitative measurements on hydrocarbon peaks eluted immediately after them. Carbon dioxide can be removed from the sample by passing it through a tube containing Ascarite. Carbon monoxide can be converted to carbon dioxide by treatment with Hopcalite, or by passing it through a tube containing copper oxide at 410°C. The carbon dioxide is then removed by Ascarite. Unfortunately, both oxidation methods result in partial losses of some components. Therefore, the method is not entirely satisfactory. In view of the higher sensitivity and selectivity of both the flame and argon detectors, it seems unlikely that infrared methods will achieve widespread application in this area.

However, there are drawbacks attendant on the employment of ionization detectors that must be overcome before they can be used to fullest advantage. They are sensitive to minute traces of contaminants, so extreme care is needed to prevent solvent vapors from cooling baths, cigarette smoke, and other extraneous air pollutants from becoming mixed up with the sample and being recorded. In addition, bleeding of the column packing through the detector can be a serious problem. This can be minimized by conditioning the column with carrier gas at as high a temperature as the packing will tolerate without undergoing excessive bleeding or thermal cracking. If columns are being used continuously, it is convenient to have replacements conditioning at all times. Even with these precautions difficulties sometimes occur, because some of the more selective stationary liquids used for the separation of hydrocarbons have comparatively high vapor pressures and will continue to give high background signals after conditioning. The only practical solutions to this problem proposed to date are the use of high-molecular-weight (and in some cases less selective) partition liquids, or interposition of a cold trap between the column and detector. Feinland *et al.* (1960) reduced the background signal caused by elution of stationary liquid from a dimethylsulfolane column by the cold trap method. They state that hydrocarbons from C_1 through C_6 are not condensed in the trap. The coolant and length of tubing are not specified in this preliminary report.

IV. Subtraction Techniques

The identification of peaks in chromatograms of complex mixtures of hydrocarbons can be simplified considerably if selected groups of compounds are removed by subtraction in a pre-column or in a reactor placed between the partition column and the detector. Thus olefins can be absorbed quantitatively on a packing containing concentrated sulfuric acid on silica gel (see method E,IV.a.1). Only acetylene and ethylene are not removed, and these are taken up if the sulfuric acid is saturated with silver sulfate (Martin, 1960). The reactor is placed between the partition column and the detector, so most of the components pass through it separately or in the form of simple mixtures. This is done to minimize the possibility of interactions between sample components catalyzed by the sulfuric acid. Saturated hydrocarbons pass through the reactor quantitatively and are recorded on the chromatogram. As a result, the pattern of the saturated homologues is simplified considerably, and the peaks for olefins are readily distinguished (Fig. 28).

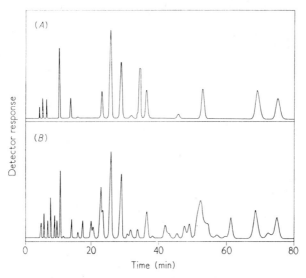

Fig. 28. Subtraction of olefins from a hydrocarbon mixture with silica gel–sulfuric acid. A, with absorber in the gas line. B, chromatogram of original sample. (Martin, 1960)

Another useful technique is to reduce the sample catalytically and compare chromatograms before and after reduction. This makes it possible to find out what paraffins are present and also to determine the nature of the carbon skeletons of the olefins. First, the olefins and aromatics are removed from an aliquot of the sample through acid absorption by ASTM method D 1019-58T to obtain a fraction containing only paraffins and naphthenes (Nelson et al., 1960). This material is then chromatographed, and the amount of each saturated compound is determined by the peak area method. Another aliquot of the original sample is reduced by hydrogen at atmospheric pressure with palladium on charcoal as a catalyst (Mitchell et al., 1956) or alternatively by hydrogen at 204°C and 500 psig over a nickel catalyst. The reduced sample is then chromatographed. The difference between peak areas after subtraction of olefins and peak areas after reduction of olefins gives the amounts of the various unsaturates present that have the same carbon skeletons as the paraffins.

A general procedure is described by Rowan (1961) for the identification of hydrocarbons by the sequential application of class reactions, which makes use of the foregoing techniques and several others. The operations are carried out in a closed system which is an integral part of the gas chromatography apparatus. A sample is injected, and a chromatogram representative of all its components is obtained by passing it through a partition column. The gases emerging from the column pass through a reactor placed after the detector which quantitatively removes a specific group of compounds. This process is repeated so that a series of chromatograms is ob-

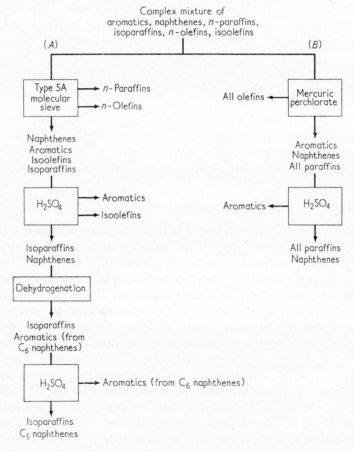

FIG. 29. Schematic diagram for systematic removal of components from a complex hydrocarbon mixture by subtraction methods. (Rowan, 1961)

tained, each lacking components recorded in the preceding cycle. A schematic diagram of one possible system for doing this is shown in Fig. 29. A mixture containing aromatics, naphthenes, *n*-paraffins, isoparaffins, *n*-olefins, and isoolefins is chromatographed per se and then passed through a column containing molecular sieve to subtract unbranched paraffins and olefins (see Chapter 7, Section B.III.a.1). The effluent from the subtraction columns contains only cyclic compounds and branched-chain alkanes and alkenes. The residual sample is rechromatographed, and the effluent gases are passed through a second reactor containing sulfuric acid. This removes aromatics and isoolefins, leaving only isoparaffins and naphthenes in the original sample. The naphthenes are dehydrogenated in a third reactor and subsequently are removed by recycling the remaining material through the sulfuric acid reactor. This leaves only the isoparaffins and cyclopentanes to be recorded in the final chromatogram. An alternative route (B) is to remove all the olefins with mercuric perchlorate, and all the aromatics with sulfuric acid, leaving only naphthenes and normal and isoparaffins to be separated on the last passage of the sample through the partition column. The total information from these parallel operations leads to a knowledge of composition according to hydrocarbon class.

These techniques will be of interest in air pollution studies only when complex mixtures containing compounds with 5 or more carbon atoms must be analyzed, since chromatographic methods have been developed for the separation of all the paraffins and olefins from C_1 through C_4, as well as many C_5 compounds. Consequently, only the method for subtracting olefins on sulfuric acid–silica gel is described in detail here.

a. Subtraction Method

*1. *Removal of Olefins on Silica Gel–Sulfuric Acid* (Martin, 1960). The absorbing mixture is prepared by shaking together 3 parts by weight of concentrated sulfuric acid and 2 parts of Davison grade 70 silica gel (60/200 mesh). By covering the surface of the silica gel completely with the large amount of acid, adsorption of sample components on the solid and resulting tailing of peaks are eliminated. The mixture is stored in a closed container, since olefins are incompletely removed when the mixture contains 12% or more water.

The mixture is packed in a glass tube 2 cm long and 0.5 mm in diameter which is placed in the carrier gas stream between the column and the detector. This position is chosen since many of the compounds are separated on emergence from the column, and the likelihood that the acid will catalyze interactions is diminished. When operated at 20° to 50°C, this packing will quantitatively remove monoolefins, diolefins, and cycloolefins through at least 8 carbon atoms, except ethylene and acetylene. When these latter must be subtracted, an absorber containing sulfuric acid saturated with silver sulfate is used. Saturated hydrocarbons pass through the tube quantitatively.

V. Chromatography of Lower Hydrocarbons

Air pollutants and the gaseous emanations of plants and bacteria are often hydrocarbons. Oxygenated compounds may coexist with them; the chromatography of these is described in Chapter 3. Consequently, the present discussion will be confined to conditions for the separation of paraffins and olefins having 1 to 10 carbon atoms. At first glance, the upper limit of this range seems high to include in a chapter on gases and vapors. Yet Los Angeles smog contains compounds such as *n*-hexane and 2,3-dimethylpentane in amounts as high as 20 parts per 100,000,000 of air. Therefore, the possibility of finding sizable molecules in gas samples cannot be excluded.

The separation of complex mixtures of hydrocarbons devolves into a number of subproblems that can be attacked individually. Firstly, it is sometimes necessary to separate aliphatic compounds as a group from aromatic compounds before proceeding with the analysis. This can be accomplished on a liquid stationary phase with high aromatic selectivity such as Carbowax 400 (Chapter 4, Section A.II.a.1). Aliphatic compounds move through columns packed with this material very rapidly without much resolution, whereas aromatic compounds of equivalent or lower molecular weight travel much more slowly. Secondly, it may be necessary to separate aliphatic compounds or groups of aliphatic compounds from one another in order of their boiling points. This is best accomplished on nonpolar stationary phases such as squalane, which do not show much selectivity for olefins (see method E.V.a.2). Thirdly, it may be desirable to separate paraffins as a group from olefins. This can be done with a solution of silver nitrate in ethylene glycol or diethylene glycol coated on an inert solid support (see method E.V.a.4). Paraffins pass through such columns very rapidly and can often be collected as a group, whereas olefins travel at much slower rates and are resolved. Fourthly, the problem may require separation of a complex mixture of olefins having the same carbon number, including *cis* and *trans* isomers. Silver nitrate in ethylene glycol, dimethyl sulfoxide, and dimethylsulfolane (3,4-dimethyltetrahydrothiophene-1,1-dioxide) are useful for this. Fifthly, separation of a mixture of paraffins having the same molecular weight but differing in chain branching may be necessary. Liquid substrates such as isoquinoline may be useful for this, since they are able to resolve such closely related paraffins as 2,3-dimethylbutane from 2-methylpentane (see method E.V.a.5). Finally, a general-purpose packing may be necessary that will permit the resolution of as many of the lower hydrocarbons as possible in a single chromatographic run. Some of the GSC and GLC packings that have been found useful in these applications are discussed in more detail below.

GSC columns are most useful for separating the C_1 to C_3 hydrocarbons from one another and from the atmospheric gases. Methane can be separated from the inorganic gases on molecular sieve, the order of elution being oxygen, nitrogen, methane, and carbon monoxide on a 2-meter column at 50°C (Carugno and Giovannozzi-Sermanni, 1958). Ethane and ethylene can be eluted by programming the temperature (see method B.II.d.2). Silica gel, or silica gel modified with a small amount of 2-ethylhexyl sebacate (Perkin-Elmer S column), can be used to separate air, methane, ethane, carbon dioxide, ethylene, propane, and propylene, in the order given, at a temperature of 50°C. The organic ester is added to the silica gel to improve reproducibility and to lower retention times. Activated charcoal is suitable for separating hydrogen, oxygen, nitrogen, carbon monoxide, and methane. The gases are eluted from a 25-foot column operated at 20°C in the order given (Madison, 1958). The methane peak tends to tail. At higher temperatures (150°C and a 20-foot column) the C_4 hydrocarbons are eluted and partially resolved, cis-2-butene emerging from the column in approximately 105 minutes. The peaks obtained on chromatographing hydrocarbons on charcoal tend to tail, but this can often be remedied by adding about 1.5% of a liquid such as squalane (Eggertsen et al., 1956). This causes the peaks to become sharper and more symmetrical and reduces retention times. However, it may also reduce the paraffin–olefin selectivity of the column. The C_4 hydrocarbons can be eluted from magnesium silicate at lower temperatures (Crespi and Cevolani, 1959), the retention time of butadiene on a 1-meter column being less than 6 minutes at 80°C. However, methane is not separated from air, and a number of hydrocarbons including isobutane and butane are not completely resolved. Better resolution can be obtained on a 20-foot column containing two adsorbents packed serially (McKenna and Idleman, 1960). The first 10 feet of column nearest the injection port contains Davison grade 62 silica gel activated at 310°C, and the second 10 feet contains activated alumina. If the column order is reversed, the separations will be affected. Either packing alone will separate the C_1 to C_3 hydrocarbons and the C_4 saturates in 4 minutes at 100°C. However, the combination of solids is necessary to separate the C_4 unsaturates. Butadiene is eluted in under 25 minutes at 91°C. Column resolution is not affected measurably by flow rate as long as the rate is maintained between 100 and 200 ml/min. The first four peaks representing hydrogen, air, carbon monoxide, and methane are crowded, but this could be improved by reducing the column temperature to 30° to

50°C. All the saturated and unsaturated hydrocarbons through butadiene are resolved, except for a slight degree of overlapping of the peaks for 1-butene and *trans*-2-butene (Fig. 30).

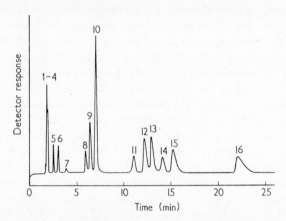

FIG. 30. Separation of low-molecular-weight hydrocarbons on silica gel–alumina. (1) Hydrogen. (2) Air. (3) Carbon monoxide. (4) Methane. (5) Ethane. (6) Ethene. (7) Propane. (8) Propene. (9) Isobutane. (10) *n*-Butane. (11) 2,2-Dimethylpropane (neopentane). (12) 1-Butene. (13) *trans*-2-Butene. (14) Isobutene. (15) *cis*-2-Butene. (16) 1,3-Butadiene. (McKenna and Idleman, 1960)

In general, hydrocarbons can be separated by GLC at lower temperatures and with less tailing than obtained on GSC packings. Furthermore, a greater variety of liquids are available, and a higher degree of selectivity is often possible. However, for the separation of the lighter hydrocarbons such as methane, GSC on silica gel or activated charcoal (see method E.V.c.1) is preferable, since this compound is not separated readily from air on most liquid packings. GSC is advantageous also when ionization detectors are used, since the packings are nonvolatile and therefore will not bleed unless contaminated with organic compounds. Nevertheless, GLC packings are very useful for the separation of lower hydrocarbons. As mentioned above, squalane is the best nonselective partition liquid for separating all classes of hydrocarbons in order of their boiling points (see method E.V.a.2). It can be used up to a temperature of 160°C. Compounds emerge from such columns in order of their boiling points, the influence of molecular structure on retention volumes being secondary. Other nonselective and semiselective packings include esters of aromatic and aliphatic dibasic acids. Examples are di-isodecyl phthalate and di-2-ethylhexyl sebacate. In general, polarity, and hence selectivity, increases as the hydrocarbon chains become shorter. Thus, di-2-ethylhexyl sebacate does not resolve 2,3-dimethylbutane from 2-methylpentane, whereas the separation factor for this pair on dibutyl phthalate is 1.18 (see method E.V.c.2). Dibutyl phthalate has been investigated as a substrate for the separation of a number of compounds of interest as air pollutants. Retention values are given in Table IV.

TABLE IV

RELATIVE RETENTION TIMES (2,3-DIMETHYLBUTANE = 1.0) OF HYDROCARBONS AND
OXYGENATED COMPOUNDS ON A 61-CM DI-n-BUTYL PHTHALATE COLUMN AT 25°C [a]

Compound	Relative retention time	Compound	Relative retention time
Hydrocarbons			
n-Butane	0.16	3,3-Dimethylhexane	5.94
Isopentane	0.38	Benzene	7.45
n-Pentane	0.49	3-Methylheptane	7.96
2,2-Dimethylbutane	0.69	2,2,5-Trimethylhexane	7.96
2,3-Dimethylbutane	1.00	3-Ethylhexane	7.97
2-Methylpentane	1.18	3-Methyl-3-ethylpentane	8.13
3-Methylpentane	1.38	3,4-Dimethylhexane	8.21
2,4-Dimethylpentane	1.80	1,1-Dimethylcyclohexane	10.3
Methylcyclopentane	2.03	1-Methyl-1-ethylcyclopentane	11.2
n-Hexane	2.15	*trans*-1,2-Dimethylcyclohexane	11.9
3,3-Dimethylpentane	2.48	Isopropylcyclopentane	13.7
2-Methylhexane	2.70	1,1,3-Trimethylcyclohexane	17.5
2,3-Dimethylpentane	2.87	Toluene	21.7
2,2,4-Trimethylpentane	3.25	3,3-Diethylpentane	24.3
3-Ethylpentane	3.34	Isobutylcyclopentane	30.6
trans-1,3-Dimethylcyclopentane	3.46	Isopropylcyclohexane	40.5
cis-1,3-Dimethylcyclopentane	3.61	p-Xylene	59.4
trans-1,2-Dimethylcyclopentane	3.75	n-Decane	87.6
n-Heptane	4.92		
2,4-Dimethylhexane	5.17		
Methylcyclohexane	5.46		
Oxygenated Compounds			
Ethyl ether	0.93	Methyl ethyl ketone	7.47
Isopropyl ether	2.24	Isopropyl acetate	8.45
Ethyl formate	2.52	Ethyl alcohol	9.7
Methyl acetate	2.84	Isovaleraldehyde	10.5
Acetone	3.06	Isobutyl formate	13.2
Isobutyraldehyde	3.35	n-Propyl acetate	15.4
Isopropyl formate	4.05	*sec*-Butyl acetate	22.2
Ethyl acetate	6.46	Diethyl ketone	36.6
n-Propyl formate	6.98		

[a] From Farrington *et al.* (1959).

Other semipolar columns that have been used to chromatograph C_1 to C_5 hydrocarbons include tetraisobutylene, dibenzyl ether, and 2,5-hexanedione. These are used at low or intermediate temperatures because of their high volatilities and would no doubt give trouble if employed with ionization detectors. Hexanedione will give partial resolution of isobutene from 1-butene at 0°C, but much better separations of this pair of isomers are now possible under more convenient operating conditions.

Separation of aliphatic compounds as a group from aromatic compounds is best accomplished on Carbowax 400, β,β'-oxydipropionitrile, or alkyl esters of tetrachloroterphthalic acid. Specific procedures are discussed in Chapter 4, Section A.

Paraffins are best separated from olefins on β,β'-oxydipropionitrile, or solutions of silver nitrate in glycols. These latter liquids cause the elution of the paraffins as a group, and at the same time yield excellent resolution of the olefins. The solvent may be triethylene, diethylene, or ethylene glycol, and it may contain as much as 30% silver nitrate. The separation of a mixture of C_3 and C_4 paraffins and olefins on 30% silver nitrate in ethylene glycol is shown in Fig. 31. The paraffins are eluted as a single peak a few

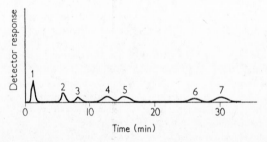

FIG. 31. Separation of unsaturated hydrocarbons on ethylene glycol–silver nitrate. (1) Paraffins. (2) Propadiene. (3) *trans*-2-Butene. (4) Propene. (5) Isobutene. (6) *cis*-2-Butene. (7) 1-Butene. (Bua *et al.*, 1959)

minutes after the sample is applied to the column (Bua *et al.*, 1959), and all the C_3 and C_4 olefins, including the *cis* and *trans* isomers of 2-butene, are resolved. 1-Butene and isobutene are eluted 30 minutes apart at a column temperature of 25°C. By contrast, these isomers are barely separated on 2,5-hexanedione at 0°C.

Branched- and straight-chain saturated hydrocarbons can be separated from one another on heterocyclic bases (Zlatkis, 1958). Quinoline mixed in a 7:1 ratio with either quinine or brucine is an efficient stationary phase. Quinoline when used alone gives only partial resolution of 2,3-dimethylbutane and 2-methylpentane. However, pure isoquinoline gives better resolution than quinoline or either of the mixtures (see method E.V.a.5).

When isoquinoline is used in series with a 3-foot squalane column, all the isomeric C_6 paraffins are resolved from one another, and cyclopentane is partially resolved from n-hexane (Fig. 32). These packings also give good resolution of mixtures of alkanes and naphthenes.

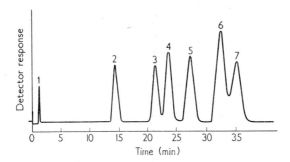

FIG. 32. Chromatogram of isomeric hexanes and cyclopentane by using squalane and isoquinoline columns in tandem at 25°C. (1) Air. (2) 2,2-Dimethylbutane. (3) 2,3-Dimethylbutane. (4) 2-Methylpentane. (5) 3-Methylpentane. (6) Cyclopentane. (7) n-Hexane. (Zlatkis, 1958)

Complex mixtures of alkanes and alkenes having the same molecular weights are well resolved on dimethylsulfolane, separate peaks being obtained for members of both the saturated and the unsaturated series (see method E.V.a.6). The C_4 hydrocarbons are eluted in the order: isobutane, n-butane, 1-butene plus isobutene, $trans$-2-butene, cis-2-butene, and butadiene. Better resolution of the C_4 unsaturates is obtained on silver nitrate–glycol columns, but the paraffins emerge as one peak. The selectivity of the sulfones and sulfoxides for unsaturated compounds increases as the hydrocarbon part of the sulfone or sulfoxide molecule becomes smaller (van der Weil, 1960). Thus, dimethyl sulfoxide and sulfolane both retain alkenes and alkynes longer than dimethylsulfolane. In Table V, the retention volumes of various homologous series of compounds on these substrates are compared. The values are adjusted graphically so that all the homologous series are represented by hypothetical compounds with boiling points of 30°C. As would be anticipated, the nonpolar comparison liquid, squalane, has very little selectivity except for chloroalkanes, alkynes, and cycloalkenes, and even these differences are small compared to those calculated for the three polar packings. Dimethyl sulfoxide shows a considerably higher degree of selectivity than dimethylsulfolane, particularly for alkynes, chloroalkanes, and alkadienes. This would be a particularly promising solvent for the resolution of complex mixtures were it not for its low boiling point. Isobutene and 1-butene are separated completely, and resolution of 2,3-dimethylbutane and 2-methylpentane is comparable to that obtained with isoquinoline.

Complex mixtures of hydrocarbons up to and including *cis*-2-butene can be analyzed in 25 minutes on a 14.4-meter column operated at 30°C.

TABLE V

CALCULATED RETENTION VOLUMES FOR HYPOTHETICAL COMPOUNDS BOILING
AT 30°C REPRESENTING VARIOUS HOMOLOGOUS SERIES[a]

Homologous series of compounds	Calculated retention volume on partition liquid (*n*-alkanes = 1.00)			
	Dimethyl sulfoxide	Sulfolane	Dimethyl-sulfolane	Squalane
2,2-Dimethylalkanes	0.8	0.86	0.81	0.96
2-Methylalkanes	0.9	0.95	0.89	1.00
n-Alkanes	(1.00)	(1.00)	(1.00)	(1.00)
1-Alkenes	2.0	2.1	1.7	1.00
trans-2-Alkenes	2.2	2.1	1.8	1.00
2-Methyl-1-alkenes	2.45	2.4	1.9	1.00
cis-2-Alkenes	2.5	2.5	1.9	1.00
Unbranched cycloalkenes	2.5	2.4	1.9	1.3
1,2-Alkadienes	6.5	5.9	3.7	1.00
1-Chloroalkanes	11.0	11.7	6.4	0.77
1-Alkynes	15.3	11.7	5.4	0.69

[a] From van der Weil (1960).

Isobutene and 1-butene also can be separated on a 50-foot column packed with propylene carbonate coated on Chromosorb (McKenna and Idleman, 1959). A number of other liquids including γ-butyrolactone, sulfolane, and adiponitrile were evaluated for this purpose but are not so effective. All the C_4 isomers are resolved, but propene is separated only partly from isobutane. This is overcome by mixing glutaronitrile with the propylene carbonate in a 30:70 ratio. When this is done, the propene peak pops up between isobutane and *n*-butane, thereby giving complete separation of all the C_4 compounds and lighter hydrocarbons. Any C_5 compounds present are eluted as separate peaks, except that isopentane partly overlaps 1-butene, and *n*-pentane is not completely resolved from *trans*-2-butene. Propylene carbonate alone produces a better separation of the saturated C_5 compounds than does the mixture. The separation of isobutene and 1-butene is not affected by the presence of the glutaronitrile.

Even better separations are obtained by coating propylene carbonate on activated alumina (see method E.V.a.7). This packing will separate neopentane from *n*-butane (Fig. 33), and by decreasing the ratio of liquid to active solid it is possible to separate most C_5 paraffins and olefins from the lower hydrocarbons. The column has an efficiency of approximately 350 plates per foot. Although this is presumably a combined GSC–GLC column, it is interesting to note that isobutene and *trans*-2-butene are eluted in the same order obtained with propylene carbonate coated on Chromosorb. On alumina alone, the order is reversed. Otherwise, the elution pattern is the same. However, the hybrid column is operated at a temperature 65°C lower than the GSC column.

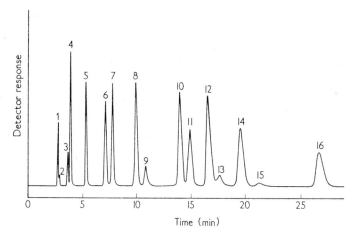

FIG. 33. Separation of low-molecular-weight hydrocarbons on alumina modified with propylene carbonate. (1) Air. (2) Methane. (3) Ethane. (4) Ethene. (5) Propane. (6) Propene. (7) Isobutane. (8) *n*-Butane. (9) 2,2-Dimethylpropane (neopentane). (10) 1-Butene. (11) Isobutene. (12) *trans*-2-Butene. (13) Isopentane. (14) *cis*-2-Butene. (15) *n*-Pentane. (16) 1,3-Butadiene. (McKenna and Idleman, 1960)

It is possible to separate all the C_5 mono-, cyclo-, and di-olefins by serial chromatography on columns packed with 1.5% squalane on Pelletex (a furnace black), dimethylsulfolane, diisodecyl phthalate, β,β'-oxydipropionitrile, and squalane on firebrick (Knight, 1958). Fractions are collected after each run and rechromatographed. All the C_6 olefins can be resolved except for one pair. The general scheme for analysis is shown in Fig. 34. Multiple-column methods with the collection of intermediate fractions and their analysis by mass spectrometry and other physical methods have proved extremely useful in the petroleum industry for the analysis of complex mixtures of hydrocarbons, but a complete discussion is beyond the scope of this book.

Special techniques are required for the analysis of traces of hydrocarbons in air because of their low concentrations and dilution with enormous amounts of atmospheric gases. Andreatch and Feinland (1960) describe a portable apparatus for the determination of C_1 to C_3 hydrocarbons in air which contains an 8-inch silica gel column for separation, and a flame ionization detector for measurement. It is said to be sensitive at the p.p.b. level. More recently, this same detector has been used for the determination of C_1 through C_6 hydrocarbons by a dual-column system (Feinland *et al.*, 1960). One column is packed with dimethylsulfolane on Chromosorb (1:4),

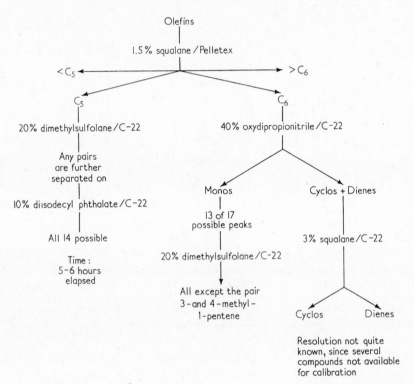

FIG. 34. Scheme for the separation of C_5 and C_6 olefins by gas chromatography. (Knight, 1958)

and the other with diisodecyl phthalate on Chromosorb W (1:9). The carrier gas is a mixture of nitrogen and hydrogen, and the column temperature is 25°C. A flame detector is placed at the outlet of each column, with a cold trap between the dimethylsulfolane packing and its detector to reduce background caused by elution of the stationary liquid. By combining data from both columns, a mixture containing twenty-six components from methane through hexane can be analyzed in 40 minutes. The minimum detectable amount of *n*-butane is 0.02 ppm in a 1-ml sample.

Methane at the 1- to 6000-ppm level can be measured with a thermal conductivity cell combined with a high-sensitivity amplifier (see method E.V.c.2). Separation from air is accomplished on a 6-foot activated charcoal column at room temperature. The column consists of a 2-foot section and a 4-foot section separated by a three-way valve and bypass line. The air travels ahead of the methane, and, after transversing the first 2 feet of column, most of it is vented to the atmosphere through the bypass line. The methane and some air travel through the remainder of the column to complete the separation. Methane appears as a small peak on the tail of the air peak. The lower limit of detection is 5 ppm, but this can be reduced to 0.5 ppm by including a concentration step in which the methane is adsorbed on charcoal cooled with dry ice.

As mentioned in Section E.II, GLC packings have been used in precolumns for concentrating hydrocarbons from air samples prior to analysis. After sample collection, the individual components are chromatographed on dimethylsulfolane (method E.V.a.6) or on di-*n*-butyl phthalate (method E.V.c.2). Retention data on potential air pollutants on this latter packing are given in Table IV.

Sometimes it is desirable to analyze for permanent gases and organic vapors in the same sample. As pointed out previously, no single packing is suitable for this, so it is necessary to use GLC and GSC columns in series (see method E.V.b.1), with the GLC packing nearest the gas sampling valve. The air passes through the liquid packing rapidly and is condensed and held in a charcoal trap cooled with liquid air while the hydrocarbons are being partitioned. When the last hydrocarbon peak registers on the recorder, the charcoal trap is warmed, and the permanent gases are swept onto the GSC column. Dimethylsulfolane and activated charcoal were used in the original publication (Madison, 1958), but any of the GSC and GLC packings mentioned above are suitable. Methane appears with the inorganic gases and ethane with the hydrocarbons.

Gaseous hydrocarbons generated by bacteria and higher plants have been analyzed by gas chromatography. Methane formed during sludge digestion has been separated from inorganic gases on activated charcoal, and the amount present measured with an argon detector (Chmielowski *et al.*, 1959; Chmielowski and Isaac, 1959). Of course this detector is really not sensitive to methane, but it was present as a major component, so probably no harm was done. Ethylene produced by fruit has been chromatographed on aluminum oxide (Burg and Thimann, 1959), liquid paraffin (Meigh, 1960), and 550 silicone oil (Meigh *et al.*, 1960), with both thermal and flame ionization detectors. The flame detector seems to be coming into increasing prominence for this type of investigation.

a. General Methods of Chromatography

1. *Separation of Methane and Ethylene from Permanent Gases by GSC. (I) Resolution of Oxygen, Nitrogen, Methane, and Carbon Monoxide on Molecular Sieve. (II) Resolution of Air, Ethane, Carbon Dioxide, and Ethylene on Silica Gel* (Carugno and Giovannozzi-Sermanni, 1958)

Chromatograph	Carlo Erba Fractovap.
Column dimensions	(I) 2 meters. (II) 1 meter. Stainless-steel U tubes, 0.6-cm i.d.
Active solids	(I) Type 5-A molecular sieve activated at 350°C. (II) Silica gel (20/60 mesh) activated at 130°C.
Temperatures	(I) 50°C. (II) 17°C.
Carrier gas	(I) and (II). Hydrogen at 10 liters/hour.
Detector	T/C cell at 8 ma.
Recorder	Honeywell-Brown.
Sample size	6 ml.
Analysis time	(I) 15 minutes. (II) 10 minutes.

*2. *Separation of C_5 to C_7 Hydrocarbons on Squalane by Boiling Point* (Eggertsen and Groennings, 1958)

Chromatograph	Laboratory-built.
Column dimensions	1500 × 0.63-cm coiled copper tube.
Solid support	C-22 firebrick (14/48 U. S. mesh).
Stationary liquid	Squalane (3:97).
Temperatures	Injection port: 100°C. Column: 25°C. Detector: ambient.
Carrier gas	Helium at 65 ml/min. Inlet pressure: 160 mm Hg. abs. Outlet pressure: atmospheric.
Detector	Gow-Mac convection-diffusion type T/C cell operated at 100-ma bridge current. Sample combusted to CO_2 before entering detector.
Recorder	1 mv; 2 seconds; 24 inches/hour.
Sample size	About 1 to 15 mg of liquid sample.
Analysis time	About 3 hours.

3. *Separation of Alkanes as a Group from Aromatics.* See Chapter 4, Section A.II.a.1.

*4. *Separation of C_3 and C_4 Alkanes from Alkenes and Resolution of Isomeric Olefins* (Bua et al., 1959)

Chromatograph	Perkin-Elmer 154-A equipped with gas sampling valve.
Column dimensions	2000 × 0.45-cm. i.d. stainless-steel tubing.
Solid support	Sil-O-Cel C-22 firebrick (30/80 mesh).
Stationary phase	Ethylene glycol containing 30% silver nitrate (35:65).
Temperatures	Injection: 25°C. Detector: 25°C.
Carrier gas	Helium at 30 ml/min. Inlet pressure: 1520 mm Hg. abs. Outlet pressure: atmospheric.
Detector	Thermistor operated at 2000 ohms and 14 ma.
Recorder	0 to 5 mv; 2 seconds; 1 cm/min.

Sample size   25 ml containing minimum of 5 ppm of trace component.
Analysis time   20 to 30 minutes.

*5. Separation of Isomeric Alkanes on Isoquinoline (Martin, 1960)

Chromatograph	Laboratory-built.
Column dimensions	34-foot × ¼-inch coiled copper tubing.
Solid support	Alkali-washed Johns-Manville Chromosorb (35/48 U. S. mesh).
Stationary phase	Isoquinoline (10:90).
Temperatures	Injection port: 100°C. Column: 25°C.
Carrier gas	Nitrogen at 60 ml/min.
Detector	Gas density balance (Nerheim, A.G., patent applied for).
Recorder	1 mv; 1 second; 1.3 cm/min.
Sample size	5-μl liquid sample.
Analysis time	About 80 minutes to 3-methylhexane.

*6. Separation of C_2 to C_5 Paraffins and Olefins on Dimethylsulfolane (Eggertsen and Nelsen, 1958)

Chromatograph	Laboratory-built.
Column dimensions	750 × 0.63-cm coiled copper tubing.
Solid support	Firebrick (20/30 U. S. mesh).
Stationary phase	Dimethylsulfolane (40:100).
Temperatures	Column: 0°C. Detector: 75°C. 60 × 0.31-cm copper preheating coils placed between column and detector.
Carrier gas	Helium at 60 ml/min and 12-psig inlet pressure. Outlet pressure: atmospheric.
Detector	Gow-Mac Model 9285 four-filament T/C cell operated at 300 ma.
Recorder	1 mv; 24 inches/hour.
Sample size	Hydrocarbons from 300 ml of exhaust gas or 5 to 10 liters of air concentrated on a 30 × 0.79-cm pre-column containing GLC packing at liquid oxygen temperature.
Analysis time	1 to 2 hours.
Remarks	Ethane not satisfactorily resolved from air and ethylene; nitrous oxide emerges with propane. Try dimethyl sulfoxide as alternate partition liquid (van der Wiel, 1960).

*7. Complete Resolution of C_1 through C_4 Paraffins and Olefins on Propylene Carbonate-Activated Alumina (McKenna and Idleman, 1960)

Chromatograph	Perkin-Elmer Model 154-B Vapor Fractometer modified to handle 60 psig carrier gas, and with drying tube containing 9 gm of Ascarite connected to inlet of gas sampling valve.
Column dimensions	915 × 0.64-cm o.d. coiled copper tubing.
Active solid	Alcoa F-10 alumina (60/80 U. S. mesh) activated overnight at 110°C.
Stationary liquid	Propylene carbonate (20.8:79.2).

Temperature	26°C.
Carrier gas	Helium at 100 ml/min. Inlet pressure: 3090 mm Hg. Outlet pressure: atmospheric.
Detector	Thermistor.
Recorder	2 mv.
Sample size	0.25 ml.
Analysis time	About 30 minutes.

b. Chromatography of Air Pollutants

*1. *Methane in Air with a Thermal Detector and a Charcoal Column with Bypass Valve* (Lawrey and Cerato, 1959). *Procedure:* A sample of air is introduced into the chromatograph with a hypodermic needle. The carrier gas sweeps the sample through the first 2 feet of column, effecting preliminary separation of air and methane. The major portion of air is bypassed to the detector and is measured at low sensitivity. At a predetermined time, usually 1 minute after the air peak registers on the chromatogram, the three-way valve is turned so that the oncoming methane zone passes through an additional 4 feet of packing before it enters the detector. The methane is then measured at a high sensitivity setting. Concentrations are calculated from the ratio of the area of the methane peak to the ratio of the area of the air peak (corrected for amplifier settings), and from a predetermined calibration factor.

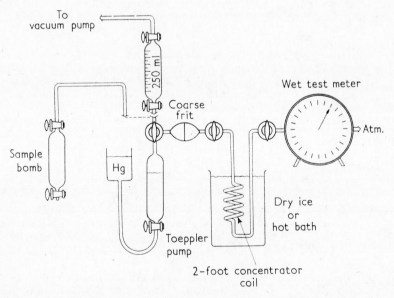

Fig. 35. Apparatus for concentrating methane from air samples. (Lawrey and Cerato, 1959)

If the sample contains less than 5 ppm of methane, it is concentrated by passing it through a 2-foot $\times$ $\frac{1}{4}$-inch section of copper tubing packed with the same adsorbent as in the chromatographic column. The coil is immersed in acetone–dry ice. The methane is desorbed from the concentration coil by immersing it in an oil bath heated to 350°F and removing the gas with a Toeppler pump (150-ml volume). Impurities should be removed from the packing by this procedure before samples are condensed. In this way it is possible to achieve a tenfold concentration of the gas, starting with a 0.1-cubic foot sample. A diagram of the apparatus is shown in Fig. 35.

c. Conditions for Chromatography

*1. Determination of Methane in Air (Lawrey and Cerato, 1959)

Chromatograph	Laboratory-built.
Column dimensions	2-foot section and 4-foot section of $\frac{1}{4}$-inch copper tubing separated by three-way valve and bypass leg.
Active solid	Activated charcoal (20/50 U. S. mesh) plus 1.5% dinonyl phthalate purged for 2 hours at room temperature with helium.
Temperature	Room temperature.
Carrier gas	Helium at 20 ml/min. Outlet pressure: atmospheric.
Detector	Gow-Mac T/C cell with TE-III geometry and tungsten filaments insulated with Styrofoam.
Recorder	2.5 mv; 1 second; equipped with high-gain DC voltage amplifier (Leeds and Northrup, Model 9835A).
Sample size	20 ml of air for sample containing 5 ppm of methane.
Analysis time	15 to 20 minutes.

*2. Separation of C_4 to C_7 Hydrocarbons on Di-n-butyl Phthalate with a Thermionic Ion Gauge for Detection (Farrington et al., 1959). Procedure: Details on sample collection and introduction are described in Section E.II.b.3.

Chromatograph	Laboratory-built with special gas handling system.
Column dimensions	61 $\times$ 0.5-cm o.d. straight glass tubing.
Solid support	Sil-O-Cel C-22 firebrick (60/80 U. S. mesh).
Stationary phase	Di-n-butyl phthalate (25:75). Carbowax 600 and dimethylsulfolane used as alternates.
Temperature	25°C.
Carrier gas	Helium at 81 ml/min. Helium purified by passing it through a column containing KOH, Drierite, Anhydrone, Ascarite, a dry ice trap, and Ti sponge heated to 800°C to remove H_2O, CO_2, and N_2. Outlet pressure: atmospheric.
Detector	Ionization gauge (Ryce and Bryce, 1957) made from RCA 1949 electron tube. Grid voltage: 16. Plate voltage: −16. Grid current: 2.0 to 2.5 ma. Detector pressure: 0.2 mm Hg.

Recorder   Varian Model G10 with 1-megohm resistor; 10 mv;
                       1 second.
Sample size   16-liter air sample dried with potassium carbonate. Limit
                       of detection: about 0.01 ppm.
Analysis time   56 seconds to 2,3-dimethylbutane under above condi-
                       tions.

*3. *General Procedure for Analysis of Condensable and Permanent Gases in the Same Sample with GLC and GSC Columns in Series with a Cold Trap between Them* (Madison, 1958). *Apparatus:* The equipment is shown in Fig. 36.

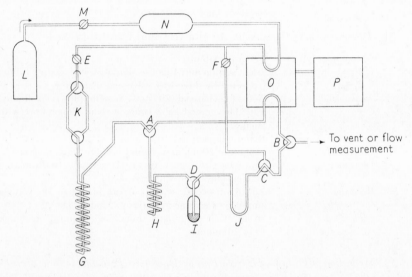

FIG. 36. Equipment for two-stage chromatography of permanent gases and organic vapors. (Madison, 1958)

L is the carrier gas supply, M a pressure regulator, O a thermal conductivity cell, P a recorder, K a gas sampling valve, and I a bubbler. G is a chromatographic column filled with a packing suitable for GLC, and H a column containing an absorbent for separating permanent gases. J is a trap for condensing permanent gases prior to passage through H. It is packed with activated charcoal (8/20 mesh). *Procedure:* The operating conditions are set at predetermined values, and trap J is cooled with liquid nitrogen. The gas sample is introduced at K with the stopcocks positioned so that the carrier gas takes route $KGAB$, venting to air at B. When the first peak (due to permanent gases) begins to appear on the recorder, stopcocks B, C, and D are turned so that the carrier gas follows the route $KGABCD$ and vents to the atmosphere through bubbler I. The permanent gases, including oxygen, nitrogen, carbon monoxide, and methane, are condensed in the cold trap (J). When stopcock B is turned, the base line of the recorder may shift, owing to a change in carrier gas flow rate arising from a difference in resistance between the two pathways. To minimize this, the vent of stopcock B is fitted beforehand with a piece of capillary tubing of a length and diameter chosen to equal the combined resistance of the charcoal trap and the bubbler. When the second peak (arising from a condensable gas) starts to appear on the chromatogram, stopcock B is turned so that the remainder of the effluent from the GLC column vents to air. The permanent gases are caught in the charcoal trap and stored there at liquid nitrogen temperature, while the remaining condensable compounds elute from the partition column. Dead space in the cell, and in the line from the cell to stopcock B, is kept to a minimum to avoid timing errors in routing the effluent gas from the GLC column. After the last component emerges from the GLC column, stopcock F is opened and E is closed. Stopcocks B, C, D, and A are then positioned so that the carrier gas follows route $FCJDHAB$, venting to the atmosphere at B. The gases within J are liberated and swept onto the GSC column on exchanging the liquid nitrogen bath surrounding the trap for a water bath heated to about 90°C. If the GSC and GLC columns are operated at different pressures, the pressure regulator must be adjusted before beginning the second stage.

VI. ANESTHETICS IN RESPIRATORY GASES

Nitrous oxide, cyclopropane, carbon dioxide, ether, and fluothane can be analyzed simultaneously by two GLC columns connected in parallel (see method E.VI.a.1). Since these gases and vapors are present in relatively large quantities in mixtures expired by anesthetized patients, a thermistor can be used for detection. Oxygen, nitrous oxide, carbon dioxide, and cyclopropane are separated on columns packed with propylene carbonate or dimethyl sulfoxide coated on Sil-O-Cel, the latter liquid being most efficient. If separation of oxygen from nitrogen is required, this must be carried out separately on a molecular sieve column (see method B.II.a.1). When ether and fluothane are present, they are separated on a 2-foot column containing dinonyl phthalate, in parallel with a dimethyl sulfoxide column. Automatic valves are employed which inject different-sized samples into the two columns simultaneously (Hill and Hook, 1960). The dinonyl phthalate column is operated at 75°C, and the sulfoxide column at 20°C, making separately thermostatted ovens necessary. The light components of the mixture pass through the dinonyl phthalate column unresolved, but ether and fluothane are separated from them and from each other (Fig. 37). The effluents from the two columns pass through opposite channels of a thermal conductivity cell. The recorder contains a device so that a negative signal actuates a polarity switch. Therefore, all the peaks on the chromatograph are in the same direction. Figure 37 shows the results obtainable on a respired anesthetic mixture containing six components. The complete analysis requires only 4½ minutes.

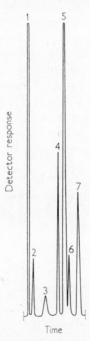

FIG. 37. Chromatogram of a respired anesthetic mixture on dimethyl sulfoxide and dinonyl phthalate columns connected in parallel. (1) Oxygen, nitrous oxide, carbon dioxide, and cyclopropane. (2) Ether. (3) Fluothane. (4) Oxygen. (5) Nitrous oxide. (6) Carbon dioxide. (7) Cyclopropane. (Adlard and Hill, 1960)

a. Conditions for Chromatography

*1. Separation of O_2, CO_2, N_2O, Cyclopropane, Ether, and Fluothane on Parallel Columns (Adlard and Hill, 1960)

Chromatograph	Laboratory-built with separately thermostatted columns in parallel, valve for automatically injecting different-sized samples into two columns simultaneously, and switch for automatically reversing direction of negative peaks.
Column dimensions	(I) 20 feet × ¼ inch. (II) 2 feet × ¼ inch.
Solid support	Sil-O-Cel (52/60 B.S. mesh).
Stationary phase	(I) Dimethyl sulfoxide (20:80). (II) Dinonyl phthalate (15:85).
Temperatures	(I) 20°C. (II) 75°C.

Carrier gas	(I) Helium at 30 ml/min and 280 mm Hg inlet pressure.
	(II) Helium at 30 ml/min. and 40 mm Hg inlet pressure.
Detector	Four-thermistor bridge with effluent from I passing through sensing side and effluent from II through reference side. Equipped with automatic reversing switch so that negative signals give positive peaks.
Sample size	3 ml.
Analysis time	4½ minutes.

VII. Summary

Hydrocarbons and other organic compounds found in low concentrations in air samples can be analyzed by gas chromatography after concentration on pre-columns, or without the use of a concentration step by employing an ionization detector. Sensitivity by both methods is of the order of a few hundredths of a part per million. All the alkanes and alkenes from C_1 through C_4 can be separated by GSC or GLC, and many C_5 compounds can be resolved. More complex mixtures can be analyzed by serial column and subtraction methods. Anesthetics in respiratory gases can be determined by GLC with a dimethylsulfolane column for the separation of nitrous oxide and cyclopropane, and a dinonyl phthalate column in parallel with it for the separation of chlorinated hydrocarbons.

References

Adlard, E. R. and D. W. Hill. 1960. Analysis of anaesthetic mixtures by gas chromatography. *Nature* **186**: 1045.

Andreatch, A. J. and R. Feinland. 1960. Continuous trace hydrocarbon analysis by flame ionization. *Anal. Chem.* **32**: 1021–1024.

Arnett, E. M., M. Strem, N. Hepfinger, J. Lipowitz, and D. McGuire. 1960. Deuterium analysis—a simple and precise method. *Science* **131**: 1680–1681.

Anon. 1960a. CO_2 with other gases. Aerograph Research Notes, Spring Issue, p. 7. Wilkens Instrument and Research Corp., Walnut Creek, Calif.

Anon. 1960b. Personal communication. F & M Scientific Corp., Avondale, Penn.

Bazinet, M. L. and J. T. Walsh. 1960. Combination gas sampler and fraction collector for gas chromatography and mass spectrometer application. *Rev. Sci. Instr.* **31**: 346–347.

Berry, R. 1960. An ultra-sensitive ionization detector for permanent gas analysis. *Nature* **188**: 578–579.

Bethune, J. L. and F. L. Rigby. 1958. Determination of the oxygen content of air in beer by gas-solid chromatography. *J. Inst. Brewing* **64**: 170–175.

Bovijn, L., J. Pirotte, and A. Berger. 1958. Determination of hydrogen in water by means of gas chromatography. *In* "Gas Chromatography: Proceedings of the Second Symposium, Amsterdam, 1958." (D. H. Desty, ed.), pp. 310–319. New York, Academic Press.

Brenner, N. and E. Cieplinski. 1959. Gas chromatographic analysis of mixtures containing oxygen, nitrogen, and carbon dioxide. *Ann. N. Y. Acad. Sci.* **72**: 705–713.

Brenner, N. and L. S. Ettre. 1959. Condensing system for determination of trace impurities in gases by gas chromatography. *Anal. Chem.* **31**: 1815–1818.

Bua, E., P. Manaresi, and L. Motta. 1959. Determination of propadiene traces in propene. *Anal. Chem.* **31**: 1910–1911.

Burg, S. P. and J. A. A. Stolwijk. 1959. A highly sensitive katharometer and its application to the measurement of ethylene and other gases of biological importance. *J. Biochem. Microbiol. Technol. Eng.* **1**: 245–259.

Burg, S. P. and K. V. Thimann. 1959. The physiology of ethylene formation in apples. *Proc. Natl. Acad. Sci. U. S.* **45**: 335–344.

Carugno, N. and G. Giovannozzi-Sermanni. 1958. Ricerche analitiche sul tabacco mediante cromatografia in fase di vapore. Nota 1. Alcuni componenti gassosi del fumo di sigarette. II *Tobacco* **62**: 265–268; *Chem. Abstr.* **53**: 7517b (1959).

Chmielowski, J. and P. C. G. Isaac. 1959. Gas chromatographic observation of the reduction of carbon dioxide to methane during anaerobic digestion. *Nature* **183**: 1120–1121.

Chmielowski, J., J. R. Simpson and P. C. G. Isaac. 1959. Use of gas chromatography in sludge digestion. *Sewage Ind. Wastes* **31**: 1237–1258.

Crespi, V. and F. Cevolani. 1959. Analisi cromatografica in fase gassosa di idrocarburi da C_1 a C_4 mediante l'impiego di silicato di magnesio. *Chim. e ind. (Milan)* **41**: 215–217.

Dominguez, A. M., H. E. Christenson, L. R. Goldbaum, and V. A. Stembridge. 1959. A sensitive procedure for determining carbon monoxide in blood or tissue utilizing gas-solid chromatography. *Toxicol. Appl. Pharmacol.* **1**: 135–143.

Drabkin, D. L. 1946. Spectrophotometric studies. XIV. The crystallographic and optical properties of the hemoglobin of man in comparison with those of other species. *J. Biol. Chem.* **164**: 703–723.

Dressler, D. P., G. J. Mastio, and F. F. Allbritten, Jr. 1960. The clinical application of gas chromatography to the analysis of respiratory gases. *J. Lab. Clin. Med.* **55**: 144–148.

Eggertsen, F. T., and S. Groennings, 1958. Determination of five- to seven-carbon saturates by gas chromatography. *Anal. Chem.* **30**: 20–25.

Eggertsen, F. T. and F. M. Nelsen. 1958. Gas chromatographic analysis of engine exhaust and atmosphere. Determination of C_2 to C_5 hydrocarbons. *Anal. Chem.* **30**: 1040–1043.

Eggertsen, F. T., H. S. Knight, and S. Groennings. 1956. Gas chromatography. Use of liquid-modified solid adsorbent to resolve C_5 and C_6 saturates. *Anal. Chem.* **28**: 303–306.

Farrington, P. S., R. L. Pecsok, R. L. Meeker, and T. J. Olson. 1959. Detection of trace constituents by gas chromatography. Analysis of polluted atmosphere. *Anal. Chem.* **31**: 1512–1516.

Feinland, R., J. J. Andreatch, and D. P. Cotrupe. 1960. Automotive exhaust gas analysis by gas-liquid chromatography using flame ionization detection. Presented at the 138th meeting, Am. Chem. Soc., New York, Abstr. of Papers: 7B.

Furuyama, S. and T. Kwan. 1961. Gas chromatography of parahydrogen, orthohydrogen, hydrogen deuteride and deuterium. *J. Phys. Chem.* **65**: 190–191.

Gant, P. L. and K. Yang. 1959. Separation of hydrogen isotopes by gas-solid chromatography. *Science* **129**: 1548–1549.

Gil-Av, E. and Y. Herzberg-Minzly. 1959. Separation of nitrogen and oxygen by gas liquid partition chromatography using blood as the stationary phase. *J. Am. Chem. Soc.* **81**: 4749.

Glueckauf, E. and G. P. Kitt. 1957. Gas chromatographic separation of hydrogen isotopes. *In* "Vapour Phase Chromatography" (D. H. Desty, ed.), pp. 422–427. New York, Academic Press.

Graven, W. M. 1959. Gas chromatograph. Ionization by alpha-particles for detection of the gaseous components in the effluent from a flow reactor. *Anal. Chem.* **31**: 1197–1199.

Greene, S. A. and H. Pust. 1958. Determination of nitrogen dioxide by gas-solid chromatography. *Anal. Chem.* **30**: 1039–1040.

Greene, S. A., M. L. Moberg, and E. M. Wilson. 1956. Separation of gases by gas-adsorption chromatography. *Anal. Chem.* **28**: 1369–1370.

Hamilton, L. M. and R. C. Kory. 1960. Application of gas chromatography to respiratory gas analysis. *J. Appl. Physiol.* **15** (5): 829–837.

Hill, D. W., and J. R. Hook. 1960. Automatic gas sampling device for gas chromatography. *J. Sci. Instr.* **37**: 253–255.

Hissel, J. 1958. Microdosage des gaz dans la vapeur d'eau. *Bull. centre belge étude et document. eaux (Liége)* **42**: 269–275.

Huelin, F. E. and B. H. Kennett. 1959. Nature of the olefins produced by apples. *Nature* **184**: 996.

Jay, B. E. and R. H. Wilson. 1960. Adaptation of gas adsorption chromatographic technique for use in respiratory physiology. *J. Appl. Physiol.* **15**: 298–302.

Kent, T. B. 1960. The determination of trace impurities in gases by gas chromatography. *Chem & Ind. (London)* pp. 1260–1261.

Knight, H. S. 1958. Gas chromatography of olefins. Determination of pentenes and hexenes in gasoline. *Anal. Chem.* **30**: 9–15.

Lard, E. W. and R. C. Horn. 1960. Separation and determination of argon, oxygen and nitrogen by gas chromatography. *Anal. Chem.* **32**: 878–879.

Lawrey, D. M. G. and C. C. Cerato. 1959. Determination of trace amounts of methane in air. *Anal. Chem.* **31**: 1011–1012.

Linde, H. W. and L. B. Rogers. 1958. Determination of water vapor in nitrogen. Thermal conductivity measurement of hydrogen liberated from calcium hydride. *Anal. Chem.* **30**: 1250–1252.

Lipsky, S. R. 1960. Comments of the theory and practice of ionization techniques in gas chromatography. Eastern Analytical Symposium. New York, No. 21. November.

MacKay, D. A. M., D. A. Lang, and M. Berdick. 1959. The objective measurement of odor. III. Breath odor and deodorization. *Proc. Sci. Sect. Toilet Goods Assoc.* **32**.

McKenna, T. A., Jr. and J. A. Idleman. 1959. Separation of C_4 and lighter hydrocarbons by gas-liquid chromatography. *Anal. Chem.* **31**: 2000–2003.

McKenna, T. A., Jr. and J. A. Idleman. 1960. Gas-solid chromatographic separation of some light hydrocarbons. *Anal. Chem.* **32**: 1299–1301.

Madison, J. J. 1958. Analysis of fixed and condensable gases by two-stage gas chromatography. *Anal. Chem.* **30**: 1859–1862.

Martin, R. L. 1960. Gas chromatographic analysis of olefinic naphthas in the three-to-six-carbon range with the aid of a subtraction technique. *Anal. Chem.* **32**: 336–338.

Massart, R. and L. Missa. 1960. A propos de la détermination des gaz dissous dans les eaux et vapeurs par chromatographie en phase gazeuse. *Bull. centre belge étude et document. eaux (Liége)* **47**: 43–49.

Meigh, D. F. 1960. Use of gas chromatography in measuring the ethylene production of stored apples. *J. Sci. Food Agr.* **11**: 381–385.

Meigh, D. F., K. H. Norris, C. C. Craft, and M. Lieberman. 1960. Ethylene production by tomato and apple fruits. *Nature* **186**: 902–903.

Mitchell, J., Jr., I. M. Kolthoff, E. S. Proskauer, and A. Weissberger, eds. 1956. "Organic Analysis," Vol. III, pp. 256–263. New York, Interscience.

Moore, W. R. and H. R. Ward. 1958. The separation of orthohydrogen and parahydrogen. *J. Am. Chem. Soc.* **80**: 2909–2910.

Moore, W. R. and H. R. Ward. 1960. The gas-solid chromatography of H₂, HD and D₂. Isotopic separation and heats of adsorption on alumina. *J. Phys. Chem.* **64:** 832.

Nelson, K. H., W. J. Hines, M. D. Grimes, and D. E. Smith. 1960. Gas chromatographic determination of C₆, C₇, and C₈ olefins according to their carbon structures. *Anal. Chem.* **32:** 1110–1114.

Ohkoshi, S., Y. Fujita, and T. Kwan. 1958a. Gas chromatographic separation of hydrogen isotopes D₂ and HD. *Bull. Chem. Soc. Japan* **31:** 770–771; *Chem. Abstr.* **53:** 13,869g (1959).

Ohkoshi, S., S. Tenma, Y. Fujita, and T. Kwan. 1958b. Gas chromatography as a tool for analysis of hydrogen isotopes. *Bull. Chem. Soc. Japan* **31:** 772; *Chem. Abstr.* **53:** 9883i (1959).

Ohkoshi, S., S. Tenma, Y. Fujita, and T. Kwan. 1958c. Enrichment of deuterium by low-temperature gas adsorption chromatography. *Bull. Chem. Soc. Japan* **31:** 773–774.

Palmer, R. C., D. K. Davis and W. Van Willis. 1960. Solenoid-operated gas sampler for use in gas chromatography. *Anal. Chem.* **32:** 894–895.

Peters, J. P. and D. D. Van Slyke. 1956. "Quantitative Clinical Chemistry." Vol. 2: Methods, rev. ed. Baltimore, Williams & Wilkins.

Ramsey, L. H. 1959. Analysis of gas in biological fluids by gas chromatography. *Science* **129:** 900-901.

Riedel, O. and E. Uhlman. 1959. Fractometrische Analyse von Deuterium im Wasserstoffstrom. *Z. anal. Chem.* **166:** 433–439.

Roberts, M., S. Laufer, and E. D. Stewart. 1947. *Proc. European Brewers' Conv., Scheveningen, Netherlands*, p. 100.

Rowan, R., Jr. 1961. Identification of hydrocarbon peaks in gas chromatography by sequential application of class reactions. *Anal. Chem.* **33:** 658–665.

Ryce, S. A. and W. A. Bryce. 1957. An ionization gauge detector for gas chromatography. *Can. J. Chem.* **35:** 1293–1297.

Seidell, A. 1958. "Solubilities of inorganic and metal organic compounds" (W. F. Link, ed.), Vol. 1. Washington, D. C., American Chemical Soc.

Smith, D. H. and F. E. Clark. 1960. Some useful techniques and accessories for adaptation of the gas chromatograph to soil nitrogen studies. *Soil Sci. Soc. Am. Proc.* **24:** 111–115.

Smith, H. A. and P. P. Hunt. 1960. Separation of hydrogen, hydrogen deuteride, and deuterium by gas chromatography. *J. Phys. Chem.* **64:** 383–384.

Smith, D. H., F. S. Nakayama, and F. E. Clark. 1960. Gas-solid chromatographic determination of nitrogen dioxide in the presence of oxygen. *Soil Sci. Soc. Am. Proc.* **24:** 145–146.

Smith, R. N., J. Swinehart, and D. G. Lesnini. 1958. Chromatographic analysis of gas mixtures containing nitrogen, nitrous oxide, nitric oxide, carbon monoxide and carbon dioxide. *Anal. Chem.* **30:** 1217–1218.

Stahl, W. H., W. A. Voelker, and J. H. Sullivan. 1960. A gas chromatographic method for determining gases in the headspace of cans and flexible packages. *Food Technol.* **14:** 14–16.

Taylor, B. W. and J. Presseau. 1959. The determination of gases in whole blood by gas chromatography. Presented at a meeting of the American Physiological Society, September 8–11, University of Illinois, Urbana, Illinois.

Thomas, C. O. and H. A. Smith. 1959. Gas chromatography with hydrogen and deuterium. *J. Phys. Chem.* **63:** 427–432.

van de Craats, F. 1958. Some quantitative aspects of the chromatographic analysis of gas mixtures, using thermal conductivity as detection method. "Gas Chromatography" (D. H. Desty, ed.), pp. 248–261. New York, Academic Press.

van der Weil, A. 1960. Two highly selective solvents for gas-liquid chromatography analysis of C_2–C_6 hydrocarbons. *Nature* **187**: 142–143.

Van Hook, W. A. and P. H. Emmett. 1960. The gas chromatographic determination of hydrogen, deuterium and HD. *J. Phys. Chem.* **64**: 673–675.

Weinstein, A. 1959. Anomalous calibration curves in gas chromatography. *Chem. & Ind.* (*London*) pp. 1347–1348.

Weinstein, A. 1960. Analytical accuracy in gas chromatography using thermal conductivity detectors. *Anal. Chem.* **32**: 288–290.

West, P. W., B. Sen, and N. A. Gibson. 1958. Gas-liquid chromatographic analysis applied to air pollution. Sampling. *Anal. Chem.* **30**: 1390–1397.

Young, R. E., H. K. Pratt, and J. B. Biale. 1952. Manometric determination of low concentrations of ethylene. *Anal. Chem.* **24**: 551–555.

Zlatkis, A. 1958. Resolution of isomeric hexanes by gas-liquid chromatography. *Anal. Chem.* **30**: 332–333.

Chapter 3

Volatile Components of Tissues
and Biological Fluids

General Introduction

Volatile materials classified under this heading include lower alcohols, thiols, sulfides, aldehydes, ketones, esters, fatty acids, amines, and complex mixtures of these substances. They may occur naturally in tissues, milk, blood, or urine, or be produced from them by autolysis, heating, microbial action, or pyrolysis. This chapter includes methods for the isolation and chromatography of compounds that contribute to the flavors of foods and beverages, and in fact the majority of practical examples of analysis by GLC are borrowed from this area of research. Terpenes and flavoring materials containing them are discussed in Chapter 5.

The volatile fraction is defined arbitrarily as the materials isolated in whole or in part by the specific method of separation employed, whether it be steam distillation, vacuum distillation, or aeration. In general, compounds comprising this fraction contain one or, rarely, two functional groups, and not more than 8 to 10 carbon atoms. The volatile fraction can be chromatographed directly, or it may be separated first into acidic, basic, and neutral subfractions by auxiliary chemical and physical methods. The neutral components can be separated further as sulfur compounds, carbonyls, etc., by use of the appropriate precipitating or complexing reagent. This chapter is organized around these groups and the methods for isolating them. Inevitably some overlapping must occur because of the extreme versatility of the methods of chromatographic separation and detection, compared to the crudity of the isolation steps.

A. Chromatography of Complex Mixtures

I. METHODS OF ISOLATION

This section includes general methods for the separation and analysis of volatile components of tissues and fluids without special regard for the functional groups they contain until after the various components emerge from the chromatograph. However, the isolation methods described below are important to all the succeeding sections, since they are useful for collecting heterogeneous mixtures which can be separated later into acidic, basic, or any of several neutral fractions by auxiliary methods.

The procedures in most common use include extraction, vacuum distillation, steam distillation, entrainment in a current of air or inert gas, or some combination of these. Separations may be made at low or high temperatures. Low temperatures minimize thermal decomposition of labile compounds but allow time for enzyme-catalyzed reactions to occur. High temperatures inactivate enzymes but promote hydrolysis and other spontaneous reactions. When volatile components are trapped at low temperatures, the main constituents are water and carbon dioxide. These are of little interest analytically and will overload the columns used for chromatography. Therefore, the two main factors that must be considered in selecting a separation procedure are avoidance of artifacts arising from temperature effects and finding of methods for the selective concentration of organic volatiles.

When volatile compounds are extracted from tissues with solvents, nonvolatile metabolites, such as lipids or carbohydrates, may be extracted also. These metabolites must be removed in some subsequent step. Furthermore, extraction with solvents such as petroleum ether is ineffective for the recovery of water-miscible compounds from wet samples, and extraction with polar solvents makes it difficult to recover neutral volatiles without prohibitive losses during solvent evaporation. Nevertheless, Hornstein *et al.* (1960) used water at room temperature to extract the flavor components of ground meat. The extract was frozen and lyophilized, yielding a dry powder that amounted to 3.5% of the fresh weight of the tissue. It seems likely that low-boiling neutrals were lost along with the water. The dry powder was vacuum-sublimed at $100°C$ and a pressure of 10^{-5} mm Hg, and fractions were condensed in traps cooled with isopropanol–dry ice and liquid nitrogen. The principal products found were tentatively identified as ammonia, ammonium lactate, and lactic acid, together with traces of methylamine, formaldehyde, acetaldehyde, and acetone.

Distillation at low temperature under reduced pressure is also employed, since artifacts arising from the application of heat can be avoided. Niegisch and Stahl (1956) applied this technique to isolate the volatile essence of onions. The tissue was minced, frozen in liquid nitrogen, and placed in a distillation flask connected to a series of traps. The system was evacuated to a pressure of less than 0.1 μ. The flask containing the frozen sample was allowed to warm to room temperature, and fractions were collected in each of three traps maintained at $-30°C$, $-80°C$, and $-190°C$. The contents of each trap were then fractionated by low-temperature distillation. Compounds tentatively identified include carbon dioxide, hydrogen sulfide, methanol, acetaldehyde, propionaldehyde, and propyl mercaptan. At least 8 hours was required to provide large enough samples for analysis, and overnight runs were sometimes made. Since the sample was held at room temperature to 30°C throughout the distillation period, it is possible that hydrolytic and other reactions occurred.

As noted above, fractions trapped at low temperatures contain large amounts of water and carbon dioxide. These must be removed at least partially, and the organic volatiles concentrated to avoid overloading of the chromatographic column. Merritt *et al.* (1959) describe a method by which volatile fractions can be enriched in aromatic components by collecting them at a series of temperatures. The sample is ground and placed in an apparatus consisting of two vacuum bottles. The bottle containing the sample is cooled to −196°C with liquid nitrogen. The pressure is reduced to 1 μ, and the vacuum is turned off, after which the coolant is removed from the sample flask and applied to the condensing flask. As the sample warms up to room temperature, the volatiles distill over into the second flask. At this point they consist mostly of carbon dioxide and water. Carbon dioxide is removed by distilling from a flask held at −80°C into a trap held at −196°C. Hydrogen sulfide, carbonyl sulfide, and the organic volatiles are found in the −196°C trap along with carbon dioxide, while water and a trace of the volatiles remain in the −80°C flask. The aromatic materials are separated from CO_2, H_2S, and COS by distilling at −140°C and 1 μ of pressure into a trap held at −196°C. The organic volatiles remain in the boiler, while CO_2, H_2S, and COS are trapped in the receiver. Further separations can be made by the same procedure, with the sample flask held at any predetermined temperature with suitable coolant mixtures. The general procedure is outlined in Table I.

This procedure does not give clean-cut separations, but it does provide a means by which aromatic components can be separated partially from

TABLE I

CONDITIONS FOR SEPARATION OF ORGANIC VOLATILES
FROM CARBON DIOXIDE AND WATER[a]

| | Distillation flask | | Receiver | |
Step	Temperature (°C)	Final contents	Temperature (°C)	Final contents
1	Room	Nonvolatiles	−196	Total volatiles
2	−80	Water plus slightly volatile components	−196	CO_2 plus volatiles
3	−140	Main volatile fraction	−196	CO_2 plus H_2S

[a] From Merritt *et al.* (1959).

carbon dioxide and water prior to chromatography. A better system for accomplishing this on a pre-column connected directly to the chromatograph is described in detail below (Rhoades, 1958).

Distillation at reduced pressure and a temperature of 40°C was used by Haagen-Smit *et al.* (1945) to isolate the volatile components of pineapple. Fractions were collected at 0°C, −80°C, and −185°C. The low-temperature trap contained mostly carbon dioxide. The −80°C and wet ice traps contained water–oil condensates consisting of esters, carbonyl compounds, sulfur-containing compounds, and alcohols. This method can also be used to isolate volatiles from liquids. Wynn *et al.* (1960) distilled milk under 1 inch of vacuum at a temperature of 50°C. Nitrogen was bubbled through the milk to displace the air and entrain the aromatic materials. Volatile compounds were fractionated by passing the gas stream through a series of traps held at 0°C, −60°C, and −185°C. Most of the water condensed at 0°C, and most of the flavor components at −185°C. Small amounts of water and aromatics condensed in the −60°C traps and were transferred to the liquid air trap by an additional distillation. Most of the flavor components were removed from the milk in 3 hours. The contents of the −185°C trap were vaporized at 100°C and introduced into a chromatograph through a modified gas sampling valve.

Distillation at reflux temperature with or without a current of air or inert gas to entrain the volatiles has been employed by a number of workers. This probably results in decomposition of some heat-labile compounds and leads to the creation of others through hydrolysis. However, such techniques are of value for reproducing the odors of cooked foods. Jackson and Hussong (1958) isolated lower fatty alcohols and ketones from cheese by steam distillation at atmospheric pressure. The distillate was neutralized, saturated with salt, and extracted with diethyl ether. The neutral components in the ether layer were recovered by careful evaporation of the solvent. This method is probably satisfactory for the range of compounds studied (C_5 to C_9) but homologues of lower molecular weight would be lost through unfavorable partition ratios or during solvent removal.

Kramlich and Pearson (1960) studied the compounds responsible for the odors of cooked meat by making a slurry of the ground material with water and cooking it for 5 to 7 hours with a stream of nitrogen constantly bubbling through it. The volatiles entrained by the nitrogen were condensed in traps cooled by wet ice, ethanol–dry ice, and liquid air, connected in series. Water condensed in the wet ice traps and was discarded. Volatiles in the dry ice and liquid air traps were vaporized by a hot oil bath or Bunsen flame and swept into the chromatograph with carrier gas.

Nawar and Fagerson (1960) have developed a simple method for the entrainment of volatiles from food samples by recycling a gas through the food sample and a cold trap. A tube packed with K_2CO_3 is placed between the sample flask and the collection tube to remove moisture and still allow sample volatiles to pass through. A pulsating pump circulates the gas and permits continuous gas–liquid extraction which gives high recovery of volatiles. Since the system is closed and at atmospheric pressure, sample loss is at a minimum.

The sample is then introduced into the chromatograph by an attachment at the injection port. The collection trap is transferred to the introduction assembly where the sample is volatilized under reduced pressure and then injected by passing a stream of gas through the assembly under pressure 5 psig higher than the column pressure. This system of sample introduction gives good recoveries of the components tested with boiling points ranging from 27° to 175.5°C.

Rhoades (1958) described an excellent method for the collection of volatiles and their partial separation from water and carbon dioxide. The method was originally devised for the study of coffee aroma, but it can be used to strip volatiles from any partially dry ground material through which gas will flow freely. The sample is placed in a chamber heated to 100°C (or any other convenient temperature), and the volatiles are removed by a stream of warm, moist helium. The gas is passed through a cold condenser that removes most of the water. The volatiles that pass through the condenser are collected in a trap cooled with liquid nitrogen. The sample at this stage consists mostly of water and carbon dioxide. The greater part of these components is removed by including a pre-column in the gas stream so that compounds with retention times greater than that of carbon dioxide but less than that of water can be re-collected. Small amounts of carbon dioxide and water are also re-collected, but not enough to overload the analytical column. The re-collected sample is vaporized and swept into the chromatograph with carrier gas. Provision is made for the introduction of an internal standard during sample collection.

Two types of sample introduction system are described below, one by Rhoades (1958) and one by Nawar and Fagerson (1960). The Rhoades system is connected with the sample collection system, and the sample is introduced at the gas sampling valve. This has an advantage over the Nawar and Fagerson method, since in the Rhoades method the trap is not dismounted from the collection system and remounted in the introduction assembly. However, good recoveries of sample volatiles are obtained with the Nawar and Fagerson procedure, where the assembly is mounted at the injection port. Short tubing lengths minimize condensation of sample in the introduction tube, and, since good vacuum can be achieved, rapid volatilization of high-boiling materials is obtained.

a. Separation of Volatiles at Low Temperatures

1. Water Extraction and Lyophilization (Hornstein *et al.*, 1960). *Extraction:* Meat (1.5 kg) is trimmed and ground in an electric grinder at 32°F. The macerated tissue (1 kg) is blended for 1 minute with ice-cold distilled water (1.5 liters). After standing overnight at 32°F, the slurry is reblended for 1 minute and centrifuged at 4000 rpm for 20 minutes in a refrigerated centrifuge regulated at a temperature of 28°C. The supernatant liquid is decanted, mixed with 1% (w/v) Filter-aid, and filtered under vacuum through a Büchner funnel. The filtrate is frozen in a dry ice–propanol bath and lyophilized. The yield of dry powder is about 3.5% of the weight of the fresh tissue. *Fractionation:* A schematic diagram of the apparatus for fractionation is shown in Fig. 1. *A* is the sample chamber, and *C* a vapor jacket

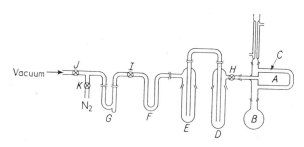

Fig. 1. Vacuum system for fractionation of volatile flavor components: (*A*) sample chamber; (*B*) boiling flask; (*C*) jacket; (*D, E, F, G*) traps; (*H, I, J, K*) vacuum stopcocks. (Hornstein *et al.*, 1960).

which heats the contents of *A* with steam from boiling water contained in flask *B*. *D*, *E*, *F*, and *G* are traps. A vacuum of better than 10^{-5} mm Hg is maintained on the system by a two-stage oil diffusion pump backed by a mechanical vacuum pump. Dried powder obtained by lyophilization (30 to 35 gm) is placed in *A*, and traces of moisture are removed by evacuating the system to a pressure of 10^{-5} cm of mercury for 4 hours at room temperature. A Dewar flask containing liquid nitrogen is then placed around trap *D*. With the same vacuum maintained, the solvent (water) in *B* is brought to a boil, and heating is continued for 6 hours. At the end of the heating period, the vacuum stopcocks at *H* and *J* are turned off, and the liquid nitrogen container is removed from *D* and placed around *G*. A dry ice–propanol mixture is placed around trap *E*. Spontaneous distillation takes place as trap *D* heats to room temperature. After 16 hours, dry nitrogen is admitted into the system. Trap *D* contains a small amount of a colorless viscous water-soluble liquid. Trap *G* contains the very low-boiling materials, and trap *E* the intermediate-boiling materials. The apparatus is so designed that an additional fraction can be collected in F if desired.

2. *Low-Temperature Distillation* (Haagen-Smit *et al.*, 1945). A 12-liter Pyrex balloon flask is connected in turn to a spiral glass condenser, a flask held at room temperature, three flasks immersed in an ice–salt bath, three flasks cooled to $-80°C$, and finally a trap cooled with liquid air. Fruit is chopped into small pieces and placed in the 12-liter flask. Distillation is carried out at a pressure of 20 mm Hg with the temperature of the flask kept below 40°C at all times. The condensates in the flask held at room temperature, and in the traps cooled with wet ice, are returned to the boiler and topped to remove volatile materials. By this procedure the desired components are collected in the third receiver cooled with wet ice and in the $-80°C$ traps. The trap cooled with liquid air contains mostly carbon dioxide. The oil–aqueous condensates from the traps are combined, and the water phase is saturated with ammonium sulfate. The oil layer is separated and dried over anhydrous sodium sulfate. The water remaining in the still and the aqueous condensates in the traps are extracted repeatedly with ethyl ether. The ether layers are combined, dried over anhydrous sodium sulfate, and the solvent carefully removed by evaporation.

b. Separation of Volatiles at Reflux Temperature

1. *Steam Distillation of Cheese Volatiles* (Jackson and Hussong, 1958). The cheese sample (2 pounds) is mixed with distilled water in a Waring blendor. The suspension is transferred to a round-bottomed flask and steam-distilled until 1 liter of solution is collected. The distillate is adjusted to a phenolphthalein end point with sodium carbonate and saturated with sodium chloride. Next, it is extracted with 2 × 150-ml portions of diethyl ether, and the extracts are dried over anhydrous sodium sulfate. The volatiles are concentrated by cautious evaporation of the solvent, and an aliquot of the ether solution is injected into the chromatograph.

*2. *Separation from Aqueous Slurries by Nitrogen Entrainment* (Kramlich and Pearson, 1960). Ground meat (1 kg) is added to deionized distilled water (3 liters) and mixed thoroughly in a food blendor. The slurry is then poured into a three-necked round-bottomed flask of 12-liter capacity. The flask is connected to four traps in series. The first trap is surrounded by a beaker of wet ice, the second by a beaker containing ethanol and dry ice, and the third and fourth traps are immersed in liquid air. The meat slurry is cooked for 5 to 7 hours with a stream of nitrogen gas constantly bubbling through it and the traps. After cooking is completed, the traps are disconnected and stoppered. The trap immersed in wet ice contains mostly condensed water and is discarded. Each trap cooled with dry ice or liquid air is connected in turn to a gas chromatograph, and its contents are vaporized by immersing the trap in a hot oil bath, or by heating it directly with a Bunsen flame. Carrier gas is then swept through the trap for 15 seconds to flush the volatiles out of the trap and onto the analytical column.

*3. *Separation from Aqueous Slurries by Recycling a Sweep Gas and Introduction into the Chromatograph* (Nawar and Fagerson, 1960; Nawar *et al.*, 1960). The food slurry (about 500 ml) is placed in a 1-liter two-necked round-bottomed flask (*A*, Fig. 2). Gas is cycled through the system. A tube with a

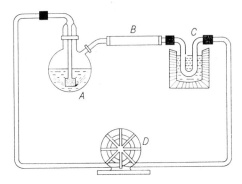

FIG. 2. System for the collection of food volatiles. (Nawar and Fagerson, 1960).

sintered-glass tip extends into the slurry to aid in sweep gas dispersion. *B* is a drying tube packed with anhydrous K_2CO_3 to remove moisture from the gas with minimal adsorption of sample volatiles. *C* is a stainless-steel U tube cooled with a refrigerant for collection of volatile materials, and *D* is a pulsating pump (Model OV-20, Sigmamotor, Inc.). The sweep gas, time of sweeping, and temperature of sample depend on the materials to be studied.

To introduce the sample into the chromatograph, the sample collection tube (*C*) in Fig. 2 is removed and fitted to the sample introduction assembly by Swagelok fittings while still immersed in liquid nitrogen (*A* in Fig. 3). Serum caps are fitted over the ends of the trap during the transfer to avoid contamination. Valve *C* is opened, and vacuum is applied at *E* to reduce the pressure to about 50 μ. Valve *C* is then closed, the liquid nitrogen is removed, and heat is applied to trap *A* by passing an electric current through the trap by means of a filament transformer (*F*) and a variable transformer (*G*). Time and temperature of heating can be determined experimentally. The volatilized sample is injected by passing a stream of helium through *E* at a pressure 5 psig higher than the column pressure, and opening valves *C* and *B*.

*4. *Entrainment of Volatiles from Solids in a Helium Stream and Introduction into the Chromatograph* (Rhoades, 1958). A diagram of the apparatus is shown

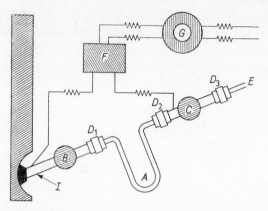

Fig. 3. Assembly for the introduction of volatile sample condensates into the chromatograph; (A) ¼-inch stainless-steel trap; (B, C) toggle valves; (D) stainless-steel fittings with O rings; (E) lead; (F) filament transformer; (G) variable transformer; (I) injection block. (Nawar *et al.*, 1960).

in Fig. 4. The ground sample is placed in tube E, the dimensions of which are such that it can be immersed in a 2-liter beaker (P) of boiling water to a depth sufficient to avoid water condensation at the top of E-3. H is a Carbowax column 10 inches in over-all length, which removes excess water and carbon dioxide from the sample. Before using this column it is first necessary to find out how long it takes carbon dioxide and water to elute from it so that the correct time for collecting the main sample can be judged. This is done by connecting the pre-column directly to the detector of the chromatograph and finding out how long it takes carbon dioxide and water to give a

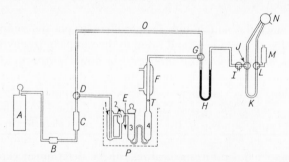

Fig. 4. Apparatus for the entrainment of volatiles from solids, and introduction into the chromatograph: (A) helium source; (B) flow throttle; (C) flowmeter; (D) three-way stopcock; (E) coffee sampling apparatus; (F) ice water condenser; (G) three-way stopcock; (H) preliminary column; (I) three-way stopcock, vent and vacuum line; (J) three-way stopcock; (K) trap; (L) three-way stopcock; (M) flowmeter; (N) sampling valve; (O) bypass helium line; (P) two-liter beaker; (T) silicone seal. (Rhoades, 1958).

trace on the recorder when volatiles condensed from a preliminary sample are swept through it. The flow rate of the helium is controlled by a glass capillary (B) and a pressure regulator at the helium tank (A). The pressure regulator is set at 10 psig. Rotameters at C and M measure the flow rate of the helium. Stopcocks at D and G direct the gas stream either through the sample chamber (E) or through the bypass line (O). Stopcocks at I, J, and L control the flow of the gas stream at various steps in the sample collection procedure, during evacuation of trap K, and on introduction of the sample into the chromatograph. The sample chamber (E) consists of four parts: (1) a bubble chamber for moistening the helium, (2) a trap to prevent entrained liquid from being swept into the sample, (3) the chamber which holds the sample, and (4) an auxiliary chamber to hold the liquid condensed by F. A silicone rubber seal is placed in the line at T for introducing the internal standard with a syringe. The components of the sampling equipment are connected to one another by butt joints and small pieces of Tygon tubing. All connecting lines are 0.7-cm glass tubing with the exception of the connections between the gas sampling valve (N) and stopcocks J and L. These lines are ¼-inch copper tubing. They are connected to the stopcock arms by butt joints and Tygon tubing.

Preparation of pre-column: Carbowax 1500 is coated on 40/60 mesh C-22 firebrick in the usual way at a 20:80 ratio of liquid to support. The material is packed into a 10-inch × 7-mm glass U tube. A plug of glass wool 1 inch long is placed above the column packing in the arm of the U tube directly connected to the sample holder.

Sampling procedure: The stopcocks are turned so that the flow of helium bypasses the sample container and takes the route *DOGHIJKL*, venting to the atmosphere through rotameter M. Distilled water (25 ml) is placed in the bubbler tube E-1, and a sample of the material to be analyzed (10 to 15 gm) is ground to about 20/40 mesh and placed in the sample compartment E-3. The internal standard is injected into the gas line at T with a syringe equipped with a Chaney adaptor. Column H is immersed in liquid nitrogen contained in a Dewar flask. The liquid nitrogen level should be about 1½ inches above the column packing so that the volatile materials condense on a plug of glass wool placed in tube H just above the partitioning liquid. Stopcocks D and G are now positioned so that the sweep gas flows through the sample compartment. The sampling unit, with the exception of condenser F, is immersed in hot water, and volatiles are collected for a period of 1 hour. At the end of the collection period the gas stream is diverted once more along the route *DOGHIJKL*, and the unit holding the sample is removed from the system. The flask holding the liquid nitrogen is removed from column H and is replaced by an empty Dewar flask. A stop watch is started at the time of removal of the coolant from H, and, when enough time has elapsed for elution of carbon dioxide from H as determined by previous experiments, trap K is immersed in liquid nitrogen so that the volatiles (other than carbon dioxide and water) can be re-collected. After 4 minutes, the empty Dewar flask is removed from H and replaced by a flask containing water at 60°C. The level of the warm water should be above that of the condensate in H to ensure rapid vaporization of the water and higher-boiling volatiles. Re-collection of the sample in trap K should be continued until water begins to elute from H as determined by preliminary experiments. This usually happens in about 13 minutes. Next, the helium stream is momentarily vented to the atmosphere through stopcock I which is now disconnected from the sample holder. A vacuum line is connected to stopcock I, and the level of liquid nitrogen is raised on trap K so that it will be above any condensate in the trap. Stopcocks I, J, and L are properly positioned, and the trap K is evacuated by means of the vacuum line attached at I. Stopcocks J and L are now positioned so that trap K is connected directly to the gas sampling valve at N. The Dewar flask containing liquid nitrogen is removed from trap K and replaced by hot water to vaporize the re-collected sample. The gas sampling valve at N is turned so that the carrier gas stream of the chromatograph sweeps through K along route $NJKLN$, carrying the volatilized sample with it onto the partitioning column. During chromatography the pre-column H is swept free of water with helium in preparation for the next sample.

II. IDENTIFICATION OF FUNCTIONAL GROUPS

Samples of volatile materials isolated by the foregoing methods are complex mixtures which may contain amines, thiols, esters, etc. These can be separated into subfractions prior to chromatography by methods described in the following sections, or else they can be analyzed per se, making use of the high resolving power of the gas chromatograph to separate compounds having the same and different functional groups. In such cases, it is usually desirable to trap fractions and characterize them by the functional groups they contain. Identification by mass, infrared, or nuclear magnetic resonance spectra is mandatory for unequivocal results, but simple chemical tests frequently will yield useful preliminary information.

These tests can be carried out by bubbling the effluent gas through test solutions just after the appearance of each peak, or by collecting the fractions in cold traps and analyzing them later. When time is not a factor, the latter technique is preferred, since smaller volumes of solvents can be used and higher sensitivities attained. Furthermore, portions of the sample can be reserved for infrared analysis.

Volatile acids and amines can be detected with acid-base indicators. With a titration cell as the detector, these are the only materials that appear on the chromatograph. Amines can be identified also by the Hinsberg test. Primary or secondary amines yield yellow colors. With tertiary amines a rose to purple color is obtained.

Carbon dioxide can be identified by the formation of a white precipitate of calcium carbonate when the effluent gas is bubbled through lime water. Primary, secondary, and tertiary alcohols form red solvates when solutions containing them are mixed with vanadium oxinate in benzene. Alternatively, they can be detected by the xanthate–molybdenum reaction, but this test is not so sensitive (Feigl, 1956) as the oxinate method. Carbonyl compounds yield insoluble hydrazones on reaction with 2,4-dinitrophenylhydrazine solution in 2 N mineral acid. Aldehydes can sometimes be distinguished from ketones by the fact that they react rapidly with o-anisidine to form colored Schiff bases, whereas ketones give colors only when present in very large amounts. The presence of esters can be shown by converting them to hydroxamic acids and developing violet colors with ferric chloride. Or they can be hydrolyzed to their component alcohols and acids with aqueous sodium hydroxide solution, and these constituents measured independently by isolating and chromatographing them (see Section B). The presence of thiols is indicated by the formation of yellow to yellow-brown precipitates on treatment with aqueous cupric chloride, but the catalytic production of gaseous nitrogen when solutions containing them are treated with sodium azide–iodine reagent is a much more sensitive indicator. Methyl sulfide precipitates mercury from mercurous acetate even when water is absent (Faragher et al., 1929). Other alkyl sulfides react similarly but only in the presence of water. Thus, the formation of metallic mercury on treating the condensate with aqueous mercurous chloride should indicate the possible presence of organic sulfides. Aromatic nuclei and aliphatic unsaturation can be detected by the LeRosen test. A wine-red color is obtained when compounds of this type are collected in a formaldehyde–sulfuric acid solution. Details of these tests are described below.

a. Qualitative Tests for Functional Groups

1. *Detection of Amines* (Walsh and Merritt, 1960). *Hinsberg test:* The effluent is bubbled into 5 drops of pyridine and 1 drop of 5% NaOH. After the sample is collected, 1 to 2 drops of benzenesulfonyl chloride are added. With primary or secondary amines, the solution will be colorless to yellow. With tertiary amines a rose to deep purple color will be obtained. The minimum detectable amount is about 100 μg.

2. *Detection of Alcohols* (Feigl and Stark, 1955). One milliliter of a sodium vanadate solution containing 1 mg of vanadium is treated with 1 ml of a 2.5% solution of 8-hydroxyquinoline in 6% acetic acid solution. The mixture is shaken with 30 ml of benzene to extract the complex that is formed.

The benzene solution is gray-green in color. It will keep for about 1 day. *Procedure:* The condensate in the fraction collector is dissolved in 1 drop of benzene and transferred to a microtest tube together with 4 drops of vanadium oxinate in benzene. The mixture is heated in a water bath at 60°C with occasional shaking. The color of the benzene solution changes from gray-green to red in about 2 to 8 minutes if measurable amounts of alcohols are present. Primary, secondary, and tertiary alcohols all form red solvates with the vanadium oxinate. Thiols give a green color under these conditions. The minimum detectable amount is about 20 μg of alcohol.

3. *Detection of Carbonyl Compounds.* A drop of 0.2% solution of 2,4-dinitrophenylhydrazine in 2 N hydrochloric acid is added to the contents of the fraction collector. A yellow-red precipitate forms if aldehydes or ketones are present. Aldehydes can frequently be distinguished from ketones by treatment with *o*-dianisidine, since the ketones do not give color tests with this reagent unless present in large amounts (Wasicky and Frehden, 1937). The condensate is dissolved in a drop of glacial acetic acid and added to 3 to 4 drops of a saturated solution of *o*-dianisidine in glacial acetic acid. The mixture is transferred to a microcrucible and heated. Orange to yellow colors appear if aldehydes are present. The lower limit of detection for acetaldehyde is about 30 μg.

4. *Detection of Esters by the Hydroxamic Acid Method* (Feigl, 1956). The condensate is dissolved in a drop of ether and transferred to a porcelain microcrucible together with a drop of saturated alcoholic hydroxylamine hydrochloride solution and a drop of saturated alcoholic potassium hydroxide solution. The mixture is heated over a microflame until slight bubbling begins. Next it is cooled, acidified with the minimum amount of 0.5 N hydrochloric acid, and a drop of 1% ferric chloride solution added. A violet color develops if an ester is present. A minimum of 2 μg of ethyl acetate can be detected.

5. *Detection of Thiols by Catalysis of Azide–Iodine Reaction* (Feigl, 1934). *Reagent:* Three grams of sodium azide is dissolved in 100 ml of 0.1 N iodine solution. *Procedure:* The condensate is dissolved in 1 drop of ethanol and transferred to a watch glass together with 1 drop of iodine–azide reagent. If thiols are present, small bubbles of nitrogen will appear, owing to catalysis of the reaction between iodine and the azide by the sulfur compound. In the

$$2NaN_3 + I_2 \rightarrow 2NaI + 3N_2$$

absence of catalysts this does not take place at an observable rate. Thioethers and disulfides have little or no effect on the rate of the reaction. The method is sensitive to 10^{-2} to 10^{-4} gm of thiol.

6. *Detection of Aromatic Nuclei and Aliphatic Unsaturation* (Walsh and Merritt, 1960). *LeRosen test:* The eluate is bubbled into a solution of 10 drops of

concentrated sulfuric acid plus 1 drop of 37% formaldehyde. A wine-red color will develop if aromatic nuclei or aliphatic unsaturation is present.

III. CHROMATOGRAPHY

Complex mixtures of volatile compounds usually contain alcohols, aldehydes, ketones, esters, and smaller amounts of hydrocarbons, thiols, and sulfides. Carboxylic acids (Zlatkis and Sivetz, 1960) and amines (Hornstein *et al.*, 1960) are found in some samples, but often they are absent either because they are lost during sample collection or because they are not eluted from the column under the conditions for chromatography. Heterocyclic compounds such as furan are sometimes present, and it is always possible that aglycones may be engendered through the hydrolysis of glycosides. Occasionally mixtures appear to be comparatively simple, but probably some components of these are lost during isolation, and many others occur in amounts too small to detect. In view of the variety of compounds likely to be present, chromatographic methods ordinarily used for the separation of related analogous and homologous series of compounds will not suffice.

Up to the present, methods having general applicability for the chromatography of complex mixtures have not been disclosed; only a few are given in enough detail to warrant inclusion here. Very often, essential information such as column dimensions, nature of the solid support, packing ratio, and flow rate of the carrier gas is omitted. Consequently, the best that can be done now is to give a few typical examples, and to summarize column packings, temperatures, and results obtained on the others (Table II). Even here it was necessary to omit a few potential examples, for in one case the column temperature was not given, and in others the stationary liquids were not defined adequately. With these limitations in mind, the following general rules are suggested for setting up conditions for the separation of complex mixtures of volatile compounds by GLC.

Selection of partition liquid. Polar liquids that have been used for the separation of complex volatile mixtures include ethylene and propylene carbonates, tetraethylene glycol dimethyl ether, phenoxyethanol, polyesters, and Carbowaxes of different molecular weights. As many as twenty to thirty peaks can be resolved on these substrates in 1 to 2 hours. If only one column is used, it is likely that best results can be obtained with members of this group. Semipolar or nonpolar columns that have been used include various silicone oils, di(ethylhexyl) sebacate, various dialkyl phthalates, tricresyl phosphate, and paraffin oil.

Columns in parallel. Complex mixtures usually can be resolved into more components with two columns differing in polarity. Generally a nonpolar packing is used in conjunction with a polar liquid, the sample being chromatographed independently on the two columns. For example, isobutyl alco-

TABLE II

Analysis of Complex Mixtures

Source	Column packings[a]	Column temperature (°C)	Number of peaks	Components identified	Supplementary methods[b]	Ref.
Strawberry oil	I. G.E. SF–96 silicone	150	8	16	RV, IR, C	Corse and Dimick (1958)
	II. Carbowax 1540	100	15 + 8 + 8			
Coffee aroma essence	II. Silicone oil	25	10	19	MS	Zlatkis and Sivetz (1960)
	II. Ethylene–propylene carbonates (1:1)	25	27	23		
Dry vacuum coffee aroma	I. Tetraethylene glycol dimethyl ether	100	9	17	MS	Zlatkis and Sivetz (1960)
Tobacco volatiles	I. Tetraethylene glycol dimethyl ether	0–26	22	6	MS, IR	Irby and Harlow (1959)
	II. Silicone 702					
Fresh onions	I. Di(ethylhexyl) sebacate	—	2 + 3	5	MS	Niegish and Stahl (1956)
		25	4	5		
Roasted coffee	I. Carbowax 1500	45	19	19	IR, RV, O	Rhoades (1960)
Irradiated meat	I. Carbowax	60	9	9	MS	Merritt et al. (1959)
Cheese volatiles	I. Carbowax 1500	125	9	6	RV, C	Jackson and Hussong (1958)
Pear essence	I. Poly(diethylene glycol succinate)	175	33	None	Taste panel	Jennings et al. (1960)
Fungus exudate	I. Carbowax 1500	80	6	8	RV	Collins and Morgan (1960)
	I. Di-n-decyl phthalate	100	8	4	RV, C	
Milk	I. Dioctyl phthalate	75	5 + 6	0	—	Wynn et al. (1960)
Skim milk	I. Carbowax 400	75	6			Patton (1958)
Irradiated milk	I. Carbowax 400	75	6	6	MS	Day et al. (1957)
	II. Paraffin oil	65	5			
Synthetic mixture	II. Dinonyl phthalate	65	5	17	MS	Seligman et al. (1957)
	II. Tricresyl phosphate	25	7			
	II. Silica gel	25	3			
	II. Phenoxyethanol	25	4			

[a] I. For primary separation. II. For secondary separation.

[b] RV = retention values. IR = infrared. C = chemical tests. MS = mass spectrometer. O = odor.

hol and isoamyl acetate are not resolved on Carbowax 1500, while the separation factor for these two compounds on di-*n*-decyl phthalate is 4.13.

Columns in series. The use of columns in parallel is valuable in certain specific cases, but better resolution can be obtained if the analysis is made in series. In this method, the sample is chromatographed on a column giving moderate resolution, and the components representing each peak are collected as they emerge from the column. Each fraction is then rechromatographed on a second column having different polarity. The subfractions eluting from the second column are then collected for optical analysis. Best results are obtained with a polar packing in conjunction with a semipolar or nonpolar column. The order in which the columns should be used is debatable, but in any event it is essential that the second column does not bleed if samples are to be collected for optical analysis. As an example of this technique, Corse and Dimick (1958) used Silicone G.E. SF-96 for the separation of strawberry oil at 200°C. Eight primary peaks were obtained, the first three being collected together. The sample was then rerun on the same liquid at 150°C, and the first three fractions were collected individually. This was repeated a number of times to amass large amounts of material. The first three fractions were then rechromatographed on Carbowax 1540 at temperatures of 100°C and 150°C. Fraction 1 yielded fifteen peaks, fraction 2 eight peaks, and fraction 3 eight peaks. Sixteen of these components were identified by optical or chemical methods. Thus, three of the eight fractions separated on silicone yielded a minimum of thirty-one individual components when rechromatographed on Carbowax. Results were not given on the other five fractions eluted from silicone, but it is likely that some of them were complex.

It is customary to trap fractions from the first column for rechromatography. However, this need not be done if a chromatograph is available having two columns and two detectors connected in series. Peaks registered by the first detector can be rechromatographed automatically on the second column. Overcrowding of the chromatogram can be prevented by including a bypass valve between the two columns so that fractions of no interest are vented to air.

Fraction analysis. Composite peaks may result even when analyses are made in series, so supplementary chemical or physical tests are necessary to obtain unequivocal results. Color tests and infrared spectra are frequently used, but mass spectrometry is the preferred method, since it will easily handle multicomponent mixtures. An example of the value of the mass spectrometer employed in conjunction with the dual-column method is given by the work of Seligman *et al.* (1957). These authors chromatographed a seventeen-component mixture on tricresyl phosphate and obtained seven primary peaks. One of these was rechromatographed on silica and yielded three secondary peaks. The first of these was extremely sharp and symmetrical and gave no evidence of the presence of a mixture. This fraction was analyzed on a mass spectrometer and shown to contain carbonyl sulfide and propane. Without this analysis the fraction would have been identified incorrectly.

Operating parameters. Operating temperatures vary from 0° to 125°C, depending on the type of sample being analyzed. The lower limit is for the analysis of mixtures containing inorganic gases and low-boiling hydrocarbons, and the upper limit for samples containing C_9 compounds. Most analyses are carried out at temperatures of 25° to 75°C. Flow rates are in the neighborhood of 25 to 100 ml of gas per minute. The carrier gas is usually helium, since thermal conductivity cells are employed most frequently. However, if fractions are collected and rechromatographed, it would be desirable to use an ionization detector with the second column, since the peaks are likely to be small if many components are present. In such cases it would not be possible to collect large enough samples for instrumental analysis.

In summary, complex mixtures are best chromatographed by employing polar and semipolar liquid substrates in series. The fractions collected from the second column should then be analyzed by mass spectrometric, infrared, or chemical methods to determine whether they are pure compounds or mixtures. Often this procedure can be simplified by modifying the isolation method so that only compounds having specific functional groups are collected. Methods for doing this are described in Sections C through G inclusive.

a. Chromatography on Polar Substrates

*1. *On Carbowax 1500* (Rhoades, personal communication)

Chromatograph	Perkin-Elmer Model 154-A with gas sampling valve.
Column dimensions	200 × 0.635-cm o.d. copper tubing.
Solid support	Johns Manville C-22 firebrick (40/60 U. S. mesh), water-washed.
Stationary phase	Carbowax 1500, a polyethylene glycol supplied by Union Carbide Chemicals (20:80).
Temperature	45°C.
Carrier gas	Helium at approximately 100 ml/min. Inlet pressure: 1280 mm Hg. Outlet pressure: atmospheric.
Detector	Thermistor at 5.6 volts.
Recorder	0 to 10 mv; 1 second.
Sample size	About 3 to 5 μl.
Analysis time	About 30 minutes to diacetyl.

*2. *On poly(diethylene Glycol Succinate)* (Jennings *et al.*, 1960)

Chromatograph	Commercial model.
Column dimensions	10-foot × ¼-inch stainless-steel tube.
Solid support	Chromosorb.
Stationary phase	Poly(diethylene glycol succinate (20:80).
Temperatures	Injection: 250°C. Column and detector: 175°C. Outlet: 275°C.
Carrier gas	Helium at 50 ml/min.
Detector	Four-filament T/C cell.
Recorder	Brown (Minneapolis-Honeywell), 1 mv; 2 seconds; 30 inches/hour.
Sample size	1.5 μl of ethyl chloride extract of fruit essence.
Analysis time	45 minutes.

IV. SUMMARY

Complex mixtures of volatile compounds can be isolated from plants by aeration, steam distillation, vacuum distillation, or extraction with solvents. If the chromatograph is equipped with a thermal detector, special steps must be taken to reduce the water and carbon dioxide content of the isolates so that peaks arising from minor components will not be masked. With a flame ionization detector, a considerable amount of these substances can be tolerated, since this device is not highly sensitive to the presence of inorganic compounds in the gas stream. However, in no case should the column be overloaded.

Complex mixtures have been chromatographed on a wide variety of liquid substrates at temperatures ranging from 0° to 175°C. No single set of operating parameters is satisfactory for all isolates. Usually it is best to chromatograph such mixtures on both polar and nonpolar liquids to obtain the maximum number of peaks. Very often, additional information can be obtained by collecting unresolved fractions and rechromatographing them on a liquid having different polarity.

The substances giving rise to the chromatographic peaks can be classified according to functional group by collecting fractions and applying chemical tests. However, interpretation of chromatograms is simplified considerably if the sample is prefractioned according to functional group by methods described in the following sections of this chapter.

B. Chromatography of Smoke Constituents

I. INTRODUCTION

The chromatography of volatile mixtures obtained by condensing tobacco smoke is treated separately from that of other complex natural mixtures, since the sample collection differs in some important details, and pyrolysis products, such as isoprene and acrolein, are present. It should be noted that a number of fractions other than the one discussed here have been isolated from tobacco smoke and separated by GLC. Among these are inorganic gases and low-molecular-weight hydrocarbons, phenols, pyridine alkaloids, and nonvolatile organic acids. Details are given elsewhere in this book.

II. Isolation and Sample Injection

A number of procedures have been described for the isolation of volatile components from tobacco smoke, but the method of Irby and Harlow (1959) is the only one that will be considered here, since it is specifically designed to meet the requirements of gas chromatography. It is similar in one important respect to the method of Merritt *et al.* (1959), referred to in Section A, for the collection of volatiles from meat, in that it provides for the partial removal of water and carbon dioxide from the condensate by low-temperature distillation. This prevents overloading of the chromatographic column.

Cigarettes are smoked on an automatic machine, and water, carbon dioxide, and organic volatiles are condensed at −196°C. Permanent gases are discharged to a vacuum line. The sample is fractionated by distilling it from a boiler held at −40°C into a trap held at −145° to −150°C. Most of the water remains in the boiler, and the organic volatiles are condensed in the trap, while almost all the carbon dioxide passes through the trap and exits via the vacuum line. The reader should consult the paper of Merritt

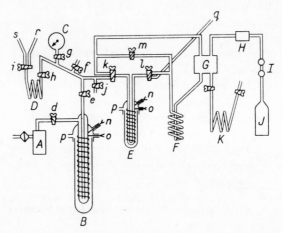

Fig. 5. Apparatus for the isolation of volatile components from tobacco smoke: (*A*) smoking machines; (*B*) LeRoy still; (*C*) vacuum gauge; (*D*) trap; (*E*) temperature-controlled trap; (*F*) chromatographic column; (*G*) Gow-Mac cell; (*H*) flow gauge; (*I*) pressure control gauges; (*J*) helium tank; (*K*) exit trap; (*n*) thermocouple leads; (*o*) heater leads; (*p*) vacuum jacket connections; (*q, r*) vacuum line connections; (*s*) Toepler pump connection. (Irby and Harlow, 1959).

et al. (1959) for the principles involved. The trap containing the organic volatiles is then heated, and the sample is swept directly into the chromatographic column by a stream of carrier gas. Details are as follows:

a. Sample Collection (Irby and Harlow, 1959)

1. *Apparatus.* "A schematic diagram is shown in figure 5. It consists of three major parts: (a) filter holder, filter, smoking machine and associated valves, (b) the low temperature evaporation still B, connecting traps D and E and the vacuum system, and (c) the chromatograph and fraction collector.

"The smoking machine is of the conventional type, hand or machine operated, adjusted to take a 35 ml puff of two seconds' duration once per minute. The vapor and gas phase smoke are drawn into a small latex rubber bag and exhausted into the still immersed in liquid nitrogen. The still B and the trap E are so constructed that by proper regulation of the voltage applied to the heater and the vacuum applied to the case surrounding them, any desired temperature from $-196°C$ upward can be obtained when they are immersed in liquid nitrogen. One part of the three-way stopcock i leads to a Toepler pump and gas burette (not shown in diagram). This enables quantitative removal and measurement of the noncondensable gases, if so desired. Depending on the positions of the three-way stopcocks k and l, trap E serves both as a trap for the fractions collected from the still and as a sample inlet trap to the chromatographic column. Stopcock m allows helium to flow through the chromatographic column at all times except during the introduction of the sample." F is the chromatographic column, G a thermal detector, K the fraction collector, and J a helium tank. The fraction collector (Fig. 6) is a radiator trap designed according to Christman *et al.* (1955).

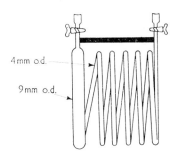

4 mm o.d.

9 mm o.d.

Fɪɢ. 6. Radiator trap for the collection of volatile fractions. (Irby and Harlow, 1959).

For efficient operation it is essential that the trap be positioned so that the lower one-third is immersed in liquid nitrogen and the upper two-thirds exposed to the air.

2. *Sampling Procedure.* "Two cigarettes are smoked for each determination and are selected so the weight is within ±20 mg of the average weight of the sample. The still and connecting vacuum system are evacuated to a pressure of less than 0.2 mm. Liquid nitrogen is placed around the still and trap D. Stopcocks i, k and e are closed, and d is opened. The cigarettes are placed in the holder, lighted with a small electrical heater, and the number of puffs necessary to smoke a 47 mm length of each cigarette is recorded. At the completion of the final puff of the first cigarette, stopcocks e and i are carefully opened and a portion of the noncondensables is exhaused by the vacuum system. This prevents any buildup of back pressure to the smoking machine during the smoking of the second cigarette. When the smoking of the last cigarette is complete, it is removed and ten air puffs are taken. This serves to remove traces of vapor constituents that might be retained by the Cambridge filter and clears the small dead space of all gases. Stopcock d is closed and e and i are carefully opened. The noncondensables at −196°C are removed through r at a pressure of less than 0.2 mm. Stopcock i is closed and trap D is allowed to warm to room temperature. Any materials which condense in this trap diffuse rapidly over into the still, which is held at −196°C. The temperature of trap E is adjusted to −145° to −150°C during the smoking period. Stopcock h is closed and k and l are opened to the still and vacuum line q. The voltage to the heater of the still is adjusted so that a temperature of −40°C is obtained in approximately 15 minutes. The evaporative distillation is carried out for a total time of 80 minutes. By this procedure only a small portion of the relatively large amount of water collected in the still evaporates, and almost all of the carbon dioxide passes through the trap E to the vacuum system.

"During the evaporative distillation, a Dewar flask containing ice water is placed around the chromatographic column, and the temperature is held at 0°C. At the end of the distillation period (80 minutes), k and l are closed, and trap E is heated rapidly to room temperature. Stopcock m is closed, and k and l are opened to the helium line." The sample is thus introduced into the chromatographic column.

III. CHROMATOGRAPHY

Irby and Harlow (1959) chromatographed the volatile components of cigarette smoke on a stationary phase consisting of tetraethylene glycol dimethyl ether on Celite. The column temperature was maintained at 0°C until the emergence of acetaldehyde. This occurred in about 17 minutes. The temperature was then raised to 26°C for the remainder of the run. About twenty-two peaks were resolved or partly resolved, of which eight were identified. These were: isoprene, acetaldehyde, composite 1, acetone, composite 2, methanol, methylfuran, and methyl ethyl ketone, in order of increasing retention time (Fig. 7). Composite peak 1 was resolved into furan and propionaldehyde by condensing it in a radiator trap and rechromatographing it on a Silicone 702 column. Composite peak 2 was eluted just after acetone. Rechromatography on Silicone 702 showed that it contained acrolein together with smaller quantities of methyl acetate and isobutyraldehyde. In collecting it, care must be taken not to contaminate it with the preceding (acetone) peak, since acetone and acrolein are not resolved on the silicone column.

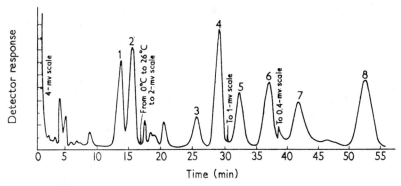

FIG. 7. Chromatogram of condensable fraction of cigarette smoke; 20% tetraethylene glycol dimethyl ether column: (1) isoprene; (2) acetaldehyde; (3) furan and propionaldehyde; (4) acetone; (5) acrolein, methyl acetate and isobutyraldehyde; (6) methyl alcohol; (7) methyl furan; (8) methyl ethyl ketone. (Irby and Harlow, 1959).

Column stability was excellent if the temperature was never raised above 100°C. However, under the experimental conditions employed, peak areas were sensitive to minor variations in flow rate. Therefore, peak heights were used for quantitative calculations. Calibration curves were run with pure compounds under identical conditions as for the separation of tobacco volatiles. The volume of trap E was determined prior to connecting it to the apparatus by weighing the amount of mercury required to fill it. Standard materials were then introduced through stopcock j. The pressures produced were read on the absolute manometer (C) (pressure range 0.2 to 50 mm in 2-mm divisions). If the samples were of such size that pressures less than 1 mm or greater than 15 mm were obtained, a trap of appropriate volume was attached at j, evacuated, and then filled with the desired sample previously stored in trap D.

The sample weight in milligrams (W) was calculated from the relation

$$W = \frac{27.3 \times MVP}{22.4 \times 760\,T}$$

where M is the molecular weight of the pure constituent, P the pressure of the sample in millimeters of Hg, V the volume of the trap in milliliters, and T the temperature of the sample contained in trap K. Pressures were kept low enough so that adherence to the ideal gas law can be assumed. Recoveries of better than 98% were obtained on the analysis of synthetic mixtures containing isoprene, acetaldehyde, acetone, and acrolein.

Seligman *et al.* (1957) chromatographed a seventeen-component synthetic mixture whose composition was suggested by previous literature reports on the composition of cigarette smoke. The boiling-point range was $-161.5°C$ (methane) to $100°C$ (water). Since both gases and liquids were included, it was necessary to introduce the sample into the chromatograph in two separate portions from traps connected in series to the column, the gas flow being arranged so that the components mixed on entry. Seven primary peaks were obtained by partition on tricresyl phosphate at 25°C. These fractions were collected in cold traps and rechromatographed on silica, Hyvac oil, or 2-phenoxyethanol. The synthetic mixture was completely resolved except for two pairs of compounds consisting of methane–ethane and carbonyl sulfide–propane. The peak obtained on this latter pair was extremely sharp and symmetrical, but analysis by mass spectrometry showed that this fraction contained two compounds. Therefore, it can be seen that serial chromatography on two or more partition liquids in conjunction with a secondary method of analysis is necessary for the complete characterization of complex mixtures.

a. Chromatography of Condensate (Irby and Harlow, 1959)

1. Primary Separation

Chromatograph	Laboratory-built.
Column dimensions	2½-meter × ¼-inch coiled copper tubing.
Solid support	Celite (45/100 mesh).
Stationary phase	Tetraethylene glycol dimethyl ether (20:80).
Temperatures	Column: 0°C to acetaldehyde (17 minutes). 26°C to methyl ethyl ketone. Detector: 25°C.
Carrier gas	Helium at 100 ml/min. Inlet pressure: 10 psig. Outlet pressure: atmospheric.
Detector	Gow-Mac T/C cell TE-II of ½-ml volume operated at 130 ma.
Recorder	10-mv Leeds and Northrup recorder with a preamplifier.
Sample size	Condensables from two cigarettes.
Analysis time	55 minutes to methyl ethyl ketone.

2. Secondary Separations

Column dimensions	2-meter × ¼-inch coiled copper tubing.
Stationary phase	Silicone 702 on Celite (20:80).
Carrier gas	Helium at 100 ml/min (25°C).
Analysis time	8 minutes for composite mixture 1; 13 minutes for composite mixture 2.
Other conditions	Same as above.

IV. Summary

Cigarettes are smoked on an automatic machine, and the organic vapors are condensed and fractionated in such a way that water and carbon dioxide are partly removed. This avoids overloading of the chromatographic column. The condensate is then chromatographed on tetraethylene glycol dimethyl ether at 0°C and 26°C, and on Silicone 702 at 25°C.

C. Volatile Fatty Acids and Esters

Volatile fatty acids containing 1 to 8 carbon atoms are found in the free state in most plant and animal tissues or can be derived from esters, including glycerides. They may be saturated or unsaturated and may contain straight or branched chains. Most of the naturally occurring fatty acids contain an even number of carbon atoms, but it is becoming increasingly evident that this is a broad generalization rather than an inflexible rule. Prominent exceptions are n-valeric (C_5), n-oenanthic (C_7) and n-pelargonic (C_9) acids. Because of the occurrence of chain branching, unsaturation, and acids with an odd number of carbon atoms, it is necessary to have available methods that can be used to separate closely related homologues and analogues. Gas chromatography is well suited for this purpose, since it is possible to resolve such closely related isomers as caproic and isocaproic acids without serious overlapping of the peaks.

Fatty acids are considerably less volatile than the corresponding alcohols and aldehydes owing to higher polarity and to the fact that they dimerize in solution. Nevertheless, they can be chromatographed successfully in the free state up to carbon number 10 at column temperatures in the neighborhood of 125°C. Sometimes they are chromatographed as their methyl esters, but this is resorted to less frequently than for the higher fatty acids.

I. Methods of Isolation

Volatile fatty acids can be removed from tissues or biological fluids by any of the general methods described in Section A, including solvent extraction and distillation. They can be separated from amines and neutral volatiles by converting them in solution to their alkali metal salts and evaporating the solvent. The neutral and basic components of the mixture are lost with the solvent, and the residue that remains consists of salts of the fatty acids.

Hankinson *et al.* (1958) extracted the volatile acids from acidified milk with a mixture of ethanol, ethyl ether, and petroleum ether. The extracts were neutralized with alcoholic sodium hydroxide, and the sodium salts of the acids were recovered by removal of the solvent at room temperature. Hughes (1960) extracted free fatty acids from fish with 80% ethanol. They were then removed from solution and concomitantly separated from neutral and basic materials by adsorbing them on a basic ion-exchange resin in the hydroxide form. The acids were eluted with sulfuric acid and steam-distilled. The distillate was neutralized with alkali, and the salts of the acids were recovered by evaporation.

Sometimes it is necessary to analyze for volatile fatty acids in mixtures containing higher fatty acids. If the relative proportions of the two fractions are not too disparate, this can be accomplished by running the analytical column at a temperature that will elute the volatile components and retain the higher homologues (Vorbeck *et al.*, 1960). Alternatively, the column can be run at a temperature that will give separation of the higher homologues (Beerthuis *et al.*, 1959). The lower fatty acids will be eluted as a group within the first few minutes and can be collected in a cold trap. This fraction can then be rechromatographed with the column at a lower temperature.

If the proportion of volatile fatty acids in the mixture is relatively small, it is often desirable to concentrate them in advance of chromatography. This can be accomplished by azeotropic distillation in toluene (James, 1960) or by steam distillation. Weenink (1958) studied the behavior on steam distillation of a mixture of normal saturated fatty acids from formic to decanoic. It was found that the volatilities of the C_4 to C_{10} acids were considerably reduced by the presence of higher homologues. Generally, the reduction in volatility resulting from the addition of C_{14} to C_{18} acids to a mixture of volatile acids was greatest for decanoic and least for formic. Indeed, the volatilities of nonanoic and decanoic acids were so reduced under these conditions that they must be considered to be only slightly volatile. Therefore, recovery can be considered quantitative only up to octanoic acid. This is in general agreement with the findings of Hawke (1957), who previously used this method for the recovery of volatile acids from butterfat for separation by GLC.

Naturally occurring esters are more difficult to isolate than free acids, since they are neutral and their volatilities cannot be changed by adjustment of pH. However, peaks arising from them can be tentatively identified by comparing chromatograms before and after alkaline hydrolysis (Collins and Morgan, 1960). Peaks that disappear on hydrolysis can reasonably be assigned to esters, particularly if new peaks engendered by the liberated alcohols appear, or if the areas of existing alcohol peaks increase. It is also possible to identify the acid component of the ester by isolating it and chromatographing it as its methyl ester or the free acid, if the free acids are removed before alkaline hydrolysis.

a. Isolation of Volatile Fatty Acids

1. *Extraction from Milk* (Hankinson *et al.*, 1958). The milk sample (100 ml) is acidified with 5% (v/v) sulfuric acid (5 ml), and the mixture is filtered

through Whatman No. 1 filter paper. A portion of the filtrate (50 ml) is transferred to a separatory funnel, and 5% (v/v) sulfuric acid (5 ml), ethanol (50 ml), ethyl ether (100 ml), and petroleum ether (100 ml) are added. The mixture is shaken ten times after the addition of the first two reagents and forty times after the addition of the latter two reagents. The extraction is repeated twice with the same volumes of ether and petroleum ether but no alcohol. The water layer is drawn off. The combined extracts are then neutralized to a Phenol Red end point by the addition of $1N$ alcoholic sodium hydroxide. The solvent is evaporated at room temperature, and the residue is transferred to a 50-ml flask and acidified with 0.2 ml of 5 N hydrochloric acid. A measured volume of ether is then added, and the water from the hydrochloric acid is removed with anhydrous sodium sulfate. The ether solution is kept in a tightly stoppered flask at 4°C until ready for chromatography. Recoveries of formic, acetic, and butyric acids are 57%, 86%, and 81%, respectively. Recoveries of propionic, valeric, caproic, and caprylic acids are quantitative. Recoveries are reproducible to within 5%.

*2. *Isolation from Fish* (Hughes, 1960). The tissue (20 gm) is macerated in a homogenizer with 4 × 50-ml portions of 80% ethanol (v/v). The combined extracts are made up to a volume of 250 ml with 80% ethanol, filtered, and stored at −30°C until used. Before analysis the acids must be concentrated and transferred to a nonaqueous medium. This is accomplished by passing an aliquot of the extract through a 2 × 1-cm column of a basic ion-exchange resin (Dowex 2, 100/120 mesh) in the hydroxide form. The column is washed with water to remove neutral materials, and the acids are eluted quantitatively from the column with N sulfuric acid (15 ml). The eluate is transferred to a Markham micro-Kjeldahl apparatus (Markham, 1942) and steam-distilled. All the acids are recovered in the first 120 ml of distillate. The distillate is neutralized with dilute sodium hydroxide to a thymolphthalein end point to give the salts of the acids, and concentrated under reduced pressure to a volume of 5 ml. The solution is then transferred to a 10-ml ampoule and evaporated in a centrifugal freeze-dryer.

3. *Separation from Butterfat by Steam Distillation* (Hawke, 1957). The fat sample (about 2.5 gm) is saponified by refluxing it with concentrated aqueous sodium hydroxide solution. The soaps are transferred to a microdistillation apparatus with a minimum volume of water, acidified with sulfuric acid, and steam-distilled until the amount of acid coming over in the distillate is negligible. The distillate is neutralized with dilute alkali solution to give the salts of the volatile acids, and the water is removed under reduced pressure in a rotary evaporator at 60°C. The salts are converted to free acids for chromatography by the addition of acid (see Section C.II). Quantitative recoveries are obtained up to C_8, but the C_{10} acid is found in both volatile and nonvolatile fractions.

TABLE III

RETENTIONS RELATIVE TO *n*-BUTYRIC ACID OF LOWER FATTY ACIDS AND ESTERS

	Free fatty acids Stationary phase			
	Silicone–10% stearic acid (James and Martin, 1952)		Dioctyl sebacate– 15% sebacic acid (Raupp, 1959)	Poly(diethylene glycol adipate) (Hunter *et al.*, 1960b)
Acid	100°C	137°C	150°C	125°C
Formic	0.076	—	0.25	—
Acetic	0.20	0.26	0.40	0.60
Propionic	0.47	0.54	0.57	0.75
Acrylic	—	—	0.69	—
Isobutyric	0.77	0.81	0.81	0.80
n-Butyric	1.0	1.0	1.0	1.0
Crotonic	—	—	1.58	—
Isovaleric	1.51	1.48	—	1.20
n-Valeric	2.17	1.91	1.82	1.55
Isocaproic	—	—	—	2.05
n-Caproic	—	3.58	—	2.4

	Ethyl esters		Methyl esters	
	Stationary phase			
	Silicone–15% stearic acid (Ralls, 1960a) 80°C	LAC 446 glycol– adipate polymer (Ralls, 1960a) 80°C	Dioctyl phthalate (James and Martin, 1956)	
			78.6°C	100°C
Formic	0.16	0.37	0.098	0.124
Acetic	0.29	0.46	0.216	0.256
Propionic	0.53	0.67	0.485	0.51
Acrylic	0.50	0.78	—	—
Isobutyric	0.66	0.63	0.71	0.706
n-Butyric	1.0	1.0	1.0	1.0
Crotonic	1.41	2.15	—	—
Isovaleric	1.26	1.11	1.56	1.45
n-Valeric	2.02	1.78	2.31	2.12
Isocaproic	2.85	2.26	3.96	3.24
n-Caproic	4.16	3.04	5.16	4.36

II. Chromatography of Free Acids and Esters

Lower fatty acids may be chromatographed as free acids or as esters. Free acids will tend to dimerize on a column and produce tailing unless special precautions are taken. Therefore, James and Martin (1952) add 10% stearic acid to the D.C. 550 silicone oil used as stationary phase for their separations. A small amount of orthophosphoric acid may also be added to give better separations of formic and acetic acids. A polar packing, dioctyl sebacate, containing 15% sebacic acid, is also used and has given very good separations of saturated and unsaturated free acids from C_1 to C_5 (Raupp, 1959). Peak symmetry is good with this column, as is the resolution of formic and acetic acids (Table III).

The acids must be free of water before chromatography on these columns. Even a small percentage will interfere with separations. Since the acids are so volatile and must be anhydrous, the samples are introduced by special methods to avoid losses before chromatography. The acids are isolated as their nonvolatile sodium salts and converted to free acids just prior to chromatography. They may be volatilized onto the chromatographic column (James and Martin, 1952; Hughes, 1960), or aliquots may be injected into the chromatograph (Gehrke and Lamkin, 1961; Hawke, 1957) (details are given below).

Hunter et al. (1960b) have developed a method for the chromatography of free fatty acids through C_8 whereby either anhydrous solutions or solutions containing up to 50% water are analyzed. Poly(diethylene glycol adipate) is the stationary phase in a specially designed all-glass chromatograph. The emerging acids are combusted to CO_2 and H_2O; the H_2O is taken up by magnesium perchlorate, and the CO_2 is measured with a thermal conductivity cell at room temperature (see below).

This is a convenient method of analysis, since the acids do not have to be anhydrous. However, separation at 125°C is not so good as with the other methods described (Table III), and complete separations of propionic and isobutyric, butyric and isovaleric, and isocaproic and caproic acids are not obtained under the conditions used. It was suggested that C_2 to C_5 acids could be separated at less than 125°C to improve separations, and above 125°C for the C_5 to C_8 acids to lower retention times.

It should be possible to use this method with conventional chromatographic equipment, with helium or nitrogen as the carrier gas, the only disadvantage being the slight corrosiveness of the acids to metal. The combustion technique could be adapted to any instrument with the combustion tube placed after the chromatographic column and in series with a magnesium perchlorate drying tube and a thermal conductivity detector. The thermal conductivity cell has greatly increased sensitivity at lower temperatures, and with the combustion technique the detector can be operated at room temperature or lower.

The flame ionization detector also can be used to circumvent interference caused by tailing of the water peak in the analysis of aqueous solutions, since this detector is insensitive to water (Emery and Koerner, 1961). However, only part of the column effluent could be passed through it under the experimental conditions employed because of high background, possibly caused by bleeding of the stationary liquid (method C.II.c.4). An aqueous solution (about 25 μl) containing 0.01 to 0.1% of an organic acid is applied to a column packed with Tween 80 which is operated at 110°C. The water peak passes through the column within a few minutes and extinguishes the flame. However, it can be relit easily before the first organic acid peak appears. Volatile fatty acids through n-valeric are eluted in under 30 minutes and yield symmetrical peaks. There is no reason why this method should not be useful for the analysis of dilute water solutions of organic compounds of all types, although it must be conceded that a pilot light to rekindle the hydrogen flame would be a distinct advantage.

This is one instance in which the flame detector has an advantage over the argon detector, since the sensitivity of the latter to organic compounds is reduced by the presence of water vapor in the carrier gas (Swoboda, 1960). However, this can be overcome by including a pre-column containing diglycerol on Celite to hold back the water while organic components are being partitioned on an analytical column packed with polyethylene glycol on Celite. The pre-column is then backflushed to vent the water to the atmosphere while the analysis is in progress.

The elution of free fatty acids from the chromatograph may be followed with a recording burette (James and Martin, 1952). Stepwise integrated curves are obtained, and the amount of material in each zone is given directly by measurement of the step height. This is easier than measuring peak areas; another advantage is that it is specific for free acids. Neutral components will not be recorded and so will not interfere if they are still present in the mixture being titrated.

Standard detectors may be used for the free acids as well as for the esters. However, the free acids are somewhat corrosive to metallic elements of the detection system. Also, with the argon ionization detector, calibration is necessary for fatty acids, since there is a marked increase in detector response per unit mass up to a molecular weight of around 150 (Böttcher et al., 1960).

When lower fatty acids and long-chain acids are isolated together, they may all be methylated (see Chapter 7, Section G) and chromatographed as methyl esters. It is not possible to run the whole series at one temperature. The C_1 to C_6 esters can be separated by azeotropic distillation in toluene and chromatographed, or the complete mixture can be chromatographed at

78.6°C on dioctyl phthalate to separate the esters (James and Martin, 1956) (see below). The longer-chain esters are not volatile at this temperature and will not be chromatographed, although the column will have to be cleaned by running carrier gas through it by backflushing to remove slightly volatile components. Symmetrical peaks are obtained with good resolution (Table III). However, the methyl esters are more volatile than the free acids, and special care must be taken to avoid losses before injection into the chromatograph.

Ralls (1960a) has developed a flash exchange method for the formation and introduction of the C_1 to C_7 acids as ethyl esters. Here the fatty acids are also isolated as salts, in this case as potassium salts. They are dried, and the ethyl esters are formed by dry distillation at 300°C with potassium ethyl sulfate in a capillary tube inserted in the injection port (details below). A low column temperature is used (80°C) with resultant good resolution (Table III). However, as yet this method has not been quantitated.

a. Methods of Detection

1. *Titration* (James and Martin, 1952). Phenol Red is used in the titration cell, an 0.001% aqueous solution for visual titration and an 0.01% aqueous solution for automatic control. The gas emerging from the column is bubbled into the titration cell. The acids are absorbed in the water where they are continuously titrated with NaOH (0.02 to 0.04 N) from a recording burette (see James and Martin, 1952, for construction details for a burette of this type). The solution may be stirred by an additional stream of carrier gas if necessary. The titration curve is plotted, and the height of each step gives the amount of acid in each fraction.

*2. *Combustion* (Hunter et al., 1960b). The combustion tube is made of a $\frac{1}{4}$-inch-diameter glass U tube filled with 20 mesh copper oxide. It is closely wound with Nichrome wire and enclosed in a metal container filled with magnesium oxide. The copper oxide is heated to dull redness, and the eluted organic materials are combusted to carbon dioxide and water.

The combustion tube is connected to a drying tube, a 12-inch length of $\frac{1}{4}$-inch-diameter glass tubing filled with magnesium perchlorate to remove the water of combustion. The CO_2 passes through to the thermal conductivity cell which is held at room temperature. Helium or nitrogen may be used as carrier gas, but helium is preferable.

*3. *Flame Ionization Detector* (Emery and Koerner, 1961). The flame ionization detector is bypassed with a line containing a Perkin-Elmer No. 0 restriction needle so that only part of the effluent gas passes through it. The detector is operated with a carrier gas flow rate of 40 ml/min and a hydrogen flow rate of 8 ml/min. Air flow through the detector is maintained at 430 ml/min, and the direct-current potential across the flame is 300 volts. When the sample contains a large amount of water, the flame is extinguished, but it can be re-ignited easily after most of the water passes through the detector within 2 minutes after injection, and well before the first fatty acid is eluted.

b. Sample Introduction

*1. *Concentration of Acids on Column* (Hughes, 1960). The dried sodium salts of the fatty acids are dissolved in 2 drops of distilled water, and the solution is acidified with 1 drop of 60% phosphoric acid solution. The ampoule containing the salts is previously treated with a water-repelling silicone compound (Desicote–Beckman Instruments Co., or Repelcote–Hopkins and Williams, Ltd.) so that the water forms one large globule, thus making it easy to dissolve the salts completely in a relatively small volume of liquid. A short column (4-mm i.d.) is prepared containing 1 cm of anhydrous sodium sulfate overlayered with 4 cm of Celite which is previously dried at 300°C. The aqueous solution containing the acids is carefully poured on top of the column, and the container is washed with 4 × 0.5-ml portions of ethyl ether, each portion being transferred to the column and slowly forced through it with compressed air. The ether solution eluting from the column is collected in a 2-ml glass bulb with a long stem. The chromatographic column is removed from the chromatograph; one end is placed inside the long stem just above the surface of the ether, and the other end is connected to a vacuum line. Air is drawn through the column, carrying the ether and volatile acids with it. The bulb containing the ether is immersed for 5 minutes in a water bath at 60°C followed by 15 minutes in an oil bath at 100°C. The volatile acids move into the column and condense there and are now ready to be chromatographed.

*2. *Concentration by Low-Temperature Evaporation* (Gehrke and Lamkin, 1961). An aqueous solution of the sodium salts of the acids is evaporated to dryness on a steam bath with a stream of filtered air. One milliliter of distilled water is added to the residue to redissolve the salts. The samples are cooled to 0°C, and 0.4 ml of concentrated H_2SO_4 at 0°C is added. Water is then removed on a liquid–solid chromatographic column. The column is 7 mm in diameter, packed to a height of 12 cm with 20/40 U. S. mesh anhydrous $CaSO_4$, with 7 cm of Celite 545 over it. The Celite and $CaSO_4$ are first dried by heating overnight at 300°C. The solution containing the free acids is poured onto the top of the column, and the acids remaining in the flask are washed onto the column with several small portions of alcohol-free ethyl ether (about 5 ml total). Small portions of ethyl ether (1 to 2 ml) are added until 15 ml of eluate is collected in an evaporation tube shown in Fig. 8.

The anhydrous ether eluate is concentrated to a small volume (0.5 to 2.0 ml) at −50°C in a dry ice–Methyl Cellosolve bath at a pressure of 6 mm of Hg. After evaporation, the samples are allowed to come to room temperature. They are made up to a known volume (2.0 ml) with ethyl ether dried by passage through a column of anhydrous $CaSO_4$. The free fatty acids are now determined by injection of an aliquot of the ether solution into the gas chromatograph.

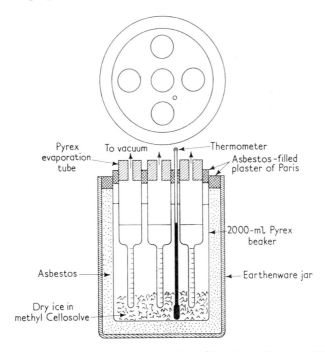

Pyrex evaporation tube — To vacuum — Thermometer — Asbestos-filled plaster of Paris — 2000-ml Pyrex beaker — Asbestos — Earthenware jar — Dry ice in methyl Cellosolve

FIG. 8. Low-temperature concentration bath. (Gehrke and Lamkin, 1961).

*3. *Flash Esterification* (Ralls, 1960a,b).[1] The potassium salts of the fatty acids are isolated and stored dry in desiccators over phosphorus pentoxide. A mixture is weighed and mixed with an equal weight of potassium ethyl sulfate. The compounds are ground and mixed until uniform. A 4.1- to 4.9-mg sample is placed in a weighed borosilicate glass capillary, 1.5-mm o.d. $\times$ 115 mm $\times$ 0.25-mm wall thickness, sealed at one end. The sample is then weighed, and the capillary tube is forced through two $\frac{1}{8}$-inch thick silicone rubber gaskets until the top gasket is $1\frac{1}{8}$ inches from the open end of the tube. The tube is placed in a $\frac{1}{4}$-inch elongated injection chamber packing nut with the lower gasket seated against the back face of the nut. The tube is bent 90° at the back face of the nut and is mounted in the sample injection chamber. The nut is tightened until the capillary tube rotates with

[1] Also see Hunter *et al.* (1960b) on use of this method for introduction of higher-boiling acids with smaller sample sizes.

difficulty. After the instrument returns to equilibrium, the lower part of the capillary up to the bend is heated for 10 seconds at 300°C in a silicone oil bath contained in a borosilicate glass test tube. The ethyl esters of the fatty acids are formed and volatilized into the instrument.

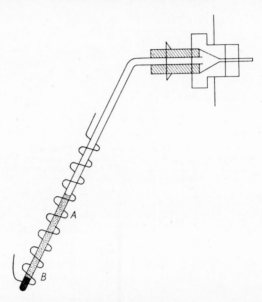

Fig. 9. Reaction capillary attached to the injection port for the flash esterification of volatile fatty acids: (A) test sample of carbonyl derivative–Celite–α-keto acid; (B) formaldehyde 2,4-dinitrophenyl hydrazone with α-ketoglutaric acid chaser. (Stephens and Teszler, 1960).

Stephens and Teszler (1960) have modified the capillary attachment to the injection port. The capillary tube is attached to a No. 27 hypodermic needle by a rubber adapter and inserted through the silicone septum. The capillary is heated to 300°C, and the assembly is removed after the prescribed reaction time (10 seconds) (Fig. 9).

c. Conditions for Chromatography of Free Acids

*1. On Silicone Oil–Stearic Acid Packing (Gehrke and Lamkin, 1961)

Chromatograph	Perkin-Elmer 154-C equipped with microdipper sample introduction system, and two columns in series.
Column dimensions	100 × 0.4-cm i.d. and 50 × 0.4-cm i.d. hairpin-shaped stainless-steel tubing.
Solid support	Johns-Manville Celite 545 size-graded by allowing the particles to settle for 3 minutes in a beaker of water 18 cm deep, washed with concentrated HCl and distilled water, and dried at 300°C.

Stationary phase	D.C. Silicone 550 + 10% (w/w) stearic acid (50:100).
Temperatures	Injection: 200° to 250°C. Column and detector: 137°C.
Carrier gas	Helium at 34 ml/min. Inlet pressure: 1432 mm. Hg. Outlet pressure: atmospheric.
Detector	Two 8000-ohm thermistor T/C cells at 8 volts.
Recorder	5 mv; 1 second; ½ inch/min.
Sample size	20 μl of 10% (w/v) solution.
Analysis time	45 minutes.

*2. On Diocytl Sebacate–Sebacic Acid (Raupp, 1959)

Chromatograph	Perkin-Elmer Fractometer Type 116.
Column dimensions	200 × 0.64-cm straight stainless-steel tubing.
Solid support	Johns-Manville Celite 545 (60/100 U. S. mesh).
Stationary phase	Diocytl sebacate containing 15% sebacic acid (10:30).
Temperature	150°C.
Carrier gas	Helium at 50 ml/min.
Detector	Thermistors operated at 8 volts.
Recorder	Leeds and Northrup, 10 mv; 1 second; ½ inch/min.

*3. On Polyester Packing with CO_2 Combustion Method (Hunter et al., 1960b)

Chromatograph	Laboratory-built all glass.
Column dimensions	244 × 0.4-cm i.d. coiled glass tubing.
Solid support	C-22 firebrick (35/40 mesh).
Stationary phase	Poly(diethylene glycol adipate) (15:100) (LAC 296, Cambridge Industries).
Temperatures	Column: 125°C. Detector: room temperature.
Carrier gas	Helium at 106 ml/min at outlet.
Detector	Sample combusted to CO_2 and measured with four-filament (W) T/C cell at 200 ma.
Recorder	Leeds and Northrup, 5 mv; 1 second; 0.25 cm/min.
Sample size	0.2 mg of each acid.
Analysis time	About 60 minutes to caprylic acid.

*4. Analysis of Aqueous Solutions by Flame Ionization Method (Emery and Koerner, 1961)

Chromatograph	Perkin-Elmer 154-C with 75-watt heater attached to injection block.
Column dimensions	100 × 0.64-cm. o.d. stainless-steel tubing.
Solid support	Chromosorb W (60/80 U. S. mesh).
Stationary phase	Mixture of Tween 80 (9 parts) and phosphoric acid (1 part) (22:78).
Temperatures	Injection: 210°C. Column: 110°C.
Carrier gas	Nitrogen at 40 ml/min. Inlet pressure: 260 mm Hg. Outlet pressure: atmospheric.
Detector	Flame ionization (see method C.II.b.3).
Recorder	5 mv; 1 second; ½ inch/min.
Sample size	20 to 25 μl of water containing 0.01 to 0.1% of each acid.

d. Conditions for Chromatography of Esters

*1. Ethyl Esters by Flash Esterification (Ralls, 1960a)

Chromatograph	Aerograph 110-C.
Column dimensions	¼-inch × 5- or 10-foot stainless-steel tubing.
Solid support	Firebrick.
Stationary phase	Silicone (Dow Corning 550) with 15% stearic acid added (25:75, w/w).
Temperature	80°C.
Carrier gas	Helium at 50 ml/min flow rate. Inlet pressure: 8 to 11 psi. Outlet pressure: atmospheric.
Detector	Thermal conductivity cell.
Recorder	1 mv.
Sample size	4.1 to 4.9 mg of K salt.
Analysis time	About 55 minutes to ethyl caproate.

2. Methyl Esters (James and Martin, 1956)

Chromatograph	Laboratory-built.
Column dimensions	4-foot × 0.4-cm i.d. straight columns.
Solid support	Size-graded Celite 545 pretreated with dilute ethanolic alkali.
Stationary phase	Di(2-ethylhexyl) phthalate.
Temperature	78°C.
Carrier gas	Nitrogen at 40 ml/min. Inlet pressure: 440 mm Hg.
Detector	Gas-density balance.
Recorder	Not given.
Sample size	Not given.
Analysis time	75 minutes to methyl caproate.

e. Detection and Identification of Esters (Collins and Morgan, 1960)

Esters in the neutral volatile fraction are saponified by refluxing the volatile material (1 ml) with 1 M potassium hydroxide solution (10 ml) for 3 hours. The mixture is extracted exhaustively with ether, and most of the ether is removed from the extract by careful distillation. A portion of this solution is then chromatographed. Comparison of this chromatogram with one obtained on an equivalent amount of unsaponified volatiles will show which peaks on the latter chromatograph represent esters, since they will be absent in the saponifiable material. Peaks representing the alcohol components of esters will increase in area, or new peaks will appear.

The acid components of the esters can be isolated as their salts as described in isolation procedures and chromatographed by the methods of Hughes (1960) or Ralls (1960a) as already described.

III. SUMMARY

Volatile fatty acids can be isolated from tissues by extraction, aeration, or distillation. Usually they can be separated from other volatile components by making the isolate alkaline and steam-distilling or extracting it. Neutral and basic compounds are removed, while the acids remain behind as their alkali metal salts. These salts are then decomposed with mineral acid, either in a separate step, or directly in the gas stream of the chromatograph. Free fatty acids are often chromatographed on nonpolar packings containing stearic acid to reduce association effects. They can be resolved also on polyesters. Aqueous solutions of acids can be analyzed directly with a flame ionization detector or by combusting the column effluent to carbon dioxide and taking up water vapor in a drying tower.

Volatile fatty acids are chromatographed most often in the free state. However, it is sometimes convenient to flash esterify them in an apparatus attached directly to the chromatograph by causing their alkali metal salts to react with potassium ethyl sulfate.

D. Volatile Amines and Amino Alcohols

The methylamines, the lower aliphatic amines, and a number of polybasic, aromatic, and heterocyclic amines are found in a variety of plant and animal tissue, or are generated during their putrefaction. As a class, the primary aliphatic amines tend to be considerably more volatile than the fatty acids and somewhat more volatile than alcohols having the same carbon number. Thus, in the C_6 series, caproic acid boils at about 205°C, 1-hexanol at 157°C, and n-hexylamine at 133°C. Although these differences tend to become proportionately smaller as chain length increases, it is possible to chromatograph most aliphatic amines without converting them to more volatile derivatives. Nevertheless, amines are sufficiently polar to be bound to solid supports, a condition which leads to tailing. Earlier work on their analysis by GLC was somewhat hampered by this, but solid supports have now been developed which give symmetrical well-resolved peaks for primary amines up to carbon number 18 (Chapter 7). Amines can be chromatographed on both nonpolar and polar stationary liquids, and their relative retention volumes on the latter are governed by their capacities for forming hydrogen bonds with liquids, as well as by their vapor pressures. It is possible to separate very closely related amines such as m- and p-toluidine by GSC.

I. Isolation from Tissues

Amines must be isolated from plant or animal tissue by aeration, steam distillation, lyophilization, or extraction before they can be chromatographed. James et $al.$ (1952) isolated ammonia and triethylamine as the mixed hydrochlorides from leaves of $Chenopodium$ $vulvaris$ by passing a stream of air through an aqueous mascerate and trapping the bases in dilute hydrochloric acid. Hughes (1959) separated volatile amines from fish by steam-distilling a trichloroacetic acid extract of the tissues into 0.1 N hydrochloric acid. In both cases the amines were determined in the effluent gas from the chromatograph by automatic titration with sulfuric acid to a Methyl Red end point. This detection device is a selective one, responding only to basic compounds. Therefore, complete separation of amines from neutral compounds is unnecessary. However, if the more commonly used and less selective thermal conductivity or ionization detectors are employed, a more extensive clean-up procedure may be required to reduce background. To accomplish this, Burks *et al.* (1959) separated the amines from alkaline solution by lyophilization, acidified the condensate, and then lyophilized again to remove neutral compounds, the amines remaining behind in the lyophilization flasks as the hydrochlorides.

Sometimes chromatography can be simplified if a preliminary separation of volatile from less-volatile substances can be made by fractional distillation. Thus Honegger and Honegger (1959) separated amines extracted from brain and other tissues by steam distillation under reduced pressure. Ammonia and methylamine were obtained in the early fractions, and dimethylaminoethanol was obtained at a higher temperature. These workers also differentiated between unbound amines and amines bound to protoplasmic constituents by extracting the tissue both before and after alkaline hydrolysis.

Block and Bolling (1951) have described an extraction procedure for isolating some of the less-volatile amines such as would be obtained through the decarboxylation of α-amino acids. The amines are extracted from alkaline solution with ether in a liquid–liquid extractor and trapped in aqueous phosphoric acid. The acid is neutralized, and the amines are extracted from the aqueous phase with 1-butanol. This procedure was developed for the isolation of amines for paper chromatography, but it should be equally applicable in the field of gas chromatography. Amines can also be isolated by means of ion-exchange resins by a procedure similar to the one used for amino acids (Chapter 8, Section A). These methods are described in detail below.

a. Isolation of Volatile Amines

1. *Isolation by Aeration* (James *et al.*, 1952). Leaves (100 gm) are macerated in a Waring blendor and extracted with 0.001 N hydrochloric acid (1 liter). The extract is filtered, centrifuged, and made alkaline with sodium hydroxide solution. Air is drawn through the mixture to volatilize the free bases. These are trapped by bubbling the air stream through 0.001 N hydrochloric acid contained in a wash bottle. At the end of an hour the wash bottle is removed from the air stream and its contents are evaporated almost to dryness. The volume is made up to 2 ml, and 100-μl portions are taken for chromatography.

*2. *Isolation by Steam Distillation* (Hughes, 1959). The tissue (30 to 40 gm) is comminuted and thoroughly extracted with 6 × 60-ml portions of 10% trichloroacetic acid in water. The combined extracts are made up to 500 ml and filtered. A portion (50 ml) of the extract is adjusted to pH 11 to 12 with sodium hydroxide solution with thymolphthalein as an indicator. The amines are steam-distilled into 0.1 N hydrochloric acid (10 ml). The volume of the distillate is reduced to about 5 ml, and the remainder of the water is removed in a centrifugal freeze-dryer. The residue is dissolved in water (0.3 ml), and a suitable aliquot is injected into the chromatograph with a syringe.

*3. *Separation from Neutral Components* (Burks *et al.*, 1959). Ground tissue (200 gm) is macerated in a Waring blendor with water (200 ml) for 5 minutes, and the slurry is clarified by centrifugation. An aliquot (100 ml) of the clear aqueous solution is withdrawn, and saturated potassium carbonate solution is added until it is alkaline. The extract is then divided among three 100-ml round-bottomed flasks and frozen in dry ice. Water, amines, and neutral compounds are removed by lyophilization at 10 to 50 μ of pressure for 6 to 10 hours. The distillate is thawed, and the pH is reduced to below 2 with dilute hydrochloric acid. The solution is then frozen and lyophilized again to remove neutral components. The residue from this procedure is a white crystalline solid weighing 6 to 25 mg. The authors state that recovery of amines is only 40 to 60%.

*4. *Preliminary Fractionation of Amines* (Honegger and Honegger, 1959). The tissue is homogenized in 80% ethanol and adjusted to pH 2 to 3 with concentrated hydrochloric acid. The mixture is then centrifuged, and the supernatant is retained. The precipitate is re-extracted three to four times, and the supernatants are combined. The ethanol solution containing the unbound amine hydrochlorides is concentrated under vacuum at a water-bath temperature of 40° to 50°C. The solution is then saturated with barium hydroxide and subjected to a fractional steam distillation at 15 to 25 mm Hg under a nitrogen atmosphere. Four fractions are collected in hydrochloric acid solution at different water-bath temperatures. Fraction 1 comes over at 14° to 19°C in 90 minutes, fraction 2 comes over at 19° to 36°C in 10 to 15 minutes, fraction 3 is obtained at 36° to 55°C in 60 to 75 minutes, and fraction 4 at 55° to 60°C in 60 to 75 minutes. The excess hydrochloric acid is removed from the fractions at reduced pressure. These are unbound fractions.

To liberate the bound amines, the residue from the steam distillation and the ethanol-insoluble precipitate are combined and refluxed for 6 hours in saturated barium hydroxide solution. The hydrolyzate is steam-distilled under vacuum in a nitrogen atmosphere, and the volatile amines are collected in N hydrochloric acid. The crude amines are then fractionated by the same procedure as for the unbound amines.

Most of the ammonia and methylamine comes off in fractions 1 and 2, and 2-(dimethylamino)ethanol is found in fraction 3.

b. Isolation of Less Volatile Amines

*1. *Liquid–Liquid Extraction* (Block and Bolling, 1951). An aliquot of the aqueous solution containing the amines (5 ml) is added to a 1:6 mixture of K_3PO_4 and Na_2SO_4 (6 gm) dissolved in 15 ml of water. The amines are extracted from this solution with peroxide-free ether in a continuous liquid–liquid extractor (Scientific Glass Apparatus Co.). Aqueous 4% phosphoric acid (1 ml) is placed in the receiver flask, and the extraction is continued for 24 to 48 hours. At the end of this time the ether is separated from the solution in the receiver flask, and the aqueous layer is adjusted to pH 7 with sodium hydroxide solution. The solution is then saturated with K_3PO_4–Na_2SO_4 mixture (see above), and the amines are extracted with *n*-butanol. The butanol is dried over anhydrous sodium sulfate, and the amines are converted to their hydrochlorides with gaseous hydrochloric acid. The solvent is then removed under vacuum.

2. *Ion-Exchange Method* (Thompson *et al.*, 1959). See Chapter 8, Section A.

II. CHROMATOGRAPHY OF AMMONIA AND METHYLAMINES

Ammonia and the methylamines were among the first compounds to be separated by gas chromatography (James *et al.*, 1952), and this is still probably the easiest and fastest way to analyze mixtures of these compounds. Ammonia can be precipitated selectively with cobaltous chloride (von der Horst, 1957), and dimethylamine can be converted to dimethylhydrazine by nitrosation and reduction, and the latter compound treated with KIO_3 (Alekseev and Dvinenina, 1955). These compounds can also be resolved by LSC (Fuks and Rappoport, 1948), and some of them can be resolved by paper chromatography. However, GLC is by far the most rapid method, since ammonia, methylamine, dimethylamine, and trimethylamine can be separated from one another in about 30 to 40 minutes, exclusive of the time required for sample preparation.

The amines are isolated from animal or plant tissue as their hydrochlorides and are converted to the free bases by treatment with alkali in a reactor placed just before the injection port. This technique is used because application of the free bases in aqueous solution to the column leads to poor separations. Two simple methods for generating the free bases *in situ* are described below.

James *et al.* (1952) obtained good separation of ammonia, methylamine, trimethylamine, and dimethylamine on a stationary phase of hendecanol (5-ethylnonan-2-ol) containing 15% liquid paraffin with nitrogen as a carrier gas. The amines are eluted from the column in the order of their boiling points (ammonia $-33.4°C$, methylamine $-6.5°C$, trimethylamine $3.5°C$, and dimethylamine $7.4°C$). Almost as good separation is obtained on hendecanol alone; however, on pure liquid paraffin di- and trimethylamines are not resolved from one another, although they are separated from ammonia and methylamine. Hughes (1959) was able to resolve all four compounds on a stationary phase composed of n-hendecanol and n-octadecane, in a 4:1 ratio (v/w). The compounds were resolved in less than 50 minutes at a temperature of 65°C and a flow rate of 5 ml of nitrogen per minute. Burks *et al.* (1959) chromatographed these materials, as well as a number of amines of higher molecular weight, on a column containing triethanolamine on C-22 firebrick. At a temperature of 60°C and a flow rate of 50 ml/min, retention times were: trimethylamine 1.8 minutes, ammonia 2.3 minutes, dimethylamine 4.7 minutes, and methylamine 6.5 minutes, the order of elution being quite different from that found on hendecanol–paraffin oil. The compounds did not come off the column in order either of boiling point or of basic strength. However, except for ammonia, they were eluted in order of the number of protons available for hydrogen-bond formation with the polar liquid. It can be argued that the lower capacity of the column for binding ammonia is occasioned by the inorganic nature of this compound with a concomitant reduction in van der Waals attraction forces. In any event, the separation factors obtained in these experiments suggest that triethanolamine would be a satisfactory liquid substrate for the separation of these compounds if column resolution in terms of theoretical plates is satisfactory. Data on this are not given.

James *et al.* (1952) observed that the solid support they used (Celite 545) was not inert and adsorbed the amines, producing a tail on each zone. Pretreatment of the support with methanolic sodium hydroxide reduced tailing but failed to eliminate it altogether. This condition generally occurs on the chromatography of polar compounds, such as alcohols and amines, when the support has not been completely deactivated. It should be of interest to find out if the specially deactivated supports used for the chromatography of fatty amines, or the inorganic salts used for the separation of pyridine derivatives, would help to reduce tailing encountered during the separation of the methylamines (Chapter 1, Section C). James *et al.* (1952) state that the lowest amount of amine that can be detected with a titration cell is 0.3 μg equivalents. This represents 2 μg of ammonia, 4 μg of methylamine, 7 μg of dimethylamine, and 8 μg of trimethylamine. The maximum amounts of amines that can be used without overloading the column are 160 μg of ammonia, 180 μg of methyl- or dimethylamine, and 220 μg of trimethylamine with a 4-foot column having an internal diameter of 0.4 mm.

a. Conversion of Hydrochlorides to Free Bases

1. *With Soda Lime in a Pre-column* (James *et al.*, 1952). A small vertical column about 8 cm long and terminating in a short horizontal capillary is

filled with dry soda lime (50 mesh). Glass wool plugs are placed above and below the packing. This pre-column is attached to the chromatograph just before the injection port. A piece of loose-fitting glass rod is placed in the line leading to the injection port to reduce the volumn. A solution containing the amine salts is transferred to the top of the pre-column with a syringe or micropipette. When the soda lime has absorbed the liquid, the glass wool plug is washed with 2 × 25 μl of distilled water. The carrier gas supply is then connected to the top of the pre-column, and the gas stream is started. The wet part of the tube is warmed with a microburner until the water front has moved almost to the end of the column attached to the chromatograph and the whole tube is hot. Hughes (1959) found it necessary to include a short plug (1 cm long) of anhydrous sodium sulfate below the soda lime to prevent entry of water into the main column. However, he used 10/14 mesh soda lime in place of the 50 mesh size, and this might not have retained water as effectively.

*2. *With Sodium Hydroxide in a T Tube* (Burks *et al.*, 1959). A T tube is mounted in the gas stream of the chromatograph just before the column. The single arm of the tube projects upward and is sealed with a silicone rubber diaphragm. A weighed sample of amine hydrochloride is placed in a depression in the T tube just below the vertical arm. The connections are made, the carrier gas is turned on, and an excess of concentrated sodium hydroxide is added to the amine salt by injecting it through the silicone diaphragm with a hypodermic needle. The bases are set free by applying heat rapidly with a microburner immediately after the addition of alkali. It should be noted that this injection method is used in conjunction with a triethanolamine column, which would be expected to retain water better than a hendecanol column.

b. *Conditions for Chromatography*

*1. *On a Nonpolar Stationary Phase* (Hughes, 1959)

Chromatograph	Apparatus described by James and Martin (1952) and James *et al.* (1952) with pre-column described in method D.II.a.1. above.
Column dimensions	4-foot × 0.4- to 0.5-cm i.d.
Solid support	Acid- and alkali-washed Celite.
Stationary phase	*n*-Hendecanol plus 20% *n*-octadecane (30:70).
Temperature	65°C.
Carrier gas	Nitrogen at 5 ml/min at outlet. Inlet pressure: 150 mm Hg. Outlet pressure: atmospheric.
Detector	Automatic titration cell containing 0.02 N sulfuric acid and 0.007% Methyl Red.
Sample size	10 to 50 μl.
Analysis time	About 45 minutes to dimethylamine.

*2. *On a Polar Liquid* (Burks *et al.*, 1959)

Chromatograph	Burrell Kromo-Tog Model K-1 modified with sample injection tube as described in method D.II.a.2.
Column dimensions	200 × 0.6-cm i.d. Pyrex column.
Solid support	Johns-Manville C-22 firebrick (30/50 U. S. mesh) washed with aqueous HCl, freed of excess acid with water, and dried at 110°C.
Stationary phase	Triethanolamine (20:100).
Temperatures	Column, 60°C; detector, 150°C.
Carrier gas	Helium at 50 ml/min.
Detector	Four-filament hot-wire T/C cell at 130 ma.
Recorder	Wheelco, 1 mv; 1 second; 1 inch/min.
Sample size	39 to 48 mg of amine hydrochlorides.
Analysis time	23 minutes.

III. Identification of Volatile Aliphatic Amines

Aliphatic amines containing as many as 12 carbon atoms and with boiling points as high as 214°C have been separated by gas–liquid partition chromatography with liquid paraffin and polyethylene oxide (Lubrol MO) as stationary phases (James, 1952). Retention volumes on liquid paraffin at 100°C relative to ethylamine vary from 0.61 for methylamine to 62.1 for di-*n*-butylamine (Table IV). Of twenty-seven amines examined, only two pairs, isobutylamine and *sec*-butylamine, and diisobutylamine and di-*sec*-butylamine cannot be separated on 4-foot columns of either solvent.

The use of two stationary liquid phases not only permits the separation and analysis of a large variety of amines but also provides information on their structures. Retention volumes of a homologous series of amines increase regularly with chain length for any given stationary liquid. On liquid paraffin, the retention volumes of the primary straight-chain amines above ethylamine increase by a factor of 2.1 to 2.2 for an increase in chain length of one methylene group, so that a straight line is obtained when the logarithm of the relative retention volume is plotted against carbon number (Fig. 10). The slope of the line obtained on the isoalkylamines is the same as for the straight-chain amines, as would be expected. However, their retention volumes are lower by a constant difference, reflecting a difference in van der Waals forces between the branched- and straight-chain homologues in their interactions with the paraffin substrate.

The slope of the line connecting the points for the secondary straight-chain amines is slightly less than that for the primary amines, and the slope of the tertiary amine line is markedly less. This confirms the suggestion made by James *et al.* (1952) that in the series NH_2R, NHR_2, and NR_3 each additional alkyl group contributes less to the van der Waals forces of interaction with the stationary phase.

TABLE IV

RETENTION VOLUMES OF AMINES RELATIVE TO ETHYLAMINE AT 100°C*

Amine	Boiling point (°C)	Column liquid phase†	
		Paraffin	Lubrol MO
Methylamine	−6.5	0.61	0.68[b]
Dimethylamine	7.4	0.93[a]	0.81
Ethylamine	16.6	1[a]	1
Trimethylamine	3.5	1.17	0.67[b]
Isopropylamine	34	1.49	1.42
n-Propylamine	48.7	2.20	2.10[c]
Diethylamine	55.5	3.25[d]	2.10[c]
sec-Butylamine	63	3.57[d]	2.8[e]
Isobutylamine	68	3.70[d]	3.1[e]
Ethylenediamine	118	4.65[f]	15.5
n-Butylamine	77.8	4.7[f]	4.4
Ethanolamine	172.2	5.25	25.8
Diisopropylamine	83	6.8	3.00[e]
Triethylamine	89.5	8.6[g]	3.1[e]
Isoamylamine	95	8.8[g]	7.3[h]
n-Amylamine	104	10.5	9.7
Di-n-propylamine	110.7	13.2	7.2[h]
4-Methylpentylamine	123.9	17.8	13.8
n-Hexylamine	132.7	22.6	19.6
Di-sec-butylamine	132.0	27.6[i]	9.74[i]
Cyclohexylamine	134	28.4[i]	25.9
Diisobutylamine	139	30.4[i]	10.9[i]
n-Heptylamine	158.3	49.5[k]	40.05
Tri-n-propylamine	156	49.6[k]	15.1
Di-n-butylamine	159	62.1	27.6
Tri-n-butylamine	214	—	85.5
Benzylamine	185	81.0	91.5

* From James (1952).

† Those amines marked with the same small letters cannot be completely resolved on a 4-foot column.

Thus for each homologous series of amines, a line with a characteristic slope is obtained when log retention volume is plotted against carbon number. Therefore, it should be possible to determine the molecular weight of an unknown amine from its retention volume by locating its position on the appropriate line. First it is necessary to determine which group it belongs to, and this can be done by chromatographing it on a second stationary phase having different polarity.

A nonpolar liquid phase such as paraffin allows no hydrogen bonding

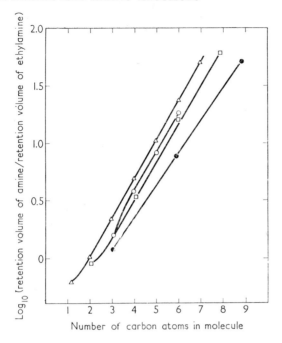

FIG. 10. The relationship between $\log_{10}$ (retention volume of amine/retention volume of ethylamine) and total number of carbon atoms in the amine molecule. △–△—primary straight-chain amines; O–O—primary isoalkylamines; □–□—secondary straight-chain amines; ●–●—tertiary straight-chain amines. (James, 1952).

between the solvent and the solute molecules, and so differences in retention volume are caused solely by differences in van der Waals interactions between the solute and stationary liquid. On the other hand, solvents such as polyethylene glycol contain many oxygen atoms with unshared electron pairs that can function as proton acceptors in hydrogen-bond formation. Hydroxyl groups occur only at the ends of long chains and are relatively unimportant. Therefore, compounds containing labile protons, such as primary aliphatic amines, should have longer residence times in columns packed with polyethylene glycol than in paraffin columns. However, the residence time of tertiary amines should be about the same in both polar and nonpolar columns, since they cannot form hydrogen bonds with either solvent. Consequently, a comparison of the residence times of a compound in a polar and nonpolar column will often reveal what homologous series it belongs to.

The most convenient way to make this comparison is to obtain chromatographic data on known members of homologous series. When the logarithms of the relative retention volumes on the polar liquids are plotted against the

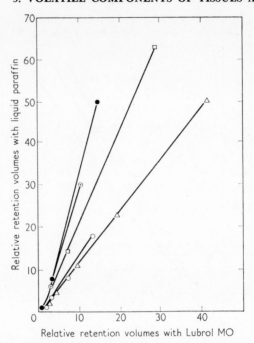

FIG. 11. The relationship between relative retention volumes (retention volume of amine/retention volume of ethylamine) for aliphatic amines on columns having stationary liquid phases of (1) liquid paraffin and (2) Lubrol MO, showing the relative speeding up of secondary and tertiary amines on changing from a solvent not allowing to one allowing hydrogen bonding. △–△—primary straight-chain amines; O–O—primary isoalkyl-amines; ☐–☐—secondary straight-chain amines; ⊙–⊙—secondary isoalkylamines; ●–●—tertiary straight-chain amines. (James, 1952).

logarithms of the retention values on the nonpolar liquids, a family of straight lines is obtained, one for each homologous series (Fig. 11). The series to which an unknown compound belongs can be determined by finding out which line the point lies on when logarithms of the two retention values are plotted against one another. Once the series is known, the carbon number can be determined also from this graph or from a plot of retention values against number of carbon atoms in the molecule.

a. Conditions for Chromatography

1. On Polar and Nonpolar Stationary Liquids (James, 1952)

Chromatograph	Laboratory-built (James and Martin, 1952).
Column dimensions	4-foot × 0.4-mm i.d. straight glass tube.
Solid support	Celite 545 prepared as described in Chapter 1, method C.III.a.1.

Stationary phase	(I) Liquid paraffin (30:70). (II) Lubrol MO (obtained from Imperial Chemical Industries Ltd.) (30:70).
Temperature	100°C.
Carrier gas	Nitrogen at 18.7 ml/min. Inlet pressure: 225 mm Hg. Outlet pressure: atmospheric.
Detector	Titration cell with 0.04 N sulfuric acid.
Sample size	0.3 to 10 gm equivalents of each amine.
Analysis time	80 minutes to di-n-butylamine on paraffin oil.

IV. POLYBASIC AMINES

Very little work has been done on the gas chromatographic separation of di- and polybasic aliphatic amines such as cadaverine, putrescine, spermine, or spermidine, despite the fact that they are important in metabolism or are produced during the bacterial degradation of organic matter. James (1952) compared the retention values of ethylenediamine on paraffin oil and on polyethylene glycol. He found that it chromatographs much more slowly (relative $V_r = 15.5$) on the polar solvent than on the hydrocarbon ($V_r = 4.65$) when compared to ethylamine. This probably arises from increased hydrogen bonding of the diamine with oxygen atoms of the polyglycol. Therefore, it should be possible to separate di- and polybasic amines from monoamines having the same carbon number by choosing a polar column packing.

Like almost all nitrogen compounds, these amines tend to tail badly when chromatographed on column packings made with solid supports containing polar sites. Wilkens Instrument and Research Inc. has published a preliminary report in the Aerograph Research Notes (Anon., 1960a) showing how this can be prevented with a solid support called Fluoropak. This material is a synthetic polymer produced as a foam which is ground to a particle size suitable for chromatography. It is nonreactive and nonpolar and therefore has little tendency to adsorb amines or other similar compounds. This column packing, when used with silicone as the stationary phase, gives good separation of putrescine and cadaverine at 119°C, the retention times being 5.1 and 9.1 minutes, respectively. The peaks are symmetrical and show essentially no tailing (Fig. 12). The amines were injected into the chromatograph as aqueous solutions, and the water peak also shows little tailing.

It is also possible to separate spermidine from spermine with this column at a temperature of 208°C. The retention times are 4.6 minutes for spermidine and 21 minutes for spermine.

The maximum efficiency that can be obtained with these columns is about 50 theoretical plates per foot, possibly because the specific surface of the ground Fluoropak is less than those of the diatomaceous earths commonly used as solid supports. However, efficiency compares favorably with that obtained by Nelson and Milun (1960), who used sodium chloride (52 plates

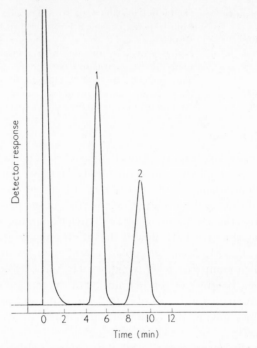

FIG. 12. Separation of (1) putrescine and (2) cadaverine on a silicone oil column with Fluoropak as the inert column packing. Temperature 119°C. (Anon., 1960a).

per foot) and deactivated Chromosorb W (35 plates per foot) for the chromatography of fatty amines on silicone grease and silicone oil, respectively.

a. Conditions for Chromatography

*1. On Silicone G.E. SF-96 (Anon., 1960a)

Chromatograph	Aerograph Model A-110-C.
Column dimensions	300 × 0.635-cm o.d. coiled stainless-steel column.
Solid support	Fluoropak 80.
Stationary phase	Silicone G.E. SF-96 (10:90).
Temperatures	(I) For putrescine–cadaverine: injection, 250°C; detector, 119°C; column, 119°C. (II) For spermine–spermidine: injection, 250°C; detector, 208°C; column, 208°C.
Carrier gas	Helium at 100 ml/min. Inlet pressure: 1200 mm Hg. Outlet pressure: atmospheric.
Detector	Four-filament hot-wire (W) T/C cell at 250 ma.
Recorder	0 to 1 mv; 1 second; 0.85 cm/min.
Sample size	200 μg of each amine.
Analysis time	22 minutes to spermine; 10 minutes to cadaverine.

V. Amino Alcohols

2-(Dimethylamino)ethanol is found in brain, fish roe, rat liver, and other tissues and has been considered to be a possible precursor of choline. Honegger and Honegger (1959) devised a procedure for extracting it from tissues and separating it from ammonia and methylamine by fractional steam distillation under reduced pressure (Section D.I.a.4). The efficiency of the procedure as measured by the recovery of C^{14}-labeled dimethylaminoethanol added to fish roe is 99%.

This compound can be separated from related amines by GLC on a Carbowax 20 M column at 125°C. 1-Dimethylamino-2-propanol, 2-(dimethylamino)ethanol, 2-(diethylamino)methanol, 2-(methylamino)ethanol, and phenylethylamine are eluted in that order. The smallest amount of dimethylaminoethanol detectable with a thermal conductivity cell at highest sensitivity is 0.1 to 0.5 μg. In a later publication (Honegger and Honegger, 1960), this compound was analyzed by means of an ionization detector with argon as the carrier gas. This method is preferred, since it is more sensitive and the detector does not respond to water, thus making it possible to inject aqueous solutions of the free bases directly into the chromatograph.[1] It should be noted (Section D.II) that James et al. obtained poor separations when the amines were applied directly to the columns in aqueous solution, but that their stationary phase (hendecanol–paraffin) is strictly nonpolar.

In the method employing the thermal detector, the amines are converted to the free bases by treating them with a 1% solution of sodium hydroxide in methanol and injecting this solution into the column. The error of the quantitative estimation calculated by the peak height × half-width method is 1 to 2% for quantities of amine above 20 μg, and 10% for smaller amounts. Significant amounts of 2-(dimethylamino)ethanol in both the bound and unbound forms are found in salmon roe, human brain, and pig brain.

a. Conditions for Chromatography

*1. On Carbowax (Honegger and Honegger, 1959)

Chromatograph	Wilkens Aerograph.
Column dimensions	150 × 0.6-cm o.d. coiled copper tubing.
Solid support	Johns-Manville Chromosorb regular (30/60 U. S. mesh) washed with 5% methanolic NaOH and dried at 120°C.
Stationary phase	Carbowax 20 M (25:100).
Temperature	125°C.
Carrier gas	Helium at 96 ml/min.
Detector	Four-filament hot-wire (W) T/C cell at 250 ma.
Recorder	0 to 1 mv; 1 second.
Sample size	1 to 10 μl of 1% (w/v) solution.
Analysis time	20 to 40 minutes.

[1] The flame ionization detector would be a better choice since the sensitivity of the argon detector is reduced by the presence of water vapor in the gas stream.

VI. SUMMARY

Ammonia and the methylamines can be separated from one another in the order of their boiling points on a stationary phase consisting of hendecanol with 15% added paraffin oil. Tailing occurs because of adsorption on the solid support. The free bases are generated from the amine hydrochlorides *in situ* in a reactor placed in advance of the column. With a titration cell as detector, the method is specific for amines isolated from biological systems. However, with a "universal" detector more care is required to eliminate neutral compounds from the material injected into the chromatograph. The lower limit of detection is about 0.3 μg equivalents of amine with a titration cell as a detector.

Values for separation factors suggest that triethanolamine would be a satisfactory liquid for the separation of the methylamines, but complete experimental details have not been worked out.

Aliphatic primary, secondary, and tertiary amines containing from 1 to 12 carbon atoms can be separated by GLC on stationary phases composed of paraffin oil or polyethylene glycol. Of twenty-six amines examined, only two pairs could not be separated on either column. It is possible to determine what group unknown amines belong to by comparing retention volumes on the two stationary liquids.

Other nitrogenous bases that can be analyzed by gas chromatography include polybasic compounds and amino alcohols.

E. Aldehydes and Ketones

Bound carbonyl compounds, such as glyceraldehyde-3-phosphate, are found in all tissues and may often occur free as minor constituents. Saturated aldehydes containing from 1 to 10 carbon atoms, and many α,β unsaturated aldehydes are found in the leaves of various species of plants. Methyl alkyl ketones with odd and even numbers of carbon atoms also occur in nature, many of them in species of *Ruta*. A variety of carbonyl compounds are found in cooked and processed foods. Cooked chicken contains biacetyl, acetone, methyl ethyl ketone, and other saturated and unsaturated aldehydes up to *n*-undec-2-en-1-al. Blue cheese contains pentanone-2, heptanone-2, and nonanone-2; cooked peas contain biacetyl, acetone, and saturated aldehydes up to valeraldehyde. It must be kept in mind that aldehydes are very reactive compounds compared to the corresponding fatty alcohols and acids. Therefore, care must be taken that they do not undergo reactions or aldol condensations during isolation or chromatography.

I. Methods of Isolation

Aldehydes or ketones can be stripped from plant and animal tissues by any of the general procedures given in Section A. They are part of the neutral fraction of the extract or distillate, inasmuch as they cannot be isolated from alcohols, ethers, or sulfur-containing compounds by adjustment of pH. However, they can be separated from other neutrals by making use of the well-known capacity of the carbonyl group for condensing with reagents containing labile hydrogen, such as hydroxylamine, or 2,4-dinitrophenylhydrazine. Precipitation through reaction with this latter compound and regeneration of the free carbonyls by a flash exchange reaction with α-ketoglutarate form the basis of the principal method for analysis of these compounds in foods by GLC (Ralls, 1960a). Pippen *et al.* (1958) stripped the carbonyl compounds free from cooked chicken by aerating an aqueous slurry of the macerated tissue under reflux. The carbonyls were collected by passing the air stream through a trap containing 2,4-dinitrophenylhydrazine in dilute acid solution. Aeration was continued for 20 hours, after which the insoluble hydrazones were collected by filtration and divided into monocarbonyl and polycarbonyl fractions by selective solubility in hot alcohol or chloroform. Ralls (1960b) isolated carbonyls from green peas by steam-distilling them at atmospheric pressure for 2 hours and collecting the first 250 ml of distillate. The carbonyls in the distillate were precipitated with 2,4-dinitrophenylhydrazine and recovered by filtration.

Carbonyl compounds react with 2-diphenylacetyl-1,3-indandione-1-hydrazone in the presence of acid catalysts in chloroform, ether, ethanol, or dioxane solution to form azines (Braun and Mosher, 1958). Mecke and deVries (1959) recommend this reagent for the subtraction of carbonyl peaks from complex mixtures prior to chromatography. Similarly, Bassette and Whitnah (1960) have shown that it is possible to remove carbonyl compounds from complex mixtures by partition between aqueous sodium sulfite and carbon tetrachloride. However, some carbonyl compounds do not react, and many α,β unsaturated aldehydes cannot be regenerated from their bisulfite addition products. Stanley *et al.* (1961) have worked out a method for the recovery of carbonyls from citrus oils by extraction with Girard reagent. Details are given in Chapter 5.

a. Isolation of Carbonyl Compounds from Cooked Foods

*1. *By Aeration at Reflux Temperature* (Pippen *et al.*, 1958). The equipment for aeration is illustrated in Fig. 13. Trap A, containing 400 ml of a saturated solution of 2,4-dinitrophenylhydrazine in $2N$ sulfuric acid, removes carbonyls from the air that sweeps the volatiles from the sample. Trap B contains glass wool. C is a 22-liter flask containing the sample, D. Traps E and F collect the carbonyls and contain 400 ml each of a 0.2% solution of 2,4-dinitro-phenylhydrazine solution in 2 N hydrochloric acid. *Procedure:* The macerated tissue (5 kg) is placed in flask C together with an equal weight of distilled water. The flask is closed, and air is drawn through the system by reducing the pressure sufficiently at trap F to cause approximately two bubbles per second to pass through the liquid in traps E and F. With water circulating through the condenser, sufficient heat is applied to flask C to maintain a gentle reflux throughout the run. Aeration is continued for a period of 20 hours. At the end of the run, hydrazones in traps E and F are recovered by filtration, washed with water, and dried under vacuum at 60°C. Presumably additional hydrazones could be recovered by liquid–liquid extraction of the filtrate as described in procedure E.I.a.2 below.

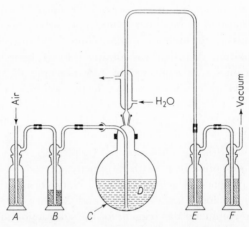

FIG. 13. Apparatus for isolating volatile carbonyl compounds from cooked foods: (A) 400 ml of a saturated solution of 2,4-dinitrophenylhydrazine in 2 N H_2SO_4; (B) trap containing glass wool; (C) 22-liter flask; (D) chicken and water heated to slow boil; (E, F) 400 ml of 2,4-dinitrophenylhydrazine solution (2 gm/liter in 2 N HCl). (Pippen *et al.*, 1958).

2. By Steam Distillation at Atmospheric Pressure (Ralls, 1960b). The sample (2 kg) is mixed with distilled water (1 liter) and macerated in a food blendor. The mixture is transferred to a flask and steam-distilled at atmospheric pressure for 2 hours, with a boiling-water bath as a heat source. About 1 hour is required to reach distillation temperature, after which clean steam is passed through the mixture for about ½ hour, and the first 250 ml of distillate is collected. A trap containing 2,4-dinitrophenylhydrazine reagent is placed after the receiver to ensure that all the volatile carbonyls are retained. The distillate is treated with a 1% solution of 2,4-dinitrophenylhy-drazine reagent in concentrated hydrochloric acid (20 ml) to precipitate the carbonyls as their 2,4-dinitrophenylhydrazones. The suspension is heated to boiling for 5 minutes, cooled slowly to room temperature, and stored overnight in a refrigerator. The precipitate is collected by filtration, washed with 2N hydrochloric acid, then with water, and finally dried under reduced pressure over phosphorus pentoxide. Aldehydes and ketones are liberated for chromatography by the flash exchange method (Ralls, 1960a). Soluble hydrazones are recovered by diluting the filtrate and washings from the DNPH precipitation to 450 ml with water, and extracting continuously with purified petroleum ether (250 ml) for 16 hours in a liquid–liquid extractor. The extract is washed with 3 × 50-ml portions of water, dried over anhydrous sodium sulfate, and the solvent evaporated.

b. Separation of Mono- and Polycarbonyl Compounds

*1. *Isolation of Polycarbonyls* (Pippen *et al.*, 1958). Separation is based on the fact that dinitrophenylhydrazones of polycarbonyl compounds are only slightly soluble in hot alcohol or chloroform, whereas monocarbonyl derivatives are quite soluble in these solvents. The mixed hydrazones are digested with large amounts of hot alcohol and chloroform, and the supernatants are filtered. The solvent is evaporated from the combined filtrates on a steam bath under a stream of nitrogen. The residue, consisting largely of monohydrazones, gives a characteristic red color when a portion of it is dissolved in alcoholic KOH. The residue on the filter consists mostly of hydrazones of di- and polyfunctional carbonyl compounds and gives a violet color on treatment with alcoholic potassium hydroxide. The free carbonyls can be liberated by Ralls' flash exchange technique and chromatographed, as described under chromatography of aldehydes and ketones.

II. Chromatography of Aldehydes and Ketones

Carbonyls have been separated successfully on several types of columns. Stephens and Teszler (1960) use dinonyl phthalate at 87°C as the stationary phase for the separation of C_2 to C_5 aldehydes. Ralls (1960a) uses Carbowax 1540 or LAC 446 (glycol adipate polymer) at 90°C and 150°C for separation of C_2 to C_6 aldehydes and ketones (Table V). Hawke *et al.* (1957) compared several types of column and found that Pluronic F 68 and tri-*m*-tolylphosphate gave better separations at 110°C than paraffin wax, D.C. 550 silicone oil or dicapryl phthalate. There was some tailing of peaks under the conditions employed by Hawke *et al.*, and the column temperatures were higher than those of the first two workers.

The C_7 to C_{11} aldehydes and ketones are found as constituents of essential oils and have been separated on a poly(1,4-butanediol succinate) column by Stanley *et al.* (1961). Cartoni and Liberti (1960) have also separated mixtures of these materials with D.C. 550 silicone oil, a nonpolar stationary phase, and

TABLE V

Retention Times for Carbonyl Compounds Regenerated from
2,4-Dinitrophenylhydrazine by Exchange with α-Ketoglutaric Acid[a,b]

Carbonyl compound	Column temperature (°C)	Retention time (min)	Remarks
Aldehydes			
Formaldehyde	90	—	Polymerizes ?
Acetaldehyde	90	4.5	
Propionaldehyde	90	6.8	
Isobutyraldehyde	90	7.7	
n-Butyraldehyde	90	10.4	
Isovaleraldehyde	90	13.1	
n-Valeraldehyde	90	17.0	
2-Methyl-1-butanal	90	12.0	
Acrolein	90	9.2	
Crotonaldehyde	90, 150	26.9, 6.9	
2,4-Pentadienal	150	12.2	
2-Hexenal	150	12.7	
Methional	150	—	Decomposes
Benzaldehyde	150, 210	>32, >20	210° on LAC
Ketones			
Acetone	90	7.6	
Butanone	90	11.7	
2-Pentanone	90, 150	17.8, 4.6	
3-Pentanone	90, 150	19.1, 5.3	
3-Methyl-2-butanone	90	14.0	
2-Hexanone	90, 150	30.0, 6.6	
4-Methyl-3-penten-2-one	150	12.3	
Cyclohexanone	150	24.6	
Biacetyl(bis)	90	>25	Not regenerated

[a] From Ralls (1960a).
[b] 10-foot Carbowax, flow rate 32 ml/min, theoretical plates = 1150 (propionaldehyde).

octakis(2-hydroxypropyl) sucrose, a strongly polar phase. Details of the chromatography of these compounds will be found in Chapter 5.

Aldehydes and ketones of low molecular weight (C_2 to C_6 carbon atoms) can be separated from the neutral volatile fraction of plant and animal tissues by forming the nonvolatile 2,4-dinitrophenylhydrazones. The free carbonyls must then be regenerated before chromatography. Ralls (1960a) has developed a flash exchange method for doing this which Stephens and Teszler (1960) have made quantitative. The crystalline 2,4-dinitrophenylhydrazones are mixed with crystalline α-ketoglutaric acid. The aldehydes and ketones are regenerated when the mixture is heated quickly to 250°C. The mixture is contained in a capillary attached at the injection port of the chromatograph, and the volatile aldehydes and ketones are swept onto the column.

Formaldehyde is regenerated rapidly and is not detected, and this forms the basis of the modification of Stephens and Teszler for the quantitative recovery of low-boiling carbonyls. A mixture of formaldehyde 2,4-dinitrophenylhydrazone and α-ketoglutaric acid is added to the capillary tube first. Next, the 2,4-dinitrophenylhydrazones of the carbonyls to be separated are adsorbed on Celite from methanol solution. The mixture of Celite, 2,4-dinitrophenylhydrazones, plus added α-ketoglutaric acid is placed on top of the formaldehyde 2,4-dinitrophenylhydrazone/α-ketoglutaric acid mixture. When the tube is heated quickly to 250°C, the regenerated formaldehyde sweeps the test carbonyls rapidly into the column (details below). This method has given quantitative recoveries with known mixtures of aldehydes.

Cason and Harris (1959) have chromatographed the C_2 to C_4 aldehydes and ketones as their oxime derivatives and obtained satisfactory separation on a di-(2-ethylhexyl) phthalate column at 88°C. The free volatile aldehydes and ketones are collected by steam distillation of tissue components. The oximes are then prepared in the aqueous solution by using hydroxylamine hydrochloride and sodium carbonate. They are next extracted into ether, and the ether extract is concentrated by distillation until a small volume remains, which is then injected into the chromatograph (details below).

Formaldehyde is not separated by the chromatographic procedures discussed above. There are several sensitive specific methods for its detection, however, one being a spectrophotometric method with chromotropic and sulfuric acids (Bricker and Johnson, 1945). As little as 2 ppm can be detected by this procedure.

Relatively high concentrations of formaldehyde can be determined in aqueous solutions by gas chromatography (Smith, 1959; Kelker, 1960). However, these methods are not applicable to the determination of trace amounts of this material as would be found in aqueous tissue extracts.

a. Sample Preparation and Injection

*1. Flash Exchange Method (Ralls, 1960a; Stephens and Teszler, 1960). A saturated solution of the 2,4-dinitrophenylhydrazone mixture is made up in methanol. Standard solutions of known 2,4-dinitrophenylhydrazones are made in this same way, and aliquots are dried at 105°C. The solids are weighed to determine their concentrations in solution. A 10- to 20-μl portion of the appropriate concentration of material is pipetted into 8 mg of Celite in a 1-ml glass vial and dried for 3 to 5 minutes at 105°C to remove the solvent. The mixture is cooled, and α-ketoglutaric acid is added, three times the weight of the derivative, and mixed thoroughly. The mixture is transferred quantitatively into a 1 × 100-mm borosilicate glass tube which contains about 1 mg of a 2:1 (w/w) mixture of α-ketoglutaric acid and formaldehyde 2,4-dinitrophenylhydrazone. The capillary tube is attached to a No. 27 hypodermic needle by a rubber adapter and inserted through the silicone septum of the injection port (Fig. 9). The capillary is heated to 250°C for 30 seconds either in a silicone oil bath or with a small resistance wire heater surrounding the capillary tube. The assembly is immediately removed from the injection port after the prescribed reaction time.

*2. *Chromatography as Oximes* (Cason and Harris, 1959). Hydroxylamine hydrochloride (3.13 gm, 45 mmoles) is added to a solution of 10 to 100 mg of the carbonyls in about 10 ml of water. Then 2.39 gm (22.5 mmoles) of anhydrous sodium carbonate is added slowly to control effervescence. The mixture is continuously extracted for 1 hour with ether which has been distilled from sulfuric acid and stored over sodium. The ether extract is dried over sodium sulfate, distilled until about 1 ml of solution remains, and then transferred to a 2-ml volumetric flask with a syringe. The distillation flask is washed with ether which is used to bring the volume to 2 ml. Aliquots of this solution are now injected into the gas chromatograph.

b. Conditions for Chromatography as Free Carbonyls

*1. *On a Nonpolar Liquid* (Stephens and Teszler, 1960)

Chromatograph	F & M Model 119.
Column dimensions	4-foot × 0.5-cm o.d. stainless-steel tube.
Solid support	Celite.
Stationary phase	Dinonyl phthalate prepacked by F. & M. Ratio not known.
Temperature	87°C.
Carrier gas	Helium at 40 ml/min. Inlet pressure: 12 psig. Outlet pressure: atmospheric.
Detector	4000-ohm matched thermistors.
Recorder	Brown recorder, 1 mv; 1 second; ½ inch/min.
Sample size	About 0.5 mg of mixed 2,4-dinitrophenylhydrazones.
Analysis time	About 14 to 15 minutes to valeraldehyde.

*2. *On a Polar Liquid* (Ralls, 1960a)

Chromatograph	Aerograph Model 110-C.
Column dimensions	10-foot × ¼-inch stainless-steel tubing.
Stationary phase	Carbowax 1540 (30:70).
Temperatures	90°C, 150°C.
Carrier gas	Helium at 32 ml/min.
Detector	Four-filament thermal conductivity cell.
Recorder	1 mv.
Sample size	4 to 5 mg of 2,4-dinitro-phenylhydrazones.
Analysis time	17 minutes to *n*-valeraldehyde at 90°C.

c. Conditions for Chromatography as Oximes

*1. *On a Nonpolar Liquid* (Cason and Harris, 1959)

Chromatograph	Laboratory-built.
Column dimensions	200 × 0.8-cm o.d. Pyrex tubing.
Solid support	Firebrick (30/60 mesh).
Stationary phase	Di-2-(ethylhexyl) phthalate (3:77).
Temperature	88°C.
Carrier gas	Helium at 35 ml/min.
Detector	Thermistor.
Recorder	Varian G-10, 10 mv.
Sample size	0.1 to 1.0 mg.
Analysis time	11 minutes to 3-methyl-2-butanone.

III. Summary

Carbonyls can be isolated from other components of the volatile fraction of tissues by precipitating them as 2,4-dinitrophenylhydrazones. They can be regenerated in the gas stream of the chromatograph through an exchange reaction of the hydrazones with α-ketoglutarate. The free aldehydes are partitioned on dinonyl phthalate at 87°C. Aldehydes and ketones containing 2 to 4 carbon atoms can be chromatographed as their oximes on di-2-(ethylhexyl) phthalate at 88°C.

F. Thiols and Sulfides

I. Occurrence and Isolation

Thiols including methylmercaptan and propylmercaptan, and thioethers like dimethyl sulfide and diallyl sulfide, have been reported to occur in traces in a number of plants and probably contribute substantially to food aroma. They are part of the neutral volatile fraction, but like aldehydes they can be separated from other neutrals by selective precipitating or complexing reagents. Very little work has been reported on the isolation of these materials for GLC. Kramlich and Pearson (1960) passed the volatiles from cooked beef through an aqueous lead acetate solution and obtained a black precipitate which they believed to indicate the presence of volatile sulfur compounds. No attempt was made to identify or chromatograph them.

Thiols react with heavy metal salts in aqueous solution to form highly insoluble mercaptides, and this can be applied as a general method of isolation. Mercury, lead, zinc, and copper derivatives have been most widely investigated, but other salts, such as those of silver, nickel, iron, and cadmium, have been prepared. Mercaptides are covalent compounds that are insoluble in water but soluble in organic solvents. Precipitation of some mercaptides is complete even when the salts of strong acids are used. However, to ensure quantitative separation, the liberated mineral acid should be neutralized, or the thiol precipitated with the salt of a weak acid, such as acetic.

Alkyl sulfides form addition compounds with salts of heavy metals, such as mercury and gold. These form as a result of the donor properties of the unshared electron pair(s) on the sulfur and can be represented as shown,

$$\begin{array}{c} R_1 \\ \diagdown \\ S \rightarrow HgX_2 \\ \diagup \\ R_2 \end{array}$$

where X is the anion. Mercurous salts react with alkyl sulfides to form metallic mercury and an addition compound of the sulfide with mercuric mercury (Faraghar et al., 1929). The addition compounds are usually solids. They are more soluble in water than in organic solvents. Therefore, aqueous solutions of mercurous salts can be used to extract sulfides from organic solvents. The alkyl sulfides can be recovered by treatment of the addition complex with hydrogen sulfide. Bassette and Whitnah (1960) subtracted alkyl sulfides from volatile mixtures by the addition of mercury salts. They found that addition of mercuric chloride to an aqueous solution of methyl sulfide, followed by extraction with carbon tetrachloride and analysis by GLC, eliminated the peak arising from this substance. The same treatment had no effect on carbonyl or alcohol peaks but reduced the height of an unresolved propanal and methyl sulfide peak to the expected height of the propanal peak alone.

II. Chromatography

Thiols and dialkyl sulfides have been chromatographed on a number of stationary phases including tricresyl phosphate (Amberg, 1958), dioctyl phthalate (Sunner et al., 1956), dinonyl phthalate (Spencer et al., 1958), β,β'-iminodipropionitrile (Karchmer, 1959), Carbowax 1540 (Carson et al., 1960), commercial wetting agents (Adams and Koppe, 1959), and squalane (Sullivan et al., 1959). Some of the retention data relative to 1-butanethiol are summarized in Table VI. Log_{10} retention value increases linearly with carbon number on nonpolar liquids such as dinonyl phthalate, but on polar liquids like Carbowax and Triton marked deviations occur at low carbon numbers. On dinonyl phthalate, the separation factor is about 2.74 per carbon atom for the homologous series consisting of primary straight-chain thiols. On Triton X-305, α varies from 1.6 for C_2/C_1 to 1.9 for C_5/C_4. Primary thiols are bound more strongly to the stationary phase than secondary thiols whether the solvent is polar or nonpolar, separation factors being about 1.5 for these isomers. Chain branching also decreases affinity for the stationary phase. This is illustrated by the fact that retention values of 2-methylpropanethiol are less than for 1-butanethiol on all the liquids investigated. Tertiary compounds are bound less tenaciously than any other thiols investigated, as shown by the finding that retention values of 2-methyl-2-propanethiol are less than for 1-propanethiol on all the stationary phases listed (Table VI), even though the latter compound has one less carbon atom.

TABLE VI

RELATIVE RETENTION VALUES OF THIOLS ON VARIOUS STATIONARY PHASES[a]

Compound	A	B	C	D	E	F	G
Hydrogen sulfide	—	—	0.15	0.03	—	—	—
Methanethiol	0.27	0.10	0.23	0.10	—	—	0.05
Ethanethiol	0.35	0.18	0.36	0.19	—	—	0.14
2-Propanethiol	0.37	0.25	0.36	—	0.33	0.29	0.21
2-Methyl-2-propane-thiol	0.37	0.33	0.41	—	0.33	0.34	0.28
1-Propanethiol	0.57	0.42	0.54	—	0.57	0.42	0.37
2-Butanethiol	0.62	0.65	—	—	—	—	0.61
2-Methyl-1-propane-thiol	0.76	0.73	0.79	—	0.76	0.75	0.70
1-Butanethiol	1.00	1.00	1.00	1.00	1.00	1.00	1.00
1-Pentanethiol	—	—	1.90	—	1.71	2.35	2.74

[a] (A) Carbowax 1540 at 80°C. (B) Apiezon M at 60°C. (C) Triton X-305 at 100°C. (D) Tricresyl phosphate at 100°C. (E) β,β' Iminodipropionitrile at 84°C. (F) White oil at 84°C. (G) Dinonyl phthalate at 50°C.

Primary normal, primary iso, and tertiary mercaptans can be identified by determining retention values on polar and nonpolar liquids and plotting logarithms of these against one another. A family of straight lines is obtained, one for each homologous series. Karchmer (1959) used β,β'-iminodipropionitrile for the polar liquids, and white oil for the nonpolar liquid. Conventional log-log plots yielded separate straight lines for each of the three groups of compounds (Fig. 14). These groups were readily distinguished from thiophene derivatives by the positions of the lines.

The retention times of dialkyl sulfides also increase in a regular manner with chain length (Table VII): the separation factor for higher members of the series is about 2.5 per methylene group, or slightly less than for thiols. Cyclic sulfides are bound more avidly than the corresponding open-chain compounds. Thus, the relative retention of thiacyclopentane on dinonyl phthalate is 2.89, compared to 0.80 for 3-thiapentane. Substitution of a methylene group for sulfur greatly reduces the degree of binding, as shown by the fact that the separation factor for thiapentane–pentane is about 11.

TABLE VII

RELATIVE RETENTION TIMES OF DIALKYL SULFIDES
ON DINONYL PHTHALATE AT 50°C
(1-Butanethiol = 1.00)

Compound	Relative retention value
2-Thiapropane	0.16
2-Thiabutane	0.31
3-Thiapentane	0.80
Thiacyclopentane	2.89
n-Pentane	0.07
2-Methyl-3-thiapentane	1.27
3-Thiahexane	1.99
5-Methyl-3-thiahexane	3.25
3-Thiaheptane	5.15

In general, the retention values of sulfides are somewhat less than for thiols having the same carbon number on both polar and nonpolar substrates (Fig. 15). However, an important exception occurs in the case of methanethiol and thiapropane. Here the thiol emerges from the chromatographic column just ahead of the sulfide. Inability to separate this pair of

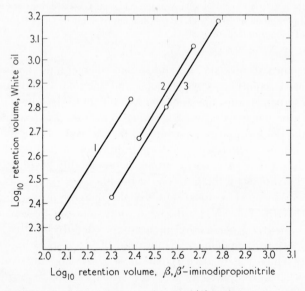

FIG. 14. Relation of relative retention volumes of (1) tertiary mercaptans, (2) primary isomercaptans, and (3) primary normal mercaptans. (Karchmer, 1959).

compounds on tricresyl phosphate led Adams and Koppe (1959) to investigate a series of commercial wetting agents (the Tritons) as stationary liquids for the separation of thiols, mercaptans, hydrogen sulfide, and sulfur dioxide. The Tritons are polyethylene glycols of various chain lengths, terminating in a hydroxyl group at one end and a *p*-octylphenyl group at the

$$CH_3—C(CH_3)_2—CH_2—C(CH_3)_2—\langle\bigcirc\rangle—(OCH_2CH_2)_xOH$$

other end. It was found that the retention times of sulfur dioxide and water increased with the number of units, *x*, in the polyether chain, whereas those of sulfides and thiols decreased. This made it possible to elute sulfur dioxide between thiapropane and 3-thiapentane with no overlapping of peaks. Moreover, the resolution of ethanethiol and thiapropane increased with chain length even though absolute retention times decreased, making it feasible to secure satisfactory analyses of these compounds on a substrate having a chain length of 30 units (Triton X-305). With this compound as a partition liquid it was possible to secure good resolution of a mixture containing methanethiol, ethanethiol, thiapropane, sulfur dioxide, 3-thiapentane, *n*-butanethiol, dimethyl disulfide, and diethyl disulfide, elution occurring in the order given.

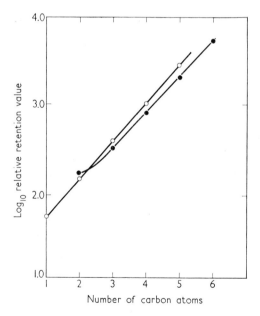

FIG. 15. Relation between carbon number and $\log_{10}$ retention value relative to *n*-butanethiol for straight-chain thiols and alkyl disulfides on dinonyl phthalate. ○—*n*-Alkane thiols; ●—*n*-dialkyl sulfides. (Data from Spencer *et al.*, 1958).

Separations were started at an initial column temperature of 30°C. After elution of 3-thiapentane, the temperature was rapidly and reproducibly increased to 100°C. Base-line drift was minimized by thermostating the detector in a separate housing from the column. Temperature programming in steps or continuously has been used by a number of workers for the separation of sulfides and disulfides having wide boiling-point ranges. Sullivan *et al.* (1959) modified an Aerograph Model A-100 chromatograph for separation of these compounds by nonlinear temperature programming. The detector was a Gow-Mac thermal conductivity cell containing four tungsten-wire filaments and having TE geometry. It was placed about 8 inches from the chromatograph and thermostatted at 150°C. The helium stream to the refer-

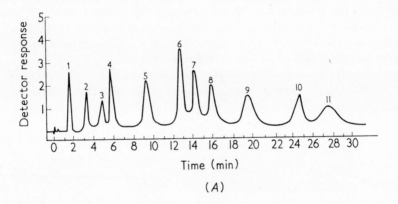

(A)

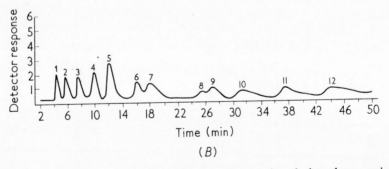

(B)

FIG. 16. (A) nonlinear temperature-programmed separation of a homologous series of sulfides: (1) dimethyl; (2) methyl ethyl; (3) methyl isopropyl; (4) diethyl; (5) ethyl-*n*-propyl; (6) di-*n*-propyl; (7) isopropyl-*n*-butyl; (8) diisobutyl; (9) di-*n*-butyl; (10) diiso-amyl; (11) di-*n*-amyl. (B) linear temperature-programmed separation of a homologous series of mercaptans, 3°C per minute: (1) ethyl; (2) isopropyl; (3) *n*-propyl; (4) isobutyl; (5) *n*-butyl; (6) isoamyl; (7) *n*-amyl; (8) *n*-hexyl; (9) *tert*-octyl; (10) *n*-heptyl; (11) *n*-octyl; (12) *n*-nonyl. (Sullivan *et al.*, 1959).

ence side of the detector was also thermostatted at 150°C. Chromatography was started at a column temperature of 20°C. The variable voltage transformer used to control the Aerograph oven temperature was turned on full-scale, and the temperature was allowed to increase to 150°C. This required about 30 minutes, during which time thiols and sulfides up to C_{10} were eluted (Fig. 16). Temperature did not increase linearly with time, and the flow rate of the carrier gas was not constant owing to the increase in its viscosity with temperature. Nevertheless, good separation by carbon number was obtained on a squalane–firebrick stationary phase. The peaks were less crowded at low retention times than on a run in which linear temperature programming was used. This probably resulted from the fact that the oven used for this work showed a temperature lag during the first 10 minutes after the heat was turned on, and thereafter warmed more rapidly. Undoubtedly this unequal temperature-time distribution tended to mask in part the logarithmic nature of the elution pattern obtained in chromatographing homologous series of compounds.

In working with complex mixtures of thiols, it is difficult to introduce samples quantitatively into the chromatograph without losing some of the more-volatile components. Losses can be avoided by generating the thiols *in situ* through a flash exchange reaction between mercuric mercaptides and a thiol. This technique is similar in principle to ones previously described for the introduction of volatile fatty acids and carbonyls (Sections C and E). The method (Carson *et al.*, 1960) is convenient, since thiols are best isolated from natural sources as their mercuric salts. The solid mercaptides are mixed with toluene-3,4-dithiol and placed in a capillary tube attached to the injection port of the chromatograph. The C_1 to C_4 thiols are liberated rapidly by heating the tube to 245° to 260°C in an oil bath and are swept into the chromatograph with the carrier gas stream. Mercuric sulfide does not react with the reagent, and the C_5 and C_6 thiols are not sufficiently volatile to produce definite peaks under the experimental conditions employed. Thus the method is useful for straight- and branched-chain thiols having 1 to 4 carbon atoms.

No evidence was found for thermal decomposition of mercuric mercaptides to disulfides under the conditions of the reaction. Complexes of dialkyl sulfides with mercuric chloride yielded free sulfides along with small amounts of the corresponding thiols on reaction with toluene dithiol. Thus, this method is potentially useful for introducing dialkyl sulfides into the chromatograph if a way can be found to minimize partial conversion to thiols. Lead salts of thiols react much less rapidly with the reagent than do mercuric salts.

Thiols can be detected by the conventional thermal and ionization methods, but Sunner *et al.* (1956) describe a potentiometric method that may be of value if selective detection of thiols in the presence of other neutral volatiles is desired. Briefly, the fractions are eluted into a solution containing iodine and an alkali metal iodine. Thiols are oxidized quantitatively to disulfides, simultaneously reducing a stoichiometric quantity of iodine. This produces a change in potential of a Pt–I_2–I^- half cell, which is detected electrometrically. Results are recorded as integral curves similar to the ones obtained on the determination of volatile fatty acids in titration cells (Fig. 17). The concentration of each thiol is approximately proportional to the length of the step corresponding to it.

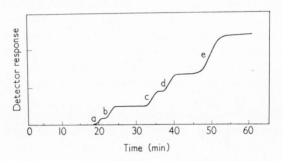

FIG. 17. Potentiometric selective detection of thiols in the presence of other neutral volatiles: separation of a mixture of (*a*) *tert*-butyl mercaptan, (*b*) *n*-propyl mercaptan, (*c*) *sec*-butyl mercaptan, (*d*) isobutyl mercaptan, and (*e*) *n*-butyl mercaptan and *tert*-amyl mercaptan on dioctyl phthalate + 5% diphenylamine. (Sunner *et al.*, 1956.)

The proportionality is not exact because there is not a linear relation between the change in electromotive force and the amount of thiol oxidized by the iodine. In the first place, the pH is not kept constant during elution of the fractions. Thus the redox potential of the half-cell is changed by the hydrogen ions liberated in the reaction

$$2RSH + I_2 \rightarrow RSSR + 2H^+ + 2I^-$$

Furthermore, on addition of a constant amount of thiol, the ratio $[I_2]/[I]^-$ decreases more rapidly at low than it does at high concentrations of iodine. Consequently, during a run the sensitivity increases, and when the remaining amount of iodine is very small, even traces of thiols cause appreciable changes in potential. However, the amount of iodine present at the beginning of a run is 5 μmoles. Therefore, if the thiols eluted during the run total less than 1 μmole, the sensitivity at the end of the run will be only 5% higher than at the beginning. For all practical purposes, a linear relation can be assumed between step height and amount of thiol if this condition is met. Otherwise, a calibration curve should be constructed, or the standard iodine–iodide solution should be changed during the run. It should be noted that some thiols (cysteine, for example) are oxidized past the disulfide stage by iodine. If unrecognized, such a phenomenon would give abnormally high results.

a. Sample Introduction and Detection

1. *Flash Exchange with Toluene Dithiol* (Carson et al., 1960). Mercuric mercaptides (3 to 5 mg) are introduced into a glass capillary melting-point tube, and an equal weight of warmed (liquid) toluene-3,4-dithiol is added. The tube is centrifuged to produce a slurry of mercaptides in toluene-3,4-dithiol. The open end of the tube is connected to the sample port of a gas chromatograph, and the lower part of the tube is heated at 245 to 260°C for 15 seconds in an oil bath. The exchange reactions take place, and the liberated mercaptans are swept onto the column by the carrier gas and are chromatographed. Further details concerning the flash exchange method are described in Sections C and E. The reaction is slow, and mercaptans having more than 4 carbon atoms are not volatile enough to give well-defined peaks. Organic sulfide-mercuric chloride complexes produce the free sulfide together with small amounts of the corresponding thiol.

2. *Potentiometric Detection of Thiols* (Sunner et al., 1956). Thiols are oxidized quantitatively by iodine to disulfides. Consequently, the amount of thiol eluted from the chromatographic column can be found by measuring the change in redox potential of a standard iodine–iodide solution, since the relative amounts of the two substances will change as peaks are eluted. The solution is prepared by adding 0.025 M iodine solution (0.2 ml) in absolute ethanol and 0.05 M potassium iodide solution (0.4 ml) in water to 70% (v/v) aqueous ethanol (50 ml). The solution is mixed in an electrode vessel which is fitted with a small stirrer and a platinum electrode. The exhaust line from the chromatograph leads into this solution. This half-cell is connected to an $Ag + Ag^+$ half-cell with an agar–agar salt bridge. This cell is connected to a recorder in series with a 20-kΩ resistance. The relation between the change in redox potential and the amount of thiol eluted into the cell is not exactly linear, since the pH is not kept constant, and the ratio of iodine to iodide decreases more rapidly at lower than at higher concentrations of iodine. However, the sensitivity of the detector at the end of a run will be only 5% higher than at the beginning if the total moles of thiol eluted is less than 20% of the initial molarity of the iodine (5 μmoles). Otherwise, the solution should be changed during the run.

b. Conditions for Isothermal Chromatography

*1. *Polar Column* (Karchmer, 1959)

Chromatograph	Perkin-Elmer Model 154-B Vapor Fractometer.
Column dimensions	2-meter × ¼-inch stainless-steel tubing.
Solid support	Size-graded Celite 545.

Stationary phase	β,β'-iminodipropionitrile (28.6:71.4).
Temperature	84°C.
Carrier gas	Helium at 70 ml/min.
Detector	Thermistor.
Recorder	Leeds and Northrup, 20 mv; 1 second.
Sample size	3 μl.
Analysis time	About 20 minutes to 3-methylthiophene.

*2. Nonpolar Column (Spencer et al., 1958)

Chromatograph	Perkin-Elmer 154-B Vapor Fractometer.
Column dimensions	152 × 0.64 cm o.d. stainless-steel tubing.
Solid support	C-22 firebrick (20/30 U. S. mesh).
Stationary phase	Dinonyl phthalate (20:50).
Temperature	50°C.
Carrier gas	Helium at 92 ml/min at exit. Inlet pressure: 200 mm Hg. Outlet pressure: atmospheric.
Detector	Thermistor.
Recorder	5 mv; 1 second; ½ inch/min.
Sample size	10 μl.
Analysis time	45 to 90 minutes.

c. Conditions for Temperature-Programmed Chromatography

*1. Polar Column (Adams and Koppe, 1959)

Chromatograph	Podbielniak Chromacon Model 9400-3A.
Column dimensions	6 feet × ¼ inch.
Solid support	Chromosorb (30/60 U. S. mesh).
Stationary phase	Triton X-305 (20:80).
Temperatures	30°C to dimethyl sulfide; 30° → 100°C for remainder of run.
Carrier gas	Helium at 50 ml/min. Inlet pressure: 716 mm Hg. Outlet pressure: atmospheric.
Detector	Thermistor.
Recorder	Brown, 10 mv; 1 second.
Sample size	5 ml of gas; 1 to 5 μl of liquid.
Analysis time	50 minutes.

*2. Nonpolar Column (Sullivan et al., 1959)

Chromatograph	Wilkins Instrument Co. Aerograph Model A-100 modified for nonlinear temperature programming.
Column dimensions	200 × 0.25-cm o.d. coiled stainless-steel tubing.
Solid support	Acid-washed firebrick (30/60 U. S. mesh).
Stationary phase	Squalane preconditioned at 135°C for 24 hours before coating (25:75).
Temperatures	Injection: 150°C. Column: 20° → 150°C in 30 minutes, nonlinear. Detector: 150°C.
Carrier gas	Helium at 100 ml/min.
Detector	Gow-Mac 4-filament (W) T/C cell with TE geometry at 275 ma.

Recorder	10 mv; 2 seconds; 2 cm/min.
Sample size	5 to 10 μl.
Analysis time	30 minutes.

III. SUMMARY

Thiols can be isolated as heavy metal mercaptides while dialkyl sulfides will form complexes with mercuric salts. The dialkyl sulfides can be recovered by treatment of the addition complex with hydrogen sulfide. Thiols can be introduced into the chromatograph by flash exchange of the corresponding mercuric mercaptides with toluene dithiol in the carrier gas stream. Complex mixtures of thiols and disulfides can be separated on polar or nonpolar liquid phases either isothermally or by programming the column temperature. Polar liquids for these separations include β,β'-iminopropionitrile and Triton X-305; nonpolar liquids include dinonyl phthalate and squalane. If desired, sulfhydryl compounds can be detected selectively by a potentiometric method of analysis.

G. Volatile Alcohols

I. OCCURRENCE AND ISOLATION

Straight- and branched-chain alcohols containing from 1 to 8 carbon atoms are found in many plants and plant products in free and combined form. 2-Propanol and n-propanol occur in apples; the isomeric butyl and amyl alcohols occur in fusel oil and fruits; and heptanol and octanol are constituents of various essential oils such as geranium, cloves, and essence of lavender, where they contribute to aroma. Optically active straight-chain alcohols such as d-3-methylpentanol-1 are present in etherial oils. Lower alcohols rarely occur free in foods in large amounts unless they have been fermented or subjected to bacterial spoilage. However, methanol, as well as butyl and amyl alcohols, are important minor constituents of alcoholic beverages. The determination of ethanol in blood and body fluids is of considerable interest from a clinical and legalistic point of view.

Alcohols can be recovered from tissues by any of the extraction or distillation procedures described in Section A. Since they are neutral, they can be separated from lower fatty acids by distillation or extraction from alkaline solution, or from amines by distillation or extraction from dilute aqueous acid. Similarly, they could be distilled or extracted from bisulfite solutions to separate them from carbonyls, or from aqueous mercuric acetate to isolate them from thiols and sulfides. Treatments of this type may result in artifacts: acid or alkaline hydrolysis, for example, will liberate combined alcohols from esters. Alcohols can be isolated as water-insoluble derivatives, the phthalates (Sabetay, 1939) and 3,5-dinitrobenzoates (Holley and Holley,

1952) being the most useful. Alcohols can be recovered from these compounds by hydrolysis. Mecke and deVries (1959) subtracted the alcohol peaks from a concentrate of cognac by treatment with 3,5-dinitrobenzoyl chloride prior to GLC.

Several procedures have been described for the removal of alcohols from beverages and body fluids for analysis. Since these should be used in conjunction with specific chromatographic methods to secure optimum results, details are included under the appropriate headings.

II. General Methods of Chromatography

The chromatography of lower alcohols is rendered difficult by the fact that water is usually present in the sample, often as a major component. This happens because alcohols are more difficult to separate from water than compounds containing other functional groups, because of similarities in vapor pressures, solubility relationships, and chemical reactivities. In certain cases alcohols are concentrated by steam distillation and extraction, or isolated as their 3,5-dinitrobenzoates, but in the main it is necessary to chromatograph them in the presence of water and sometimes to determine the amount of water as well. Three general procedures are used for the chromatography of aqueous solutions of lower alcohols. In the first of these, a non-polar stationary phase is employed so that water elutes first, followed by the alcohols in order of increasing carbon number. The difficulty with this is that water appears on most chromatograms as a large asymmetrical peak with a high degree of tailing. This makes quantitative analysis of compounds immediately after it very difficult, since the peaks may appear on the tail of the water curve. The second procedure is to use a highly polar stationary liquid, such as glycerol or a polyethylene glycol. These retain water for a long time, so the lower alcohols are eluted before it. Consequently, complications arising from tailing of the water peak are avoided. An alternative method to these that may be helpful in some cases is to select a detector insensitive to water. The hydrogen flame detector, for example, gives a small positive response to water, but the response to alcohols is several orders of magnitude greater (Fig. 18). Consequently, it is possible to "see" a comparatively small amount of alcohol on the tail of the scaled-down water peak. Alternatively, a thermal detector can be used and the sample burned in a combustion tube containing CuO placed after the column (Hunter *et al.*, 1960a). Water introduced with the sample and water of combustion are taken up in a drying tower containing magnesium perchlorate before the carrier gas enters the detector. Consequently, only the carbon dioxide derived from the alcohol is measured. With either of these methods, care should be taken that peak resolution is not impaired by overloading the column, for, even though water peaks may not appear on the final chromatogram, an excess of water in the column during partitioning might interfere with the separation of other components.

Tailing is most pronounced when polar solutes are chromatographed on nonpolar solvents. Consequently, the chromatographic separation of water and the lower alcohols on liquids such as the dialkyl phthalates is severely hampered by peak asymmetry. Smith (1959) attempted to determine small amounts of water in ethanol on dioctyl phthalate coated on Celite. He found that the retention time for water varied with its concentration in the mixture and increased as the water content decreased. Good resolution was obtained on mixtures containing several per cent water, but quantitative measurements became impossible when the water content was reduced to a few tenths of a per cent.

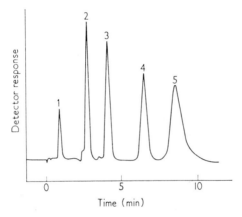

FIG. 18. One microliter of an aqueous solution containing 0.001% acetone and 0.01% each of ethanol, n-propanol, and n-butanol. Hydrogen flame detector, 8-X attenuation: (1) acetone; (2) ethanol; (3) n-propanol; (4) n-butanol; (5) H_2O. (Anon., 1960c.)

Tailing is usually caused by adsorption of the solute on the solid support that holds the stationary liquid. Thus, on chromatographing ethanol on a silicone–Celite packing, peak asymmetry would not be caused by interactions between the ethanol and silicone, but rather by adsorption of the ethanol on the Celite. The bulk of the solute is bound loosely to the partition liquid, but traces of it adhere firmly to the Celite and are eluted slowly. Hence tailing occurs. Knight (1958) found that tailing could be reduced by avoiding concentration ranges where the adsorption isotherm is strongly curved. In practice this was best accomplished by keeping the concentration of solute on the column low at all times. He also showed that a marked reduction in tailing of water and alcohol peaks could be achieved by feeding a constant amount of water with the helium used as the carrier gas, to maintain relative humidity at the column entrance at 50%. A moist carrier gas improved the shapes of water and methanol peaks on silicone fluid and dialkyl phthalates, but it was less effective with polyol-type solvents. Moisture failed to prevent tailing of amine peaks. It was necessary to control the temperature of the saturator and the chromatographic column carefully to prevent drifting of the base line, arising from fluctuations of the He/H_2O ratio in the carrier gas. Harva *et al.* (1959) found that tailing of saturated alcohols on liquid paraffin–Celite columns could be suppressed by addition of 0.1 to 0.5% of a surface-active substance to the partition liquid. Span 20, Manoxol OT, stearic acid, and glycerol monostearate were effective. On the other hand, 1% of polyethylene glycol 400 or hexylene glycol in the paraffin did not make the peaks symmetric. It was shown that the partition coefficients of the solutes remained unchanged until a threshold concentration of the surfactant was reached, after which the coefficient increased linearly with concentration. This threshold concentration was 1.5% for Manoxol OT, and as little as 0.1% of the compound gave good peak symmetry. This observation may prove very useful, since Tenney (1958) has shown that nonpolar liquids such as Silicone D.C. 703, Convoil-20, and Convachlor-12 are more effective than oxygenated solvents for the chromatography of alcohols.

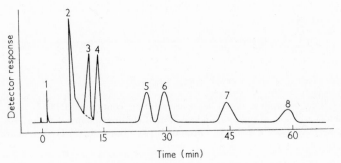

Fig. 19. Separation of water and alcohols. Stationary liquid, Armeen SD 33% on 30/60 mesh Chromosorb. Column temperature 88°C. (1) air; (2) water; (3) ethyl alcohol; (4) isopropyl alcohol; (5) *n*-propyl alcohol; (6) *sec*-butyl alcohol; (7) isobutyl alcohol; (8) *n*-butyl alcohol. (Zarembo and Lysyj, 1959).

Zarembo and Lysyj (1959) described the use of Armeen SD as a partition liquid for chromatographing aqueous solutions of the lower alcohols. This substance consists of the following normal primary amines: hexadecyl 20%, octadecyl 17%, octadecenyl 26%, and octadecadienyl 37%. Chromatograms (Fig. 19) show that all alcohols produce essentially symmetrical peaks, and that only the water fraction exhibits some degree of tailing. For quantitative measurements, the tailing side of the water peak was extended to the base line, and only the area under it was used for calculating water content. The area under the tail was not included in calculating ethanol content. The results (Table VIII) obtained on the analysis of standard samples containing water and C_2 to C_4 alcohols showed good agreement between the amounts present and those calculated by the peak area–internal normalization method. Absolute errors were generally less than 1%, even for the ethanol peak.

TABLE VIII

DETERMINATION OF ALCOHOLS AND WATER ON ARMEEN SD COLUMN AT 88°C[a]

Compound	Per cent present	Per cent found	Absolute error
Water	75.00	75.57	+0.57
Ethanol	4.17	4.16	−0.01
2-Propanol	4.17	4.03	−0.14
1-Propanol	4.17	3.90	−0.27
2-Butanol	4.17	4.28	+0.11
2-Methyl-1-propanol	4.17	3.78	−0.39
1-Butanol	4.17	4.28	+0.11

[a] From Zarembo and Lysyj (1959).

This packing can be classified as nonpolar, since water was eluted first, even though it has a higher boiling point than the first four alcohols to come off the column (Table IX). The order of elution was much the same as previously described for the thiols (Section F). The straight-chain primary alcohols were eluted in order of increasing retention time, the separation

TABLE IX

RETENTION TIME OF ALCOHOLS AND WATER ON ARMEEN SD AT 88°C[a]

Compound	Boiling point (°C)	Retention time (min)[b]
Water	100.0	6.0
Ethanol	78.3	10.0
3-Propanol	82.3	11.9
1-Propanol	97.2	22.7
2-Butanol	99.5	26.8
2-Methyl-1-propanol	107.9	39.6
1-Butanol	117.7	51.6

[a] From Zarembo and Lysyj (1959).
[b] Measured from air peak.

factor averaging about 2.5 per methylene group. Secondary alcohols were bound to the column less tenaciously than primary alcohols with the same carbon number; chain branching as in isobutyl alcohol also decreased affinity for the stationary phase.

Polar liquids for the chromatography of aqueous alcohol solutions include glycerol, triethanolamine, diglycerol, triethylene glycol, and polyethylene glycols of various molecular weights (Table X). Glycerol is used frequently for the separation of C_1 to C_5 alcohols, but it does not give as good resolution as triethanolamine. This latter compound will resolve active and isoamyl alcohols. Glycerol is sometimes mixed with 10% by weight of tricresyl phosphate (Smith, 1959). Because of the relatively long retention time of water on this column, it can be used to determine water in all the lower alcohols including the C_4 alcohols. The performance of columns packed with diglycerol is similar. The lower alcohols appear a good distance below the water peak, but they are not well resolved. Thus methyl, ethyl, and n-propyl alcohol give only one peak. Triethylene glycol separates ethanol from water but does not separate ethanol from isopropanol. Polyethylene glycols of molecular weight 200, 400, and 600 have been used for separating water from the lower alcohols. Smith (1959) states that there is no special advantage in using polymers of high molecular weight, since thermal stability is less, and the vapor pressures of the lower ones are small enough to permit operation at 100°C. However, Carbowax 1500 has been widely used for the analysis of complex mixtures of volatile compounds (Rhoades, 1960) and for the direct analysis of congeners in alcoholic beverages (Carroll and O'Brien, 1959). Bodnar and Mayeux (1958) described a method for the analysis of lower alcohols and other volatile compounds in aqueous solutions on polyethylene glycol 400 at 100°C. Isopropanol, ethanol, and water were eluted in the order given. The separation factor for isopropanol–ethanol was only 0.96, but for ethanol–water it was 0.314. Water was retained for almost an hour. These columns are useful for the analysis of alcohols in the presence of water, since the former are eluted first. Therefore, tailing of the water peak does not interfere. However, these liquids are not so effective for separating closely related alcohols as the nonpolar packings.

The best separation of lower alcohols up to C_5 so far achieved was obtained on a 100-foot capillary column coated with Armeen SD (Fig. 20). The order of elution was the same as that obtained on a packed column with this liquid, but all the C_1 to C_5 alcohols were included. Resolution of all the components of the mixture was satisfactory except that 3-pentanol was not cleanly resolved from 2-pentanol although it was eluted slightly before it.

This is a much better resolution that that obtained by Kuffner and Kallina (1959) on chromatographing a mixture of the eight isomeric C_5 alcohols on a column packed with polyethylene glycol 300, at a temperature of

TABLE X

Partition Liquids for the Chromatography of Lower Alcohols

Stationary phase	Tempera-ture (°C)	Compounds chromatographed	Ref.
Glycerol	95	C_2 to C_5 alcohols	
Glycerol	109	Isomeric cyclohexanols	Komers et al. (1958)
Diglycerol	—	Water, lower alcohols	Smith (1959)
Triethylene glycol	110	EtOH, H_2O	Bodnar and May-eaux (1958)
Erythritol	130	Isomeric cyclohexanols	Komers et al. (1958)
2,4-Dihydroxymethyl-pentane	—	MeOH, EtOH, H_2O	Smith (1959)
Triethanolamine	100	Lower alcohols, H_2O	Smith (1959)
Polyethylene glycol 200	100	MeOH, EtOH, PrOH, H_2O	Smith (1959)
Polyethylene glycol 300	100, 163	Isomeric C_5 and C_8 alcohols	Kuffner and Kallina (1959); Kallina and Kuffner (1960)
Polyethylene glycol 400	100	EtOH, i-PrOH, H_2O	Bodnar and May-eaux (1958)
Polyethylene glycol 600	100	Lower alcohols, H_2O	Adlard (1957)
Polyethylene glycol 1500	106	EtOH, H_2O	Maricq and Molle (1959)
Emulphor 0	70, 130, 190	C_1 to C_9 alcohols	Kovats (1958)
Polyoxyethylene sorbitan monoleate (Tween 80)	100	EtOH, H_2O	Smith (1959)
Flexol plasticizer 8N8	130	H_2O, fusel oil	Bouthilet and Lowry (1959)
Armeen SD	88	H_2O, EtOH, PrOH, BuOH	Zarembo and Lysyj (1959)
Lanolin	162	Isomeric C_5 and C_8 alcohols	Kuffner and Kallina (1959); Kallina and Kuffner (1960)
Silicone D.C. 703	100	Separation of alcohols from other oxy com-pounds	Tenney (1958)
Tritolyl phosphate	130	C_1 to C_6 alcohols	Grob et al. (1960)
Dibutyl sebacate	65.3	C_1 to C_4 alcohols	Bethea and Smutz (1959)
Dibutyl phthalate	65.3	C_1 to C_4 alcohols	Bethea and Smutz (1959)
Di(2-ethylhexyl) phthalate	—	EtOH, H_2O	Haskin et al. (1958)

TABLE X (Continued)

Stationary phase	Tempera-ture (°C)	Compounds chromatographed	Ref.
Castor oil	90, 145	Isomeric C_5 and C_8 alcohols	Kuffner and Kallina (1959); Kallina and Kuffner (1960)
Apiezon L	70, 130, 190	C_3 to C_9 alcohols	Kovats (1958)
Convoil-20	100	Separation of primary, secondary, and terti-ary alcohols	Tenney (1958)
Convachlor-12	100	Separation of primary, secondary, and terti-ary alcohols	Tenney (1958)
Glycerol–tricresyl phosphate (1:1)	—	H_2O, C_4 to C_4 alcohols	Smith (1959)
Glycerol–tricresyl phosphate (3:2)	106	MeOH, EtOH, H_2O	Fox (1958)
Flexol 8N8–diisodecyl phthalate–polyethylene glycol 600 (15:10:3)	110	MeOH, EtOH	Cadman and Johns (1958)
Liquid paraffin plus 0.1 to 0.5% Manoxol OT	60	C_3 to C_5 alcohols	Harva et al. (1959)

101°C. The peaks of 2-pentanol and 3-pentanol coincided, and this composite peak was not cleanly resolved from 3-methyl-2-butanol. Furthermore, 1,1-dimethylpropanol and 2,2-dimethylpropanol were not completely separated,

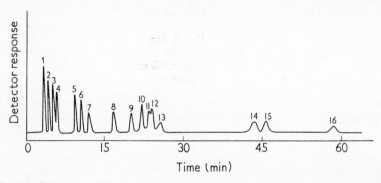

FIG. 20. Separation of C_1 to C_5 alcohols on a 100-foot stainless-steel capillary column coated with Armeen SD. (1) methanol; (2) ethanol; (3) isopropanol; (4) tert-butanol; (5) n-propanol; (6) sec-butanol; (7) 2-methyl-2-butanol; (8) isobutanol; (9) 2-methyl-3-butanol; (10) n-butanol; (11) 3-pentanol; (12) 2-pentanol; (13) 2,2-dimethyl-1-propanol; (14) 3-methyl-1-butanol; (15) 2-methyl-1-butanol; (16) 1-butanol. (Anon,. 1960d.)

and the peaks for 2-methyl-1-butanol and 3-methyl-1-butanol coincided. Thus the eight components yielded four main peaks, two of which were double. Only one compound, 1-pentanol, was satisfactorily resolved from all the others. Kallina and Kuffner (1960) applied the same technique to the separation of a mixture of saturated C_8 alcohols with a column temperature of 163°C. A mixture of fifteen isomeric alcohols yielded ten maxima, but few of the peaks were cleanly separated from adjacent ones, and the chromatogram was crowded.

a. Conditions for Chromatography

*1. *Chromatography in a Packed Column on Armeen SD* (Zarembo and Lysyj, 1959)

Chromatograph	Cenco Vapor Phase Analyzer.
Column dimensions	670 × 0.635-cm o.d. coiled copper tubing.
Solid support	Chromosorb W (30/60 U. S. mesh).
Stationary phase	Armeen SD, (33:67) (Armour & Co.).
Temperatures	Injection: 140°C. Column and detector: 88°C.
Carrier gas	Helium at 85 ml/min. Inlet pressure: 1290 mm Hg. Outlet pressure: atmospheric.
Detector	Four-filament (W) Gow-Mac T/C cell operated at 100 ma.
Recorder	Varian, 10 mv; 1 second; ½ inch/min.
Sample size	10 to 50 μl.
Analysis time	60 minutes to *n*-butanol.

*2. *Chromatography on Armeen SD by Capillary Method* (Anon., 1960d)

Chromatograph	Barber-Coleman Model 20.
Column dimensions	3050 × 0.025-cm i.d. stainless-steel capillary tube.
Solid support	Column wall.
Stationary phase	Armeen SD applied in 5% (v/v) solution.
Temperatures	Flash heater: 140°C. Column: 60°C. Detector: 110°C.
Carrier gas	Argon at 760 mm Hg. 2 ml/min through column at STP; 200 ml/min through flash heater at STP.
Detector	Argon ionization.
Sample size	0.5 μl total; 0.005 μl to column.
Analysis time	About 58 minutes to 1-pentanol.

*3. *Chromatography in a Packed Column on Polyethylene Glycol* (Bodnar and Mayeaux, 1958)

Chromatograph	Laboratory-built.
Column dimensions	214 × 0.95-cm o.d. coiled copper tubing.
Solid support	C-22 firebrick (30/60 U. S. mesh).
Stationary phase	Carbowax 400 (ratio not given) (Carbide Chemicals).
Temperature	100°C.
Carrier gas	Helium at 80 ml/min. Inlet pressure: 1070 mm Hg. Outlet pressure: atmospheric.

Detector	Gow-Mac direct-pass T/C cell with MT/T filaments operated at 138 ma.
Recorder	5 mv; 1 second; 0.85 cm/min.
Sample size	10 μl.
Analysis time	About 1 hour to water peak.

III. Ethanol in Body Fluids and Tissues

The determination of ethanol in blood or other body fluids is often important from a clinical or legal point of view, and GLC is the basis of the most rapid and reliable analytical methods currently available. Several techniques are employed: The sample can be injected directly into the chromatograph; it can be injected after precipitation of the proteins; or the alcohol can be concentrated by solvent extraction or distillation. Since the conditions for chromatography often depend on the method of sample preparation, the two are described together. The following are representative of current methods.

*a. Direct Injection Method (Anon., 1960b)

1. *Sample Introduction. Equipment:* An Aerograph Model A-110-C chromatograph with a specially modified injection block is used. The large bore of this interchangeable injector allows insertion of a rolled stainless-steel screen. This traps any solid blood particles without restricting the flow of the carrier gas. After about thirty samples have been injected, the screen should be removed and cleaned with sodium hypochlorite solution. *Method:* A 50-μl sample of blood is taken up in a dilution pipette. A standard solution of *n*-propanol in water (100 μl) is also taken up and mixed thoroughly with the blood in the mixing chamber of the pipette. An aliquot of this solution is then injected into the chromatograph.

2. *Conditions for Chromatography*

Chromatograph	Aerograph Model A-110-C with modified injection block.
Column dimensions	300 $\times$ 0.32-cm o.d. stainless-steel tubing.
Solid support	Johns-Mansville C-22 firebrick (30/42 U. S. mesh).
Stationary phase	Carbowax 400 (30:100).
Temperature	Injector: 260°C. Column and detector: 108°C.
Carrier gas	Helium at 30 ml/min. Inlet pressure: 900 mm Hg. Outlet pressure: atmospheric.
Detector	Four-filament hot-wire (W) T/C cell operated at 250 ma.
Recorder	1 mv; 1 second; 0.85 cm/min.
Sample size	10 μl.
Analysis time	6 minutes to elution of water peak.

3. *Results.* Acetone, ethanol, *n*-propanol, and water are cleanly resolved and are eluted in that order. A straight-line relation between peak height

and concentration of ethanol is found with *n*-propanol as the internal standard. Accuracy is 1% at 150 mg % ethanol.

b. Injection after Precipitation of Protein (Maricq and Molle, 1959)

1. *Sample Preparation.* A sample of preserved blood (1 ml) is placed in a microcentrifuge tube, and phosphotungstic acid solution (0.1 ml) containing 150 gm of the solid per 100 ml of water is added. The mixture is homogenized and then centrifuged for about 15 minutes at 2500 to 3000 rpm. An aliquot of the supernatant is injected into the chromatograph. Results are calculated by the peak area method with a blood sample fortified with 0.15% ethanol as a standard.

2. *Conditions for Chromatography*

Chromatograph	Perkin-Elmer Model 116 Vapor Fractometer.
Column dimensions	400 × 0.44-cm copper U tube.
Solid support	Celite.
Stationary phase	Carbowax 1500 (20:80).
Temperature	106°C.
Carrier gas	Hydrogen at 25 ml/min. Inlet pressure: 600 mm Hg. Outlet pressure: atmospheric.
Detector	Thermistor operated at 8 volts.
Recorder	Leeds-Northrup Speedomax 1 mv; 1 second; 1.3 cm/min.
Sample size	10 μl.
Analysis time	45 minutes.

3. *Results.* Ethanol, methanol, and water are eluted in that order, but the methanol and ethanol peaks are not cleanly resolved. About 45 minutes is required to flush out the water, but this time could be greatly reduced by using a chromatograph equipped with a backflush valve. Accuracy is 2 to 4%.

*c. Solvent Extraction Method (Cadman and Johns, 1958)

1. *Sample Preparation.* The blood sample (1 ml) is placed in a 3-ml centrifuge tube containing *n*-propyl acetate (1 ml) and potassium carbonate (1 gm). The tube is capped and shaken vigorously. Next it is centrifuged for 2 minutes to break the emulsion. The supernatant is decanted into a 1-ml serum bottle and capped. An aliquot is withdrawn with a microsyringe and injected into the chromatograph. The alcohol content of the blood is interpolated from a calibration curve obtained by extracting and chromatographing blood samples fortified with known amounts of alcohol. The solvent peak (*n*-propyl acetate) is used as an internal standard. The amount of alcohol extracted from the blood is reproducible but not complete, so it is not recommended that known concentrations of ethanol in *n*-propyl acetate be used as standards.

2. *Column Modification.* The end of the column next to the injection port should contain 1.5 inches of absorbent before the main packing to take up traces of water in the extract. The absorbent is made by coating 30/60 mesh calcium sulfate with polyethylene glycol 600 in a ratio of 1 part of liquid to 10 of solid.

3. *Conditions for Chromatography*

Chromatograph	Beckman Model GC-2.
Column dimensions	366 × 0.63-cm o.d. coiled stainless-steel tubing.
Solid support	Johns-Manville C-22 firebrick (42/60 U. S. mesh).
Stationary phase	Mixture of 15 parts Flexol 8N8 (Carbide and Carbon Chemicals Co.), 10 parts diisodecyl phthalate, and 3 parts polyethylene glycol 600 (Carbide and Carbon Chemicals Co.) (28:100).
Temperatures	Injection: 160°C. Detector and column: 110°C.
Carrier gas	Helium at 60 ml/min. Inlet pressure: 1250 mm Hg. Outlet pressure: atmospheric.
Detector	Four-filament hot-wire (W) T/C cell at 330 ma.
Recorder	1 mv; 1 second; ½ inch/min.
Sample size	35 μl.
Analysis time	8 minutes to ethanol.

4. *Results.* The order of elution is methanol, acetone, ethanol, isopropanol, and n-propyl acetate in that order, all the peaks being symmetrical and well resolved. The solvent is eluted completely in 24 minutes. Samples containing 0.007 to 0.171 weight % ethanol were analyzed. The average difference between the GLC method and the Kozelka-Hine method was 0.006 weight per cent.

*d. *Distillation Method Applicable to Blood, Urine, or Tissue* (Fox,[2] 1958)

1. *Sample Preparation.* The sample (1 to 5 gm) is placed in a 250-ml distilling flask containing water (25 ml), 50% sodium tungstate (3 ml), and 1N sulfuric acid (5 ml). A heated fractionating column (Eck and Krebs No. 3470) 55 cm in length, 1 cm in diameter, and filled with glass helices, is attached to the flask. The flask is heated electrically, and 20 to 25 ml of distillate is collected in an ice-cooled receiver over a period of an hour. An aliquot of the distillate is injected into the chromatograph. Results are calculated by the peak height method with known concentrations of ethanol in water as standards.

2. *Conditions for Chromatography*

Chromatograph	Perkin-Elmer Model 154-B.
Column dimensions	100 × 0.64-cm o.d. copper U tubes.
Solid support	C-22 firebrick (30/60 mesh).

[2] Deceased; method checked by T. A. Loomis, M.D.

Stationary phase	(I) Glycerol–tricresyl phosphate–support (30:20:50).
	(II) Glycerol–tricresyl phosphate–support (18:22:60).
Temperature	106°C.
Carrier gas	Helium at 20 ml/min.
Detector	Thermistor.
Recorder	5 mv; 12 inches/hour.
Sample size	50 to 100 μl of distillate prepared according to above directions.
Analysis time	About 10 minutes.

3. *Results.* Column I gives symmetrical ethanol peaks but does not separate ethanol from either formaldehyde or methanol. Column II separates these binary mixtures and eliminates the need for separate methanol tests. Blood samples containing 0.1 to 3 mg of ethanol per milliliter were analyzed with an accuracy of 5 mg %.

IV. Congeners in Alcoholic Beverages

Alcoholic beverages, including beer, wines, and distilled spirits, contain small amounts of congeners of ethanol, including methanol and the butyl and amyl alcohols. They may also contain esters of these alcohols as well as other low-molecular-weight compounds that contribute to flavor and aroma. Techniques for the isolation of these materials for GLC are similar to those for the determination of ethanol in body fluids, except here ethanol as well as water is a major interference. Carroll and O'Brien (1959) analyzed for these materials by injecting distilled spirits directly into a chromatograph containing a Carbowax 1500 column. The two main peaks represented ethanol and water, but a number of minor peaks arising from other lower alcohols, esters, and aldehydes were also observed. Cacace *et al.* (1959) separated the alcohol fraction of distilled spirits from water by saturation with potassium carbonate so that two layers were formed, the lower layer consisting of saturated aqueous potassium carbonate, and the upper of ethanol and congeners. The upper layer was then chromatographed on didecyl phthalate and polyethylene glycol (molecular weight unspecified) columns connected in series. This combination of substrates afforded good resolution of methanol from ethanol and permitted quantitative analysis of the former component in trace amounts. Mecke and deVries (1959) separated congeners from distilled spirits by extraction with a mixture of pentane and diethyl ether. This solvent combination is effective for removing aromatic materials from the beverage and at the same time does not extract large amounts of ethanol and water. Furthermore, the ether and pentane form an azeotrope boiling at 33°C, so the solvent can be evaporated readily without undue loss or overheating of the aromatic materials. The evaporation residue was then chromatographed on polyethylene glycol.

Distillation has also been used as a means of concentrating ethanol congeners. In one example cited here, the distillate was chromatographed, and in another the residue in the still was. Obviously such methods are empirical and cannot result in total recovery of the aromatic fraction. Bavisotto and Roch (1959) distilled decarbonated beer and collected the first 5 ml of distillate from a 100-ml sample. On chromatography on a glycerol substrate, this yielded peaks representing several esters and amyl alcohols. It should be noted that glycerol is a particularly valuable liquid for the chromatography of fusel oil, since good resolution of active amyl from other amyl alcohols can be obtained. Bouthilet and Lowrey (1959) concentrated propyl, butyl, and amyl alcohols in brandy by reducing a 20-ml sample to a volume of less than 1 ml by distilling at 95°C. The residue was then diluted to a standard volume and chromatographed on a column containing Flexol 8N8 plasticizer as a stationary liquid. Details of these methods are described below.

a. Direct Injection Procedure (Carroll and O'Brien, 1959)

1. *Conditions for Chromatography*

Chromatograph	Perkin-Elmer Model 154-C Vapor Fractometer.
Column dimensions	2-meter × ¼-inch copper or stainless-steel tubing.
Solid support	C-22 firebrick, Celite 545, or Chromosorb at 60/80 mesh.
Stationary phase	Carbowax 1500 at 15, 20, or 25%.
Temperature	95°C.
Carrier gas	Helium at 90 ml/min. Inlet pressure: 10 psig. Outlet pressure: atmospheric.
Detector	Thermistor.
Recorder	5 mv.
Sample size	10 to 50 μl.
Analysis time	Not given.

2. *Results.* The predominant peaks arise from ethanol and water. These are scaled down by attenuation. Acetaldehyde, formaldehyde, ethyl formate, ethyl acetate, and methanol are eluted in that order before the ethanol peak. *n*-Propanol is eluted between ethanol and water, and isoamyl alcohol after water.

b. Removal of Water in Drying Tower after Combustion of Sample (Hunter *et al.*, 1960a)

1. *Conditions for Chromatography*

Chromatograph	Laboratory-built with a CuO combustion tube and magnesium perchlorate drying tube connected in series between column and detector (see Chapter 1, Section D.VI.a.1).
Column dimensions	5-foot × ¼-inch copper tube wound in the form of a helix 6 inches in diameter.

Solid support	Firebrick (60/80 U. S. mesh).
Stationary phase	β,β'-Oxydipropionitrile (15:100).
Temperature	75°C.
Carrier gas	Helium at 85 ml/min.
Detector	T/C cell operated at 200 ma.
Recorder	3 inches/min.
Sample size	30 μl of cell-free fermentation liquid.
Analysis time	8 minutes.

2. *Results.* This method has been used only for the quantitative determination of ethanol in yeast fermentation liquids, but other alcohols, if present, could be analyzed.

c. Methanol in Cognac by Salting-Out Method (Cacace et al., 1959)

1. *Procedure.* A sample of cognac is treated with an excess of finely divided anhydrous potassium carbonate. The solution separates into two phases, the lower one consisting of a saturated aqueous solution of potassium carbonate,[3] and the upper one of an alcohol solution of the congeners. The lower layer is drawn off in a separatory funnel and discarded, and the upper layer is dried over anhydrous copper sulfate for 2 days with occasional shaking. It is then centrifuged, and an aliquot of it is injected into the chromatograph.

2. *Conditions for Chromatography*

Chromatograph	Carlo Erba Model B.
Column dimensions	(A) 1 meter × 0.4 cm. (B) 2 meters × 0.6 cm. (A) and (B) are connected in series.
Solid support	C-22 firebrick (30/60 mesh).
Stationary phase	(A) Didecyl phthalate. (B) Polyethylene glycol.
Temperature	85°C.
Carrier gas	Hydrogen at 4 liters/hour. Inlet pressure: 1000 mm Hg. Outlet pressure: atmospheric.
Detector	T/C cell.
Recorder	10 mv; 1 second; 2 cm/min.
Sample size	50 μl of alcohol layer.
Analysis time	15 minutes to ethyl alcohol.

3. *Results.* Good separations of isobutyl and isoamyl alcohols and their respective acetates are obtained on didecyl phthalate, but a polyethylene glycol column connected in series with it is necessary to obtain resolution of methanol from ethanol. The order of elution is acetaldehyde, ethyl acetate, acetal, methanol, and ethanol. Under these conditions it is possible to determine as little as 0.05% methanol in ethanol with an accuracy of 2%.

---

[3] *Authors' note:* The use of alkali could result in artifacts arising from the formation of alcohols through the catalytic hydrolysis of esters.

d. Ether–Pentane Extraction Method for Distilled Spirits
(Mecke and deVries, 1959)

1. *Procedure.* A 300-ml sample of the beverage is extracted with 3 × 50-ml portions of a 1:2 mixture of *n*-pentane and diethyl ether. The combined extracts are freed of traces of ethanol by shaking them repeatedly with water, and then dried over anhydrous calcium chloride or sodium sulfate. The volume is reduced to approximately 0.2 ml on a water bath at 32°C. An aliquot of this solution is injected directly into the chromatograph, or portions of it are treated with various reagents to subtract groups of compounds selectively. For example, esters are removed by saponification with sodium hydroxide, aldehydes, and ketones by precipitation from ether solution with 2-(diphenylacetyl)-1,3-indanedione-1-hydrazone, and alcohols by treatment with 3,5-dinitrobenzoyl chloride.

2. *Conditions for Chromatography*

Chromatograph	Perkin-Elmer Model 154-B Vapor Fractometer.
Column dimensions	3 meters × ¼ inch.
Solid support	Not given.
Stationary phase	Polyethylene glycol.
Temperature	70°C.
Carrier gas	Hydrogen at 45 ml/min.
Detector	Thermistor.
Recorder	Not given.
Sample size	10 μl.
Analysis time	30 minutes to 1 hour.

3. *Results.* More than twelve compounds are resolved from cognac by this method. Identities of individual compounds and retention values are not given.

e. Chromatography of Distillate from Beer (Bavisotto, 1958; Bavisotto and Roch, 1959)

1. *Procedure.* The beer is chilled overnight and decarbonated by shaking. A 100-ml sample is placed in a 1-liter round-bottomed flask connected to a condenser and calibrated receiver. The receiver is cooled in an ice bath, and an air filter packed with carbon is attached to it to prevent contamination of the distillate by solvent vapors from the surrounding atmosphere. The flask containing the beer is then heated, and exactly 5 ml of distillate is collected. An aliquot of the distillate is injected into the chromatograph. After the amyl alcohols are eluted, the column is backflushed for about 50 minutes to remove water in preparation for the next run.

2. *Conditions for Chromatography*

Chromatograph	Beckman Model GC-2 equipped with backflush valve.
Column dimensions	$\frac{2}{3}$ × 0.63-cm o.d. coiled copper tubing.
Solid support	Firebrick (30/60 U. S. mesh) (Fisher Scientific Co.).
Stationary phase	Glycerol (30:100).
Temperature	75°C.
Carrier gas	Helium at 40 ml/min. Inlet pressure: 15 psig. Outlet pressure: atmospheric.
Detector	Four-filament hot-wire (Pt) T/C cell operated at 350 ma.
Recorder	Brown Electronik, 1 mv; $\frac{1}{2}$ inch/min.
Sample size	50 μl of distillate.
Analysis time	About 80-minute cycle including backflushing.

3. *Results.* The order of elution is ethyl acetate, amyl acetate, ethanol, *d*-amyl alcohol, and isoamyl alcohol. The ethanol peak is very large and may obscure minor components. If present, *n*-amyl alcohol can be detected beyond isoamyl alcohol by continuing the run. Quantitative results obtained from calibration curves relating peak height concentration are reproducible to within 1% absolute.

*f. Chromatography of Distillation Residue from Brandy
(Bouthilet and Lowrey, 1959)

1. *Procedure.* The brandy sample (20 ml) is placed in a distillation flask which has a tapered graduated tube with a capacity of about 2 ml sealed onto the bottom (Fig. 21). Boiling chips are added, and the flask is placed

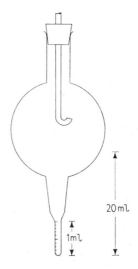

Fig. 21. Flask for the recovery of the distillation residue from brandy. (Bouthelet and Lowrey, 1959).

in a water bath adjusted to a temperature of 95°C. The solution is distilled until the liquid level is below the 1-ml mark on the tapered part of the flask. The flask is then removed from the bath, cooled, and the liquid in it diluted to 1 ml with absolute ethanol. An aliquot of this solution is injected into the chromatograph.

2. Conditions for Chromatography

Chromatograph	Beckman Model GC-2.
Column dimensions	6-foot stainless-steel tube.
Solid support	Firebrick.
Stationary phase	Flexol plasticizer 8N8 (packing ratio not given).
Temperature	130°C.
Carrier gas	Hydrogen at 20 psig. inlet pressure.
Detector	Hot-wire T/C cell operated at 350 ma.
Recorder	1 mv; 1 second.
Sample size	15 μl of concentrate.
Analysis time	Not given.

3. *Results.* n-Propyl, isobutyl, and isoamyl alcohols are eluted in that order and appear on the tail of a large ethanol peak.

V. CHROMATOGRAPHY OF ALCOHOL DERIVATIVES

Lower alcohols are volatile enough to be chromatographed directly. However, as noted in foregoing sections, they frequently occur in dilute aqueous solution, and quantitative concentration by extraction, fractional distillation, or formation of water-insoluble derivatives is impractical. Drawert *et al.* (1960a, 1960b) and Drawert and Kupfer (1960) describe methods for the conversion of alcohols to volatile nonpolar derivatives that can be dried conveniently. The conversion processes and the drying operations are conducted in-stream so that the process is continuous. The procedures include conversion (1) to alkyl nitrites by esterification with nitrous acid, (2) to olefins by dehydration with phosphoric acid, or (3) to paraffins by reduction with Raney nickel. All three operations are carried out in heated reaction tubes placed before the analytical columns. Unfortunately, the dimensions of these tubes and methods for packing them are not given, so the methods cannot be evaluated critically. In all cases, water contained in the original sample or produced by the conversion reaction is removed by passing the gas stream through a column containing calcium hydride. This converts the water to hydrogen and does not alter the reaction products of the alcohols. The carrier gas for chromatography is hydrogen, so water peaks are not recorded. Alcohols also react with alkali or alkaline-earth hydrides to yield hydrogen. However, by converting them to alkyl nitrites, olefins, or paraffins prior to drying, this reaction is bypassed.

Alcohols in dilute aqueous solution are converted to nitrites by acidifying them with 50% tartaric acid and injecting the mixture into a pre-column containing a 1:1 mixture of sodium nitrite and Sterchamol. Alternatively, the alcohol solution can be treated with nitrite and injected into a pre-column containing tartaric (or oxalic) acid and Sterchamol. The effluent gas stream is dried in a calcium hydride column and chromatographed on a D.C. 550 silicone oil stationary phase. At 80°C and a flow rate of 35 ml/min of hydrogen, methyl, ethyl, isopropyl, and n-propyl nitrites are eluted in that order within 20 minutes. Retention volumes are given in Table XI. This method is useful for determining the methanol content of wines, distilled

TABLE XI

RELATIVE RETENTIONS OF NITRITE ESTERS AND OLEFINS DERIVED FROM ALCOHOLS[a,b]

Derivative	Nitrite ester					Olefin		
Standard	Benzene			Pentane		Benzene		
Column	C_1	C_1	C_2	C_2	C_3	C_2	C_3	C_3
Temperature	70°C	100°C	70°C	70°C	75°C	100°C	100°C	125°C
Methanol	0.06							
Ethanol	0.12		0.009	0.050		0.016		
Isopropanol	0.20	0.30	0.028	0.163	0.043	0.039		
n-Propanol	0.27	0.38	0.028	0.163	0.043	0.039		
2-Methyl-propanol-(1)		0.47	0.069	0.400		0.092		
2-Methyl-propanol-(2)		0.46	0.069	0.400		0.092		
Butanol-(1)		0.60	0.084	0.488	0.129	0.100		
Butanol-(2)			0.097	0.562		0.104		
Isopentanol		1.00	0.238	1.39		0.285		
Pentanol-(1)			0.210	1.23	0.290	0.242		
Pentanol-(2)			0.210	1.23	0.290	0.242		
2-Methyl-butanol-(2)						0.292		
Hexanol-(1)			0.480	2.80	0.580	0.438	0.505	0.696
Heptanol-(1)					1.26	1.04	1.28	1.16
Octanol-(1)					2.53		2.27	1.98
Nonanol-(1)							3.95	3.46
Decanol-(1)								6.05

[a] From Drawert et al. (1960a, 1960b).
[b] C_1 = column packed with Silicone oil D.C.–Sterchamol (30:100); column length: 3.1 meters. C_2 = column packed with dinonyl phthalate–Sterchamol (35:100); column length: 6.3 meters. C_3 = Two columns: (1) Silicone oil D.C.–Sterchamol (30:100), 3.1 meters in length; (2) Dinonyl phthalate–Sterchamol (35:100), 1.60 meters in length.

spirits, or fusel oils. Ethanol in excess does not interfere. Methyl formate also yields methyl nitrite when analyzed under these conditions, but methyl acetate is split scarcely at all. The authors state that the method is also applicable to the analysis of sugar and polyhydric alcohols. In so far as preserving the structural integrity of the original alcohol is concerned, this method is the most useful of the three described, since the identities of all isomers are maintained barring rearrangements during esterification.

Alcohols can also be chromatographed as hydrocarbons by reducing them in a Raney nickel–Sterchamol (1:10) pre-column at 170°C with the carrier gas (H_2) as the reducing agent. The hydrocarbons are then separated on a dinonyl phthalate–Sterchamol (35:100) stationary phase at 100°C and a flow rate of 47.5 ml of H_2 per minute. C_2 to C_4 normal and isomeric alcohols can be resolved within 15 minutes by this method. The identities of primary and secondary alcohols are lost, but those of compounds differing only in chain branching are preserved.

The most useful method for the analysis of alcohol in blood described here is based on dehydration of the ethanol to ethylene. This is performed in a pre-column containing phosphoric acid and Sterchamol (1:2) heated to 200° to 300°C. The water in the sample and the water of reaction are removed on calcium hydride, and the olefins are separated on a 6.2-meter column packed with dinonyl phthalate on Sterchamol (35:100) (Table XI). At a temperature of 70°C and a flow rate of 51.5 ml of H_2 per minute, ethylene is eluted in about 0.6 minutes.

These methods have great potential for the analysis of aqueous solutions of the lower alcohols, but at present the techniques are not described in enough detail to be used without preliminary exploratory work.

VI. SUMMARY

Alcohols are somewhat more difficult to isolate from aqueous solution than other compounds because of their high polarities and the relatively low chemical reactivity of the un-ionized hydroxyl group. Therefore, it is often convenient to chromatograph them after the subtraction of other components. However, if necessary, crystalline 3,5-dinitrobenzoate or phthalate esters can be prepared, and the alcohols recovered by hydrolysis. Moreover, it is sometimes feasible to remove them from aqueous solutions by saturation with inorganic salts and extraction with a polar solvent.

When alcohol–water mixtures are chromatographed on nonpolar stationary liquids, the water elutes first, followed by the alcohols in order of increasing carbon number. However, the water peak is usually large and asymmetric. This makes quantitative analysis of compounds eluted immediately after it difficult, since the peaks may appear on the tail of the water curve. With highly polar liquids such as glycerol, water is retained for a long period and the lower alcohols elute before it. Therefore this type of packing is preferable. Interference from water can be reduced further by means of detection systems insensitive to it. These include the flame ionization detector, or combustion of column effluents to carbon dioxide, and removal of the water in a drying tower placed between the end of the combustion tube and the detector (T/C cell). Argon ionization detectors also are relatively insensitive to water. However, the presence of moisture vapor in the carrier gas stream alters sensitivity to organic compounds.

Alcohols are usually chromatographed unchanged. However, if desired, they can be converted to alkyl nitrites or to olefins in reaction chambers connected into the gas stream of the instrument. This is advantageous in that these derivatives are more volatile than the parent alcohols, and also can be dried more conveniently.

References

Adams, D. F. and R. K. Koppe. 1959. Gaschromatographic analysis of hydrogen sulfide, sulfur dioxide, mercaptans, and alkyl sulfides and disulfides. *Tappi* **42**: 601–605.

Adlard, E. R. 1957. An evaluation of some polyglycols used as stationary phases for gas-liquid partition chromatography. *In* "Vapour Phase Chromatography" (D. H. Desty, ed.), pp. 98–113. New York, Academic Press.

Alekseev, N. F. and M. P. Dvinyanina. 1955. Hydrazine method of determining dimethylamine in mixtures containing ammonia and methylamines. *Zavodskaya Lab.* **21**: 1166–1168. *Chem. Abstr.* **50**: 4722f, 1956.

Amberg, C. H. 1958. Gas-liquid partition chromatography of organic sulphur compounds. *Can. J. Chem.* **36**: 590–592.

Anon. 1960a. Amines. Aerograph Research Notes. Spring page 1. Wilkens Instrument and Research, Inc., Walnut Creek, California.

Anon. 1960b. Blood alcohol and acetone. Aerograph Research Notes. Summer page 6. Wilkins Instrument and Research, Inc. Walnut Creek, California.

Anon. 1960c. Flame ionization kit. Aerograph Research Notes. Fall. Wilkins Instrument and Research, Inc. Walnut Creek, California.

Anon. 1960d. [Advertisement] Barber-Coleman Chromatogram. *Federation Proc.* **19** (2): xxiii.

Bassette, R. and C. H. Whitnah. 1960. Removal and identification of organic compounds by chemical reaction in chromatographic analysis. *Anal. Chem.* **32**: 1098–1100.

Bavisotto, V. S. 1958. Application of gas chromatography to flavor definition in beer. *Comm. Master Brewers Assoc. Am.* **19**: 11–14.

Bavisotto, V. S. and L. A. Roch. 1959. Gas chromatography of volatiles in beer during its brewing. *Proc. Am. Soc. Brew. Chem.*, 63–75.

Beerthuis, R. K., D. Dijkstra, J. G. Keppler, and J. H. Recourt. 1959. Gas-liquid chromatographic analysis of higher fatty acid methyl esters. *Ann. N. Y. Acad. Sci.* **72**: 616–632.

Bethea, R. M. and M. Smutz. 1959. Gas chromatography. Effect of sample size on height of equivalent theoretical plate and retention volume. *Anal. Chem.* **31**: 1211-1214.

Block, R. J. and D. Bolling. 1951. "The Amino Acid Composition of Proteins and Foods," 2nd ed., 576 pp. Springfield, Illinois, Charles C. Thomas.

Bodnar, S. J. and S. J. Mayeux. 1958. Estimation of trace and major quantities of lower alcohols, ethers and acetone in aqueous solutions by gas-liquid partition chromatography. *Anal. Chem.* **30:** 1384–1387.

Böttcher, C. J. F., G. F. G. Clemens, and C. M. van Gent. 1960. Response of the β-ray ionization detector to unesterified lower fatty acids in gas-liquid chromatography. *J. Chromatog.* **3:** 582–584.

Bouthilet, R. J. and W. Lowrey. 1959. The use of the gas chromatograph in the determination of fusel oil in grape brandy. *J. Assoc. Offic. Agr. Chemists.* **42:** 634–637.

Braun, R. A. and W. A. Mosher. 1958. 2-Diphenylacetyl-1,3-indandione 1-hydrazone— A new reagent for carbonyl compounds. *J. Am. Chem. Soc.* **80:** 3048–3050.

Bricker, C. E. and H. R. Johnson. 1945. Spectrophotometric method for determining formaldehyde. *Ind. Eng. Chem., Anal. Ed.* **17:** 400–402.

Burks, R. E., Jr., E. B. Baker, P. Clark, J. Esslinger, and J. C. Lacey, Jr. 1959. Detection of amines produced on irradiation of beef. *J. Agr. Food Chem.* **7:** 778–782.

Cacace, F., M. Ihram, and M. L. Stein. 1959. Applicazione della cromatografia in fase gassosa all'analisi di distillati alcoolici. *Ann. Chim. (Rome)* **49:** 1383–1390.

Cadman, W. J , and T. Johns. 1958. Gas chromatographic determination of ethanol and other volatiles from blood. Presented as Pittsburgh Conf. on Anal. Chem. & Appl. Spectroscopy., March.

Carroll, R. B. and L. C. O'Brien. 1959. Gas-liquid chromatography of whiskies. Abstr. of Papers, 135th Am. Chem. Soc. meeting, April: p. 10A.

Carson, J. F., W. J. Weston, and J. W. Ralls. 1960. A rapid method for qualitative analysis of volatile mercaptan mixtures. *Nature* **186:** 801.

Cartoni, G. P. and A. Liberti. 1960. Gas chromatography of oxygen-containing terpenes. *J. Chromatog.* **3:** 121–124.

Cason, J. and E. R. Harris. 1959. Utilization of gas phase chromatography for identification of volatile products from alkaline degradation of herqueinone. *J. Org. Chem.* **24:** 676–679.

Christman, D. R., N. E. Day, P. R. Hansell, and R. C. Anderson. 1955. Improvements in isotopic carbon assay and chemical analysis of organic compounds by dry combustion. *Anal. Chem.* **27:** 1935–1939.

Collins, R. P. and M. E. Morgan. 1960. Esters produced by *Chalaropsis thielavioides*. *Science* **131:** 933–934.

Corse, J. W. and K. P. Dimick. 1958. The volatile flavors of strawberry. *In* "Flavor Research and Food Acceptance" (Arthur D. Little Inc., ed.), pp. 302–314. New York, Reinhold.

Day, E. A., D. A. Forss, and S. Patton. 1957. Flavor and odor defects of gamma-irradiated skim milk. II. Identification of volatile components by gas chromatography and mass spectrometry. *J. Dairy Sci.* **40:** 932–941.

Drawert, F. and G. Kupfer. 1960. Gas-Chromatographische Analyse von Alkoholen als Ester der salpetrigen Säure. *Angew. Chem.* **72:** 33–34.

Drawert, F., R. Felgenhauer, and G. Kupfer. 1960a. Reaktions-Gaschromatographie zur Analyse von Alkoholen und zur Blut-Alkoholbestimmung. *Angew. Chem.* **72:** 385.

Drawert, F., R. Felgenhauer, and G. Kupfer. 1960b. Reaktions-Gaschromatographie. *Angew. Chem.* **72:** 555–559.

Emery, E. M. and W. E. Koerner. 1961. Gas chromatographic determination of trace amounts of the lower fatty acids in water. *Anal. Chem.* **33:** 146–147.

Faragher, W. F., J. C. Morrell, and S. Comay. 1929. Interaction of alkyl sulfides and salts of mercury. *J. Am. Chem. Soc.* **51:** 2774–2781.

Feigl, F. 1934. Über die Verwendung von Tüpfelreaktionen zum Nachweis organischer Verbindungen. *Mikrochemie* **15**: 1–18.

Feigl, F. 1956. Spot tests in Organic Analysis. 5th Eng. ed. Ralph E. Oesper, trans. Elsevier Publ. Co., New York, 616 pp.

Feigl, F. and C. Stark. 1955. Einige Verbisserungen von Nachweisen in der organischen Tüpfelanalyse. *Mikrochim. Acta:* 996–1003.

Fox, J. E. 1958. Gas chromatographic analysis of alcohol and certain other volatiles in biological material for forensic purposes. *Proc. Soc. Exp. Biol. Med.* **97**: 236–237.

Fuks, N. A. and M. A. Rappoport. 1948. Separation of ammonia, methyl-, dimethyl-, and trimethyl-amine by the method of distributive chromatography. *Doklady Akad. Nauk S. S. S. R.* **60**: 1219–1221. *Chem. Abstr.* **43**: 121i.

Gehrke, C. W. and W. M. Lamkin. 1961. Quantitative determination of steam-volatile fatty acids by gas-liquid chromatography. *J. Agr. Food Chem.* **9**: 85–88.

Grob, R. L., D. Mercer, T. Gribben, and J. Wells. 1960. Thermal conductivity cell response and its relationship to quantitative gas chromatography. *J. Chromatog.* **3**: 545–553.

Haagen-Smit, A. J., J. G. Kirchner, A. N. Prater, and C. L. Deasy. 1945. Chemical studies of pineapple (*Ananas sativus* Lindl). I. The volatile flavor and odor constituents of pineapple. *J. Am. Chem. Soc.* **67**: 1646–1650.

Hankinson, C. L., W. J. Harper, and E. Mikolajak. 1958. Gas-liquid chromatographic method for volatile fatty acids in milk. *J. Dairy Sci.* **41**: 1502–1509. *Anal. Abstr.* **6**: 3193, 1959.

Harva, O., P. Kivalo, and A. Keltakallio. 1959. Reduction of tailing in gas-liquid chromatography. *Suomen Kemistilehti*, **32B**: 71–72.

Haskin, J. F., G. W. Warren, L. J. Priestly, Jr., and V. A. Yarborough. 1958. Gas chromatography. Determination of constituents in the study of azeotropes. *Anal. Chem.* **30**: 217–219.

Hawke, J. C. 1957. The fatty acids of butter fat and the volatile acids formed on oxidation. *J. Dairy Research* **24**: 366–371.

Hawke, J. C., W. L. Dunkley, and C. N. Hooker. 1957. The separation of fatty esters and aldehydes by gas-liquid chromatography. *New Zealand J. Sci. Technol.* **38B**: 925–938.

Holley, A. D. and R. W. Holley. 1952. Identification of alcohols in dilute aqueous solution. *Anal. Chem.* **24**: 216–218.

Honegger, C. G. and R. Honegger. 1959. Occurrence and quantitative determination of 2-dimethylaminoethanol in animal tissue extracts. *Nature* **184**: 550–552.

Honegger, C. G. and R. Honegger. 1960. Volatile amines in brain. *Nature* **185**: 530–532.

Hornstein, I., P. F. Crowe, and W. L. Sulzbacher. 1960. Constituents of meat flavor: beef. *J. Agr. Food Chem.* **8**: 65–67.

Hughes, R. B. 1959. Chemical studies on the herring (*Clupea Harengus*). I. Trimethylamine oxide and volatile amines in fresh, spoiling, and cooked herring flesh. *J. Sci. Food Agr.* **10**: 431–436.

Hughes, R. B. 1960. Chemical studies on the herring (*Clupea harengus*). III. The lower fatty acids. *J. Sci. Food Agr.* **11**: 47–53.

Hunter, I. R., E. W. Cole, and J. W. Pence. 1960a. Determination of ethanol in yeast-fermented liquors by gas chromatography. *J. Assoc. Offic. Agr. Chemists.* **43**: 769–771.

Hunter, I. R., V. H. Ortegren, and J. W. Pence. 1960b. Gas chromatographic separation of volatile organic acids in presence of water. *Anal. Chem.* **32**: 682–684.

Irby, R. M., Jr. and E. S. Harlow. 1959. Cigarette smoke. I. Determination of certain vapor constituents. *Tobacco* **148** (16): 22–26.

Jackson, H. W. and R. V. Hussong. 1958. Secondary alcohols in blue cheese and their relation to methyl ketones. *J. Dairy Sci.* **41:** 920–924.

James, A. T. 1952. Gas-liquid partition chromatography. The separation of volatile aliphatic amines and of the homologues of pyridine. *Biochem. J.* **52:** 242–247.

James, A. T. 1960. Qualitative and quantitative determination of the fatty acids by gas-liquid chromatography. *In* "Methods of Biochemical Analysis" (David Glick, ed.), Vol. 8, pp. 1–60. New York, Interscience.

James, A. T. and A. J. P. Martin. 1952. Gas-liquid partition chromatography. The separation and micro-estimation of volatile fatty acids from formic acid to dodecanoic acid. *Biochem. J.* **50:** 679–690.

James, A. T. and A. J. P. Martin. 1956. Gas-liquid chromatography. The separation and identification of the methyl esters of saturated and unsaturated acids from formic acid to *n*-octadecanoic acid. *Biochem. J.* **63:** 144–152.

James, A. T., A. J. P. Martin, and G. H. Smith. 1952. Gas-liquid partition chromatography: the separation and micro-estimation of ammonia and the methyl-amines. *Biochem. J.* **52:** 238–242.

Jennings, W. G., S. Leonard, and R. M. Pangborn. 1960. Volatiles contributing to the flavor of Bartlett pears. *Food Technol.* **14:** 587–590.

Kallina, D. and F. Kuffner. 1960. Trennung isomerer Alkohole mittels der Gas-Flüssig-Chromatographie, 2. Mitt.: Trennung gesättigter C_8-Alkohole. *Monatsh. Chem.* **91:** 289–293.

Karchmer, J. H. 1959. Gas-liquid partition chromatography of sulfur compounds with β,β'-iminodipropionitrile. *Anal. Chem.* **31:** 1377–1379.

Kelker, H. 1960. Gaschromatographische Bestimmung von Formaldehyd. *Z. Anal. Chem.* **176:** 3–8.

Knight, H. S. 1958. Gas-liquid chromatography of hydroxyl and amino compounds. Production of symmetrical peaks. *Anal. Chem.* **30:** 2030–2032.

Komers, R., K. Kochloefl, and V. Bazant. 1958. Gas-liquid partition chromatography of stereoisomeric methyl*cyclo*hexanols. *Chem. & Ind. (London),* pp. 1405–1406.

Kováts, E. 1958. Gas-chromatographische Charakterisierung organischer Verbindungen. Teil I. Retentionsindices aliphatischer Halogenide, Alkohole, Aldehyde und Ketone. *Helv. Chim. Acta* **41:** 1915–1932.

Kramlich, W. E. and A. M. Pearson. 1960. Separation and identification of cooked beef flavor components. *Food Research* **25:** 712–719.

Kuffner, F. and D. Kallina. 1959. Trennung isomerer Alkohole mittels der Gas-Flüssig-Chromatographie, 1. Mitt.: Trennung der gesättigten C_5-Alkohole. *Monatsh. Chem.* **90:** 463–466.

Maricq, L. and L. Molle. 1959. Recherches sur la determination de l'alcooémie par chromatographie gazeuse. *Bull. acad. roy. méd. Belg.* **24:** 199–230.

Markham, R. 1942. A steam distillation apparatus suitable for micro-Kjeldahl analysis. *Biochem. J.* **36:** 790–791.

Mecke, R. and M. DeVries. 1959. Gaschromatograpische Untersuchung von alkoholishcen Getränken. *Z. anal. Chem.* **170:** 326–332.

Merritt, C., Jr., S. R. Bresnick, M. L. Bazinet, J. T. Walsh, and P. Angelini. 1959. Determination of volatile components of foodstuffs. Techniques and their application to studies of irradiated beef. *J. Agr. Food Chem.* **7:** 784–787.

Nawar, W. W. and I. S. Fagerson. 1960. Techniques for collection of food volatiles for gas chromatographic analysis. *Anal. Chem.* **32:** 1534–1535.

Nawar, W. W., F. M. Sawyer, E. G. Beltran, and I. S. Fagerson. 1960. An injection system for gas chromatography. *Anal. Chem.* **32:** 1534.

Nelson, J. and A. Milun. 1960. Gas chromatography of high molecular weight fatty primary amines. *Chem. & Ind. (London)*, pp. 663–664.

Niegisch, W. D. and W. H. Stahl. 1956. The onion: gaseous emanation products. *Food Research* **21**: 657–665.

Patton, S. 1958. Chemical aspects of flavour research on milk and its products. *In* "Flavor Research and Food Acceptance" (Arthur D. Little Inc., ed.), pp. 315–323. New York, Reinhold.

Pippen, E. L., M. Nonaka, F. T. Jones, and F. Stitt. 1958. Volatile carbonyl compounds of cooked chicken. I. Compounds obtained by air entrainment. *Food Research* **23**: 103–113.

Ralls, J. W. 1960a. Rapid method for semiquantitative determination of volatile aldehydes, ketones and acids. Flash exchange gas chromatography. *Anal. Chem.* **32**: 332–336.

Ralls, J. W. 1960b. Flash exchange gas chromatography for the analysis of potential flavor components of peas. *J. Agr. Food Chem.* **8**: 141–143.

Raupp, G. 1959. Gas-chromatographische Trennung niederer Fettsäuren. *Angew. Chem.* **71**: 284–285.

Rhoades, J. W. 1958. Sampling method for analysis of coffee volatiles by gas chromatography. *Food Research* **23**: 254–261.

Rhoades, J. W. 1960. Analysis of the volatile constituents of coffee. *J. Agr. Food Chem.* **8**: 136–141.

Rhoades, J. W. 1961. Personal communication.

Sabetay, S. 1939. Phthalization in hot pyridine. *Ann. chim. anal. et chim. appl.* **21**: 289–290. *Chem. Abstr.* **34**: 692 (1940).

Seligman, R. B., F. E. Resnik, A. O'Keefe, J. C. Holmes, F. A. Morrell, D. P. Murrill, and F. L. Gager, Jr. 1957. Gas chromatography in tobacco research. *Tobacco* **145**: 24–29.

Smith, B. 1959. Analysis of aqueous mixtures by gas chromatography. *Acta Chem. Scand.* **13**: 480–488.

Spencer, C. F., F. Bauman, and J. F. Johnson. 1958. Gas oderants analysis by gas chromatography. *Anal. Chem.* **30**: 1473–1474.

Stanley, W. L., R. M. Ikeda, S. H. Vannier, and L. A. Rolle. 1961. Determination of the relative concentrations of the major aldehydes in lemon, orange and grapefruit oils by gas chromatography. *J. Food Sci.* **26**: 43–48.

Stephens, R. L. and A. P. Teszler. 1960. Quantitative estimation of low boiling carbonyls by a modified α-ketoglutaric acid-2,4-dinitrophenylhydrazone exchange procedure. *Anal. Chem.* **32**: 1047.

Sullivan, J. H., J. T. Walsh, and C. Merritt, Jr. 1959. Improved separation in gas chromatography by temperature programming. Application to mercaptans and sulfides. *Anal. Chem.* **31**: 1826–1828.

Sunner, S., K. J. Karrman, and V. Sundén. 1956. Separation of mercaptans by gas-liquid partition chromatography. *Mikrochim. Acta*, pp. 1144–1151.

Swoboda, P. A. T. 1960. The analysis of dilute aqueous solutions by gas chromatography. *Chem. & Ind. (London)*, pp. 1262–1263.

Tenney, H. M. 1958. Selectivity of various liquid substrates used in gas chromatography. *Anal. Chem.* **30**: 2–8.

Thompson, J. F., C. J. Morris, and R. K. Gering. 1959. Purification of plant amino acids for paper chromatography. *Anal. Chem.* **31**: 1028–1031.

von der Horst, H. D. 1957. The determination of ammonia and trimethylamine in amine mixtures. *Chem. Tech. (Berlin)* **9**: 478–479; *Chem. Abstr.* **52**: 976c.

Vorbeck, M. L., L. R. Mattick, F. A. Lee, and C. S. Pederson. 1960. Determination of fatty acids of lower molecular weight by gas chromatography. *Nature* **187**: 689.

Walsh, J. T. and C. Merritt, Jr. 1960. Qualitative functional group analysis of gas chromatographic effluents. *Anal. Chem.* **32**: 1378–1381.

Wasicky, R. and O. Frehden. 1937. Use of spot-plate tests in the examination of drugs. I. Aldehyde and amine tests for the recognition of ethereal oils. *Mikrochim. Acta* **1**: 55–63. *Chem. Abstr.* **31**: 5944 (1937).

Weenink, R. O. 1958. The steam distillation of volatile fatty acids. *New Zealand J. Sci.* **1**: 18–22.

Wynn, J. D., J. R. Brunner, and G. M. Trout. 1960. Gas chromatography as a means of detecting odors in milk. *Food Technol.* **14**: 248–250.

Zarembo, J. E. and I. Lysyj. 1959. Use of a new stationary liquid phase in gas chromatography determination of alcohols in the presence of large amounts of water. *Anal. Chem.* **31**: 1833–1834.

Zlatkis, A. and M. Sivetz. 1960. Analysis of coffee volatiles by gas chromatography. *Food Research* **25**: 395–398.

Chapter 4

Cyclic Compounds

General Introduction

Substances discussed in this chapter include alicyclic compounds, alkyl-benzenes, polycyclic aromatics, phenols, aromatic amines, pyridine deriva-tives, and alkaloids. They are a heterogeneous assortment as far as occur-rence and methods of isolation are concerned, the only unifying feature being their cyclic nature. Some of these groups, specifically the alicyclic compounds, the alkylbenzenes, and the phenols, are components of essential oils. However, they coexist in nature with one another and with related alcohols and ketones, so that separate treatment of the individual components of these mixtures is not feasible. Therefore, the chromatography of essential oils is discussed in a separate chapter which follows, and basic principles governing the separation of some of the compounds found in them are con-sidered here.

A. Alkylbenzenes and Polycyclic Aromatics

I. Occurrence

Alicyclic compounds and alkylbenzenes found in nature include men-thene, various menthadienes, *p*-cymene, styrene, 1-methyl-4-isopropenyl benzene, and agropyrene. *p*-Menthane, or 1-methyl-4-isopropylcyclohexane, does not occur in essential oils, but it can be prepared by hydrogenating limonene, terpinene, or *p*-cymene. Cumene (isopropylbenzene) is a degrada-tion product of many terpenes and camphors.

Among the polycyclic aromatics, naphthalene has been identified in essential oils of *Eugenia caryophyllata* and *Iris germanica*, and anthracene, 1,2-benzanthracene, pyrene, and isomeric benzopyrenes are formed during the smoking of tobacco. Since a number of these compounds are believed to be carcinogenic, their separation by GLC is of considerable interest.

Aromatic compounds in chromatograph eluates can be detected by the LeRosen test (Chapter 3, Section A).

II. Methods of Chromatography

Aromatic hydrocarbons have somewhat longer residence times in non-polar columns than aliphatic compounds with the same carbon number; for example, the retention volume of *n*-hexane on liquid paraffin at 100°C is 0.673 relative to benzene. However, the retention of *n*-heptane on this packing is 1.36, so the C_6 aromatic is eluted before the C_7 alkane. When polar substrates are used, aromatic compounds are retained relatively longer. Thus on tricresyl phosphate, normal decane (b.p. 174°C) emerges from the column well before ethylbenzene (b.p. 136°C), its retention value being only about a quarter of that obtained on liquid paraffin. When $\log_{10}$ retention values on paraffin and tricresyl phosphate are plotted against one another, as in Fig. 1, two straight lines are obtained, the lower one

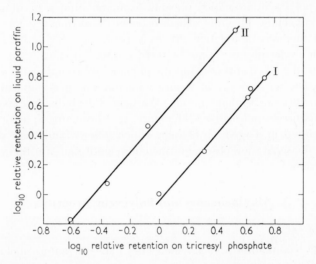

Fig. 1. Relation of relative retention volumes of (I) *n*-alkylbenzenes and (II) *n*-alkanes on liquid paraffin and tricresyl phosphate. (Plotted from data of Grant and Vaughan, 1957.)

representing the aromatic compounds, and the upper one *n*-alkanes. As a result of this selectivity for aromatic compounds, it is possible to elute most paraffin hydrocarbons ahead of benzene derivatives of the same molecular-weight range by using a polar column packing. Durrett (1960) found that Carbowax 400 is even more selective than tricresyl phosphate for aromatics, as shown by the fact that benzene emerges from columns packed with it at the same time as paraffins boiling at 90° to 100°C higher and having 4 more carbon atoms.

Aromatic compounds are separated from one another on nonpolar columns primarily because of vapor pressure differences. This is shown by the fact that a good straight line is obtained when the boiling points of cumene, isocumene, mesitylene, pseudocumene, etc., are plotted against logarithms of retention values (Grant and Vaughan, 1957). However, separation by polarity as well as by boiling point can be achieved on polar columns. Among the best substrates for this are β,β'-oxydipropionitrile and esters of tetrahalo-phthalic acids (Langer *et al.*, 1960).

The usefulness of the nitriles is limited by their volatilities. The phthalate esters form more stable column packings but with lower aromatic selectivity. The capacities of the phthalates for separating specific compounds is controllable to some extent, since it is governed by the molecular weight of the alcohol used in making the ester. Whereas *n*-octane is eluted before benzene from the dimethyl ester, it is eluted after benzene from the dibutyl and di-propyl esters. Increasing the atomic weight of the halogen has an effect similar to that of decreasing the size of the hydrocarbon chain, as evidenced by the fact that *n*-octane emerges before benzene from di-*n*-propyl tetra-bromophthalate, and after benzene from the chlorine analogue. Thus, the choice of column packing will depend on the components to be separated. Di-*n*-propyl tetrachlorophthalate at 100°C is recommended in the experimental section of this chapter, but other esters may be useful in specific cases.

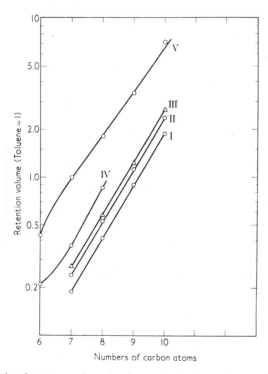

Fig. 2. Relation between carbon number and retention volumes for (I) 2-methyl-alkanes, (II) *n*-alkanes, (III) *n*-alkenes, (IV) methylcyclohexanes, and (V) *n*-alkylben-zenes. Di-*n*-butyl tetrachlorophthalate column at 100°C. (Plotted from data of Langer *et al.*, 1960.)

The selectivity of di-n-butyl tetrachlorophthalate for various classes of hydrocarbons is illustrated by a plot of carbon number against $\log_{10}$ retention volume (Fig. 2). A family of curves is obtained, each representing a homologous series of compounds. It can be seen that 2-methylalkanes (I) are eluted before n-alkanes (II) with the same carbon number. The presence of a double bond (III) increases residence time in the column compared to the corresponding n-alkane, and 6-membered rings (IV) retard elution even more. The highest retention volumes are those of the alkylbenzenes (V), which contain completely conjugated ring systems. It is anticipated that the lines representing substituted cyclohexenes and cyclohexadienes would lie between those of the cyclohexanes and the n-alkylbenzenes.

There is a general correlation between the boiling points of the alkylbenzenes and their retention volumes on the tetrachlorophthalates, but the relation is not exact (Table I). Evidently polar factors play a part here as well. Langer et al. (1960) suggest that the specificity of these packings for separating closely related isomers arises from "charge-transfer" interactions between the aromatic compounds (donors) and the tetrahalophthalates (acceptors). In any event, pairs of isomers such as m- and p-xylene which boil only a degree apart can be resolved. The separation of a 0.4-μl sample of these compounds on the di-n-propyl ester at 90°C is shown in Fig. 3. The

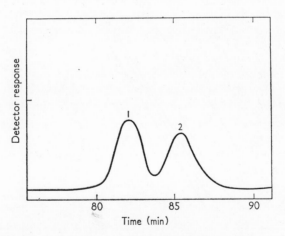

FIG. 3. Separation of (1) m-xylene and (2) p-xylene on di-n-propyl tetrachlorophthalate at 90°C. (From Langer et al., 1960.)

peaks are separated by 4.4 standard deviations on a 35-foot column operated at an efficiency of 7000 theoretical plates calculated from toluene. Other liquids capable of separating these isomers include 1-chloronaphthalene, ethylene carbonate, dimethylsulfolane (Zlatkis et al., 1959), and

1-naphthylamine (Araki and Goto, 1960). However, they can also be separated on nonselective stationary phases, such as dinonyl phthalate, if the column temperature is kept sufficiently low (Wiseman, 1960).

TABLE I

INFLUENCE OF CARBON NUMBER AND ISOMERISM ON BOILING POINTS
AND RETENTION TIMES (TOLUENE = 1.00) OF ALKYLBENZENES
ON DI-n-BUTYL TETRACHLOROPHTHALATE AT 100°C[a]

Compound	Carbon number	Boiling point (°C)	Retention volume (toluene = 1)
Benzene	6	80.4	0.44
Toluene	7	110	1.00
Ethylbenzene	8	136	1.81
m-Xylene	8	139	2.15
p-Xylene	8	138	2.23
o-Xylene	8	142	2.84
Cumene (isopropylbenzene)	9	153	2.60
Isocumene (n-propylbenzene)	9	159	3.34
1-Methyl-4-ethylbenzene	9	162	3.83
Pseudocumene (1,2,4-trimethylbenzene)	9	169	5.89
Butylbenzene	10	183	7.03

[a] From Langer et al. (1960).

Retention volumes of the n-alkylbenzenes on the phthalates increase with carbon number, but positional effects are also very important. Ethylbenzene, for example, has a retention volume of only 1.81 compared to 2.23 for p-xylene. This pattern is followed throughout, showing that single carbon atoms substituted in several positions in a benzene ring are more effective in retarding elution than the same number of carbons in one chain. Thus, the retention volume of 1-methyl-4-ethylbenzene is intermediate between those of isopropylbenzene and trimethylbenzene. Chain branching speeds up elution in the same way it does in the aliphatic series. This is illustrated by the fact that the retention volume of isopropylbenzene is 2.60 compared to 3.34 for n-propylbenzene. Conversely, unsaturation decreases rate of travel through the column, styrene being retained longer than ethylbenzene by a wide margin. However, it is interesting that the retention volume of phenylacetylene is slightly less than that of styrene. Evidently, a triple bond conjugated with a benzene ring does not interact with the liquid substrate to any greater extent than a double bond.

It has already been pointed out that alkylbenzenes are separated on nonpolar columns according to boiling point. Therefore, it should be possible to separate complex mixtures most effectively by collecting fractions from nonpolar columns and rechromatographing them on polar columns. In this way isomers could be separated on the second column without overlapping of peaks arising from compounds with the next highest carbon number. This technique is discussed in more detail under fatty acids (Chapter 7, Section G).

n-Alkylbenzenes containing 6 to 20 carbon atoms in the side chain can be separated at temperatures of 240° to 320°C on asphalt. The asphalt is preconditioned by bubbling nitrogen through it for 24 hours at 320°C to remove volatile components. Only compounds with a single phenyl group attached to a straight-chain alkyl group were investigated (Spencer and Johnson, 1960). There are 104 possible-phenyl-n-alkane isomers in this molecular-weight range. However, the largest number of isomers for any one molecular weight is 10. The retention times of phenylalkanes from phenylhexane to phenyleicosane are listed in Table II. All isomers contained in a single molecular-weight mixture from phenylhexane through phenyldecane can be separated. Isomers of phenylundecane through phenyltetradecane mixtures are all separated except the 5- and more internally substituted isomers. The 6- and more internally substituted phenylalkanes are not separated in the phenylpentadecanes through the phenyloctadecanes.

For mixtures of phenylalkanes of two or more consecutive carbon numbers, certain isomers of each molecular weight are not resolved. In runs made at 240°C, the 2-phenylalkanes are not resolved or are only partially resolved from the 5-phenylalkane of the next higher carbon number; and runs made at 270°C place the 2-phenylalkanes with the 4-phenylalkanes containing one more carbon. A family of straight lines is obtained when $\log_{10}$ retention volume is plotted against carbon number for each homologous series.

High-molecular-weight polynuclear hydrocarbons can also be separated by GLC. This is important from a biochemical standpoint, since some of these compounds are carcinogens. Carugno and Giovannozzi-Sermanni (1959) chromatographed seventeen members of this series containing 10 to 24 carbon atoms, including 3,4-benzopyrene. They used Apiezon L as the partition liquid and varied the temperature, the column length, and the liquid/solid ratio to eluate compounds of different molecular-weight ranges (Table III). C_{10} to C_{17} hydrocarbons were eluted within 70 minutes at 230°C on a 1-meter column containing 25% Celite as the stationary phase. In general, elution was in order of carbon number with structural differences superimposed. Thus fluoranthene was eluted before pyrene even though they both have the same empirical formula ($C_{16}H_{10}$). Evidently the greater symmetry of the latter compound is responsible for its slower rate of travel through the column.

TABLE II

RETENTION TIMES OF n-ALKYLBENZENES AT THREE TEMPERATURES[a]

Times in min from air

Number of carbons in n-alkyl group	Column temperatures, 240°C						Column temperatures, 270°C						Column temperatures, 320°C					
Attachment position of phenyl group to n-alkyl group →	1	2	3	4	5	6 or more internal substitution	1	2	3	4	5	6 or more internal substitution	1	2	3	4	5	6 or more internal substitution
6	8.2	5.9	5.1	+	+	+	—	—	—	+	+	+	—	—	—	+	+	+
7	11.6	8.3	7.2	6.3	+	+	—	—	—	—	+	+	—	—	—	—	+	+
8	16.5	11.8	10.2	9.0	+	+	—	—	—	—	+	+	—	—	—	—	+	+
9	23.4	16.7	14.1	12.5	11.8	+	—	8.6	7.5	6.8	6.4	+	—	—	—	—	—	+
10	33.1	23.8	20.0	17.8	16.7	+	—	11.7	10.2	9.2	8.6	+	—	—	—	—	—	+
11	46.8	33.1	28.2	25.2	23.7	23.7	—	16.6	13.9	11.7	11.7	11.7	—	—	—	—	—	—
12	66.2	47.4	39.9	35.6	33.1	33.1	—	22.3	18.6	16.6	15.4	15.4	—	—	—	—	—	—
13	95	62.8	56.3	50.0	47.4	45.7	—	29.1	25.1	22.3	21.7	21.7	—	—	—	—	—	—
14	133	94.8	79.1	70.4	66.0	63.4	—	40.0	33.9	30.3	28	27.3	—	9.7	8.8	6.9	6.9	6.9
15	188	135	112	100	96	87	—	55.2	46.4	41.0	38.4	36.8	—	12.4	10.9	9.7	8.8	8.8
16	—	192	156	142	135	120	—	73.5	62.1	55.3	51.3	49.3	—	14.4	13.9	12.4	10.9	10.9
17	—	—	220	202	192	168	—	101	84.6	74.6	69.8	66.8	—	18.7	15.3	14.4	13.9	13.9
18	—	—	—	—	—	—	—	134	113	94	88.7	88.7	—	23.9	20.8	18.7	15.3	15.3
19	—	—	—	—	—	—	—	183	157	136	127	120	—	30.3	26.3	23.9	20.8	20.8
20	—	—	—	—	—	—	—	244	208	183	170	157	—	37.0	32.0	30.3	26.3	26.3

[a] From Spencer and Johnson, 1960.

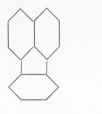
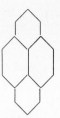

Fluoranthene   Pyrene

Hydrocarbons containing 16 to 24 carbon atoms were eluted within 45 minutes from a 1.5-meter column held at 260°C. In this case the packing contained 10% of the partition liquid. At 260°C, and a column length of 0.5
meter, dibenzopyrene, the highest-molecular-weight compound studied, was
eluted in 54 minutes. It will be interesting to investigate the behavior of
this group of materials on polar liquids when material with satisfactory
thermal stabilities becomes available.

a. Conditions for Chromatography

*1. Separation of Aliphatics from Aromatics (Durrett, 1960)

Chromatograph	Laboratory-built.
Column dimensions	305 × 0.64-cm o.d. coiled copper tubing.
Solid support	Firebrick (30/60 U. S. mesh) washed with aqua regia and neutralized with NaOH.
Stationary phase	Carbowax 400 (40:100).
Temperature	100°C throughout.
Carrier gas	Helium at 80 ml/min at exit. Inlet pressure: 1070 mm Hg. Outlet pressure: atmospheric.
Detector	Dual-pass four-filament (Pt) T/C cell operated at 200 ma.
Recorder	2 mv; 2 seconds; 1.27 cm/min.
Sample size	3 μl.
Analysis time	About 30 minutes to n-propylbenzene.

*2. Separation of C_6 to C_{10} Alkylbenzenes (Langer et al., 1960)

Chromatograph	Laboratory-built.
Column dimensions	889 × 0.5-cm coiled stainless-steel tubing.
Solid support	C-22 firebrick (35/45 mesh, ASTM).
Stationary phase	Di-n-propyl tetrachlorophthalate (7:93).
Temperature	100°C throughout.
Carrier gas	Helium at 90 ml/min. Inlet pressure: 1709 mm Hg. Outlet pressure: 740 mm Hg.
Detector	Gow-Mac T/C cell.
Recorder	Weston 2.5 mv.
Sample size	3 μl.
Analysis time	100 minutes to mesitylene.

TABLE III

Retention Times of Polycyclic Hydrocarbons on (I) 1-Meter Apiezon L–Celite (25:100) Column at 230°C; (II) 1.5-Meter Apiezon–Celite (10:100) Column at 260°C; and (III) 0.5-Meter Apiezon–Celite (10:100) Column at 260°C[a]

Compound	Melting point (°C)	Relative retention time
Column I		
Naphthalene	80	0.20
Azulene	100	0.27
Acenaphthene	95	0.40
Fluorene	116	0.52
Anthracene	217	1.00
Phenanthrene	100	1.00
Fluoranthene	110	2.16
Pyrene	156	2.65
3-Methylpyrene	58	4.36
Column II		
Pyrene	156	0.49
1,2-Benzofluorene	189	0.57
3-Methylpyrene	58	0.70
1,2-Benzanthracene	160	0.94
Chrysene	255	1.00
1,2-Benzopyrene	178	2.55
3,4-Benzopyrene	179	2.55
Perylene	264	2.88
Column III		
1,2-Benzofluorene	189	0.21
1,2-Benzanthracene	160	0.39
Chrysene	255	0.48
Perylene	264	1.00
1,2-Benzopyrene	178	1.00
3,4-Benzopyrene	179	1.00
1,2,5,6-Dibenzanthracene	266	2.51
Anthanthrene	257	2.71
3,4,9,10-Dibenzopyrene	287	6.64

[a] From Carugno and Giovannozzi-Sermanni (1959).

*3. *Separation of* C_{12} *to* C_{26} *Phenylalkanes* (Spencer and Johnson, 1960)

Chromatograph	Custom-constructed.
Column dimensions	365 × 0.63-cm o.d. coiled stainless-steel tubing.
Solid support	C-22 firebrick (42/60 U. S. mesh).

Stationary phase	Residue from 92-penetration asphalt blown with a nitrogen stream for 24 hours at 320°C (40:100).
Temperatures	Column: 240°C, 270°C, and 320°C. Detector: 240°C, 270°C, and 320°C.
Carrier gas	Helium at 35 ml/min at exit. Inlet pressure: 400 mm Hg. Outlet pressure: atmospheric.
Detector	Two-filament 75-ohm T/C cell at 12 volts.
Recorder	1 mv; 1 second; 0.5 inch/min.
Sample size	2–10 μl.
Analysis time	About 3–4 hours to C_{26} at 270°C.

*4. *Separation of Polycyclic Aromatics* (Carugno and Giovannozzi-Sermanni, 1959)

Chromatograph	Carlo Erba Fractovap.
Column dimensions	(I) 1 meter. (II) 1.5 meters. (III) 0.5 meter. 0.4-cm i.d. copper tubing.
Solid support	Celite (30/60 mesh).
Stationary phase	Apiezon L: (I) 25:100. (II) and (III) 10:100.
Temperatures	Column: (I) 230°C. (II) and (III) 260°C. Combustion tube: 750°C. Detector: 5°C.
Carrier gas	Helium at (I) 5.82 liters/hour and 380 mm Hg inlet pressure. (II) 435 liters/hour and 774 mm Hg inlet pressure. (III) 7.47 liters/hour and 380 mm Hg inlet pressure.
Detector	Eluates burned to CO_2 and measured with T/C cell.
Recorder	Honeywell-Brown.
Sample size	20–30 μl.
Analysis time	About 1 hour.

III. Summary

Alkylbenzenes are retained slightly longer on nonpolar columns than are *n*-alkanes with the same carbon number. However, on polar columns they are retained much longer, making it possible to separate aromatic compounds as a group from paraffins if the boiling-point range of the mixture is not too wide. Closely related alkylbenzenes, for example *m*- and *p*-xylenes, can be separated from one another on selective partition liquids such as di-*n*-propyl tetrachlorophthalate. Unsaturation and ring formation increase retention values relative to *n*-alkanes, whereas chain branching decreases them. Single carbon atoms substituted at several positions in a benzene ring are more effective in retarding elution from polar columns than the same number of atoms contained in a single chain.

Polynuclear aromatic hydrocarbons containing 10 to 24 carbon atoms can be chromatographed on Apiezon L columns at temperatures of 230°C and 260°C. In general, separation is in order of carbon number, but symmetrical compounds appear to be eluted more slowly than asymmetrical ones.

B. Phenols

I. ISOLATION AND IDENTIFICATION

Mono- and dihydric phenols such as the cresols, carvacrol, catechol, and hydroquinone, are widely distributed in the plant kingdom. Some of them, like salicylic acid and vanillin, contain alkoxy, carbonyl, or carboxyl groups attached directly to the aromatic nucleus, whereas others contain only alkyl or alkylene groups. Phenols are frequently components of essential oils. Consequently, some of the more important methods for analyzing them are included in Chapter 5.

Phenols are weak acids that can form salts with strong alkalis, but not with alkali metal carbonates. In general, the salts are soluble in aqueous alkali and insoluble in organic solvents, whereas the phenols are only slightly soluble in water and quite soluble in organic solvents. Thus phenols, together with carboxylic acids, usually can be removed from ether extracts of tissues by treatment with dilute aqueous sodium hydroxide solution. The salts are then decomposed by treating the aqueous layer with HCl or CO_2, and the phenols are re-extracted into ether. Carruthers and Johnstone (1960) isolated phenols as their methyl ethers by treating the extracts with diazomethane and saponifying the reaction products with ethanolic potassium hydroxide solution. Both phenols and carboxylic acids are methylated, but only the esters are saponified, leaving the phenols as volatile ethers which can be separated from the reaction mixture by distillation.

An alternative method for separating phenols from carboxylic acids is to extract the original ether solution with 2% aqueous sodium bicarbonate. This removes the carboxylic acids but not the phenols. The phenols are extracted from the ether solution by shaking it with 5% aqueous sodium hydroxide solution. In this way the free phenols are obtained. However, quantitative separations may not be obtained in all cases, since Carruthers and Johnstone (1960) used a combination of the two techniques to isolate phenols from tobacco smoke condensate as their ethers. Anisole, the methyl esters of o-, m-, and p-cresols, veratrole, and methoxyacetophenones were among the products separated by GLC and identified.

Monohydric phenols are quite stable, but polyhydric phenols are easily oxidized, especially when they contain hydroxy groups *ortho* or *para* to one another. Thus alkaline solutions of them absorb oxygen from the air and darken rapidly. There are a large number of color tests described in the literature for the detection of phenols. Among these are the ferric chloride test, the Liebermann reaction, and coupling to form an azo dye with diazotized sulfanilic acid or other aromatic amines. Some of these are relatively nonspecific, but usually a combination of tests will serve to identify a phenolic fraction in eluates collected from a chromatographic column.

a. Separation Procedure

1. *Isolation as Methyl Ethers from Cigarette Smoke* (Carruthers and Johnstone, 1960). Cigarettes are smoked mechanically with a puff 2 seconds in duration and 25 ml in volume every 15 seconds. The smoke is condensed in traps at $-60°C$, and volatile materials are removed from the condensate by codistillation with methanol. The methanol solution containing the nonvolatile components is cooled to $0°C$ to precipitate waxes and filtered. The methanol is evaporated, the residue dissolved in ether, and the ether solution extracted successively with dilute aqueous acetic acid, sodium bicarbonate solution, and sodium hydroxide solution. The sodium hydroxide solution is acidified and re-extracted with ether to recover the phenols. The phenols, together with carboxylic acids, are then methylated by the diazomethane method (Chapter 7, Section G). The solvent is evaporated, and the residue is refluxed with ethanolic potassium hydroxide to saponify the esters. The phenolic ethers are recovered by distillation and chromatographed.

b. Color Tests (Feigl, 1956)

1. *Liebermann Reaction.* The eluate is dissolved in one drop of a 1% solution of 5-nitroso-8-hydroxyquinoline in concentrated sulfuric acid, and the mixture is warmed gently. Phenols with a free *para* position form dark-brown to violet colors. Sensitivity is 1 to 5 μg.

2. *Coupling Reaction.* One drop of a 0.5% solution of sulfanilic acid in 2% aqueous hydrochloric acid solution is added to one drop of 0.5% sodium nitrite solution in the depression of a spot plate. The eluate is dissolved in one drop of water or methanol and added to the mixture with stirring. The solution is made alkaline with one drop of 10% sodium carbonate solution, and the color is compared to that of a blank solution prepared in the same way. Phenols produce red-yellow to red-brown colors. Sensitivity is in the range of 0.5 to 5 μg, depending on the derivative. Aromatic amines also give positive tests.

II. METHODS OF CHROMATOGRAPHY

Phenols can be chromatographed on nonpolar liquids like paraffin and the Apiezons, or on polar packings such as glycerol, sugar alcohols, and sugars. On polar liquids, the introduction of alkyl groups in the aromatic ring hastens elution, the retention time of 3-*n*-butylphenol being 0.64 relative to phenol on erythritol (Janák *et al.*, 1959). The relative retention time of this compound on Apiezon L at 170°C is 7.7. Thus, a tenfold increase in retention occurs in changing from a polar to a nonpolar packing. This arises from differences in van der Waals interactions between the side chain of the solute and the stationary liquids.

The introduction of substituents in one or both of the positions *ortho* to the phenolic hydroxyl group also has a marked influence on retention volumes, since it reduces hydrogen bonding of the solute with the solvent through steric hindrance. This effect is pronounced with polar packings and negligible with nonpolar packings. For example, the retention time of *o*-cresol relative to *m*-cresol on erythritol is 0.55 compared to a value of 1.00 on paraffin (Table IV). This phenomenon is also observed with the xylenols, the greatest reduction in retention occurring with the 2,6-derivative in which both *ortho* positions are blocked. Thus, it is a comparatively simple matter to separate *ortho* from *meta* or *para* isomers by making use of differences in hydrogen bonding.

TABLE IV

RETENTION TIMES OF PHENOLS WITH AND WITHOUT *Ortho* SUBSTITUENTS[a]

| | | Retention times relative to *m*-cresol (b.p. 202°C) | | |
Partition liquid	Column temperature (°C)	*o*-Cresol	2,6-Xylenol	3,5-Xylenol
Paraffin	140	1.00	1.38	1.88
Dimethyl polysiloxane	170	0.90	1.22	1.52
Glycerol monoöleate	173	0.75	1.00	1.57
Diaminodiphenyl sulfone	192	0.71	0.56	1.26
Glycerol	150	0.63	0.34	1.00
Erythritol	150	0.55	0.24	0.92

[a] Compiled from the literature by Fitzgerald (1959).

On the basis of this information, Fitzgerald (1959) proposed a method for chromatographing phenols on two different liquid substrates. They are first run on Apiezon L which separates the compounds in the approximate order of their boiling points (Table V). Actually, the *ortho* derivatives are eluted somewhat more rapidly than the *meta* and *para* derivatives, possibly because the latter tend to dimerize to a greater extent in the liquid phase. However, the differences are small and would not be satisfactory for quantitative separations. After this preliminary separation by boiling point, the individual fractions are rechromatographed on a polar column. This separates the *ortho* isomers from the *meta* and *para* compounds.

Fitzgerald examined a number of polar phases and found sodium dodecylbenzenesulfonate and 4,4'-diaminodiphenyl sulfone to be most satisfactory for these separations (Table V). The sodium sulfonate is a commercial detergent consisting of 40% active ingredient and about 60% sodium sulfate, spray-dried to a moisture content of 2%. The brand was Gardilene 40-SD.

TABLE V

RETENTION TIMES OF MONOHYDRIC PHENOLS AT 200°C[a]

Substituent(s)	Boiling point (°C)	Retention time on column packing (phenol = 1.00)		
		Apiezon L	Sodium dodecyl-benzenesulfonate	4,4'-Diaminodi-phenyl sulfone
2-Me-	190.8	1.5	0.9	0.9
2,6-Me₂-	201	2.25	0.75	0.7
2-Me-	202.1	1.6	1.35	1.3
3-Me-	202.2	1.65	1.35	1.3
2-Et-	207	2.2	1.1	1.0
2,4-Me₂-	210	2.4	1.3	1.1
2,5-Me₂-	210	2.4	1.25	1.15
2-isoPr-	216	2.7	1.2	—
2,3-Me₂-	218	2.9	1.5	1.35
2,6-Et₂-	218	3.7	0.95	0.8
3-Et-	218	2.5	1.7	1.6
4-Et-	219	2.45	1.85	1.5
3,5-Me₂-	219.5	2.6	1.8	1.65
2-n-Pr-	220	3.1	1.35	1.0
4-Et-2-Me	222	3.6	1.8	1.2
2,4,6-Me₃-	222	3.5	1.15	0.85
5-Et-2-Me-	223	3.6	1.7	1.3
2-Et-5-Me-	224.2	3.2	1.4	1.15
3,4-Me₂-	225	3.0	2.15	2.0
2-Me-6-n-Pr-	225	5.1	1.05	—
2,3,6-Me₃-	226	4.1	1.2	1.0
3-Et-2-Me-	227	3.85	1.9	1.55
2-n-Pr-	228	3.6	2.5	1.8
3-isoPr-	228	3.2	2.1	1.6
4-Me-2-isoPr-	228	3.85	1.5	0.9
4-Et-3-Me-	229	4.2	2.9	2.2
4-isoPr-	231	3.2	2.2	1.5
2,4,5-Me₃-	232	4.5	2.0	1.6
4-n-Pr-	233	3.8	2.6	1.55
3-Et-5-Me-	233	3.8	2.3	1.85
2,3,5-Me₃-	233	4.35	1.9	1.7
5-Me-2-isoPr-	234	4.2	1.6	1.1
2,3,4-Me₃-	236	5.2	2.4	2.2
2-Me-5-isoPr-	237	4.55	2.0	1.35
4-tert-Bu-	240	4.3	2.75	1.8
4-Indanol	245	6.0	3.4	3.2
2,3,5,6-Me₄-	247	7.3	1.9	1.6
3,5-Et₂-	248	5.2	3.35	2.15
3,4,5-Me₃-	248	5.5	3.3	3.35
2,6-n-Pr₂-	255	7.8	1.4	—
2,6-isoPr₂-	255	5.7	1.0	0.55
5-Indanol	255	6.5	4.3	4.3
4-tert-Am-	255	6.9	4.2	2.4
2,3,4,5-Me₄-	260	8.9	3.55	3.5
2,6-tert-Bu₂-4-Me-	266	10.5	1.1	0.3
Me₅-	267	16.0	3.8	3.4
2-Ph-	275	13.0	4.45	6.2

[a] From Fitzgerald (1959).

It may not be obtainable elsewhere than Australia, but equivalent products would probably suffice. It withstood use for prolonged periods at 140°C without noticeable deterioration. The diaminodiphenyl sulfone melted at 176°C and was shown by Grant and Vaughan (1957) to exhibit strong selectivity for *ortho* isomers. However, some decomposition occurs when columns containing it are heated above 225°C, as shown by reductions in retention times and plate efficiency.

The stationary liquids used by Fitzgerald (1959), as well as a number of sugars and related compounds suggested by Janák and Komers (1958), give good separations of *ortho* from *meta* or *para* isomers, but they are not useful for resolving the latter pair of compounds. This has been achieved by Brooks (1959) on a stationary phase consisting of tris(2,4-xylenyl) phosphate on acid-washed kieselguhr. Brooks examined the phosphate esters of a number of phenols and found this to be the most effective liquid tested. The method is of particular interest because of the close chemical resemblance of the solute to the solvent.

At a column temperature of 110°C, phenol, *o*-cresol, *p*-cresol, and *m*-cresol were eluted in that order. The fact that *o*-cresol was eluted before the other isomers by a considerable margin confirms that the packing is essentially polar in nature. The separation of the *meta* and *para* isomers is good but not complete (Fig. 4). It is interesting that the *meta* isomer boils at a tempera-

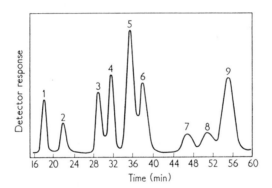

FIG. 4. Separation of phenol derivatives on tris(2,4-xylenyl) phosphate at 110°C. Peaks arise from (1) phenol, (2) *o*-cresol, (3) *p*-cresol, (4) *m*-cresol, (5) 2,4-xylenol, (6) 2,5-xylenol, (7) 2,3-xylenol, (8) *p*-ethylphenol, and (9) *m*-ethylphenol + 3,5-xylenol (coincident peaks). Temperature: 110°C. Stationary phase: 2,4-xylenyl phosphate, 5% w/w, on Celite, 100/200 mesh. Inlet pressure: 16 psig. (From Brooks, 1959.)

ture only 0.1°C higher than the *para* isomer. This is in agreement with the order of retention times, but the difference appears to be too small to account for the separation in terms of vapor pressure differences alone. This liquid was also effective for separating the isomeric xylenols, the 2,4-, 2,5-, and 2,3-derivatives being eluted in that order. 3,5-Xylenol, in which no interference with hydrogen bonding by the methyl groups is possible, has the longest retention time of the disubstituted phenols. Its peak was coincident with that of *m*-ethylphenol. Resolution of this pair on Apiezon L would also be difficult, since the separation factor is only 1.06.

Dihydric phenols have been chromatographed on Apiezon M at 190°C and on silicone E-301 at 180°C (Fitzgerald, 1959). Retention values of the unsubstituted compounds are 2.5 to 4 times as great as for phenols (Table VI). The residence time of the *ortho* isomer (catechol) on silicone is considerably less than for resorcinol and hydroquinone. The introduction of alkyl groups increases retention on this liquid in all cases. Janák and Komers (1958) have shown that retention volumes decrease in the order resorcinol > hydroquinone > catechol, with inositol at 230°C as a stationary phase. However, the substitution of methyl groups in the aromatic ring decreases rather than increases retention. These authors recommend mannitol or dulcitol at 190°C for the analysis of catechol and its derivatives, and inositol at 230°C to 240°C for the chromatography of mixtures containing hydroquinone or resorcinol.

Chlorinated phenols and anisoles have been chromatographed on a variety of stationary phases (Table VII). The retention time of *o*-chloro-

TABLE VI

RETENTION TIMES OF VARIOUS DIHYDRIC PHENOLS
ON APIEZON M AND SILICONE E-301[a]

	Retention time on liquid (phenol = 1)	
Compound	Apiezon M at 190°C	Silicone E-301 at 180°C
Catechol	2.4	2.5
4-Me-	4.1	3.9
3,5-Me$_2$-	—	4.95
3,6-Me$_2$-	—	4.1
Hydroquinone	—	3.4
2-Me-	—	4.3
Resorcinol	3.0	3.8
2-Me-	4.4	4.4
4-Me-	4.7	4.9
5-Me-	5.1	5.6
2,4-Me$_2$-	—	5.5
2,4,6-Me$_3$-	—	6.55

[a] From Fitzgerald (1959).

phenol is less than that of the *para* isomer on Apiezon L, but the two anisole isomers behave identically. Evidently an *ortho* effect is operative in the case of the phenols even on a nonpolar column packing, but this cannot occur with the anisoles because dimerization in the solvent through intermolecular hydrogen bonding is not possible. Retention times increase progressively as chlorine atoms are substituted for hydrogen when the stationary phase is Apiezon L. However, on polar media such as 4,4′-diaminodiphenyl sulfone, a chlorine atom in the *ortho* position decreases retention relative to phenol, whereas *para* substitution increases it to a marked extent. This *ortho* effect is so pronounced that the retention times of the 2,4- and 2,6-dichloro isomers are actually less than that of *p*-chlorophenol. Evidently reduction of hydrogen bonding between solute and solvent more than counterbalances the decrease in vapor pressure produced by the extra chlorine atom.

TABLE VII

Retention Times for Chlorinated Phenols Relative to Phenol[a]

Substit-uent(s)	Boiling point (°C)	Apiezon L		4,4′-Diamino-diphenyl sulfone at 180°C	Silicone DC-703 at 160°C	Benzyl-diphenyl at 160°C	Zinc stearate at 190°C
		At 200°C	At 190°C				
Phenols							
2-Cl-	176	1.3		0.6	1.15	0.6	
4-Cl-	217	1.8		2.7	1.7	3.0	
2,4-Cl₂-	210	2.4		1.25	2.6	1.3	
2,6-Cl₂-	220	2.65		1.25	3.0	1.3	
2,4,6-Cl₃-	246	4.9		2.2	—	2.4	
2,4,5-Cl₃-	246	—		3.0	—	—	
Anisoles							
2-Cl-	195		2.1				0.4
4-Cl-	198		2.1				0.4
2,4-Cl₂-	235		4.3				0.8
2,6-Cl₂-	220		3.1				0.6
2,4,6-Cl₃-	242		5.3				1.0

[a] From Fitzgerald (1959).

Phenols are converted readily to anisoles by methylation with diazomethane. This renders them more volatile and less likely to tail on nonpolar packings. Carruthers and Johnstone (1960) employed this method for the chromatographic separation of phenols recovered from tobacco smoke. Nevertheless, it is not a suitable technique for the separation of *ortho* and *para* isomers, since loss of the labile proton levels out differences in hydrogen bonding with the solvent that make such separations possible. This is also true for C-alkyl phenols. However, the separation factor obtained for 2,4- and 2,6-dichloroanisoles is 1.4 compared to 1.1 for the corresponding dichlorophenols. Hence, in this special case methyl ether formation is an asset.

Conversion of phenols to trimethylsilyl ethers prior to chromatography is more advantageous (Langer et al., 1958). This can be accomplished by treating the phenols with an excess of hexamethyldisilazane. Water does not interfere, since it is converted to hexamethyldisiloxane and dimethylsilanol, which are eluted from the column very rapidly. Consequently, it is possible to analyze aqueous solutions containing as little as 0.2% phenol by using a large enough excess of reagent to react with all the water. Excellent resolution of the trimethylsilyl ethers can be obtained by chromatography on Dow Corning 550 silicone at 125°C (Fig. 5). The 3-isomeric cresols are

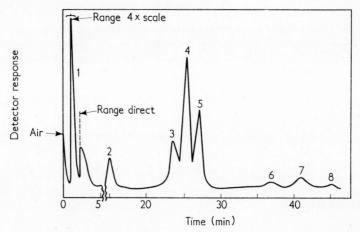

FIG. 5. Separation of trimethylsilyl ethers of phenols on Dow Corning 550 silicone packing at 125°C. (1) Hexamethyldisiloxane. (2) Phenol. (3) o-Cresol. (4) m-Cresol. (5) p-Cresol. (6) 2,5-Dimethylphenol + o-ethylphenol (trace). (7) 2,4-Dimethylphenol. (8) 2,6-Dimethylphenol + p-ethylphenol. (From Langer et al., 1958.)

partly resolved, and the 2,5-, 2,4-, and 2,6-dimethylphenols are completely resolved. Separations by this technique are comparable to those obtained by direct chromatography of the phenols on tris(2,4-xylenyl) phosphate.

a. Conditions for Chromatography

*1. Serial Chromatography on Polar and Nonpolar Stationary Phases (Fitzgerald, 1959)

Chromatograph	Laboratory-built.
Column dimensions	244 or 366 × 0.475-cm i.d. copper tubing in coil 9 cm in diameter.

Solid support	Celite 545 (85/100 B.S. mesh).
Stationary phase	(A) Apiezon L (20:80). (B) Sodium dodecylbenzene-sulfonate (12:88). (C) 4,4'-diaminodiphenyl sulfone (25:75).
Temperatures	Injection port: 250°C. Column: 200°C.
Carrier gas	Nitrogen at 300–800 mm Hg inlet pressure. Outlet pressure: atmospheric.
Detector	Scott hydrogen flame detector with two thermocouples in series.
Recorder	1–32 mv full scale.
Sample size	1–5 mg.
Analysis time	Not given.

*2. *Resolution of meta and para Isomers* (Brooks, 1959)

Chromatograph	Pye Argon.
Column dimensions	120 × 0.45 cm.
Solid support	Celite (100/120 B.S. mesh) soaked in concentrated HCl and washed chloride-free.
Stationary phase	Tris(2,4-dixylenyl) phosphate (5:95).
Temperature	110°C.
Carrier gas	Argon. Inlet pressure: 826 mm Hg above atmospheric.
Detector	Argon ionization.
Recorder	10 mv; 2 seconds; 0.635 cm/min.
Sample size	0.1 μl.
Analysis time	About 60 minutes to *m*-ethyl phenol.

III. SUMMARY

Monohydric phenols substituted in the benzene ring with alkyl groups or chlorine can be separated according to vapor pressure on Apiezon L, or by differences in hydrogen bonding with the stationary phase on polar liquids such as sodium dodecylbenzenesulfonate and erithrytol. *Ortho* isomers are eluted from polar packings much more rapidly than the corresponding *meta* or *para* isomers and consequently can be separated from them readily. To separate the latter two isomers it is necessary to use highly selective liquids, such as tris(2,4-xylenyl) phosphate, or to convert the phenols to trimethylsilyl ethers prior to chromatography. Conversion to anisoles prior to chromatography results in a marked decrease in *ortho-para* separation factors but may be useful in a few specific cases. Dihydric phenols are retained on columns much longer than monohydric compounds and are best chromatographed on sugar alcohols at high temperatures.

C. Aromatic Amines

I. METHODS OF CHROMATOGRAPHY

Gas chromatographic methods have not been worked out for the separation of aromatic amines of biological interest such as phenylethylamine, tryamine, or *p*-aminobenzoic acid. Nevertheless, sufficient data are available on other aromatic amines to obtain a general idea of the kinds of separation that can be made and the experimental conditions required. James (1956) measured the retention volumes of sixty-one aniline derivatives substituted in various positions with alkyl, alkoxy, halogen, and amino groups, using a titration cell as a detection device. Since these materials are very weak bases, it was necessary to carry out the titrations in a nonaqueous medium. Glacial acetic acid was the solvent, Crystal Violet or Metanil Yellow the indicator, and 0.04 *N* perchloric acid in glacial acetic acid the titrating reagent. Details of the operation of the automatic recording burette are given elsewhere (James and Martin, 1952; James, 1952).

The stationary liquids were paraffin wax, polyethylene glycol (Lubrol MO), and benzyldiphenyl coated on alkali-treated Celite 545. The columns were operated at 137°C. These stationary phases were not chosen to obtain the best separations possible but rather to show differences in selectivity between polar and nonpolar solvents. With a few exceptions, molecular weight is the main factor regulating retention time on paraffin columns, and many amines with similar molecular weight cannot be separated. On the other hand, primary and secondary amines can form hydrogen bonds with the polyethylene glycol packing, whereas tertiary amines cannot. Benzyldiphenyl also exhibits a degree of selectivity based on polarity. Consequently, in most cases, a pair of substances that overlap in position on the paraffin column will be well resolved on one of the other columns (Table VIII). In general, *meta* and *para* isomers cannot be separated from one another on short GLC columns containing these packings. Either long packed columns, capillary columns, or more selective stationary phases must be used. Substituent groups in a position *ortho* to the amino group which can function as proton acceptors in intramolecular hydrogen-bond formation tend to reduce retention times on both polar and nonpolar columns, the difference in retention time between isomers being greatest on the polar packing. Therefore, derivatives substituted in the *ortho* position with halogen, alkoxy groups, or amino groups can be easily separated from the corresponding *meta* and *para* isomers. This does not apply to mixtures of the *o*-, *m*-, and *p*-toluidines where intramolecular hydrogen bonding is not possible. However, *N*-alkyl isomers are readily separated from nuclear substituted isomers by polar solvents, since hydrogen bonding with the solvent will be reduced in the former case.

Jones *et al.* (1958) studied the chromatographic behavior of a series of aromatic amines containing from 6 to 10 carbon atoms during an investigation of the composition of a food dye. Since they were interested in the separation of amines up to isoduridine, they investigated the properties of liquid phases that could be used at moderately high temperatures. Poly-

TABLE VIII

RETENTION VOLUMES OF AROMATIC AMINES RELATIVE TO ANILINE IN THREE TYPES OF COLUMN AT 137°C[a]

N atom	Substituents in position					Column stationary phase		
	2	3	4	5	6	Paraffin wax	Lubrol MO	Benzyl-diphenyl
—	F	—	—	—	—	0.72	—	0.63
—	F	—	F	—	—	0.74	0.75	—
—	F	—	—	F	—	0.79	1.08	—
—	—	—	F	—	—	0.96	1.28	1.1
—	—	F	—	—	—	—	0.99	1.52
—	—	F	CH_3	—	—	1.88	2.28	—
—	—	—	CH_3	—	—	1.95	1.63	1.75
—	CH_3	—	F	—	—	2.0	2.28	—
—	—	CH_3	—	—	—	2.0	1.36	1.86
CH_3	—	—	—	—	—	2.05	1.28	1.73
—	CH_3	—	—	—	—	2.05	1.53	1.8
$(CH_3)_2$	CH_3	—	—	—	—	2.56	0.71	1.07
$(CH_3)_2$	—	—	—	—	—	2.60	1.05	1.68
—	Cl	—	—	—	—	2.8	2.34	2.6
C_2H_5	—	—	—	—	—	3.18	1.66	2.33
—	CH_3O	—	—	—	—	3.4	2.7	3.7
CH_3	CH_3	—	—	—	—	3.4	—	3.05
CH_3	—	CH_3	—	—	—	3.4	—	3.28
CH_3	—	—	Cl	—	—	3.7	5.25	4.4
C_2H_5	—	—	—	—	—	3.76	—	—
—	—	Cl	—	—	—	3.8	5.35	4.4
—	CH_3	—	CH_3	—	—	3.84	2.60	3.36
—	NH_2	—	—	—	—	3.92	7.95	6.6
—	CH_3	—	—	CH_3	—	4.0	2.7	3.14
—	—	—	CH_3O	—	—	4.1	5.5	—
—	—	NH_2	—	—	—	4.2	—	10.0
—	CH_3	—	—	—	CH_3	4.25	2.5	3.22
—	—	CH_3	CH_3	—	—	4.27	3.27	3.8
CH_3	Cl	—	—	—	—	4.3	—	3.7
—	—	CH_3O	—	—	—	4.4	5.8	6.6
—	CH_3	CH_3	—	—	—	4.6	3.34	4.0
$(CH_3)_2$	Cl	—	—	—	—	4.8	—	—
—	Br	—	—	—	—	4.9	4.5	5.0
—	—	—	CH_3O	—	—	4.9	—	5.7
$(CH_3)_2$	—	—	CH_3	—	—	5.1	1.7	2.74
C_2H_5	CH_3	—	—	—	—	5.21	2.34	3.66
$(CH_3)_2$	—	CH_3	—	—	—	5.4	1.8	2.9
$(C_2H_5)_2$	—	—	—	—	—	5.45	1.9	3.0
$n\text{-}C_3H_7$	—	—	—	—	—	5.82	2.7	4.0
C_2H_5	—	CH_3	—	—	—	5.9	3.02	4.4

TABLE VIII (*Continued*)

N atom	Substituents in position					Column stationary phase		
	2	3	4	5	6	Paraffin wax	Lubrol MO	Benzyl-diphenyl
C_2H_5	—	—	CH_3	—	—	6.0	2.9	4.4
—	—	NH_2	—	—	—	6.2	—	12.4
—	—	—	C_2H_5O	—	—	6.2	—	8.8
—	—	—	Br	—	—	6.4	10.0	8.8
—	—	Br	—	—	—	6.4	10.0	9.0
CH_3	—	—	Cl	—	—	7.35	—	6.9
—	—	Br	CH_3	—	—	8.8	—	—
—	NO_2	—	—	—	—	9.8	—	—
—	Cl	Cl	—	—	—	10.0	—	—
—	Cl	—	Cl	—	—	10.0	—	—
—	I	—	—	—	—	10.1	—	—
$(C_2H_5)_2$	—	—	CH_3	—	—	10.5	3.2	5.0
$(C_2H_5)_2$	—	CH_3	—	—	—	10.8	3.1	5.1
n-C_4H_9	—	—	—	—	—	11.0	4.7	7.0
—	—	—	I	—	—	13.0	—	23.2
—	—	I	—	—	—	13.1	22.4	23.2
—	CH_3O	—	—	CH_3O	—	14.0	—	—
—	—	Cl	Cl	8 —	—	14.6	—	—
—	CH_3O	—	—	NH_2	—	16.4	—	—
Iso-C_5H_{11}	—	—	—	—	—	16.8	6.4	—
$(CH_3)_2$	—	—	Br	—	—	17.3	6.8	13.3

[a] From James (1956).

ethylene glycol 600, dioctyl phthalate, tricresyl phosphate, and a variety of silicones gave excessive bleeding when used at 200°C. Good separations were obtained with Apiezon M, but the column was easily overloaded. Dow Corning 710 silicone oil was finally selected as the liquid phase, since it gave good resolution with sample volumes up to 25 μl, and the base line was steady. However, some bleeding must occur, for a column operated at 200°C for 56 hours loses its power to separate o-xylidines from m-xylidines. With fresh columns, good resolution of the aromatic amines was obtained at temperatures of 185° to 220°C and flow rates of 13 to 28 ml of helium per minute.

This column separates the amines into isomeric groups. Thus the toluidines, the xylidines, etc., are separated from each other, but the individual isomers are not resolved (Table IX). There are a few exceptions in which isomeric amines are resolved. Mesidine, for example, is well separated from pseudocumidine and 1-amino-2,3,4-trimethylbenzene, but, as a rule, closely related isomers such as the *m*- and *p*-xylidines are not completely separated from one another on this column.

TABLE IX

Retention Times of Aniline Derivatives on Dow Corning 710
Silicone Fluid at 200°C[a]

Substituents	Retention time (mins)	Substituents	Retention time (mins)
2-CH$_3$	8	2,3,6-Tri-CH$_3$	19½
3-CH$_3$	8	2,4,5-Tri-CH$_3$	19½
4-CH$_3$	8	2,3,5-Tri-CH$_3$	16½
2-C$_2$H$_5$	10½	2,3,4-Tri-CH$_3$	23½
4-C$_2$H$_5$	11	3,4,5-Tri-CH$_3$	23
2,6-(CH$_3$)$_2$	11½	2-CH$_3$, 5-C$_2$H$_5$	15
2,4-(CH$_3$)$_2$	11½	2-C$_2$H$_5$, 5-CH$_3$	14
3,5-(CH$_3$)$_2$	11½		
		2-CH$_3$, 6-C$_2$H$_5$	13½
2,5-(CH$_3$)$_2$	11½	2-CH$_3$, 4-C$_2$H$_5$	16
		2-C$_2$H$_5$, 4-CH$_3$	15
2,3-(CH$_3$)$_2$	13½		
3,4-(CH$_3$)$_2$	13½	2-CH$_3$, 3-C$_2$H$_5$	17
		2-C$_2$H$_5$, 3-CH$_3$	14
2,4,6-(CH$_3$)$_3$	15½	3-CH$_3$, 4-C$_2$H$_5$	16
		3-C$_2$H$_5$, 4-CH$_3$	16
		2,4,5,6-Tetra-CH$_3$	32
		2,3,5,6-Tetra-CH$_3$	32

[a] From Jones *et al.* (1958).

Separation of *o*-, *m*-, and *p*-toluidines can be achieved by GSC with a montmorillonite clay in which the naturally occurring inorganic ions are replaced by dimethyldioctadecyl ammonium ions (Hughes *et al.*, 1959). This material is supplied under the trade name B34 by F. W. Berk and Co., Ltd. The column packing is prepared by mixing 15 parts of the adsorbent with 100 parts of Celite (60/80 B.S. mesh). A 90 × 0.6-cm i.d. column gives resolution of the isomers at 200°C. Retention volumes of the *o*-, *m*-, and *p*-toluidines are 1.03, 1.24, and 1.60, respectively, relative to phenol as unity. The elution peaks are markedly asymmetric. However, this could probably be reduced by the use of smaller column loadings in conjunction with a more sensitive detection device. The sample size is not stated, but a volume of 4 μl was injected into the instrument in a parallel experiment in which a mixture of cyclohexane, benzene, and the isomeric xylene was chromatographed.

a. Conditions for Chromatography

1. *Characterization on Polar and Nonpolar Columns* (James, 1956)

Chromatograph	Laboratory-built.
Column dimensions	4-foot × 0.3–0.4-cm i.d. glass tubing.
Solid support	Alkali-treated Celite 545 (James, 1952).
Stationary phases	(I) Paraffin wax (m.p. 49°C). (II) Lubrol MO (a poly-ethylene glycol supplied by Imperial Chemical Industries Ltd.). (III) Benzyldiphenyl (40:60).
Temperature	137°C.
Carrier gas	Nitrogen: (I) Not given. (II) 120 ml/min. (III) Not given. Inlet pressure: (I) Not given. (II) 75 cm Hg. (III) Not given. Outlet pressure: (I) Not given. (II) Atmospheric. (III) Not given.
Detector	Titration cell containing Crystal Violet in glacial acetic acid. 0.04 N perchloric acid.
Sample size	About 5 microequivalents of each base.
Analysis time	40–50 minutes.

*2. *Separation into Isomeric Groups* (Jones et al., 1958)

Chromatograph	Laboratory-built.
Column dimensions	8-foot × ¼-inch o.d. copper tubing.
Solid support	C-22 firebrick (30/60 mesh).
Stationary phase	Dow Corning 710 silicone fluid (40:100).
Temperatures	Column: 200°C. Injection port: 260°C.
Carrier gas	Helium at 20 ml/min at inlet. Inlet pressure: 15–20 psig. Outlet pressure: atmospheric.
Detector	Gow-Mac Model NRL T/C cell.
Recorder	10 mv; × 20 attn. with Kin Tel 111A D.C. amplifier for concentrations less than 1%.
Sample size	5–25 μl.

II. SUMMARY

Aromatic amines can be separated from one another on paraffin or on silicone columns largely on the basis of molecular weight. The toluidines, xylidines, etc., are separated as groups, but the individual isomers are not resolved on short chromatographic columns. However, if a substituent capable of forming intramolecular hydrogen bonds is introduced into the molecule in a position *ortho* to the amino group, these isomers will have lower retention volumes than the corresponding *meta* or *para* derivatives and hence can be separated from them. Compounds with alkyl groups substituted on the nitrogen atom can be separated from nuclear substituted isomers by means of a polar stationary phase, such as polyethylene glycol, which is capable of forming hydrogen bonds with the solutes, thus retarding their passage through the column differentially. Separation of *m*- and *p*-toluidines from one another can be achieved by GSC on a montmorillonite clay in which the inorganic cations are replaced by dimethyldioctadecyl-ammonium ions.

D. Heterocyclic Nitrogen Compounds

I. Occurrence and Isolation

Compounds classified under this heading include pyridine, pyridine derivatives, and alkaloids. Alkaloids are basic compounds, the end products of nitrogen metabolism in some plants, rarely occurring in animals. They are of rather high molecular weight and are classified by the nature of the nitrogen-containing ring systems they possess. They occur abundantly in dicotyledonous plants, particularly in such families as the Apocyanaceae, Papaveraceae, Papilionaceae, Ranunculaceae, Rubiaciae, and Solanaceae. The material is usually localized in certain plant organs such as seeds, leaves, and roots.

The general procedure for removing alkaloids from plant tissue is to free the bases by treatment with alkali and extract them into an organic solvent. Manske and Holmes (1950) describe two methods which are generally applicable to plant materials. If the plant part is rich in fat (seeds), it should be extracted first with petroleum ether. In the first method they describe, the plant part is macerated and extracted with a water-miscible solvent such as methanol. The solvent is evaporated, and the residue is steam-distilled. After removal of extraneous organic matter by decantation and extraction, the aqueous solution is made alkaline, and the free alkaloids are extracted with ether or chloroform. The other procedure is milder. The tissue is macerated and made alkaline. The free alkaloids are extracted with an organic solvent which is then evaporated. The alkaloids are redissolved in aqueous acid, and organic impurities are removed by filtration and extraction. The solution is then made alkaline, and the alkaloids are extracted into ether or chloroform.

Lee (1960) describes a method for the isolation of alkaloids from opium and nux vomica which is said to avoid emulsions and the use of large volumes of solvents. The alkaloids are extracted with aqueous hydrochloric acid or ethanol and precipitated from solution with ammonium reineckate. The reineckates are then dissolved in acetone, and the free alkaloids are regenerated by passing the solution through an ion-exchange column. Crystalline mixtures containing codeine, thebaine, papaverine, narcotine, strychnine, and brucine have been isolated in this way. Morphine is obtained in pure form by selective adsorption on the ion-exchange column.

Quin (1959) collects alkaloids from cigarette smoke by passing the filtered smoke through a dry ice–ethanol trap. The residue in the trap is dissolved in dilute acid, and nonbasic materials are removed by extraction with benzene. The aqueous layer is then made alkaline, and the alkaloids are recovered from it by solvent extraction.

a. Extraction Followed by Partition (Manske and Holmes, 1950)

*1. *Extraction with Methanol.* The tissue is macerated and extracted with acetone-free methanol. The solution is concentrated to a small volume (under reduced pressure if frothing can be avoided), acidified to a pH of 2, and steam-distilled to remove traces of remaining methanol. The volume after steam distillation should be about 1 liter of water for 1 to 3 kg of plant material. To remove suspended matter, the solution is allowed to stand undisturbed for 24 hours and then placed in a refrigerator for 2 to 3 days. The aqueous solution, which should now be clear, is decanted from resins and fats and filtered through charcoal. If suspended particles are still present, they are removed by entrapment in paraffin. The aqueous acid layer is next extracted with ether or chloroform to remove water-soluble organic materials. The water layer is made alkaline with ammonia or sodium carbonate and extracted with chloroform or peroxide-free ether. Chloroform extracts all alkaloids except the quaternary bases and is to be preferred.

*2. *Extraction with Aqueous Alkali.* The plant material is macerated and made alkaline with aqueous ammonia or sodium carbonate solution in a Waring blendor. This mixture is then extracted with a water-immiscible solvent such as chloroform or ethylene dichloride. The organic layer containing the alkaloids plus other plant materials is removed, and the solvent is evaporated. A resinous mass is obtained. The crude alkaloids are dissolved by digesting the residue with dilute acid, and the nonsoluble materials are removed by filtration. The aqueous acid solution is extracted with ether. Some sparingly soluble alkaloid salts may precipitate at this point. To recover the remaining alkaloids, the aqueous acid solution is made alkaline with ammonia and extracted with peroxide-free ether or chloroform. The organic layer is removed, clarified with charcoal, and filtered. The solvent is then evaporated.

b. Isolation as Reineckates (Lee, 1960)

*1. *Opium Alkaloids.* Opium (1 gm) is digested with 10% hydrochloric acid (50 ml) for ½ hour on a water bath. The solution is filtered through No. 1 Whatman paper, and the residue is washed with 3-ml portions of warm dilute hydrochloric acid until the filtrate gives no precipitate with Mayer's reagent. A 2% ammonium reineckate solution (50 ml) is added to the acid solution, after which the mixture is cooled to 0°C and filtered through a sintered-glass funnel with the aid of gentle suction. The precipitate on the funnel is dissolved in acetone, and calcium oxide is added to remove impurities. The solution is then filtered through a sintered-glass funnel, and the lime is washed with acetone until the filtrate is colorless. The acetone solution is passed through an ion-exchange column of De-Acidite FF which has been previously activated by passing a solution of 5% sodium hydroxide solution through it, and then washing it with water until the pH of the eluate is 7 to 8. The acetone solution which percolates through the ion-exchange resin contains all the opium alkaloids but morphine, which is retained on the column. This solution is treated with water (20 ml), and the volume is reduced to 10 ml. It is made alkaline with sodium hydroxide, and the alkaloids are extracted with chloroform. Crystalline products are obtained on evaporating the solvent and triturating the residue with 50% ethanol. Morphine is recovered from the ion-exchange column by washing it first with water to remove the acetone, and then with 10% aqueous acetic acid. The acid solution is made ammoniacal and then extracted with a mixture of chloroform and isobutyl alcohol (3:1), and the morphine is recovered by evaporation of the solvent.

*2. *Nux Vomica Alkaloids.* An ethanol extract of nux vomica (20 ml) is treated with 10% hydrochloric acid solution (20 ml) and heated on a water bath to remove the ethanol. The solution is filtered through No. 1 Whatman paper, and the residue is washed with dilute hydrochloric acid until the filtrate gives no precipitate with Mayer's reagent. Strychnine and brucine are precipitated as their reineckates, and the free alkaloids are isolated as described above.

c. Isolation from Cigarette Smoke

*1. *Method of Quin* (1959). Cigarettes are smoked five at a time on an automatic machine to a butt length of 20 mm. Puffs of 2 seconds' duration and 35-ml volume are taken every minute. The smoke is passed through a 4.5 cm circular glass-fiber filter (Wartman and Harlow, 1958), the filter being replaced after each cycle. The gas from the filter is passed through a trap chilled in dry ice–ethanol to collect volatiles. The condensate is dissolved from the trap, filters, and connecting tubing by washing them thoroughly with 1 N HCl (400 ml). This solution is then placed in a liquid–liquid extractor and extracted continuously with benzene for 3 days. The benzene is removed daily, evaporated to 1 ml, and examined by GLC to determine if volatile acidic or neutral substances are present. None should be found at the end of the third day. The benzene is then discarded, and the pH of the aqueous acid solution is adjusted to 11 with solid sodium hydroxide. This solution is then extracted continuously with benzene for 3 days. The benzene extract is concentrated to 1.0 ml and stored in a refrigerator until ready for use. This solution contains about 0.5 gm of alkaloids.

II. CHROMATOGRAPHY OF PYRIDINE DERIVATIVES

James (1952), using the same column packings employed for the primary aliphatic amines (Chapter 3, Section D), chromatographed a mixture of pyridine, α-, β-, and γ-picolines, 2,4- and 2,6-lutidine, and 2,4,6-collidine at 137°C. All these compounds were resolved except for β- and γ-picoline, which appeared as one peak. Pyridine and the picolines appeared in the same relative positions on the polar and nonpolar packings, so James considered that these compounds have similar hydrogen-bonding power. However, the lutidines have lower hydrogen-bonding power, and thus they run more rapidly relative to pyridine on a polar column. As with the amines, markedly asymmetric peaks are obtained on nonpolar liquid phases owing to adsorption on the solid support. Decora and Dinneen (1960) describe a new solid support that is said to give symmetrical peaks with stationary phases such as squalane, mineral oil, or Apiezon L. This material is derived from Tide, a synthetic detergent containing sodium lauryl sulfate and other organic and inorganic compounds. It is manufactured by spray-drying; thus the inorganic and organic components are intimately mixed. When dried and extracted with petroleum ether, a porous material is obtained which will hold up to 70 gm of liquid per 100 gm of solid and still remain free-flowing. Decora and Dinneen studied the properties of this packing with a variety of liquid substrates (Table X) and fourteen pyridine deriva-

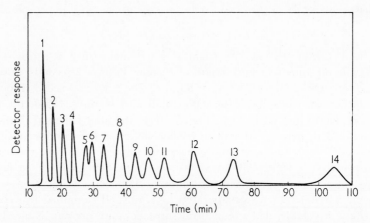

FIG. 6. Separation of fourteen pyridines by using a nonadsorbing support with nonpolar and polar columns in series. (1) Pyridine. (2) 2-Methylpyridine (α-picoline). (3) 2,6-Dimethylpyridine. (4) 2-Ethylpyridine. (5) 3-Methylpyridine (β-picoline). (6) 4-Methylpyridine (γ-picoline). (7) 2,5-Dimethylpyridine. (8) 2,3-Dimethylpyridine. (9) 2,4,6-Trimethylpyridine. (10) 4-Ethylpyridine. (11) 2-Methyl-5-ethylpryidine. (12) 4-Isopropylpyridine. (13) 4-n-Propylpyridine. (14) 3-Ethyl-4-methylpyridine. (From Decora and Dinneen, 1960.)

TABLE X

Relative Retention Values of Fifteen Pyridine Derivatives on Various Liquid Substrates[a]

Pyridine	Boiling point (°C, 760 mm)	Relative retention (2,5-dimethylpyridine = 1)										
		Squalane	Mineral oil	Apiezon L	Silicone high-vacuum grease	Silicone oil D.C. 703	Octoil	Octoil-S	TCP[b]	Tide	DPP[c]	MTE[d]
Pyridine	115.3	0.30	0.29	0.33	0.40	0.35	0.34	0.34	0.40	0.44	0.40	0.45
2-Methyl-	129.4	0.47	0.46	0.51	0.53	0.50	0.48	0.50	0.53	0.51	0.52	0.53
2,6-Dimethyl-	144.0	0.73	0.72	0.73	0.66	0.70	0.67	0.67	0.68	0.69	0.65	0.55
3-Methyl-	144.1	0.64	0.64	0.69	0.74	0.71	0.71	0.71	0.81	0.86	0.82	0.88
4-Methyl-	145.4	0.64	0.64	0.71	0.71	0.71	0.74	0.69	0.83	0.86	0.86	0.95
2-Ethyl-	148.9	0.81	0.81	0.80	0.82	0.83	0.79	0.79	0.78	0.76	0.77	0.66
2,5-Dimethyl-	157.0	1.00	1.00	1.00	1.00	1.00	1.00	1.00	1.00	1.00	1.00	1.00
2,4-Dimethyl-	158.3	1.00	1.00	1.05	0.96	1.01	1.02	1.01	1.07	1.05	1.08	1.11
2,3-Dimethyl-	160.7	1.09	1.08	1.14	1.09	1.11	1.10	1.11	1.21	1.13	1.19	1.15
4-Ethyl-	167.8	1.19	1.18	1.26	1.22	1.30	1.33	1.27	1.43	1.47	1.46	1.51
2,4,6-Trimethyl-	170.3	1.50	1.51	1.49	1.30	1.36	1.35	1.42	1.42	1.35	1.33	1.11
2-Methyl-5-ethyl-	176.8	1.79	1.80	1.82	1.57	1.74	1.75	1.72	1.70	1.49	1.65	1.60
4-Isopropyl-	182.0	1.77	1.76	1.81	1.71	1.87	1.92	1.83	1.94	1.93	1.92	1.96
4-n-Propyl-	187.8	2.07	2.09	2.15	2.07	2.15	2.23	2.19	2.40	2.28	2.32	2.31
3-Ethyl-4-methyl-	194.9	2.55	2.61	2.77	2.55	2.77	3.02	2.75	3.08	2.77	3.24	3.37

[a] From Decora and Dinneen (1960).
[b] Tri-m-cresyl phosphate (tri-m-tolyl phosphate).
[c] Diphenyl phthalate.
[d] N-Hydroxyethyl-N,N',N'-tris(hydroxypropyl)ethylenediamine.

tives. From these data they were able to select a combination of two columns that, when used in series, separated the components of the mixture (Fig. 6). The first column contained diphenyl phthalate, and the second N-hydroxyethyl-N',N',N'-tris(hydroxypropyl)ethylenediamine (MTE), both coated on the solid support. As can be seen, both peak symmetry and resolution are excellent. The β- and γ-picolines are partially resolved.

These peaks can be cleanly resolved and good symmetry obtained if highly polar liquids are used on conventional solid supports. Murray and Williams (1956) and Brooks and Collins (1956) simultaneously announced the separation of β- and γ-picolines on glycerol. The latter workers obtained partial resolution of these compounds on Carbowax 1000, and almost complete resolution on triethanolamine (Table XI). However, the picolines were completely separated on a glycerol column at 78°C (Fig. 7). The

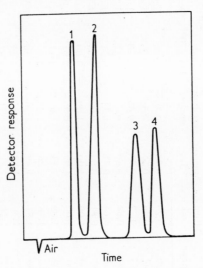

Fig. 7. Separation of (1) 2,6-lutidine, (2) α-picoline, (3) β-picoline, and (4) γ-picoline on a glycerol column at 78°C. (From Brooks and Collins, 1956.)

order of elution was: 2,6-lutidine, α-picoline, β-picoline, and γ-picoline, the lutidine being eluted before the picolines on the polar column and after them on paraffin.

The chromatography of pyridine and quinoline derivatives on polar and nonpolar liquids has been investigated by Fitzgerald (1961). The most useful nonpolar phase for separation according to boiling point was found to be silicone E-301. It will give good separations with both classes of com-

TABLE XI

RELATIVE RETENTION VALUES OF PYRIDINE DERIVATIVES
ON THREE PARTITION LIQUIDS

Compound	Boiling point (°C)	Relative retention time on liquid		
		Carbowax 1000 at 120°C	Triethanolamine at 120°C	Glycerol at 90°C
Pyridine	115.26	1.00	1.00	1.00
α-Picoline	129.41	1.22	1.13	0.82
2,6-Lutidine	144.05	1.43	1.16	0.53
β-Picoline	144.14	1.98	1.90	1.54
γ-Picoline	145.36	2.07	2.20	1.86
2-Ethylpyridine	148.70	1.74	1.25	0.62
2,5-Lutidine	157.01	2.25	2.22	1.22
2,4-Lutidine	157.90	2.43	2.55	1.55
2,3-Lutidine	160.8	2.79	2.68	1.51
2-Ethyl-6-methylpyridine	160.1	1.83	1.17	0.30
3-Ethylpyridine	165.0	2.99	3.00	1.65
4-Ethylpyridine	167.7	3.60	3.53	2.11
2,4,6-Collidine	170.3	2.83	2.34	1.00
3,5-Lutidine	172.2	3.68	3.60	2.30
2,3,5-Collidine	186.8	4.74	4.87	2.46
2,3,4-Collidine	192.7	6.80	7.98	4.03

pounds. Polar materials of equally wide applicability were not found. Diglycerol is suitable for pyridines, but not for quinolines, whereas hexa(cyanoethyl)melamine gives good results with quinolines, but not with pyridines, since its melting point is too high.

a. Conditions for Chromatography

*1. Use of Columns in Series (Decora and Dinneen, 1960)

Chromatograph	Laboratory-built.
Column dimensions	350 × 0.6-cm coiled aluminum tubing.
Solid support	Extracted Tide (see Chapter 1, method C.III.c.1).
Stationary phase	(A) Diphenyl phthalate (10:100). (B) MTE (N-hydroxyethyl-N,N',N'-tris(hydroxypropyl)ethylenediamine (10:100).
Temperature	130°C.
Carrier gas	Helium at 90 ml/min.
Detector	Thermistor.
Sample size	5 μl.
Analysis time	105 minutes to 3-ethyl-4-methylpyridine.

*2. *Resolution of Picolines on Glycerol* (Murray and Williams, 1956)

Chromatograph   Laboratory-built.
Column dimensions   124 × 0.4-cm i.d. straight glass tube.
Solid support   Celite 535 (ungraded).
Stationary phase   Glycerol (30:100).
Temperatures   Column: 78°C. Injection port: 170°C. Detector: 78°C.
Carrier gas   Nitrogen at 18 ml/min at inlet. Inlet pressure: 790 mm
                       Hg. Outlet pressure: atmospheric.
Detector   Hot-wire (Pt) T/C cell operated at 115 ma.
Recorder   Honeywell-Brown 1 mv; 1 second; 12 inch/hour.
Sample size   16–24 mg.
Analysis time   5 minutes.

III. Chromatography of Alkaloids

Work has been done on the separation and identification of alkaloids from tobacco (Quin, 1958, 1959). Nicotine, nornicotine, myosamine, anabasine, anatabine, 2,3-dipyridyl, and cotinine were separated from tobacco smoke and identified by using polypropylene glycol and polyethylene glycol packings at 190°C. Pilleri and Vietti-Michelina (1960) have shown that good separation of nicotine from pyridine can be obtained with Apiezon L at 200°C, but they have worked only with synthetic mixtures of these materials.

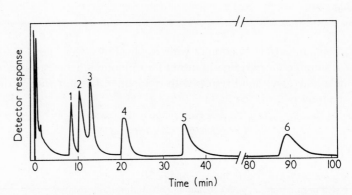

Fig. 8. Separation of papaveracine alkaloids on silicone polymer SE-30 at 204°C. (1) Codeine. (2) Morphine. (3) Thebaine. (4) Laudanosine. (5) Papaverine. (6) Gnoscopine. (From Lloyd *et al.*, 1960.)

A methyl silicone polymer manufactured by General Electric, SE-30, has been introduced recently as a stationary phase in gas chromatography. It has been used for the separation of alkaloids, steroids, and other materials of relatively high molecular weight. By keeping the ratio of stationary phase to solid support low, relatively low temperatures can be used and short retention times obtained without decomposition of the materials being chromatographed.

Lloyd *et al.* (1960) used 2 to 3% SE-30 coated on treated Chromosorb W at 204°C and obtained good separations of alkaloids of several classes having molecular weights greater than 250 (Table XII). Papaveracine alkaloids—

TABLE XII

Retention Times of Alkaloids on Silicone Polymer SE-30 [a,b]

Compound	Time (min)	Compound	Time (min)
1. Lupin alkaloids		Neopine	9.1
Cytisine	5.1	Papaverine	35.3
Methylcytisine	4.3	Thebaine	13.2
Methylcytisine		*4. Indole Alkaloids*	
N-oxide	5.8	Brucine	80.0[c]
Lupanine	5.5	Coronaridine	8.2[c]
13-Hydroxylupanine	11.6	Ibogamine	15.4
Matrina	8.5	Ibogaine	35.1
Lupinine	1.5[d]	Serpentine	16.8[c]
Sparteine	5.9[d]	Strychnine	25.9[c]
α-Isosparteine	5.2[d]	Voacangine	40.3
13-Hydroxysparteine	14.3[d]	*5. Steroidal Alkaloids*	
2. Amaryllidaceae		Solanidine	40.6[c,e]
Galanthine	19.0	Solasodine	74.3[c,e]
Acetylcaranine	10.5	Tomatidine	77.3[c,e]
Lycorenine	10.6	*6. Miscellaneous*	
Galanthamine	7.8	Atropine	5.0
Crinine	9.5	Caffeine	1.6
Powelline	15.8	Cinchonine	6.7[c]
Tasettine	15.2	Cocaine	4.8[c]
Belladine	8.7	Corydaline	16.2[c]
3. Papaveraceae		Cryptopine	50.8
Codeine	8.2	Himbacine	12.7[c]
Gnoscopine	90.6	Piperine	33.0
Laudanosine	21.0	Protopine	44.7
Morphine	11.0	Quinine	11.8[c]

[a] From Lloyd *et al.* (1960).
[b] Temperature 204°C unless otherwise noted.
[c] Temperature 222°C.
[d] Temperature 160°C.
[e] Pressure 10 psig.

codeine, morphine, thebaine, laudanosine, papaverine, and gnoscopine— show good separation with slight tailing when this partition liquid is used (Fig. 8). They have also found that commercially available analgesic mixtures can be separated with just a few cases of serious overlapping of peaks.

This method therefore shows promise in the analysis of body fluids for drug metabolites, for "fingerprinting" opium from various sources, and for screening plants for alkaloid content.

a. Conditions for Chromatography

*1. Tobacco Smoke Alkaloids (Quin, 1959)

Chromatograph	Perkin-Elmer 154B.
Column dimensions	100 × 0.6 cm.
Solid support	Firebrick washed with 2% alcoholic KOH, alcohol, and dried at 110°C.
Stationary phase	(I) Polypropylene glycol (M.W. 1025) and (II) polyethylene glycol (M.W. 20,000) (10:40).
Temperature	190°C.
Carrier gas	Helium at 45 ml/min.
Detector	Thermistor at 8 volts.
Recorder	Leeds & Northrup Speedomax Type G, 1 mv, 1 in./min.
Sample size	50 μl (about 25 mg of alkaloids).
Analysis time	About 100 minutes.

*2. Separation of Nicotine and Pyridine (Pilleri and Vietti-Michelina, 1960)

Chromatograph	C. Erba Fractovap.
Column dimensions	1000 × 0.6-cm coiled copper tubing.
Solid support	Celite C-22.
Stationary phase	Apiezon L.
Temperature	200°C.
Carrier gas	Nitrogen at 25 ml/min. Inlet pressure: 114 mm Hg. Outlet pressure: atmospheric.
Detector	T/C, fractions combusted to CO_2.
Recorder	Leeds & Northrup Speedomax Type G, 1 mv, 1 in./min.
Sample size	10 μl.
Analysis time	3 minutes.

*3. Other Alkaloids (Lloyd et al., 1960)

Chromatograph	Barber-Colman Model 10.
Column dimensions	180 × 0.4-cm i.d. glass U tube.
Solid support	Chromosorb W (80/100 U. S. mesh) washed with concentrated HCl followed by 1% methanolic KOH) dried at 100°C.
Stationary phase	General Electric Co. methyl silicone polymer, type SE-30 (2–3%).
Temperature	204°C (few exceptions).
Carrier gas	Argon. Inlet pressure: 15 psig. Outlet pressure: atmospheric.
Detector	Argon ionization with radium foil.
Recorder	Wheelco. 50 mv; 2 seconds; 1 cm/min.
Sample size	1–3 μl of 0.5–1% solution in methanol, acetone, or chloroform.
Analysis time	About 80 minutes.

IV. Summary

Alkaloids from tobacco can be separated from one another on polypropylene glycol and polyethylene glycol columns. Apiezon L has been used to separate pyridine and nicotine. A methyl silicone polymer is successful for the separation of alkaloids of rather high molecular weight, with a low ratio of stationary phase to solid support. This material also shows promise as a stationary phase for separation of other materials with relatively low vapor pressures.

References

Araki, T. and R. Goto. 1960. Gas-liquid partition chromatography of *m*- and *p*-xylenes on 1-naphthylamine. *Bull. Chem. Soc. Japan* **33** (1): 115; *Anal. Abstr.* **7:** 3813 (1960).

Brooks, V. T. 1959. Gas-liquid chromatography: separation of close-boiling phenol isomers. *Chem. & Ind. (London)* pp. 1317–1318.

Brooks, V. T. and G. A. Collins. 1956. Separation of pyridine bases by vapour-phase chromatography. *Chem. & Ind. (London)* p. 1021.

Carruthers, W. and R. A. W. Johnstone. 1960. Some phenolic constituents of cigarette smoke. *Nature* **185:** 762–763.

Carugno, N. and G. Giovannozzi-Sermanni. 1959. Determinazione del 3–4 benzopirene e di altri idrocarburi aromatici policiclici per mezzo della cromatografia in fase gassora. *Il Tabacco* **63:** 285–292.

Decora, A. W. and G. U. Dinneen. 1960. Gas-liquid chromatography of pyridines using a new solid support. *Anal. Chem.* **32:** 164–169.

Durrett, L. R. 1960. Applications of Carbowax 400 in gas chromatography for extreme aromatic selectivity. *Anal. Chem.* **32:** 1393–1396.

Feigl, F. 1956. "Spot Tests in Organic Analysis," 5th Engl. ed.) (Ralph E. Oesper, transl.), 616 pp. New York, Van Nostrand (Elsevier).

Fitzgerald, J. S. 1959. Gas chromatography applied to the analysis of phenols. *Australian J. Appl. Sci.* **10:** 169–189.

Fitzgerald, J. S. 1961. Gas chromatography applied to the analysis of pyridines and quinolines. *Australian J. Appl. Sci.* **12:** 51–68.

Grant, D. W. and G. A. Vaughan. 1957. The use of gas-liquid chromatography in the determination of the distribution of aromatic compounds in coal tar naphthas. *In* "Vapour Phase Chromatography" (D. H. Desty, ed.), pp. 413–420. New York, Academic Press.

Hughes, M. A., D. White, and A. L. Roberts. 1959. Separation of *meta*- and *para*-isomers of the xylenes, cresols, and toluidines by gas-solid chromatography. *Nature* **184:** 1796–1797.

James, A. T. 1952. Gas-liquid partition chromatography: the separation of volatile aliphatic amines and of the homologues of pyridine. *Biochem. J.* **52:** 242–247.

James, A. T. 1956. Gas-liquid chromatography. Separation and microestimation of volatile aromatic amines. *Anal. Chem.* **28:** 1564–1567.

James, A. T. and A. J. P. Martin. 1952. Gas-liquid partition chromatography. A technique for the analysis of volatile materials. *Analyst* **77:** 915–931.

Janák, J. and R. Komers. 1958. Evaluation of some sugars as stationary phases for separation of phenols by gas chromatography. *In* "Gas Chromatography" (D. H. Desty, ed.), pp. 343–348. New York, Academic Press.

Janák, J., R. Komers, and J. Šíma. 1959. Gaschromatographie einwertiger Phenole. *Collection Czechoslov. Chem. Communs.* **24**: 1492–1508.

Jones, J. H., C. D. Ritchie, and K. S. Heine, Jr. 1958. Gas chromatography of aromatic amines and nitro compounds. *J. Assoc. Offic. Agr. Chem.* **41**: 749–752.

Langer, S. H., P. Pantages, and I. Wender. 1958. Gas-liquid chromatographic separation of phenols as trimethylsilyl ethers. *Chem. & Ind. (London)* pp. 1664–1665.

Langer, S. H., C. Zahn, and G. Pantazoplos. 1960. Selective gas-liquid chromatographic separation of aromatic compounds with tetrahalophthalate esters. *J. Chromatog.* **3**: 154–167.

Lee, K-T. 1960. Quantitative isolation of alkaloids from plant materials. *Nature* **188**: 65–66.

Lloyd, H. A., H. M. Fales, P. F. Highet, W. J. A. VandenHeuvel, and W. C. Wildman. 1960. Separation of alkaloids by gas chromatography. *J. Am. Chem. Soc.* **82**: 3791.

Manske, R. H. F. and H. L. Holmes, eds. 1950. "The Alkaloids: Chemistry and Physiology," 525 pp. New York, Academic Press.

Murray, W. J. and A. F. Williams. 1956. The determination of small amounts of γ-picoline in aqueous solutions of β-picoline by vapour phase chromatography. *Chem & Ind. (London)* 1020–1021.

Pilleri, R. and M. Vietti-Michelina. 1960. Gaschromatographische Analyse von Pyridin-Nicotinmischung. *Z. anal. Chem.* **174**: 172–174.

Quin, L. D. 1958. Separation of some tobacco alkaloids by gas chromatography. *Nature* **182**: 865.

Quin, L. D. 1959. Alkaloids of tobacco smoke. I. Fractionation of some tobacco alkaloids and of the alkaloid extract of Burley cigarette smoke by gas chromatography. *J. Org. Chem.* **24**: 911–914.

Spencer, C. F. and J. F. Johnson. 1960. Analysis of phenylalkanes by gas chromatography. *J. Chromatog.* **4**: 244–248.

Wartman, W. B. and E. S. Harlow. 1958. Determination of total solids, tars, and resins, and nicotine in cigarette smoke, including a discussion of existing methods. Paper presented at the 133rd National Meeting of the American Chemical Society, San Francisco.

Wiseman, W. A. 1960. Separation factors in gas chromatography. *Nature* **185**: 841–842.

Zlatkis, A., S.-Y. Ling, and H. R. Kaufman. 1959. Resolution of isomeric xylenes by gas-liquid chromatography. *Anal. Chem.* **31**: 945–947.

Chapter 5

Essential Oils

General Introduction

Gas chromatography is an excellent tool for the separation, character-ization, and quantitative analysis of essential oils. Separations of components that formerly took days by tedious chemical and physical means, or were impossible by these older methods, can now be accomplished in minutes.

Terpenes, hydrocarbons, and related oxygenated terpenoid derivatives are the main constituents of the essential oils. These compounds are com-posed of isoprene units, monoterpenes being composed of two units (C_{10}), and sesquiterpenes of three (C_{15}). Only the monoterpenes (usually simply called terpenes) and sesquiterpenes need concern us in this chapter, since essential oils are composed to a large extent by derivatives of these two groups of compounds. Other compounds composed of larger numbers of isoprene units are also biochemically important; these include carotenoids and steroids. The chromatography of these materials is covered elsewhere (see Chapter 7).

Many geometric, positional, and optical isomers are present in the terpenes and sesquiterpenes, and many of the compounds are unstable. Gas chromatography separates many of these components and has the added advantages of being fast, of using an inert atmosphere, and of requiring small sample sizes.

The general methods of isolation of essential oils and preliminary sep-aration of components are covered in Section A. Sections B, C, and D cover chromatography of known terpenes, oxygenated terpenoid compounds, and synthetic mixtures of these materials, and Sections E, F, and G cover the chromatography of the naturally occurring oils arranged by plant families. Section H deals with special precautions necessary for chromatography of terpenoid compounds, since many are unstable and undergo decomposition easily during chromatography.

Much of the work on the chromatography of essential oils has been done in commercial laboratories and unfortunately has not been published. The list of naturally occurring oils that have been chromatographed, therefore, is not so extensive as it would be if this material were available in published literature.

Before chromatography, many essential oils are separated into constituent groups such as terpenoid hydrocarbons and oxygenated derivatives by meth-ods described in Section A. These groups then are chromatographed as de-

371

scribed in Sections B, C, and D, or under specific headings in Sections E, F, and G.

The complete essential oil mixture is often chromatographed without preliminary separation. There are several disadvantages to this type of chromatography. Complete separations of all components usually cannot be achieved at one column temperature, since the boiling-point range for the hydrocarbon and oxygenated fractions is very wide. There may be incomplete separation of components which could be isolated by preliminary functional group separation. Also, hydrocarbons sometimes constitute the major fraction in an essential oil. In lemon oil, for instance, the terpene hydrocarbons make up 96% of the essential oil. The oxygenated portion is of importance, however, since it gives the oil its distinctive flavor and aroma. When the complete oil is chromatographed, either the oxygenated fraction will be too dilute for good detection or, if a larger sample is chromatographed, the hydrocarbons will overload the column and these peaks will mask the peaks from the oxygenated components.

There are advantages to the use of the complete oil, if the limitations of the procedure are kept in mind. First, this is a very rapid method, since no preliminary separations are necessary. The essential oil, sometimes diluted with a low-boiling organic solvent, is injected directly into the chromatograph. Second, characteristic chromatograms, fingerprints of an essential oil, may be obtained if there are no major constituents present to mask the other components. This type of chromatogram is useful for quality control where the actual identification of the components is not so important as is a characteristic chromatogram of the oil. Fortification and adulteration can be detected very quickly by comparisons of chromatograms of pure and suspect mixtures.

A refined technique for the classification and identification of peppermint oil has been described (see Section G.VII.c). The ratio of certain components of the essential oil versus the ratio of other components gives information on the species of peppermint, the region in which the plants were grown, and the process of manufacture. Adulteration can be readily recognized by this technique. It should prove a valuable method for the characterization of other essential oils as well, and for the detection of subtle sophistication of these extracts.

A. Isolation and Separation

I. ISOLATION OF ESSENTIAL OILS FROM PLANT MATERIALS AND BEVERAGES

Our major interest in essential oils concerns the chromatography of commercially prepared extracts for fingerprinting, identification of flavor components, and detection of adulteration. Therefore, only a few general methods for their isolation from plant materials will be given.

Essential oils are most often separated by steam distillation at atmospheric pressure. The oils are insoluble in water and form an oil phase on the aqueous distillate. Most of the flavor and organoleptic components are found in the oil layer, little being present in the water. The oil layer is drawn off and freed from water, usually by centrifugation. When small amounts of essential oils are distilled, they can be separated from the water layer by extraction with petroleum ether. Some essential oil constituents are heat-labile, and structural rearrangements can take place during isolation by steam distillation at atmospheric pressure. Therefore, steam distillation at reduced pressure is sometimes used, or other methods of isolation are employed which are less likely to cause changes.

The essential oils of citrus fruits are found mainly in ductless glands located in the colored outer layer of the peel. The oils are present in such large quantities that they are usually recovered commercially by cold-press methods as water emulsions by squeezing the peel through grooved rollers, or by rasping the surface of the whole fruit. The oils are then separated by high-speed centrifugation and are sometimes further chilled and clarified to remove waxes. This method avoids heat but is suitable only for materials containing large quantities of essential oils.

These oils may be extracted also with volatile organic solvents at low temperatures. Petroleum ether is sometimes used to extract thermolabile compounds and is employed commercially for extracting small quantities of essential oils. The material to be extracted is finely divided and stirred for a period of several hours with petroleum ether. The extracts are filtered, and the solvent is carefully removed under reduced pressure at temperatures around 40°C.

Benzene is sometimes used for extraction, but this solvent extracts materials other than essential oils and therefore is not so desirable. Acetone has been used for extraction of dry material (Runeberg, 1960a), but here again the solvent will extract materials other than essential oils. The acetone can be removed by evaporation, and the residue suspended in diethyl ether. The ether is filtered, the filtrate evaporated, and the residue taken up in petroleum ether. This is filtered, and the essential oils are found in the filtrate.

Either concentrated or dilute ethanol is sometimes used for the extraction of dried plant materials. Like acetone, it is not generally suitable for the extraction of fresh material, since it dissolves the water contained in the tissues and becomes increasingly more dilute. Alcohol extracts not only essential oils but also alcohol-soluble resins. These materials can be precipitated and filtered off, leaving the essential oil in solution, or the essential oil can be steam-distilled away from the less-volatile resins.

Any of the volatile solvents used to extract essential oils should be evaporated with care, preferably under reduced pressure at temperatures slightly higher than room temperature. The oils should be protected from air and oxygen as much as possible to prevent oxidation of unsaturated compounds. They are best stored in petroleum ether in a cool place under an atmosphere of nitrogen.

Essential oils are used as flavoring components of beverages, and a method has been developed by Harold *et al.* (1960) for their isolation and separation by GLC. The essential oils are isolated by liquid extraction with ether, the extract is washed and neutralized, and the solvent is steam-distilled to separate the essential oils and other volatiles from the nonvolatile components.

a. Isolation Procedures

1. *Isolation by Steam Distillation* (Langenau, 1948). A sufficient quantity of ground plant material is placed in a 2-liter round-bottomed flask (Fig. 1).

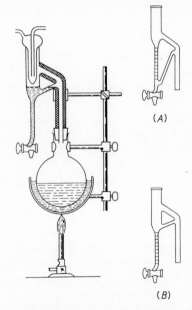

Fig. 1. Apparatus for the isolation of essential oils by steam distillation: (*A*) trap for oils lighter than water; (*B*) trap for oils heavier than water. (Langenau, 1948.)

Water is added to correspond to three to six times the weight of the plant material. Trap *A* is attached for oils lighter than water, trap *B* for oils heavier than water. Each contains a cold finger condenser. Water is added to fill the trap, and the flask is then heated in an oil bath held at 130°C so that approximately 1 drop of condensate is obtained per second. The distillation is continued, usually for 5 to 6 hours, until no further increase in the amount of oil is observed. The distillate is allowed to stand until a good separation of layers is obtained, and the oil layer is collected. The distillate may be centrifuged to separate the layers, or, if small quantities of oil are present, it may be extracted with petroleum ether.

2. *Isolation by Petroleum Ether Extraction* (Paul *et al.*, 1960). Finely divided plant material (1 part) is stirred with 2 parts of petroleum ether (b.p. 40° to 60°C) at room temperature for 2 hours. The extract is allowed to settle and is filtered. The plant material is then re-extracted twice for periods of 2 hours each with 1½ parts of petroleum ether. The filtrates are combined, and the solvent is removed under reduced pressure at 40°C.

*3. *Isolation by Extraction with Acetone* (Runeberg, 1960a). Dried, ground plant material is continuously extracted with acetone for 24 hours. The acetone is evaporated, and the remaining oil is poured, with stirring, into 10 volumes of peroxide-free ether. The ether suspension is filtered and evaporated. The residue is mixed with 10 volumes of petroleum ether (b.p. 40° to 60°C). The petroleum ether suspension is filtered, and the solvent is removed by evaporation. The essential oils are in this extract.

*4. *Isolation of Essential Oils from Beverages* (Harold *et al.*, 1960). The beverage, beer, is extracted continuously with freshly distilled ether in an inert atmosphere. The ether extract is washed with aqueous solutions of sodium bicarbonate, sodium hydroxide, and citric acid to remove acidic and basic materials. Ether and ethanol are removed by fractional distillation by using a 1-meter column containing glass helices and a reflux ratio of 1:10. The residue is steam-distilled at a pressure of 30 mm of mercury, the essential oils being found in the distillate along with other volatile components such as the lower alcohols.

II. Fractionation of Essential Oil Components Prior to GLC

Essential oils are made up mainly of terpene hydrocarbons and oxygen-containing compounds with differing chemical characteristics and wide boiling-point ranges. The best separations of individual components by GLC are obtained after preliminary separations of groups of homogeneous compounds by other methods. Thus terpene hydrocarbons are often separated from the oxygen-containing fraction prior to chromatography, and the oxygen-containing compounds are sometimes further subdivided into carboxyl, hydroxyl, and carbonyl compounds. Subtraction techniques are also employed at times to remove specific groups of materials which may interfere with chromatographic separations.

Terpene hydrocarbons can be separated from the oxygenated components of essential oils by liquid–solid chromatography on silicic acid or alumina, or by preliminary GLC on nonpolar packings with collection of the eluates. Kirchner and Miller (1952) made a detailed study of conditions necessary for the separation of the two fractions on silicic acid. They found that the hydrocarbon fraction could be eluted quantitatively from a column packed with silicic acid (Table I), with hexane as the eluting agent. The amounts of

TABLE I

SUMMARY OF ESSENTIAL OILS FROM WHICH TERPENE FRACTIONS HAVE BEEN REMOVED[a]

Oil	A[b]	B[b]	C[b]	D[b]	E[b]
Orange, cold-pressed	136	625	4.0	90.7	94.7
Grapefruit, cold-pressed	151	625	16.5	74.0	90.5
Lemon, cold-pressed	108	625	6.0	88.8	94.8
Clove	656	200	86.0	10.3	96.3
Peppermint	600	2,000	67.5	21.4	88.9
Petitgrain (Paraguay)	800	800	83.5	8.1	91.6
Bay	700	800	74.0	20.0	94.0
Cedarwood	382	900	28.8	65.8	94.6

[a] From Kirchner and Miller (1952).

[b] A, grams of silicic acid required to remove all oxygenated components from 100 gm of oil. B, approximate number of milliliters of hexane required to remove terpene hydrocarbons from 100 gm of oil. C, yield of oxygenated components (grams) from 100 gm of oil. D, yield of terpene hydrocarbons (grams) from 100 gm of oil. E, over-all yield (grams).

silicic acid and hexane required for the adsorption of the oxygen-containing fraction and the elution of the hydrocarbon fraction differ with various types of essential oils. Only 108 gm of silicic acid is required for adsorption of the oxygenated portion from 100 gm of lemon oil, but 800 gm is needed for the oil of petitgrain. The oil of peppermint requires at least 2 liters of hexane to elute the terpene hydrocarbon fraction, and even then the elution may not be complete, whereas 100 gm of the oil of clove requires only one-tenth that amount of solvent for the quantitative elution of the hydrocarbon fraction. Later, these oxygenated fractions are quantitatively eluted with ethyl acetate. It can be seen that the conditions for separation of essential oil constituents must be carefully investigated in order to obtain good results. Column chromatography is best suited for preliminary fractionation, although a slurry technique may be used at times if the procedure has been standardized. This will be discussed below. A micromethod for deterpenation has been used in which 1 to 2 drops of the essential oil is deterpenated on silicic acid with a micro-Büchner as a column (Broderick, 1961). Kirchner and Miller examined fractions eluted from a column by a fluorescein–bromine test on a small portion of the eluate spotted on a chromatostrip. The reagent is sprayed on the strip and gives a positive test (yellow spot on a pink background) for compounds with ethylenic-type double bonds. Both the hydrocarbon and the oxygenated fractions contain these double bonds, but, since they are eluted with different solvents, the spot test is used only to test for completeness of elution with each solvent. A simple test specific for oxygenated compounds would be of help in ascertaining whether oxygen-containing materials are eluted with the hydrocarbon fraction, or specific tests for different types of oxygen-containing groups might be used.

A slurry technique is sometimes applied for the separation of the hydrocarbon and oxygenated fractions on silicic acid (Kirchner and Miller, 1952; Clark and Bernhard, 1960a). The silicic acid is added to the essential oil dissolved in hexane or pentane and is allowed to stand with occasional swirling for a period of time, after which the hydrocarbon fraction in the solvent is filtered away from the oxygenated portion adsorbed on the silicic acid. The oxygenated compounds are then eluted from the adsorbent with ethyl acetate. This is a very simple technique and has been applied with partial success to the separation of citrus oil fractions (Clark and Bernhard, 1960a). However, the slurry method must be carefully evaluated for completeness of separation with each type of essential oil examined. Rigby and Bethune (1957) employed this procedure for the separation of hop oil constituents and found methyl nonyl ketone and other ketones in the hydrocarbon fraction. They were able to obtain clean hydrocarbon separations, however, with the column chromatographic technique under carefully controlled conditions.

Hydrocarbon and oxygenated components can also be separated on activated alumina by LSC prior to GLC, but, here again, there may be overlapping of groups unless care is taken to determine optimum chromatographic conditions (Paul et al., 1960). The oil is applied in a hexane solution to a column containing alumina. Hydrocarbons are eluted with light petroleum ether, there being a partial separation of the monoterpenes and sesquiterpenes of hop oil (Howard and Slater, 1957). The oxygenated components are eluted with a series of solvents, partial separations of esters and methyl ketones being obtained.

Sometimes preliminary GLC can be used to separate essential oil constituents on nonpolar packings. The compounds are eluted in the order of their boiling points, and, since the monoterpene hydrocarbons generally have higher vapor pressures than their oxygenated derivatives, the hydrocarbons are eluted first. However, several low-boiling oxygenated components, important in some essential oils, are also removed with the monoterpene hydrocarbons. Hexanol and hexenal, octyl aldehyde, and cineol are examples. The sesquiterpene hydrocarbons are eluted after the oxygenated monoterpenes, since their boiling points in general are higher than those of the oxygenated derivatives (Liberti and Cartoni, 1958b). The eluates can be collected and further separations of components made under different chromatographic conditions.

The hydrocarbon fractions of essential oils can be further subdivided into fractions by differential elution from silica gel columns. Clements (1958) separated citrus oil hydrocarbons at −78.5°C with petroleum ether followed by a 1:1 diethyl ether–petroleum ether mixture. However, hydrocarbon fractionation before GLC is usually not necessary under proper chromatographic conditions.

Oxygenated monoterpenoids containing various functional groups are often isolated and chromatographed separately. Free acids may be present in the essential oil if the oil is isolated by solvent extraction. They can be removed by extraction of the ether or petroleum ether solution with aqueous sodium carbonate. The acids are then re-extracted from the acidified aqueous solution into ether and are methylated prior to chromatography by procedures described in Chapter 7.

Aromatic compounds with phenolic groups are important constituents of some essential oils. They may be separated by extraction from an ethereal solution with aqueous sodium hydroxide or potassium hydroxide (Kelker and Rao, 1934; Naves, 1959a). Carboxylic acids also form salts with strong alkalis and will be extracted. However, they may be removed by extraction with sodium carbonate prior to phenol extraction with the strong alkali, since phenols are weak acids and will not be removed by weak bases. The extractions may not be so clear-cut in practice as in theory, and some phenols may be extracted by sodium carbonate, whereas some of the carboxylic acids may not be extracted (Carruthers and Johnstone, 1960).

Another procedure for the separation of the two groups is described in Chapter 4, Section B. In this method both the phenols and carboxylic acids are extracted into aqueous NaOH. The salts are decomposed by acidifying the aqueous layer, and the phenols and acids are extracted into ether. The compounds are methylated by using diazomethane as described in Chapter 7. The methyl ethers of the phenols and the methyl esters of the carboxylic acids are formed. The esters are saponified, leaving the phenols as volatile ethers which can be separated by distillation.

Esters are usually present in essential oils as acetates, sometimes as formates, propionates, or butyrates (Clark and Bernhard, 1960b) of terpenoid alcohols, and are usually chromatographed unchanged. Free acids, phenols, carbonyl compounds, and alcohols can be removed from the essential oil, leaving the neutral oil containing the ester fraction which can then be chromatographed. The esters also might be saponified and the alcohols removed by formation of their benzoic esters.

Stanley *et al.* (1961) have developed a method for removal of carbonyl compounds from citrus essential oils prior to gas chromatography. Water-soluble Girard derivatives are formed. They are extracted into water, formaldehyde is added to form formaldehyde–hydrazone derivatives, and the free carbonyl compounds are regenerated. These are extracted into isopentane, and the extract is concentrated and then chromatographed.

Carbonyls may also be separated by extraction of the essential oil with aqueous sodium bisulfite (Liberti and Cartoni, 1958b). Water-soluble bisulfite addition compounds are formed, the aqueous layer is separated, and the free carbonyl compounds are liberated by addition of alkali and then extracted into hexane.

Alcohols can be separated from essential oils by formation of benzoic acid esters. These esters crystallize out of solution and have been chromatographed through C_8 by Bayer *et al.* (1958), although no details were given. Perhaps C_{10} derivatives of the monoterpenoid alcohols also could be chromatographed directly if the proper conditions were chosen. Phthalic acid esters of the alcohols also can be formed for the separation of this fraction. Otherwise the esters can be saponified, the alcohol–acid mixture methylated with diazomethane–BF_3, and the mixture resaponified, forming the free acids and the methyl ethers of the alcohols. These are extracted from alkaline solution into an organic solvent. The volatile ethers can then be chromatographed.

It is often desirable to remove certain groups of compounds from the essential oil prior to chromatography. Better resolution of components of interest can often be obtained in this way; or, if a major component is removed, chromatograms of minor constituents can be obtained which might otherwise be masked. Any of the separation methods described in this section can be used as subtraction techniques. Thus, hydrocarbons can be removed from oxygenated components by liquid–solid chromatography or by preliminary gas chromatography, aldehydes and ketones by the use of Girard's T or P reagent, acids by sodium carbonate extraction, and phenols and acids by extraction with sodium or potassium hydroxide.

a. Separation of Hydrocarbon and Oxygenated Components

*1. *Separation on Silicic Acid: Column Method* (Kirchner and Miller, 1952). A slurry of 136 gm (see Table I) of silicic acid mixed with 400 ml of hexane is added to a Tswett chromatographic column $2\frac{1}{6}$ inches in diameter. The hexane is drawn down to the level of the adsorbent by using reduced pressure (2.5 inches of Hg absolute) at the bottom of the tube. One hundred grams of the essential oil (cold-pressed orange oil) is poured carefully onto the column. The oil is drawn onto the adsorbent. Next 625 ml of hexane is added and drawn through. Samples of the eluate are tested frequently by spotting on chromatostrips and spraying with 0.05% fluorescein, and then by exposing to the strips to bromine vapors. When the test first becomes positive (yellow spot on pink background), the receiver is changed and the hydrocarbon fraction is collected. The testing is continued, and when it becomes negative the hydrocarbons are eluted and the receiver is again changed. Ethyl acetate is added to the column, and the eluate is tested until it again gives a positive test with fluorescein–bromine. The receiver is changed, and the oxygenated fraction is collected. The solvent is evaporated under reduced pressure at 0°C prior to GLC. See Table I for conditions for the separation of specific oils.

*2. *Separation on Silicic Acid: Slurry Method* (Clark and Bernhard, 1960a). Fifteen grams of 100-mesh silicic acid is dried by heating at 125°C for 3 hours. This is added to a solution of 10 gm of essential oil (lemon oil) in 75 ml of *n*-pentane with shaking. The mixture is allowed to stand at room temperature with occasional shaking for 2 hours. The silicic acid containing the oxygenated fraction is filtered off on a sintered-glass crucible. The pentane fraction containing the hydrocarbon terpenes is dried over anhydrous sodium sulfate for 1 hour. It is then filtered and evaporated with a rotary flash evaporator under a vacuum of around 1.0 mm Hg and at 30°C.

The oxygen-containing fraction adsorbed on the silicic acid is eluted by placing the silicic acid in 75 ml of absolute ethanol. The mixture is allowed to stand at room temperature for 2 hours, with occasional stirring. The silicic acid is filtered off as described above. The oxygen-containing fraction in ethanol solution is dried over anhydrous sodium sulfate. It is then filtered and evaporated by means of a rotary flash evaporator and a vacuum of around 1.0 mm Hg at 30°C. See Table I for conditions for separation of specific oils.

*3. *Separation on Alumina* (Howard and Slater, 1957). A chromatographic column (1.37 cm in diameter) is packed with 50 gm of Merck Grade I alumina in a light petroleum ether (b.p. 40°C) slurry. Five milliliters of the essential oil (hop oil) is placed on the column. Light petroleum ether is used to elute the hydrocarbon fraction. One hundred and thirty-five milliliters is collected, with a partial separation of mono- and sesquiterpenes. Esters are eluted with light petroleum ether and 5% diethyl ether. One hundred milliliters is collected, and then a mixture of light petroleum ether and 20% diethyl ether is used to elute more esters plus methyl ketones. Seventy milliliters is collected. Finally, diethyl ether alone is used to elute other methyl ketones.

4. *Preliminary Separation by GLC* (Liberti and Cartoni, 1958b). See Section D.II.a.1.

b. Separation of Oxygenated Compounds

1. *Separation of Acids.* A diethyl or petroleum ether solution of the essential oil is extracted with a 3% sodium carbonate solution. The acids are

extracted into the aqueous layer and, after acidification with dilute sulfuric acid, are extracted into ether. They can then be methylated and separated by GLC, by methods described in detail in Chapter 7.

*2. *Separation of Phenols* (Naves, 1959a). Carboxylic acids are removed by extraction with aqueous sodium carbonate (see preceding paragraph). The essential oil is then extracted at room temperature with 5% aqueous sodium hydroxide followed by 1% sodium hydroxide. The combined aqueous extract is acidified with 20% phosphoric acid to a Congo Red end point and extracted with ether, and the product is dried over magnesium sulfate.

*3. *Separation of Aldehydes* (Stanley *et al.*, 1961). The essential oil sample (lemon 10 ml, lime 10 ml, orange 50 ml, or grapefruit 50 ml) is refluxed for 1 hour with 2 to 3 gm of Girard's T or P reagent, 200 ml of isopropanol, and 0.5 gm of the acid form of IRC-50 ion-exchange resin. The mixture is cooled and filtered through coarse filter paper into a 1-liter separatory funnel. The flask and filter paper are washed with 2 × 10-ml of isopropanol followed by 250 ml of distilled water, and the combined washings are added to the separatory funnel.

Redistilled hexane (75 ml) is added to the separatory funnel, shaken thoroughly, and allowed to stand for 1 to 2 hours. The aqueous phase is drawn off and washed with 2 × 50-ml portions of hexane, 1 hour being allowed for separation of the phases after each extraction.

The aqueous phase is transferred to a 1-liter glass-stoppered bottle, and 60 ml of 36% aqueous formaldehyde is added. (The formaldehyde should be freed from contaminants prior to this step by three washings with hexane in a separatory funnel.) The head space over the aqueous solution is purged with nitrogen, the solution is swirled gently, and the bottle is placed in a constant-temperature bath at 37°C for 24 hours.

The solution is cooled in an ice bath for 10 to 15 minutes; then 40 gm of sodium chloride and 50 ml of isopentane are added. The solution is extracted by swirling until the sodium chloride is dissolved, and then it is transferred to a separatory funnel. The aqueous phase is removed and extracted with another 50-ml portion of isopentane.

The isopentane extracts are combined and washed with 200 ml of distilled water, followed by 100 ml of 20% aqueous sodium chloride. The isopentane solution is dried over anhydrous sodium sulfate and evaporated to 0.5 to 1.0 ml in a rotary flash evaporator under water aspirator vacuum at 30°C. The residue is a concentrated solution of the regenerated aldehydes in isopentane and is ready to be analyzed by GLC.

4. *Separation of Alcohols* (Sterrett, 1949). One mole of dry pyridine per mole of alcohol (add slight excess) is added to the essential oil, along with about one mole of benzoyl chloride for each mole of alcohol in the essential oil. After a short period of refluxing, the solution is cooled and water is added. The benzoic esters of the alcohols will settle out. The suspension is

filtered and washed with a little cold dilute sodium hydroxide or sodium carbonate, followed by water. The esters are recrystallized from a suitable solvent such as petroleum ether. Tertiary alcohols form benzoic esters with difficulty and only in the presence of absolute pyridine. Phenols will also form esters with benzoyl chloride, so they should be removed prior to this separation (see Section A.II.b.2).

For use of this method as a subtraction technique, the essential oil in the filtrate is extracted into an organic solvent after the benzoic esters of the alcohols have been removed by filtration.

B. Terpene Hydrocarbons

I. Monoterpenes

Monoterpene hydrocarbons are a complex group of compounds containing 10 carbon atoms. They differ in degree of unsaturation and molecular configuration, some being open-chain, and others containing one, two, or even three rings. Since they have a narrow boiling-point range, fractional distillation is unsuitable for resolution of complex mixtures of monoterpenes, and gas chromatography is an excellent tool for their separation. It is possible to separate these components by boiling point and also by differences in polarity when proper columns and conditions are chosen, so that complete separations of many isomers can be obtained.

Monoterpenes can be separated at column temperatures of 130°C or lower, and many highly selective stationary liquids are stable in this range.

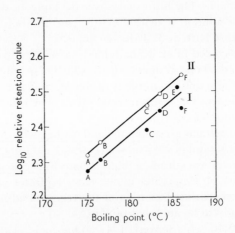

FIG. 2. Change in relative retention value with boiling point for some *p*-menthadienes. (I) Didecyl phthalate, 130°C. (II) Carbowax 4000, 130°C. (*A*) α-Terpinene. (*B*) Dipentene. (*C*) γ-Terpinene. (*D*) 3,8-*p*-Menthadiene. (*E*) 2,4(8)-*p*-Menthadiene. (*F*) Terpinolene. (Data from Zubyk and Conner, 1960.)

However, higher column temperatures are required for the separation of sesquiterpenes, as well as oxygenated terpene derivatives. Therefore columns for these components must be stable at temperatures up to 190° to 200°C.

Polar substrates separate the hydrocarbons within a group of positional isomers by boiling point, as do nonpolar packings. In addition, when hydrocarbons differ in unsaturation or molecular structure, these groups are separated further by differences in polarity. Thus within the p-menthadiene series of positional isomers, all compounds except those containing conjugated double bonds are eluted in the order of their boiling points on the polar substrate Carbowax 4000 (Zubyk and Conner, 1960). Similarly, on the nonpolar substrate didecyl phthalate, this series is also eluted in the order of their boiling points. The separation factors are the same, as can be seen in Fig. 2, where the logs of relative retention volumes are plotted against boiling points. Parallel curves are obtained on the polar and nonpolar packings.

Polar substrates show a distinct advantage when hydrocarbons differing in degree of unsaturation or molecular configuration are chromatographed. These compounds differ in polarity and are separated according to their polarities as well as boiling points, the more polar materials being retained longer on a polar stationary liquid than the less polar ones.

Relative retention values for monoterpene hydrocarbons on both polar and nonpolar substrates are given in Tables II and III. When the logs of the relative retention values on polar and nonpolar substrates are plotted against each other, differences in polarities become apparent. Families of curves are obtained showing differences in polarity between each group. This is similar to data obtained with fatty acids, with one important difference. The fatty acids differ in chain length as well as in degree of unsaturation, whereas the terpene hydrocarbons all contain 10 carbon atoms but differ in degree of unsaturation and molecular structure.

When the logs of relative retention values of fatty acid esters on polar and nonpolar substrates are plotted against each other, a family of straight lines is obtained. Each line represents a homologous series of fatty acids differing in number of double bonds (see Chapter 7, Section G). Thus, fatty acids containing one double bond are retained relatively longer on a nonpolar packing and relatively shorter on a polar packing than are homologues containing two double bonds. When the logs of the relative retentions on the two columns are plotted, two parallel straight lines are obtained, showing that the relative retentions differ by a constant factor depending on the degree of unsaturation.

Monoterpene hydrocarbons also show differences in relative retentions on polar and nonpolar substrates. These depend only on degree of unsaturation and molecular structure, since the carbon number remains constant.

TABLE II

Relative Retention Ratios for Terpene Hydrocarbons and Related Compounds on Relatively Nonpolar Substrates
(α-Pinene = 1.00)

Compound	Didecyl phthalate[a]			Tricresyl phosphate,[b] 100°C	Dimethyl polysiloxane,[c] 140°C	D.C. 550 Silicone,[b] 100°C	Silicone,[d] 100°C
	110°C	130°C	150°C				
α-Pyronene	0.99	1.00	0.98				
β-Pyronene	1.25	1.24	—				
3-p-Menthene	1.42	1.35	1.34				
trans-p-Menthane	1.43	1.35	1.35				
cis-p-Menthane	1.50	1.45	1.45				
α-Phellandrene	1.84	1.78	1.75				1.47
β-Phellandrene	2.28	2.24	2.12	3.30		2.16	1.62
α-Terpinene	2.08	1.89	1.80				
1-p-Menthene	1.90	1.83	1.77				
4(8)-p-Menthene	2.04	1.90	1.85				
Dipentene	2.16	2.04	1.90		1.64		
Limonene	2.72	2.47	2.46	2.48		1.95	
γ-Terpinene	3.06	2.79	2.56	3.24		2.10	
3,8-p-Menthadiene	3.66	3.26	2.92				
2,4(8)-p-Menthadiene	3.18	2.83	2.75	3.90		3.13	
Terpinolene	1.46	1.44	1.33	1.80		1.57	
Myrcene	1.27	1.26	1.17				
Cumene	2.45	2.25	2.12				
m-Cymene	2.46	2.35	2.13	3.40		2.42	
p-Cymene	2.94	2.38	2.40	2.90		2.08	
o-Cymene	0.80	0.83	0.86				
Bornylene	1.00	1.00	1.00	1.00	1.00	1.00	1.00
α-Pinene	1.13	1.14	1.16	1.24	1.08	1.30	1.26
α-Fenchene	1.16	1.20	1.21				
Camphene	1.52	1.44	1.41	1.76	1.24	1.40	
β-Pinene	1.45	1.40	1.40				
Isocamphane	1.31	1.34	1.37				
trans-Pinane	1.39	1.41	1.40				
cis-Pinane	1.77	1.74	1.66	1.97		1.90	

[a] From Zubyk and Conner (1960). [b] From Liberti and Cartoni (1958). [c] From Cvrkal and Janák (1959). [d] From von Rudloff (1960).

TABLE III

Relative Retention Ratios for Terpene Hydrocarbons and Related Compounds on Polar Substrates
(α-Pinene = 1.00)

Compound	Carbowax 4000,[a] 130°C	LAC-2-R446,[b] 100°C	LAC-1-R296,[b] 100°C	Methyl abietate,[b] 100°C	Squalene,[c] 100°C	Carbowax 400,[c] 100°C	Polyphenyl ether,[c] 100°C	Poly(ethylene glycol adipate),[c] 100°C
α-Pyronene	1.02							
β-Pyronene	1.35							
3-p-Menthene	1.18							
trans-p-Menthane	0.97							
cis-p-Menthane	1.10							
α-Phellandrene	1.96							
β-Phellandrene	2.46	2.64	2.93	2.16	1.60	1.98	2.08	2.10
α-Terpinene	2.09				1.69	2.06	2.26	2.26
1-p-Menthene	1.72							
4(8)-p-Menthene	1.71							
Dipentene	2.29							
Limonene	2.88	2.64	2.84	2.13				
γ-Terpinene	3.12	3.28	3.64	2.51				
3,8-p-Menthadiene								
2,4(8)-p-Menthadiene								
Terpinolene	3.51	2.36	3.51	1.81				
Myrcene	1.70	1.96	2.10	1.44				
Cumene	2.02							
m-Cymene	3.14							
p-Cymene	3.15	4.01	4.59	2.27				
o-Cymene								
Bornylene	0.86							
α-Pinene	1.00	1.00	1.00	1.00	1.00	1.00	1.00	1.00
α-Fenchene	1.22			1.22				
Camphene	1.28	1.37	1.46					
β-Pinene	1.58	1.67	1.70	1.47	1.33	1.48	1.51	1.56
Isocamphane	1.26							
trans-Pinane	1.19							
cis-Pinane	1.25							
Δ³-Carene	1.82							

[a] From Zubyk and Conner (1960). [b] From Clark and Bernhard (1960a). [c] From von Rudloff (1960).

Aliphatic monoterpenes are compounds such as myrcene and ocimine, positional isomers containing three double bonds. There is a large group of monocyclic terpenes having *p*-menthane (A) as the parent compound. A *p*-menthene contains one double bond, and a *p*-methadiene two double bonds. There are six possible isomeric *p*-methenes and many menthadienes. *p*-Cymene is a related compound having an aromatic ring. The pyronenes, which are rearrangement products of some natural terpenes, are related to the parent structure (B) and have two double bonds. Bicyclic monoterpenes are related to such parent structures as pinane (C), carane (D), camphane (E), fenchane (F), isobornylane (G), and thujane (H), and have one double bond.

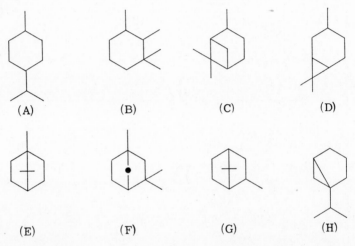

   (A)   (B)   (C)   (D)

   (E)   (F)   (G)   (H)

The logs of the retention times of monoterpene hydrocarbons on didecyl phthalate, a relatively nonpolar substrate, and on Carbowax 4000, a polar column packing, are plotted and the relationships shown in Fig. 3. A family of straight lines is obtained. When the relative retentions on the didecyl phthalate column are compared at one value with those on the Carbowax column, it can be seen that, as the series of compounds becomes less polar, the retention time is longer on the nonpolar column. Series I compounds are retained longest on this column, series II compounds for a shorter period of time, etc.

The difference between curves is a measure of the difference in relative polarity between these groups of compounds; although the relative retention times vary within the groups, the relative polarity with respect to the two substrates remains constant.

The *cis*- and *trans-p*-methanes (curve I) are synthetic saturated mono-cylic compounds and are the least polar compounds tested, since they are

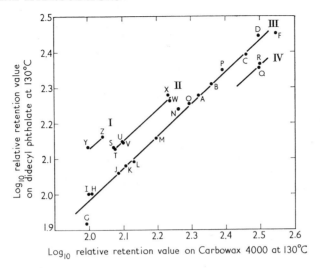

FIG. 3. Relations between relative retention values (α-pinene $= 100$) on didecyl phthalate and Carbowax 4000 for some monoterpenes. (A) α-Terpinene. (B) Dipentene. (C) γ-Terpinene. (D) 3,8-p-Menthadiene. (F) Terpinolene. (G) Bornylene. (H) α-Py-ronene. (I) α-Pinene. (J) α-Fenchene. (K) Camphene. (L) β-Pyronene. (M) β-Pinene. (N) Δ^3-Carene. (O) α-Phellandrene. (P) β-Phellandrene. (Q) m-Cymene. (R) p-Cymene. (S) 3-p-Menthene. (T) $trans$-Pinane. (U) cis-Pinane. (V) Isocamphane. (W) 1-p-Menthene. (X) 4(8)-p-Menthene. (Y) $trans$-p-Menthane. (Z) cis-p-Menthane. (Data from Zubyk and Conner, 1960.)

retained for the shortest period of time on the polar Carbowax column rela-tive to their retention on the nonpolar column. The p-menthenes (curve II) are relatively more polar than the saturated parent terpene and are retained for a longer period on the polar column relative to their retentions on the nonpolar column. The p-menthadienes series is still more polar, as is seen by the displacement of the line relating the retention volumes of these com-pounds (curve III). In this series it is also evident that the retention times vary with the positions of the double bonds in the molecule. Thus the com-pounds with two double bonds in the ring are in general retained on both columns for a shorter period of time than those with one of the double bonds in the isopropyl chain. This is also the case in the p-menthene series, as shown by the fact that the 3-p-menthene with a double bond in the ring is retained for a shorter period of time on both columns than the 4(8)-p-menthene with the double bond in the isopropyl chain.

When three double bonds are present in the ring in the p-menthane series, these constitute aromatic compounds, the cymenes. They are the most polar compounds in this group, as would be expected, and are retained for the longest period of time on the polar packing relative to the retention time on the nonpolar substrate (curve IV). When other terpene hydrocarbons are compared on these same substrates, they form groups with the same relative retention ratios as this first series, and certain relationships between structure and polarity can be discerned.

The pyronenes, for instance, are isomers of the *p*-menthadienes with methyl groups attached directly to the 6-membered ring rather than having an isopropyl group. Their retention values fall on the *p*-menthadiene curve (III) and thus have the same relative retention ratios. However, their affinities for the substrates are less than those of the *p*-menthadienes.

The presence of a second ring apparently has the same effect on the relative retentions, and therefore on the polarity of a compound, as a double bond. *cis*- and *trans*-Pinane are saturated bicyclic terpenes, and their relative polarity corresponds to the *p*-menthene series, although they have less affinity for the substrates than the unsaturated compounds. Bicyclic compounds with one double bond correspond in relative polarity to the *p*-menthadiene series, which are monocyclic compounds with two double bonds. The bicyclic compounds are retained for a shorter period of time than the dienes. As was seen earlier in the *p*-menthene series, a double bond in the ring is less effective in increasing retention than a double bond in the side chain. Thus, bornylene with a double bond in the ring is retained for a shorter period of time on both substrates than either fenchene or camphene, where the double bond is in the side chain. Also, α-pinene is retained for a shorter period of time than β-pinene, showing again that this is the case.

In addition to the position of the double bond, the size of the rings affects the relative retentions of these compounds. When the second ring is formed at the 2,4-positions of the 6-membered ring, the compound is retained for a longer period of time than when a 1,4-ring is formed, and a 3-membered ring is retained still longer. Thus bornylene is retained on both columns for a relatively shorter period of time than the pinenes. Camphene and α-fenchene are retained for a longer period of time than α-pinene, but the double bond is in the side chain of the first two compounds, and within the ring in the latter. Δ³-Carene contains a 3-membered ring plus one double bond, and the relative retention of this compound is very similar to that of the *p*-menthadiene series. This indicates that the 3-membered ring is very similar to a double bond, which also has been shown from chemical studies.

Many of these hydrocarbons do not occur in essential oils. The saturated parent compounds, for instance, such as *p*-menthane, pinane, and fenchane, are synthetic derivatives of naturally occurring materials. However, from data of this sort it is possible to predict the general structure of an unknown terpene hydrocarbon. If the logs of the relative retention values of an unknown are found to fall on line III, for instance, the compound might be a *p*-menthadiene, or it might be a mono-unsaturated compound containing two rings. The position of the point on the line would give an indication of the structure of the unknown. Thus, if it fell on the lower part of the line it might be a pyronene, or a compound containing one double bond plus two 4- to 6-membered rings; and if it fell higher up on the line it might contain one double bond plus two rings, one of which is 3-membered, or one ring plus two double bonds. From a knowledge of the behavior of known groups on the same substrates, similar information could be obtained for unknown monoterpenes falling on other lines.

Several polar packings give good separations of terpene hydrocarbons. Carbowax 4000, a polyethylene glycol, gives good separations at 130°C or lower. Ethylene glycol polyesters of succinic and phthalic acids give separations comparable to Carbowax 4000, as does poly(polyethylene glycol adipate) (von Rudloff, 1960). They have an additional advantage of being stable at temperatures up to 220°C. Poly(diethylene glycol adipate) partially cross-linked with pentaerythritol (LAC-2-R446) and the same compound without the pentaerythritol cross linkage (LAC-1-R296) also give good separations (Clark and Bernhard, 1960a). These compounds are stable at temperatures above 130°C and thus are useful for separations of oxygenated terpenes.

Esters of tetrahalophthalic acids are very polar compounds and have been shown to give good separations of various classes of hydrocarbons (Chapter 4, Section A.II). Families of curves are obtained by using di-*n*-butyl tetrachlorophthalate, each curve representing a homologous series of compounds. The 2-methylalkanes are eluted before *n*-alkanes with the same carbon number, and one double bond increases the retention time, while 6-membered rings retard elution.

This group of liquid substrates should also give good resolution of monoterpene hydrocarbons, with separations obtained by differences in polarity.

Squalene is a substrate that gives good separations of monoterpene hydrocarbons (von Rudloff, 1960). However, its use is limited specifically to these compounds, since it is unstable at 130°C and above. A similar polyunsaturated aliphatic liquid phase of higher molecular weight stable at higher temperatures, such as natural rubber, would be of more general use for the separation of both mono- and sesquiterpene hydrocarbons.

Nonpolar and relatively nonpolar substrates such as silicone, didecyl phthalate, poly(dimethyl siloxane), and the Apiezons have been used by some workers for terpene hydrocarbon separations. With these packings, separations are by boiling point alone.

a. Conditions for Chromatography

*1. *On Poly(polyethylene Glycol Adipate)* (von Rudloff, 1960)

Chromatograph	Beckman GC-2.
Column dimensions	0.6-cm o.d. × 6-foot coiled copper tubing.
Solid support	Chromosorb W.

Stationary phase	Poly(polyethylene glycol adipate) (16.5:83.5).
Temperature	100°C.
Carrier gas	Helium at 26.3 ml/min.
Detector	T/C cell.
Recorder	Bristol Dynamaster, 0.05 to 1.05 mv; ½ inch/min.
Sample size	1.5 to 40 μl.
Analysis time	About 16 minutes for d-limonene.

*2. On Carbowax 4000 (Zubyk and Conner, 1960)

Chromatograph	Laboratory assembled.
Column dimensions	¼-inch o.d. × 6-foot stainless steel.
Solid support	Chromosorb C-48560 (60/100 U. S. mesh).
Stationary phase	Carbowax 4000 (28.5:71.5).
Temperature	130°C.
Carrier gas	Helium at 45 ml/min. Inlet pressure: 5.9 psig. Outlet pressure: atmospheric.
Detector	Four-filament T/C cell, Gow-Mac Model 9285.
Recorder	10 mv, 16 inches/hour.
Sample size	5 to 20 μl.
Analysis time	About 22 minutes.

*3. On Squalene (von Rudloff, 1960)

Chromatograph	Beckman GC-2.
Column dimensions	0.6-cm o.d. × 6-foot coiled copper tubing.
Solid support	Chromosorb W.
Stationary phase	Squalene (16.5:83.5).
Temperature	100°C.
Carrier gas	Helium at 74.2 ml/min.
Detector	T/C cell.
Recorder	Bristol Dynamaster, 0.05 to 1.05 mv; ½ inch/min.
Sample size	1.5 μl and larger.
Analysis time	About 16 minutes for d-limonene.

*4. On Didecyl Phthalate (Zubyk and Conner, 1960)

Chromatograph	Perkin-Elmer 154A modified with a more sensitive temperature control.
Column dimensions	198 × 0.66-cm. o.d.
Solid support	Celite 545 (50/100 U. S. mesh).
Stationary phase	Didecyl phthalate (25:75).
Temperatures	Column: (a) 110°C. (b) 130°C. (c) 150°C.
Carrier gas	Helium at 45 ml/min. Inlet pressure: (a) 13.2 psig. (b) 13.9 psig. (c) 15.0 psig. Outlet pressure: atmospheric.
Detector	Thermistor.
Recorder	2.5 mv; 24 inches/hour.
Sample size	5 to 20 μl.
Analysis time	About 50 minutes.

II. Sesquiterpenes

Sesquiterpene hydrocarbons are major components of hop essential oils and contain 15 carbon atoms. Like the monoterpenes, some are unsaturated acyclic compounds, and others are mono-, bi-, or tricyclic compounds with varying degrees of unsaturation. As one might expect, the principles of chromatography are similar to those for monoterpene hydrocarbons, and best separations should be obtained by chromatography on polar substrates. However, since these compounds contain 15 instead of the 10 carbon atoms of monoterpenes, they are less volatile and must be chromatographed at higher column temperatures. They have been partitioned at 170°C (Howard and Slater, 1957; Harold et al., 1960) and at 185°C (Rigby and Bethune, 1957). These separations were made on nonpolar packings, but polar packings stable in this temperature range are also available. Von Rudloff (1960) has found that the polyesters of ethylene glycol with adipic, succinic, or phthalic acids and the polyphenylene ether, m-bis(m-phenoxyphenoxy)benzene (Monsanto Corp.), can be used at temperatures up to 220°C and give good separations of many terpenes. The polyesters of diethylene glycol with adipic and succinic acids should also be suitable (see Clark and Bernhard, 1960a). A high-molecular-weight polyunsaturated acyclic liquid phase more stable than squalene might also be of use for the separation of these compounds.

Harold et al. (1960) have chromatographed sesquiterpenes isolated from beer on Apiezon M at 170°C and separated caryophyllene, humulene, isocaryophyllene, and farnesene, although the resolution was not complete. These hydrocarbons differ in molecular configuration and also in unsaturation, farnesene being an acyclic compound with four double bonds, whereas humulene is monocyclic with an 11-membered ring and three double bonds. Howard and Slater (1957) have separated caryophyllene, isocaryophyllene, and humulene from hop oil by using Apiezon M at 170°C. They have shown the presence of other components also, probably sesquiterpenes. These peaks were not completely resolved under the conditions employed. No complete chromatographic data are available at the present time on the separation of sesquiterpenes on polar substrates.

a. Conditions for Chromatography

*1. On Poly(polyethylene Glycol Adipate) (von Rudloff, 1960)

Chromatograph	Beckman GC-2.
Column dimensions	0.6-cm o.d. × 6-foot coiled copper tubing.
Solid support	Chromosorb W.
Stationary phase	Poly(polyethylene glycol adipate) (16.5:83.5).
Temperature	160° to 190°C.

Carrier gas	Helium. Inlet pressure: 1000 to 2000 mm Hg. Outlet pressure: atmospheric.
Detector	T/C cell.
Recorder	Bristol Dynamaster, 0.05 to 1.05 mv; $\frac{1}{2}$ inch/min.
Sample size	1.5 to 50 μl.
Analysis time	Not given.

*2. *On Apiezon M* (Harold *et al.*, 1960)

Chromatograph	Pye Argon, Cat. No. 12350, equipped with facilities for sample addition by micropipette.
Column dimensions	125 × 0.5-cm straight stainless steel.
Solid support	Embacel (May and Baker) sieved to pass 60/80 B.S.S. mesh.
Stationary phase	Apiezon M (25:100).
Temperatures	Injection: 300°C. Column: 170°C.
Carrier gas	Argon, 20 ml/min measured at outlet. Inlet pressure: 22.5 cm Hg. Outlet pressure: atmospheric.
Recorder	Sunvic, 10-mv full-scale deflection; 2-second response.
Detector	Argon.
Sample size	0.5 to 1.0 μl.
Analysis time	About 70 minutes.

III. SUMMARY

Monoterpene hydrocarbons can be separated on polar or nonpolar substrates at temperatures of 130°C or lower. Sesquiterpenes require temperatures around 170° to 190°C. Better separations are obtained on polar packings. When the logs of the retention volumes on both polar and nonpolar packings are plotted, a family of curves is obtained yielding information on molecular structure and degree of unsaturation of the compounds.

C. Oxygenated Terpenoids from Essential Oils

I. INTRODUCTION

Oxygenated terpenoids are the components of essential oils most often responsible for their distinctive aroma and flavor, even though they are often minor constituents of the oil. Thus, their separation and identification is of interest to the essential oil, flavor, and perfume industries. There has been a recent report that compounds of this type also occur in animals. During studies of squalene and cholesterol biosynthesis from mevalonic acid in liver enzyme preparations, Popják and Cornforth (1960) found that alcohols and acids composed of isoprene units may be present.

When the oxygenated fraction is a minor constituent of the complete oil, preliminary separation from the bulk of the hydrocarbon fraction is desirable. Methods for preliminary separations are given in Section A.II. Alcohols, carbonyl compounds, esters (mostly acetates and butyrates of terpenoid alcohols), ethers, and hydroxyphenylpropane derivatives are found in the oxygenated fraction of essential oils. These compounds are theoretically derived from terpene hydrocarbons which in turn are composed of isoprene units. The alcohols are considered to be derived from the hydration of one terpene double bond, and the other derivatives from further reaction of the alcohols, so that aliphatic monoterpenoid oxygenated derivatives would contain at most two double bonds, and aliphatic sesquiterpenoids three double bonds. One or more of the other double bonds are sometimes hydrogenated. Esters will contain more than the 10 or 15 carbon atoms of the parent terpenoid alcohol, depending on the length of the acid side chain. Thus, geraniol contains 10 carbon atoms, geranyl formate 11, and geranyl acetate 12.

Other oxygenated components of essential oils considered to be terpene derivatives vary in the number of carbon atoms in the molecule. The ionones contain 13 carbon atoms, and other naturally occurring carbonyl compounds found in essential oils vary from C_7 to C_{12} (Stanley et al., 1961).

Differences in carbon number will of course aid in the ease of separation of terpenoid compounds. Most derivatives, however, contain 10, 15, or sometimes 20 carbon atoms and differ only in the positions and numbers of double bonds, the positions of the functional group, or the geometrical configuration of the molecule. Gas chromatography is ideally suited to the separation of these closely related compounds when suitable chromatographic conditions are established, and it is even possible to separate terpenes differing only in the *cis,trans* configuration about a double bond.

Terpenoid derivatives differ in relative polarity depending on the functional group, the unsaturation, and the geometrical configuration. Thus, when the logs of the relative retention volumes on polar and nonpolar substrates are plotted, families of curves are obtained, each series representing a functional group (Cartoni and Liberti, 1960) (Fig. 4). Since these materials are all quite polar, better separations are obtained on polar substrates. Temperatures and column conditions must be adjusted quite carefully, since many of these materials are unstable at high temperatures. If acid centers are present on the solid support, catalytic breakdown can occur (see Section H).

The monoterpenoids can usually be chromatographed satisfactorily at temperatures between 130° and 160°C with liquid/solid support ratios of 15 to 25%. Sesquiterpenoids require higher column temperatures, the range of 160° to 190°C usually being satisfactory. With low substrate/solid support packing ratios, in the range of 5 to 10% on Celite or 0.5 to 1.0% on glass beads, temperatures can be reduced so that monoterpenoids can be separated at column temperatures of 70° to 120°C. Low packing ratios require small sample sizes; otherwise column overloading will result. These small

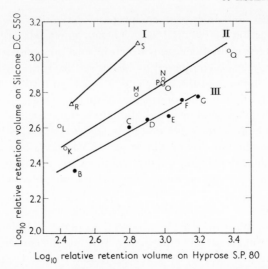

FIG. 4. Relations between relative retention volumes on D.C. 550 silicone and Hyprose S.P. 80 for some oxygenated monoterpenoids. △ Esters. ○ Carbonyl compounds. ● Alcohols. (*A*) Cineole. (*B*) Linalool. (*C*) Menthol. (*D*) α-Terpineol. (*E*) Citronellol. (*F*) Nerol. (*G*) Geraniol. (*K*) Citronellal. (*L*) Capric aldehyde. (*M*) β-Citral (neral). (*N*) α-Citral (geranial). (*O*) Carvone. (*P*) Cumic aldehyde. (*Q*) Cinnamaldehyde. (*R*) Linalyl acetate. (*S*) Geranyl acetate. (Data from Cartoni and Liberti, 1960.)

sample sizes, in turn, require very sensitive detectors such as the argon or hydrogen flame detectors.

Polar stationary liquids must be chosen that are stable at these column temperatures. The adipate polyester of polyethylene glycol and the succinate polyester of ethylene glycol are stable and give good separations of many monoterpenoids (von Rudloff, 1960), as does the polyphenylene ether *m*-bis(*m*-phenoxyphenoxy)benzene. The succinate polyester of diethylene glycol (LAC-4-R777) has also been shown to give good separations of oxygenated components (Bernhard and Marr, 1960), as well as the adipate polyester partially cross-linked with pentaerythritol (LAC-2-R466). Cartoni and Liberti (1960) have found that Hyprose S.P. 80 is a good polar packing for separation of oxygenated monoterpenoids. This compound is octakis(2-hydroxypropyl) sucrose. It contains many hydroxyl groups, making it very polar, and is stable at temperatures up to 160°C, where its volatility is less than 0.1%. Another polar packing suitable for use at high column temperatures is sucrose diacetate hexaisobutyrate (SAIB) (Smith *et al.*, 1960). It is a monomeric compound of uniform properties and is stable at temperatures up to 200°C. Its decomposition products are acetic and isobutyric acids, which will not foul hot-wire detectors. Good separations of many monoterpenoid compounds have been obtained, and it shows promise of being a valuable liquid substrate for polar compounds. Mixtures of this material with tetrakis(2-hydroxypropyl)ethylenediamine (Quadrol) (2:1) give excellent separations of monoterpenoid compounds at 140°C. One disadvantage is that the mixture cannot be used at temperatures above 150°C and so cannot be employed for high-temperature work.

Many nonpolar and relatively nonpolar packings are stable at high column temperatures and are often used for separations of these compounds. Separations are mainly by boiling point. However, valuable information can be obtained on the identification of oxygenated terpenoids when the logs of retention times on both polar and nonpolar substrates are plotted (see Section C.VII). The Apiezons and the silicones are often used as nonpolar substrates, since they are stable at high temperatures.

The oxygenated fraction can be separated from terpene hydrocarbons by methods described in Section A.II.a, or by functional group according to procedures described in Section A.II.b. These groups can then be chromatographed separately. This procedure has the advantage of making identification of components easier, since known groups of compounds are being analyzed. Also, there are no interferences from components containing other functional groups having close retention values.

The resolution of compounds can be changed with change in column temperature, so that materials not resolved at one temperature may be separated at a different one. Thus at 70°C linalool and isomenthone are resolved with a separation factor of 2.4 on poly(propylene glycol succinate) at low packing ratios, whereas at 100°C the separation factor is unity (Holness, 1961).

II. CHROMATOGRAPHY OF ALCOHOLS

Terpenoid alcohols are important derivatives contributing to the distinct flavor and aroma of many essential oils, and their separation and identification are important for characterization of natural oils and also for separation of synthetic mixtures. Both positional isomers and stereoisomers of terpenoid alcohols have been separated by gas chromatography.

Isomers. Linalool, a positional isomer of nerol and geraniol, has been separated from them on both polar and nonpolar substrates (Cartoni and Liberti, 1960; Popják and Cornforth, 1960). The polar substrate octakis(2-hydroxypropyl) sucrose (Hyprose S.P. 80) gave a separation factor of about 4, poly(ethylene glycol adipate) a factor of 2.3, the weakly polar D.C. 550 silicone a factor of 2.5, and the nonpolar Apiezon L a factor of only 1.7 under the conditions employed (Table IV). Polar packings in general give better separations of polar compounds, but the best substrates must be determined experimentally.

TABLE IV

Relative Retention Ratios for Oxygenated Compounds on Polar and Nonpolar Substrates (α-Terpineol = 1.00)

Compound	Hyprose S.P. 80	Didecyl phthalate,[b] 150°C	Silicone,[c] 130°C	D.C. 550 Silicone[a]	Silicone C-lithium capronate (9:1),[d] 187°C	Silicone C-sodium capronate (9:1),[d] 185°C	Carbowax 400,[e] 130°C	Polyphenyl ether,[e] 130°C	PEGA,[e] 130°C	PEGS,[e] 100°C	LAC-2-R446,[e] 150°C	PDEGS,[a] 112°C	Diglycerol,[e] 100°C
Hydroxy compounds													
α-Fenchyl alcohol		0.64			0.775	0.720							
β-Fenchyl alcohol		0.70											
trans-Dihydro-α-terpineol		0.70											
β-Terpineol		0.78											
cis-Dihydro-α-terpineol		0.77											
Borneol		0.89			1.14	0.880							
Isoborneol		0.99											
α-Terpineol	1.00	1.00	1.00	1.00	1.00	1.00	1.00	1.00	1.00	1.00	1.00	1.00	1.00
Citronellol	1.33		1.26	1.05	1.25		1.74	0.946	1.33	1.16	1.04	0.462	1.01
Linalool	0.384			0.509	0.615	0.720					0.465		
Menthol	0.780			0.900	1.02	0.882							
Geraniol	1.97			1.34	0.975	1.12							
Nerol	1.58			1.28							1.59		
trans-Carveol													
Eugenol				*3.10									
Carbonyl compound and ethers													
1,4-Cineole	0.098	0.23	0.449	0.347			0.108	0.256	0.114	0.0915	0.154		0.227
1,8-Cineole		0.26	0.571				0.259	0.467	0.265	0.261			0.485
Fenchone		0.47											
Estragole		0.98											
trans-Anethole		1.81										1.42	
Citral	1.13			1.58	1.13	1.28					1.26		
D-Carvone	0.338		0.820	0.690	1.25	1.20	0.327	0.640	0.334	0.365	1.36		0.494
Citronellal			0.795		0.940	0.760	0.444	0.787	0.466	0.487			0.970
Camphor					0.850	0.800							
Menthone											1.04		
Neral	0.875			1.38									
Geranial	1.08			1.68									
Cumic aldehyde	1.02			1.60									
Cinnamaldehyde	2.45			2.96									
Esters													
Linalyl acetate	0.370	1.22		1.22	1.80	1.37					0.272		
Geranyl acetate	0.890	2.68		2.68	0.840						1.14	1.34	
Terpinyl acetate			1.57		1.30		0.535	1.17	0.544	0.540	1.86		0.726
Bornyl acetate					3.00								
Geranyl butyrate													
Linalyl propionate													
Citronellyl acetate											0.516	0.617	
Geranyl formate											0.705	0.805	
Terpinyl propionate												1.17	

[a] From Cartoni and Liberti (1960).   [b] From Zubyk and Conner (1960).   [c] From von Rudloff (1960).   [d] From Bayer et al. (1958).   [e] From Clark and Bernhard (1960b).

The positional isomers of the sesquiterpenoid alcohol dehydronerolidol have been chromatographed on Apiezon L (Ofner *et al.*, 1959). However, complete separations were not obtained. In this case a polar packing stable at high column temperatures might give better separations, as in the case of the monoterpenoid linalol, nerol, and geraniol separations. The positional isomers α- and β-eudesmol have been partially resolved on polyethylene glycol adipate and ethylene glycol succinate polyesters, but are totally unresolved when chromatographed on silicone (von Rudloff, 1960). These isomers were also unresolved on the polar polyphenylene ether *m*-bis(*m*-phenoxyphenoxy)benzene, showing that separations vary with type of packing and cannot be predicted from the polarities alone.

Stereoisomeric terpenoid alcohols have also been chromatographed and separated, at least partially. Here again, more polar column packings would probably give better separations of these isomers. Nerol and geraniol, *cis,trans* monoterpenoid alcohol isomers, have a separation factor of only 1.05 on D.C. 550 silicone (Cartoni and Liberti, 1960), but on the polar substrate Hyprose S.P. 80 the separation factor is 1.25 and the isomers are completely resolved under the conditions employed (Table IV). On the polar poly(ethylene glycol adipate) the separation factor is 1.12, and on the nonpolar Apiezon L the factor is 1.09 (Popják and Cornforth, 1960), showing again that the polar packings give better separation factors.

The isomeric menthols are not well separated on silicone (Petrowitz *et al.*, 1960). Di-*n*-decyl phthalate is a better substrate, with three of the isomers being separated. Three menthol stereoisomers have also been separated on Carbowax 4000 (Tagaki and Mitsui, 1960) at a column temperature of 160°C.

cis,trans Stereoisomers of derivatives of the sesquiterpenoid alcohols nerolidol and dihydronerolidol without double bonds in the 6,7-position have been shown to have different retention times on the nonpolar Apiezon L with separation factors of 1.12 to 1.20 (Ofner *et al.*, 1959). Separation of these stereoisomers on polar substrates has not been investigated. *cis,trans* Isomers of farnesol, another sesquiterpenoid alcohol, have been chromatographed on poly(polyethylene glycol adipate) with a separation factor of 1.12, and on Apiezon L with a separation factor of 1.09.

Aliphatic and cyclic monoterpenoid alcohols. Monoterpenoid alcohols are chromatographed on polar and nonpolar liquids, but polar substrates usually give better separations (see Table IV). Octakis(2-hydroxypropyl)sucrose (Hyprose S.P. 80) is a good polar substrate for separations of these compounds (Cartoni and Liberti, 1960), as are the polyesters poly(polyethylene glycol adipate) and poly(ethylene glycol succinate) (von Rudloff, 1960). Sucrose diacetate hexaisobutyrate (SAIB) also gives very good separations (Smith *et al.*, 1960) as do poly(diethylene glycol adipate) partially crosslinked with pentaerithritol, and poly(diethylene glycol succinate).

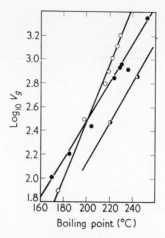

Fig. 5. Log₁₀ of retention volume versus boiling point for oxygenated terpinoids on Hyprose S.P. 80. ○ Alcohols. ◑ Esters. ● Carbonyl compounds. (Cartoni and Liberti, 1960.)

When the logs of retention volumes on the polar Hyprose S.P. 80 for both aliphatic and cyclic monoterpenoid alcohols are plotted against boiling point, a straight line is obtained, the slope of which is characteristic for the alcohols, showing that retention volume is dependent on the boiling point (Fig. 5). With this polar packing the slopes for compounds containing various functional groups are different, showing a relationship not only with the boiling points but also with the polarities of the groups. On the relatively

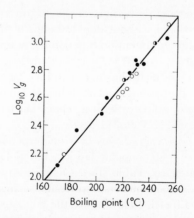

Fig. 6. Log₁₀ of retention volume versus boiling point for oxygenated terpenoids on D.C. 550 silicone. ○ Alcohols. ◑ Esters. ● Carbonyl compounds. (Cartoni and Liberti, 1960.)

nonpolar D.C. 550 silicone, the retentions for all functional groups are related to boiling points only, so that all compounds fall on one line (Fig. 6).

The retention values of both acyclic and alicyclic primary and tertiary alcohols fall on the same curve when these compounds are chromatographed on Hyprose S.P. 80 and the results are plotted against boiling points. The polarities are not greatly changed by the geometric configuration, the hydroxyl group being the main factor influencing the retention values of the compounds.

Relatively nonpolar packings such as D.C. 550 silicone and didecyl phthalate separate many monoterpenoid alcohols, although the separation factors are usually less than on more polar packings.

Sesquiterpenoid alcohols. These compounds contain 15 instead of 10 carbon atoms, are less volatile than monoterpenoid alcohols, and must be chromatographed at higher column temperatures, in the range of 160° to 200°C, with only partial separations (Ofner *et al.*, 1959). Polar and nonpolar packings have been compared for three sesquiterpenoid alcohols (von Rudloff, 1960). Occidentalol, differing only in that it contains one more double bond, was separated from the positional isomers α- and β-eudesmol on all packings tested. The separation factor on the relatively nonpolar silicone was 1.32, whereas the polar packings gave separation factors of 1.5 to 1.7, the best

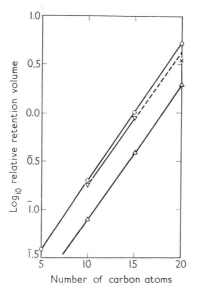

FIG. 7. Relationship between $\log_{10}$ relative retention volume on poly(ethylene glycol adipate) and the number of carbon atoms. ○ Primary *trans,trans* alcohols. ▽ Primary *cis.trans* alcohols. △ *tertiary* alcohols. (Popják and Cornforth, 1960.)

resolution being obtained on poly(ethylene glycol succinate) at 180°C. Popják and Cornforth (1960) chromatographed several aliphatic sesquiterpenoid alcohols on both Apiezon L and poly(ethylene glycol adipate) at 197°C, obtaining better separations on the polar column. The strongly polar packing sucrose diacetate hexaisobutyrate has been shown to give good separations of monoterpenoid compounds (Smith *et al.*, 1960), and, since it does not decompose at temperatures up to 200°C, it might be useful for chromatography of sesquiterpenoid compounds as well (see Section C.VII.a.1 for more details).

Acyclic mono-, sesqui-, and diterpenoid primary and tertiary alcohol mixtures. Synthetic mixtures of C_5 to C_{20} acyclic terpenoid alcohols have been chromatographed on polar and nonpolar substrates, and the relationships between the retention volumes on both substrates and the carbon number have been determined (Popják and Cornforth, 1960). Differences in retention were found between *cis,trans* and *trans,trans* primary alcohols and also terti-

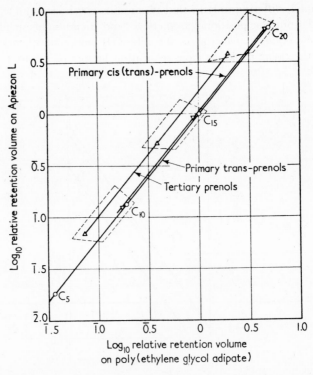

FIG. 8. Relationship between log₁₀ relative retention volumes on Apiezon L and poly(ethylene glycol adipate). O Primary *trans,trans* alcohols. ▽ Primary *cis,trans* alcohols. △ *tertiary* alcohols. (Popják and Cornforth, 1960.)

ary alcohols. When the logs of the retention volumes on poly(ethylene glycol adipate) were plotted against carbon number, three parallel lines were obtained (Fig. 7). The primary *trans,trans* alcohols were retained for the longest period of time on this packing, the primary *cis,trans* alcohols for a slightly shorter time, and the tertiary alcohols for the shortest time. These alcohols differ not only in carbon number but also in degree of unsaturation. Since they are made up of isoprene units, the C_{10} compounds contain two double bonds, the C_{15} compounds three double bonds, and the C_{20} compounds four double bonds. Therefore, the retention values of these terpenoids are governed by degree of unsaturation as well as by carbon number.

When the logs of the retention volumes on poly(ethylene glycol adipate) and Apiezon L are plotted against each other, families of parallel lines are obtained, indicating a difference in relative retentions on both liquids for the three groups of alcohols (Fig. 8). The primary *trans,trans* alcohols are retained longest on the polar packing and shortest on the nonpolar packing relative to the primary *cis,trans* and tertiary alcohols. The tertiary alcohols are retained longest on the nonpolar packing and shortest on the polar packing. This indicates that the primary *trans,trans* alcohols are relatively more polar than the *cis,trans* isomers, and the tertiary alcohols are least polar. These measurements can be used for preliminary identification of unknown terpenoid alcohols if their retentions are compared with suitable known curves.

a. Conditions for Chromatography of Isomers

See methods below for conditions for chromatography.

b. Conditions for Chromatography of Acyclic and Alicyclic Monoterpenoid Alcohols

*1. On Hyprose S.P. 80 (Cartoni and Liberti, 1960)

Chromatograph	Laboratory-built.
Column dimensions	300 × 0.4- to 0.5-cm i.d. straight glass tubing.
Solid support	Embacel (80/100 mesh) (May and Baker).
Stationary phase	Octakis(2-hydroxypropyl) sucrose (20:80).
Temperature	132°C.
Carrier gas	Nitrogen at 110 ml/min measured at outlet. Inlet pressure: 2 atmospheres. Outlet pressure: atmospheric.
Detector	Gas density balance.
Recorder	2.5 mv; 1 second; 0.5 cm/min.
Sample size	10 μl.
Analysis time	90 to 110 minutes.

*2. On Poly(polyethylene Glycol Adipate) (von Rudloff, 1960)

Chromatograph	Beckman GC-2.
Column dimensions	6-foot × 0.6-cm o.d. coiled copper tubing.
Solid support	Chromosorb W.

Stationary phase	Poly(polyethylene glycol adipate) (16.7:83.3).
Temperature	130°C.
Carrier gas	Helium at 41.6 ml/min. Inlet pressure: 1531 mm Hg. Outlet pressure: atmospheric.
Detector	T/C cell.
Recorder	Bristol Dynamaster, 0.05 to 1.05 mv; ½ inch/min.
Sample size	1.5 to 10 μl.
Analysis time	About 42 minutes to α-terpineol.

3. *On SAIB* (Smith *et al.*, 1960). See Section C.VII.a.1 for details.

*4. *On D.C. 550 silicone* (Cartoni and Liberti, 1960)

Chromatograph	Laboratory-built.
Column dimensions	300 × 0.4- to 0.5-cm i.d. straight glass tubing.
Solid support	Embacel (80/100 mesh) (May and Baker).
Stationary phase	D.C. 550 silicone oil (20:80).
Temperature	132°C.
Carrier gas	Nitrogen at 110 ml/min. Inlet pressure: 2 atmospheres. Outlet pressure: atmospheric.
Detector	Gas density balance.
Recorder	2.5 mv; 1 second; 0.5 cm/min.
Sample size	10 μl.
Analysis	90 to 110 minutes.

*5. *On Didecyl Phthalate* (Zubyk and Conner, 1960)

Chromatograph	Perkin-Elmer Vapor Fractometer Model 154-A modified with more sensitive temperature control.
Column dimensions	198 × 0.66-cm o.d.
Solid support	Celite 545 (50/100 U. S. mesh).
Stationary phase	Didecyl phthalate (25:75).
Temperature	150°C.
Carrier gas	Helium at 45 ml/min. Inlet pressure: 15.0 psig. Outlet pressure: atmospheric.
Detector	Thermistor.
Recorder	2.5 mv; 24 inches/hour.
Sample size	5 to 20 μl.
Analysis time	Not given.

c. Conditions for Chromatography of Sesquiterpenoid Alcohols

*1. *On Poly(ethylene Glycol Succinate)* (von Rudloff, 1960)

Chromatograph	Beckman GC-2.
Column dimensions	6-foot × 0.6-cm o.d. coiled copper tubing.
Solid support	Chromosorb W.
Stationary phase	Poly(ethylene glycol succinate) (16.7:83.3).
Temperature	190°C.
Carrier gas	Helium at 39.4 ml/min. Inlet pressure: 2029 mm Hg. Outlet pressure: atmospheric.
Detector	T/C cell.

Recorder	Bristol Dynamaster, 0.05- to 1.05-mv; 0.5 inch/min.
Sample size	1.5 to 10 μl.
Analysis time	About 31 minutes for β eudesmol.

*2. On Poly(ethylene Glycol Adipate) (Popják and Cornforth, 1960)

Chromatograph	Laboratory-built (Martin and James design).
Column dimensions	120 × 0.4-cm i.d.
Solid support	Celite (120/150 British mesh) washed with acid and alkali.
Stationary phase	Poly(ethylene glycol adipate (15:100 or 20:100) conditioned for 1 week at 197°C with a stream of nitrogen.
Temperature	197°C.
Carrier gas	Nitrogen at 25 to 50 ml/min at 25°C measured at outlet. Inlet pressure: 8 to 14 psig. Outlet pressure: atmospheric.
Detector	Gas density balance.
Recorder	0 to 100 μv.
Sample size	0.1 to 1.0 μl (no solvent).
Analysis time	About 25 minutes to trans,trans-farnesol.

*3. On Apiezon L (Popják and Cornforth, 1960)

Chromatograph	Laboratory-built (Martin and James design).
Column dimensions	120 × 0.4-cm i.d.
Solid support	Celite (120/150 mesh) washed with acid and alkali.
Stationary phase	Apiezon L (15:100 or 20:100) conditioned for a few hours at 197°C with a stream of nitrogen.
Temperature	197°C.
Carrier gas	Nitrogen at 25 to 50 ml/min at 25°C measured at outlet. Inlet pressure: 8 to 14 psig. Outlet pressure: atmospheric.
Detector	Gas density balance.
Recorder	0 to 100 μv.
Sample size	0.1 to 1.0 μl.
Analysis time	About 20 minutes to trans,trans-farnesol.

d. Conditions for Chromatography of Acyclic Mono-, Sesqui-, and Diterpenoid Primary and Tertiary Alcohol Mixtures.

See Sections C.II.c.2 and C.II.c.3 above for specific conditions for chromatography.

III. Chromatography of Carbonyl Compounds

Monoterpenoid aldehydes and ketones containing 10 carbon atoms are important constituents of many essential oils. Often, carbonyl compounds containing from 6 to 14 carbon atoms are also found, so the chromatography of this whole group will be covered here.

Many aliphatic monoterpenoid aldehydes such as α- and β-citral and citronellal are of commercial importance, since they are components contributing to the unique aromas and flavors of essential oils. Some cyclic monoterpenoid ketones such as fenchone and camphor are also of commercial importance. Other aldehydes and ketones, although they may be only minor constituents of essential oils, contribute to flavor and aroma, so their separation and identification are important to the essential oil industry.

Carbonyl compounds can be isolated from other terpenes prior to GLC by the procedures described in Section A.II. Aldehydes with carbon numbers to 13 or 14 can be chromatographed unchanged on either polar or nonpolar substrates. Since they are polar compounds, polar substrates usually give better separations. No work has been done on sesquiterpenoid aldehydes at this time. They are uncommon in essential oils and may undergo aldol condensations at the temperatures necessary for chromatography, ultimately forming polymers (see Chapter 7, Section F.III). Therefore, sesquiterpenoid aldehydes probably should be converted to their more stable dimethyl acetals prior to chromatography.

The monoterpenoid carbonyl compounds should be chromatographed at temperatures as low as possible in order to prevent decomposition. Temperatures between 130° and 160°C have been used with no apparent polymerization. However, ionones and methylionones, synthetic ketones containing 13 and 14 carbon atoms, have been chromatographed at column temperatures as high as 195°C and injection port temperatures of 265°C with no apparent decomposition of the samples observed (Crisler and Benford, 1959).

Isomers. The positional isomers α- and β-ionone and also α-, β-, γ-, and δ-methylionone have been chromatographed on the nonpolar substrate Apiezon L (Crisler and Benford, 1959). The α- and β-ionone isomers were separated, as were the α-, β-, and γ-methylionones. The δ-methylionone was not completely separated from the α- and γ-methylionones. Since these are C_{13} and C_{14} ketones, column temperatures were rather high—up to 195°C for the methylionones, with the injection port temperature at 265°C. Polar packings stable at these temperatures probably could also be used for their separation.

The monoterpenoid aldehyde stereoisomers α- and β-citral have been chromatographed on both D.C. 550 silicone and octakis(2-hydroxypropyl) sucrose (Hyprose S.P. 80), with a separation factor of 1.20 for the silicone and 1.23 for the Hyprose S.P. 80 (Cartoni and Liberti, 1960).

Carbonyl fraction of essential oils. Aldehydes and ketones with 6 to 14 carbon atoms can be separated on either polar or nonpolar packings. Carbonyl compounds containing the same number of carbon atoms can also be separated from each other on the same types of packing and under the same general conditions used for monoterpenoid alcohols. Since they are polar compounds, polar packings in general give better separations, although both polar and nonpolar packings can be used.

Octakis(2-hydroxypropyl)sucrose (Hyprose S.P. 80) is a good polar packing for the separation of carbonyl compounds. When the logs of the retention volumes are plotted against boiling point, a straight line is obtained for these compounds with a slope that is characteristic for them (Fig. 5). On the relatively nonpolar D.C. 550 silicone these compounds are separated by boiling point alone, and the separation factors are usually less than on polar packings (Fig. 6).

Other polar packings, such as poly(ethylene glycol succinate), poly(poly-ethylene glycol adipate), poly(diethylene glycol adipate) partially cross-linked with pentaerythritol, and sucrose diacetate hexaisobutyrate (SAIB) would probably be suitable for separations of these compounds also.

Several nonpolar packings have been used for their separation. D.C. 550 silicone is a relatively nonpolar substrate and has been used with mono-terpenoid carbonyl compounds, and the nonpolar Apiezon L has been used for C_{13} to C_{14} ketones at column temperatures from 180° to 195°C.

a. Conditions for Chromatography of Isomers

See Section C.III.b for references.

*1. Separation of (I) Ionone and (II) Methyl Ionone Isomers on Apiezon L (Crisler and Benford, 1959)

Chromatograph	Laboratory-constructed, conventional design, and sep-arately heated injection port.
Column dimensions	180 × 0.6-cm o.d. coiled copper tubing.
Solid support	Johns-Manville Celite 545 (40/140 U. S. mesh) acid-washed, neutralized, and dried.
Stationary phases	Apiezon L (25:75).
Temperatures	(I) Column: 180°C. Injection port: 210°C. (II) Column: 195°C. Injection port: 265°C.
Carrier gas	Helium at 120 ml/min. Inlet pressure: 775 mm Hg. Outlet pressure: atmospheric.
Recorder	0 to 1 mv; 1 second; 1.25 cm/min.
Detector	Gow-Mac TE III, four-filament (tungsten) T/C cell at 150 ma.
Sample size	5 μl.
Analysis time	(I) 24 minutes to β-ionone. (II) 27 minutes to β-methyl-ionone.

b. Conditions for Chromatography of the Carbonyl Fraction of Essential Oils

1. On Hyprose S.P. 80 (Cartoni and Liberti, 1960). See Section C.II.b.1 for specific conditions.

2. On Poly(polyethylene Glycol Adipate) (von Rudloff, 1960). See Section C.II.b.2 for specific conditions.

3. On D.C. 550 Silicone (Cartoni and Liberti, 1960). See Section C.II.b.4 for specific conditions.

IV. CHROMATOGRAPHY OF ESTERS

Esters of terpenoid alcohols and lower organic acids are often found as constituents of essential oils. They are also made synthetically from terpenoid alcohols. They may be chromatographed unchanged as esters, and usually are separated in this way, or they may be hydrolyzed and the alcohol and acid portions chromatographed and identified. The most common esters are acetates, but formates, propionates, and butyrates sometimes occur. They are important constituents of many essential oils such as lavandin, lavender, and ylang ylang.

Esters have been separated on both polar and nonpolar liquids at temperatures from 130° to 160°C. As with the other oxygenated groups discussed previously, they are polar compounds, and therefore better separations should be obtained on polar packings.

Most of the chromatography of these compounds has been done in admixture with other oxygenated terpenoid constituents of essential oils. References for the chromatography of these are covered in that section (Section C.VII). Bayer *et al.* (1958) have separated bornyl acetate, geranyl acetate, and geranyl butyrate on Silicone C–lithium capronate (9:1) and on Silicone C alone, and Naves (1958a) has also separated several acetates on D.C. 550 silicone.

Esters of linalool and a few other monoterpenoid alcohols have been chromatographed on the polar substrate poly(propylene glycol sebacate)

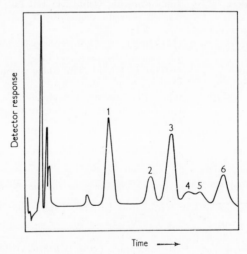

FIG. 9. Separation of some monoterpenoid alcohol esters on poly(propylene glycol sebacate). (1) Linalyl acetate, linalyl formate, and an unknown alcohol ester. (2) Neryl formate. (3) Geranyl formate. (4) Neryl acetate and terpinyl acetate. (5) Terpinyl formate. (6) Geranyl acetate. (Holness, 1959.)

(Holness, 1959) at 135°C (Fig. 9). Linalyl acetate and formate are not separated under the conditions employed. However, separations of neryl formate
and acetate and of geranyl formate and acetate are complete, although
terpenyl formate and acetate interfered in this chromatogram. It is possible
that better resolution of these latter compounds from other components
could be obtained at lower column temperatures.

Cartoni and Liberti (1960) have separated linalyl and geranyl acetates
on D.C. 550 silicone and on octakis(2-hydroxypropyl)sucrose (Hyprose
S.P. 80). They are well separated on both columns with a separation factor
of 2.2 on the silicone packing and 2.6 on the polar Hyprose S.P. 80, showing
that this substrate gives better separations of these esters as well as of the
alcohols and carbonyl compounds tested (see Table IV) than does the nonpolar silicone. When the logs of the retention values on the polar liquid are
plotted against boiling point, a characteristic curve is obtained for the esters.
At equivalent boiling points they are retained for shorter times than either
the alcohols or the carbonyl compounds, indicating that they are less polar
(see Fig. 5). On the relatively nonpolar D.C. 550 silicone, however, the
polarity of the compounds does not affect the volume of gas necessary to
elute them, and all groups are eluted in the order of boiling point alone
(see Fig. 6).

When the logs of retention volumes of esters on both D.C. 550 silicone
and Hyprose S.P. 80 are plotted against each other, a characteristic curve is
obtained differing from those found for the other oxygenated derivatives
chromatographed (see Fig. 4). Therefore, when oxygenated terpenoids are
chromatographed on both polar and nonpolar substrates, it is possible to
identify the type of compound by comparison with plots of log retention volumes of known materials on the same two phases.

a. Conditions for Chromatography

*1. On Polypropylene Glycol Sebacate or Polypropylene Glycol Adipate (Hol-
ness, 1961)

Chromatograph	Pye Argon Chromatograph.
Column dimensions	120 cm long × 4 mm in diameter borosilicate glass tubing.
Solid support	Celite (100/110 B.S.S. mesh); or spherical glass beads (0.12-mm diameter) previously cleaned with hot aqua regia.
Stationary phases	(I) Polypropylene glycol sebacate (Reoplex 100, Geigy) or (II) Polypropylene glycol adipate (Reoplex 400) at 5 to 10% (w/w) on Celite or at 0.5 to 1% (w/w) on glass beads. Columns "cured" at 150°C for 72 hours before use.

Temperature	50° to 120°C, according to sample and information sought. For work at lower temperatures, a "flash" vaporizer at 100°C is useful.
Carrier gas	Argon at 20 to 40 ml/min measured at outlet. Inlet pressure: about 1000 mm Hg. Outlet pressure: atmospheric.
Detector	Argon, voltage 1250 to 1750.
Recorder	0.10 mv; 2 seconds; 3 or 6 inches/hour.
Sample size	0.025 to 0.1 μl, according to complexity.
Analysis times	70°C, 3 hours for linalyl acetate. 90°C, 2½ hours for geraniol. 110°C, 3½ hours for eugenol.

2. *On Hyprose S.P. 80* (Cartoni and Liberti, 1960). See Section C.II.b.1 for specific conditions.

3. *On D.C. 550 Silicone* (Cartoni and Liberti, 1960). See Section C.II.b.4 for specific conditions.

V. CHROMATOGRAPHY OF PHENOLIC COMPOUNDS

The monoterpene hydrocarbon *p*-cymene, an aromatic compound having the general *p*-menthane structure, is found in many essential oils. Oxygenated compounds structurally related to *p*-cymene occur also. One group of compounds having a general hydroxyphenylpropane structure includes thy-

TABLE V

RELATIVE RETENTION RATIOS OF HYDROXYPHENYL PROPANE
COMPOUNDS ON APIEZON L AT 190°C[a]
(Borneol = 1.00)

Compound	Relative retention value
Borneol	1.00
Safrol	1.47
cis-Isosafrole	1.93
trans-Isosafrole	2.53
Eugenol	1.80
Eugenol methyl ether	2.00
cis-Isoeugenol	2.30
trans-Isoeugenol	1.47
cis-Isoeugenol methyl ether	2.67
trans-Isoeugenol methyl ether	3.34
Eugenol acetate	3.07
β-Asaron (*cis*-isoasaron)	4.54
Asaron (*trans*-isoasaron)	6.20
β-Caryophyllene	3.20

[a] From Stahl and Trennheuser (1960).

mol and carvacrol. Estragole and anethole are related materials, being
p-methoxyallylbenzene and *p*-methoxypropenylbenzene, respectively. Derivatives of guaiacol are also aromatic components of essential oils. Eugenol (4-
allylguaiacol) is the main constituent of the oil of cloves. Isoeugenol (4-pro-
penylguaiacol) is a positional isomer of eugenol, and coniferyl alcohol,
safrole, and isosafrole are related compounds occurring naturally.

Thirteen hydroxy derivatives of *p*-cymene have been chromatographed
in known mixtures on Apiezon L at 190°C, and the relative retention times
have been tabulated (Table V) (Stahl and Trennhauser, 1960). The stereoisomers *cis*- and *trans*-isosafrole are separated, as well as *cis*- and *trans*-iso-
eugenol, *cis*- and *trans*-isoeugenol methyl ether, and asaron and β-asaron.
The separation factors for many of these derivatives such as *cis*-isosafrole and
eugenol methyl ether, safrole and *trans*-isoeugenol, and *trans*-isosafrole and
cis-isoeugenol methyl ether are so close that these compounds would not be
resolved on nonpolar packings if chromatographed together under these
conditions. However, some of these are synthetic compounds that would
not be found together in natural mixtures.

The polar substrates poly(polyethylene glycol adipate) and *m*-bis(*m*-
phenoxyphenoxy)benzene have been used to separate anethole, eugenol, and
isoeugenol at 190°C and 220°C, respectively (von Rudloff, 1960). These
compounds were well separated on both substrates with no signs of decomposition.

cis- and *trans*-Anethole have been separated with D.C. 550 silicone as the
liquid substrate at a column temperature of 180°C (Naves *et al.*, 1958)
(Fig. 10).

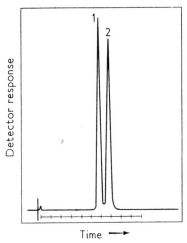

Fig. 10. Separation of (1) *cis*-anethole and (2) *trans*-anethole on D.C. 550 silicone at
180°C. (Naves *et al.*, 1958.)

In general, these polar compounds should be better separated on the polar packings that are stable at high column temperatures such as poly(polyethylene glycol adipate) and the polyphenylene ether discussed above. Other polar packings stable at high temperatures, discussed in this chapter, should also be useful.

Mono- and dihydric phenols not found in essential oils have been separated by boiling point on nonpolar substrates such as Apiezon L, or by differences in polarity on polar substrates such as sodium dodecyl sulfonate, erythritol, dulcitol, and inositol at high temperatures. These separations and chromatographic conditions are discussed in Chapter 4, Section B, and should be applicable to these terpenoid derivatives as well.

a. Conditions for Chromatography

*1. On Apiezon L (Stahl and Trennheuser, 1960)

Chromatograph	Perkin-Elmer 116.
Column dimensions	300 × 0.625-cm o.d. stainless steel.
Solid support	Celite (60/100 mesh).
Stationary phase	Apiezon L.
Temperature	190°C.
Carrier gas	Helium at 96 ml/min.
Detector	T/C cell.
Recorder	0 to 5 mv; 1 cm/min.
Sample size	5 μl.
Analysis time	47 minutes to asaron.

*2. On Poly(polyethylene Glycol Adipate) (von Rudloff, 1960)

Chromatograph	Beckman GC-2.
Column dimensions	6-foot × 0.6-cm o.d., coiled copper tubing.
Solid support	Chromosorb W.
Stationary phase	Poly(polyethylene glycol adipate) (20:80).
Temperature	190°C.
Carrier gas	Helium at 83.5 ml/min.
Detector	T/C cell.
Recorder	Bristol Dynamaster, 0.05 to 1.05 mv; 0.5 inch/min.
Sample size	Not given.
Analysis time	26 minutes to isoeugenol.

VI. CHROMATOGRAPHY OF OTHER OXYGEN-CONTAINING TERPENOID COMPOUNDS

Oxygen-containing terpenoids also include ethers, lactones, and furan derivatives. Little work has been done on the chromatography of these compounds. Cineole, an intra-annular ether occurring in many essential oils, has been separated from other oxygenated terpenoids on both polar and nonpolar substrates. It is eluted relatively rapidly on both types of column and is better separated from the other oxygenated terpenoids on polar packings (see Table IV). Thus the separation factor between cineole and linalool is 1.47 on D.C. 550 silicone and 3.9 on Hyprose S.P. 80 (Cartoni and Liberti, 1960). Sucrose diacetate hexaisobutyrate also gives good separations of cineole from other oxygenated derivatives. It is eluted with about the same retention volume as the hydrocarbon d-limonene on most packings, although here the separation factor varies from substrate to substrate.

The positional isomers 1,4-cineole and 1,8-cineole have been separated on didecyl phthalate at 130°C with a separation factor of 1.15 (Zubyk and Conner, 1960). More polar columns might improve the separation, although these ethers are not very polar themselves.

Menthofuran, a terpenoid found in the oil of peppermint, has been separated from other terpenoids on poly(diethylene glycol succinate) at 155°C and also on a mixed column packing of tetrakis(2-hydroxypropyl) ethylenediamine (Quadrol) and sucrose diacetate hexaisobutyrate (SAIB) in a ratio of 2:1 (Anon., 1960). Cineole is also well separated on this mixed column packing (see Fig. 51).

a. Conditions for Chromatography

*1. On Quadrol–SAIB (Anon., 1960). See Section C.VII.a.2 for specific conditions.

*2. On Didecyl Phthalate (Zubyk and Conner, 1960). See Section C.II.b.5 for specific conditions.

VII. Chromatography of Oxygenated Terpenoid Mixtures

The complete oxygenated fraction of an essential oil can be analyzed by GLC without prior separation according to functional group. Since there are generally many components in such a mixture, there is more chance of overlapping peaks. This is particularly true with chromatography on nonpolar substrates where the compounds are eluted by boiling point only, since the whole oxygenated fraction has a narrow boiling-point range. Compounds with different functional groups vary in their polarities, and much better separations will in general be achieved on polar packings, where the more polar compounds are retained for longer periods of time than less polar compounds. When alcohols, esters, and carbonyl compounds are chromatographed on a polar packing such as octakis(2-hydroxypropyl)sucrose, and the logarithms of the retention volumes are plotted against the boiling points of the compounds, a series of straight lines is obtained, each one being characteristic for a specific functional group (see Fig. 5) (Cartoni and Liberti, 1960). When these same compounds are chromatographed on D.C. 550 silicone, a relatively nonpolar substrate, a single straight line is obtained dependent only on the boiling points of the oxygenated terpenoids (see Fig. 6). When the logs of the retention volumes of the compounds on both the polar and the nonpolar substrates are plotted against each other, straight lines are obtained characteristic for each functional group (see Fig. 4). When unknown oxygenated terpenoids are chromatographed on two dissimilar columns such as these and the logs of the retention volumes on both columns are plotted, the nature of the functional group can be determined.

Several relationships can be seen on examining the results obtained on alcohols (see Fig. 4, curve III). The doubly unsaturated aliphatic secondary alcohols geraniol and nerol are retained for the longest length of time on both substrates, and the singly unsaturated citronellol is retained for a relatively shorter length of time. The doubly unsaturated tertiary alcohol linalool is retained for a much shorter period than the others. With the two cyclic alcohols, the tertiary α-terpeneol with one double bond is retained relatively longer than menthol, a saturated secondary alcohol.

Thus if an unknown compound has retention values such that the point falls on the alcohol curve, the compound can be tentatively identified as an alcohol, and the relative position on the line will give an indication of the degree of unsaturation of the compound and also the general molecular structure.

Other polar packings may be used for separation of these mixtures (see Table IV). The best packing depends to some extent on the mixture being separated, since different polar packings give different separations of various oxygenated components. The best substrates must usually be determined experimentally.

Poly(diethylene glycol succinate) (LAC-4-R777) has been shown to give good separations of the components present in autoxidized limonene (Bernhard and Marr, 1960), as well as poly(diethylene glycol adipate) partially cross-linked with pentaerythritol (LAC-2-R446). Carbowax 400 gives good separations of oxygenated terpenoids but cannot be used at temperatures above 130°C. The polyesters poly(polyethylene glycol adipate) and poly(ethylene glycol succinate) are efficient substrates and are stable at temperatures of 195° to 200°C (von Rudloff, 1960). Sucrose diacetate hexaisobutyrate is a useful substrate for separation of mint oil constituents (Smith *et al.*, 1960). This liquid is stable at temperatures up to 200°C. A mixed column packing also shows promise for separation of oxygenated terpenoids. This is Quadrol [tetrakis(2-hydroxypropyl) ethylene diamine] mixed with sucrose diacetate hexaisobutyrate (SAIB) in a ratio of 2:1 (Anon., 1960). This mixture cannot be used at temperatures above 150°C.

Other packings, both polar and nonpolar, are didecyl phthalate, diglycerol, polyphenylene ether, other diethylene glycol polyesters, and Apiezon greases.

The resolution of constituents of a mixture often can be changed by changing the column temperature. This is true for similar compounds as well as for compounds with different functional groups. Thus the linalool–camphor peaks are unresolved at 120°C, while relative retentions are 1.4 at 90°C and 3.9 at 70°C on poly(propylene glycol succinate) at a low liquid/solid ratio. On the same type of column, the separation factor for α-citral and β-citral is 1.9 at 110°C and 2.9 at 100°C. Nerol and citronellol almost overlap at 70°C but are resolved at 100°C (Holness, 1961).

Temperatures for chromatography should be controlled carefully, since many of these oxygenated terpenoids are thermolabile (see Section H). Most monoterpenoid oxygenated derivatives are chromatographed at column temperatures between 130° and 160°C, but compounds with higher carbon numbers may require higher temperatures.

a. Conditions for Chromatography

*1. On SAIB (Smith et al., 1960)

Chromatograph	Burrell Kromotog K-2 with column bath.
Column dimensions	215 × 0.6-cm i.d. straight glass tubing.
Solid support	Aqua regia-washed firebrick (30/60 U. S. mesh).
Stationary phase	Sucrose diacetate hexaisobutyrate (10:100).
Temperature	(I) 120°C. (II) 145°C. (III) 170°C.
Carrier gas	Helium at (I) 78 ml/min. (II) 77 ml/min. (III) 74 ml/min. Inlet pressure: 80 mm Hg above atmospheric. Outlet pressure: atmospheric.
Detector	Four-filament hot-wire T/C cell at 200°C and 200 ma.
Recorder	0 to 1 mv; 1 second; 0.5 inch/min.
Sample size	2 to 10 μl.
Analysis time	(I) 68.4 minutes. (II) 27.7 minutes. (III) 13.4 minutes for 1-menthol.

*2. On Quadrol–SAIB (Anon., 1960)

Chromatograph	Aerograph A-110-C.
Column dimensions	300 × 0.635-cm o.d., coiled stainless-steel column.
Solid support	Johns-Manville C-22 firebrick (60/80 U. S. mesh).
Stationary phase	2:1 mixture of N,N,N^1,N^1-tetrakis-(2-hydroxypropyl) ethylenediamine and sucrose diacetate hexaisobutyrate (15:85).
Temperatures	Injector: 260°C. Detector: 140°C. Column: 140°C.
Carrier gas	Helium at 100 ml/min. Inlet pressure: 1200 mm Hg. Outlet pressure: atmospheric.
Detector	Four-filament hot-wire (W) T/C cell at 250 ma.
Recorder	0 to 1 mv; 1 second; 0.85 cm/min.
Sample size	1 μl.
Analysis time	About 33 minutes.

*3. On Hyprose S.P. 80 (Cartoni and Liberti, 1960). See Section C.II.b.1 for conditions for chromatography.

*4. On Poly(*diethylene Glycol Succinate*) (Bernhard and Marr, 1960)

Chromatograph	Aerograph A-90-C.
Column dimensions	10-foot × ¼-inch o.d. stainless steel.
Solid support	Sil-O-Cel C-22 (30/60 mesh) water-graded and dried at 110°C for 17 hours.
Stationary phase	LAC-4-R777 (25:75) packing pretreated at 20° to 30°C higher than column temperature in a stream of helium.
Temperatures	Column: 150°C. Injection port: 200°C.
Carrier gas	Helium at 90 ml/min. Outlet pressure: atmospheric.
Detector	Four-channel hot-wire katharometer.
Recorder	Recording potentiometer, 1 mv; 30 inches/hour.
Sample size	5 μl.
Analysis time	About 40 minutes.

*5. On Poly(*diethylene Glycol Adipate*) *Partially Cross-Linked with Pentaerythritol* (Bernhard and Marr, 1960)

Chromatograph	Aerograph A-90-C.
Column dimensions	10-foot × ¼-inch o.d. stainless steel.
Solid support	Sil-O-Cel C-22 (30/60 mesh) water-graded and dried at 110°C for 17 hours.
Stationary phase	LAC-2-R446 (25:75) packing pretreated at 20° to 30°C higher than column temperature in a stream of helium.
Temperatures	Column: 150°C. Injection port: 200°C.
Carrier gas	Helium at 90 ml/min. Outlet pressure: atmospheric.
Detector	Four-channel hot-wire katharometer.
Recorder	Recording potentiometer, 1 mv; 30 inches/hour.
Sample size	5 μl.
Analysis time	Not given.

*6. On D.C. 550 Silicone (Cartoni and Liberti, 1960). See Section C.II.b.4 for specific conditions.

VIII. SUMMARY

Oxygenated terpenoids discussed here include alcohols, esters, carbonyl compounds, and aromatic phenolic compounds, as well as a brief mention of ethers and furan derivatives. They may be isolated and chromatographed as a single fraction, or individual groups can be isolated by functional group and chromatographed. They are generally chromatographed at temperatures between 140° and 190°C on polar substrates to obtain best separations, although nonpolar packings are sometimes used.

D. Hydrocarbon and Oxygenated Terpenoid Mixtures

I. INTRODUCTION

Chromatography of a complete essential oil is sometimes desirable. This procedure has found wide application in quality control, fingerprinting of essential oils, and determination of adulteration. Chromatographic peaks are sometimes identified by comparison with relative retention values for known compounds, or the chromatogram itself is sometimes used as a characteristic identification of a known essential oil for quality control and determination of adulteration. For either of these objectives, separation of as many components as possible is desired.

In general, better separations can be achieved if hydrocarbon and oxygenated fractions of essential oils are chromatographed separately. The compounds cover a wide boiling-point range, and, unless temperature programming is used, good separations of all components are not possible. With temperatures high enough to elute the less-volatile compounds, the more-volatile monoterpene hydrocarbons will not be well separated; and, with lower column temperatures, less-volatile components will be retained too long on the column and sharp peaks will not be obtained.

For preliminary chromatography, complete separations are not essential. The fractions are collected and rechromatographed under different conditions in order to achieve better separations. Preliminary chromatography can be carried out on preparative scale instruments in order to obtain large samples for further study, or conventional packed columns can be used, with fractions collected from several runs until a sample large enough for rechromatography is obtained.

II. Preliminary Separation of Fractions by GLC

Constituents of essential oils chromatographed on a nonpolar substrate will be eluted in the order of boiling points. If fractions are collected and rechromatographed on polar packings, further separations will be obtained depending on the polarities of the compounds. In general, the terpene hydrocarbons are more volatile than oxygenated terpenoids, and sesquiterpenes

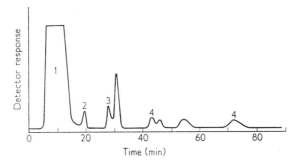

Fig. 11. Preliminary separation of components of lemon oil on D.C. 550 silicone at 156°C. (1) Monoterpenes. (2) Alcohols. (3) Carbonyl compounds. (4) Sesquiterpenes. (Liberti and Cartoni, 1958b.)

are least volatile, so a general separation according to group will be obtained (Liberti and Cartoni, 1958b) (Fig. 11). This figure shows a chromatogram of lemon oil obtained on silicone at 156°C. The monoterpene hydrocarbons are eluted first, followed by a small peak representing terpenoid alcohols, then carbonyls, and finally sesquiterpenes. If these fractions are collected in sufficient quantity they can then be separated further on other types of columns under conditions described in Sections B, and C.

This procedure has not been widely used up to the present, but it might be a convenient method for preliminary separation of essential oils. With some essential oils there would be an overlap of the monoterpene and oxygenated components, since there are several low-boiling oxygenated compounds which would be eluted with the hydrocarbon fraction. Among these are hexenol and hexenal, octanal, and cineole.

a. Conditions for Chromatography

*1. *On D.C. 550 Silicone* (Liberti and Cartoni, 1958b)

Chromatograph	Laboratory-built.
Column dimensions	300 × 0.6-cm i.d. straight glass tubing.
Solid support	Deactivated Celite (80/100 mesh).
Stationary phase	D.C. 550 silicone (20:80).
Temperature	156°C.
Carrier gas	Nitrogen at 100 ml/min. measured at outlet. Inlet pressure: 2 atmospheres. Outlet pressure: atmospheric.
Detector	Gas density balance.
Recorder	2.5 mv; 1 second; 0.5 cm/min.
Sample size	Approximately 10 μl.
Analysis time	About 80 minutes through sesquiterpenes.

III. CHROMATOGRAPHY OF KNOWN MIXTURES

Groups of known terpenoid hydrocarbon and oxygenated mixtures have occasionally been chromatographed together, most often to demonstrate separations that can be achieved. Bayer *et al.* (1958) chromatographed mixtures of a few monoterpenoid hydrocarbons and oxygenated derivatives on Silicone C–sodium caproate with partial separations of components. Artificial mixtures of terpenoid hydrocarbons and hydroxyphenylpropane derivatives have been chromatographed on Apiezon L (Stahl and Trennheuser, 1960). However, since the physical properties of these compounds differ greatly, best separations are obtained under different chromatographic conditions such as different column temperatures and column packings. Therefore artificial mixtures of terpenes are generally chromatographed in groups where optimum conditions for the group can be used.

IV. SUMMARY

Synthetic mixtures of terpene hydrocarbons and oxygenated compounds are rarely chromatographed together, since their physical properties differ greatly. Better separations can be obtained if groups are chromatographed individually so that chromatographic conditions can be adjusted for each mixture of compounds. This technique sometimes is used for preliminary separations of groups of components in an essential oil.

E. Separation and Fingerprinting of Essential Oils of Gymnospermae

I. CHROMATOGRAPHY OF PINACEAE

The essential oils from several genera of the pine family are commercially important, and constituents of some of the oils have been separated by gas chromatography.

Crude wood turpentine. Crude wood turpentine, produced from distillation of the wood of species of *Pinus*, contains mainly terpene hydrocarbons. These have been separated on didecyl phthalate at 130°C (Fig. 12) (Zubyk and

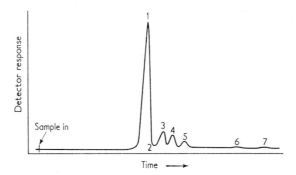

FIG. 12. Chromatogram of wood turpentine on didecyl phthalate at 130°C. (1) α-Pinene. (2) Unidentified. (3) α-Fenchene. (4) Camphene. (5) *trans-p*-Menthane, 3-*p*-menthene, *trans*-pinane—any or all. (6) Δ³-Carene. (7) Dipentene. (Zubyk and Conner, 1960.)

Conner, 1960). α-Pinene is the main constituent of turpentine and is well separated from other monoterpenes present. α-Fenchene and camphene are present as minor components, as well as several other monoterpenes. German turpentine oil has been chromatographed on tricresyl phosphate at 100°C (Fig. 13) (Liberti and Cartoni, 1958a). The major component was identified as Δ³-carene with limonene, α-pinene, and *p*-cymene also present in considerable amounts.

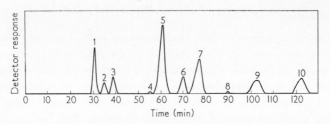

Fig. 13. Chromatogram of German turpentine oil on tricresyl phosphate at 100°C.
(1) α-Pinene. (2) Unidentified. (3) Camphene. (4) β-Pinene. (5) Δ³ Carene. (6) Unidentified. (7) Limonene. (8) o-Cymene. (9) p-Cymene terpinene. (10) Terpinolene. (Liberti
and Cartoni, 1958a.)

Juniperus species. The heartwood of some *Juniperus* species is steam-distilled to obtain cedarwood oil. The main constituents are sesquiterpenes.
Gas chromatography has been used in conjunction with fractional distillation for their isolation (Runeberg, 1960a, 1960b). Thujopsene, cuparene, α-
cedrene, and widdrol were separated from oil of *Juniperus utahensis* Lemm.
on a stationary phase composed of a mixture of 2,4-dinitrophenyl-2-naphthyl
ether and dibenzylpyridine (20:1) at 150°C. Thujopsene is the major constituent of the oil. Several other unidentified compounds were also separated
from the sesquiterpene fractions isolated by fractional distillation.

The oil of *Juniperus virginiana* L. was also separated into fractions by
distillation, and the main sesquiterpene hydrocarbon fractions were further
separated by gas chromatography on 2,4-dinitrophenyl-2-naphthyl ether
and dibenzylpyridine (20:1) at 150°C (Runeberg, 1960b). α-Cedrene, thujopsene, and cuparene were separated, as well as several unidentified sesquiterpene hydrocarbons.

The oil from berries of *Juniperus oxycedrus* L. has been separated into fractions by vacuum distillation, and the lower-boiling fractions have been
analyzed by GLC with tricresyl phosphate as a stationary phase at 136°C
(Motl *et al.*, 1960). This oil consists mainly of monoterpene hydrocarbons,
with α-pinene, myrcene, limonene, and a small amount of p-cymene identified. The sesquiterpene hydrocarbons compose about 20% of the oil, the
oxygen-containing terpenes only a minor fraction, about 15%.

Other genera of Pinaceae. The oils of several other genera of Pinaceae have
been investigated by gas chromatography, and fingerprints characteristic
for each species have been obtained (Cvrkal and Janák, 1959). *Picea excelsia*
oil was examined exhaustively by separation of constituents first by fractional
distillation and then by gas chromatography. The fractions were chromatographed on poly(dimethyl siloxane) as the stationary liquid at 140°C and
180°C. Twenty-three fractions were separated, and the major constituents
were identified as β-pinene, dipentene, β-phellandrene, and bornyl acetate.

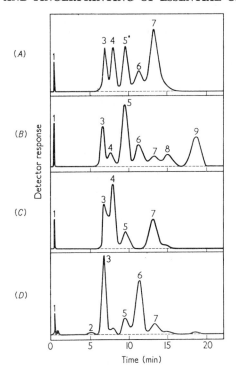

Fig. 14. Chromatograms of the monoterpene hydrocarbon fraction of several genera of Pinaceae on poly(dimethyl siloxane) at 140°C. (*A*) *Pinus mugo* Turr. (*B*) *Abies concolor* Lindl. et Gord. (*C*) *Pseudotsuga Douglasii* Lindl. (*D*) *Picea excelsa* Link. (Cvrkal and Janák, 1959.)

Comparative chromatograms were obtained on the monoterpene hydro-carbons of *Pinus mugo* Turr., *Abies concolor* Lindl. et Gord, *Pseudotsuga Douglasii* Lindl., and *Picea excelsia* Link (Fig. 14). The per cent composition of different components varies with the species, and the presence or absence of specific terpenes is typical for the various species.

a. Conditions for Chromatography

1. Of Wood Turpentine (Zubyk and Conner, 1960)

Chromatograph	Perkin-Elmer Model 154A modified with a more-sensitive temperature control.
Column dimensions	396 × 0.66-cm o.d.
Solid support	Celite 545 (50/100 U. S. mesh).
Stationary phase	Didecyl phthalate (25:75).
Temperature	130°C.
Carrier gas	Helium at 45 ml/min.
Detector	T/C cell (thermistor type).

Recorder   2.5 mv; 24 inches/hour.
Sample size   10 μl.
Analysis time   Not given.

*2. Of Monoterpene Hydrocarbons of Pinaceae (Cvrkal and Janák, 1959)

Chromatograph   Griffin and George Type MK II.
Column dimensions   160 × 0.7-cm glass U tubing.
Solid support   (I) Celite C-545 (Johns-Manville). (II) Sterchamol
                     (Dortmund, Germany).
Stationary phase   (I) Poly(dimethyl siloxane) (30:70). (II) Glycerol
                     (30:70).
Temperatures   (I) 140°C. (II) 120°C.
Carrier gas   Hydrogen.
Detector   T/C cell.
Recorder   Honeywell-Brown, 3 mv.
Sample size   10 to 40 μl.
Analysis time   About 20 minutes at 140°C for monoterpene hydrocar-
                     bons.

F. Separation and Fingerprinting of Essential Oils
of Angiosperma—Monocotyledoneae

I. CHROMATOGRAPHY OF ESSENTIAL OILS OF GRAMINAE

Citronella, palmarosa, and lemon grass (all members of the *Andropogon* genus) produce essential oils which are important commercially. Certain oxygenated terpenoid perfume and flavor components are derived from them. The analysis of these oils and identification of components has been accomplished by gas chromatography. Since the oxygenated fraction is predominant, the oils can be chromatographed quickly and quantitatively without preliminary separation from the hydrocarbon fraction.

The grass species differ in their terpenoid contents, and even varieties differ, some being more desirable commercially than others.

a. Citronella and Palmarosa

Both Java-type and Ceylon citronella grass essential oils have been chromatographed and compared on the polar Carbowax 20M substrate at 190°C (Rogers, 1959). Ceylon citronella oil has a more complex composition than Java types or palmarosa grass oil (Figs. 15, 16, 17). The Ceylon type, for instance, contains higher-boiling eugenol derivatives that are not present in the other two types of oil. The oils were chromatographed also at 160°C, giving better separations of the lower-boiling components. Twenty-four peaks were separated from the Ceylon citronella grass oil, twenty-three peaks from the Java type, and twelve peaks from palmarosa grass oil.

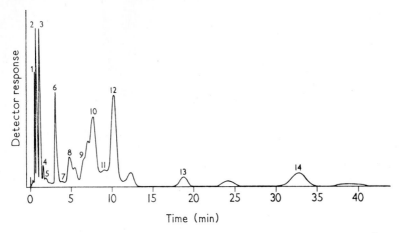

Fig. 15. Chromatogram of citronella Ceylon Estate on Carbowax 20M at 190°C. (1) α-Pinene. (2) Camphene. (3) Limonene. (4) *p*-Cymene. (5) Methyl heptenone. (6) Citronellal. (7) Linalool. (8) Sesquiterpene "x." (9) Citronellyl acetate. (10) Citronellol and geranyl acetate. (11) Nerol. (12) Geraniol. (13) Methyl eugenol. (14) Methyl isoeugenol. (Rogers, 1959.)

Fractions were collected and identified by infrared spectrophotometry, and quantitative analyses of components of these oils were made. It was found that the free geraniol content of the citronella oils was similar, ranging from 12.2 to 14.1%. Geraniol and citronellol are obtained commercially

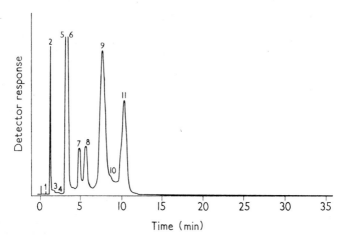

Fig. 16. Chromatogram of Java-type citronella on Carbowax 20M at 190°C. (1) Myrcene. (2) Limonene. (3) *p*-Cymene. (4) Methyl heptenone. (5) Citronellal. (6) Linalool(?). (7) Sesquiterpene "x." (8) Citronellyl acetate. (9) Citronellol and geranyl acetate. (12) Nerol. (11) Geraniol. (Rogers, 1959.)

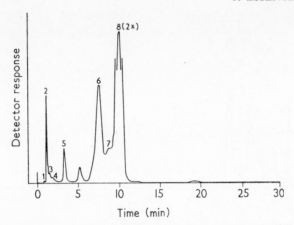

FIG. 17. Chromatogram of Palmarosa E.I. on Carbowax 20M at 190°C. (1) Myrcene. (2) Limonene. (3) *p*-Cymene. (4) Methyl heptenone. (5) Linalool. (6) Geranyl acetate. (7) Nerol. (8) Geraniol. (Rogers, 1959.)

from these oils, and the Java-type oils have been considered superior. In practice the oils are saponified, thus releasing geraniol and citronellol from the esters, and when this is done the total geraniol–citronellol content of the Java types is higher than that of the Ceylon citronella oil. The per cent composition of other components varies between the two types of oil, the aldehyde citronellal, for instance, being present from 32 to 40% in the Java types and only 5.5 to 9% in the Ceylon oil. Palmarosa oil has a different composition from that of the citronella oils, containing 69 to 75% free geraniol and no citronellol.

A Carbowax 20M column with a low packing ratio (5%) also has been used with success for the chromatography of these oils (Rogers, 1961). With column temperatures of 160°C, the elution of components is very rapid. On the Carbowax 20M column with a 30% packing ratio operated at 190°C, the elution time to geraniol is 10.2 minutes; at 160°C with the same 30% packing it is 26.0 minutes; but with the same stationary phase at a 5% packing ratio operated at 160°C, the elution time to geraniol is only 3.8 minutes. Resolution is also very good.

Ucon LB-550-X is another liquid used with success for these essential oils (Rogers, 1959). Its polarity is slightly different from that of Carbowax 20M. On this column geranyl acetate was separated from citronellol, and geranyl butyrate from geraniol, although they were not resolved on Carbowax 20M.

Oil of citronella also has been chromatographed on Reoplex 100 and D.C. 550 silicone (Lamparsky, 1959; Naves and Odermatt, 1958). Separations of citronellal, citronellol, and geraniol were obtained on both columns.

*1. *Chromatography on Carbowax 20M or Ucon LB-550-X* (Rogers, 1961)

Chromatograph	Perkin-Elmer 154-C, two columns in series.
Column dimensions	200 × 0.6-cm o.d. (0.4-cm i.d.) U-shaped Pyrex glass tubing.
Solid support	Chromosorb W (60/80 U. S. mesh), steeped in concentrated HCl, washed neutral with distilled water, washed with 1% alcoholic NaOH, drained, and dried at 125°C. Conditioned at 200°C with nitrogen.
Stationary phase	(I) Carbowax 20M (30:70). (II) Ucon LB-550-X (25:75). (III). Carbowax 20M (5:95).
Temperatures	Injection: (I*a*) 220°C. (I*b*) 190°C. (II) 220°C. (III) 190°C. Column and detector: (I*a*) 190°C. (I*b*) 160°C. (II) 190°C. (III) 160°C.
Carrier gas	Helium at: (I*a*) 42 ml/min. (I*b*) 55 ml/min. (II) 55 ml/min. (III) 67 ml/min. Inlet pressure: 950 mm Hg. Outlet pressure: atmospheric.
Detector	Thermistor operated at 8 volts.
Recorder	Leeds and Northrup, 1 second; 5 mv; 30 inches/hour.
Sample size	4.5 to 6.0 μl.
Analysis time	(I*a*) 10.2 minutes to geraniol. (I*b*) 26.0 minutes to geraniol. (II) 14.6 minutes to geraniol. (III) 3.8 minutes to geraniol.

b. Lemon Grass

Lemon grass oil also is of commercial interest because it contains both

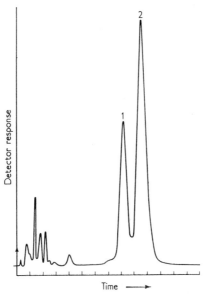

Fig. 18. Chromatogram of lemon grass oil on Reoplex 100 at 180°C. (1) β-Citral. (2) α-Citral. (Lamparsky, 1959.)

α- and β-citral. These have been separated on Reoplex 100 at 180°C (Fig. 18) (Lamparsky, 1959). They are the major components of the oil, and the ratios of the two isomers remain constant in oils from different regions.

Citrals in lemon grass oil have also been separated by Naves and Odermatt (1958) on D.C. 550 silicone at 180°C.

Other substrates that should prove useful in the separation of the oxygenated terpenoids of the Graminae are polar liquid packings stable at high column temperatures such as poly(diethylene glycol succinate), sucrose diacetate hexaisobutyrate, LAC-2-R446, and others discussed in Sections C and G.V.

*1. *Chromatography on Reoplex 100* (Lamparsky, 1959)

Chromatograph	Consolidated Electrodynamics type 26.201.
Column dimensions	180 × 0.45-cm o.d. coiled glass tubing.
Solid support	Celite.
Stationary phase	Reoplex 100 (25:75).
Temperature	180°C.
Carrier gas	Hydrogen at 60 ml/min. Outlet pressure: atmospheric.
Detector	Katharometer.
Recorder	Philips, 3 mv; 0.5 second.
Sample size	2 to 3 μl.
Analysis time	20 minutes.

II. CHROMATOGRAPHY OF ORCHIDACEAE (VANILLA)

The detection of adulteration of commercial vanilla extract is a problem for which gas chromatography has proved useful (Burchfield and Prill, 1959a; Anon., 1961). Vanilla beans sometimes are extracted under conditions other than the Flavoring Extract Manufacturer's Association procedure used to obtain a typical pure vanilla extract. Alkali may be added, and sometimes the temperatures are higher than standard. Synthetic flavors, and extracts from other plant materials may be added as adulterants. The pure extract is diluted with these materials, and it is difficult to detect the adulteration with most analytical procedures. Gas chromatography is a quick and accurate method for the detection of extraction using a menstruum containing alkali, and also for the detection of many foreign botanicals. Paper chromatography can also detect these foreign adulterants (Burchfield and Prill, 1959b).

Since vanillin is present in large amounts in all vanilla extracts, it is removed prior to chromatography so as not to interfere with the separations of minor components (Burchfield and Prill, 1959a). The extracts are treated with 2,4-dinitrophenylhydrazine to precipitate carbonyl compounds.

Authentic samples of extracts of vanilla beans from different parts of the world, treated as described above, revealed chromatograms which were similar. Four main peaks were resolved when the samples were chromatographed

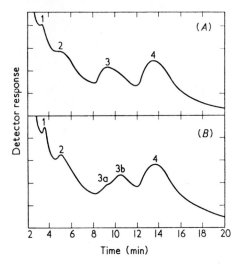

Fig. 19. Chromatograms of the noncarbonyl portion of authentic vanilla bean extracts on Carbowax 1500 at 200°C. (*A*) Type A, Guadeloupes. (*B*) Type B, whole Mexican Buenas. (Burchfield and Prill, 1959a.)

on Carbowax 1500 at 200°C (Fig. 19). Differences were found in the relative peak heights, depending on the types of beans extracted, so the beans were classified as types A, B, or C. Tahiti beans are a different botanical variety from other vanilla beans, and they revealed a different chromatographic pattern (Fig. 20).

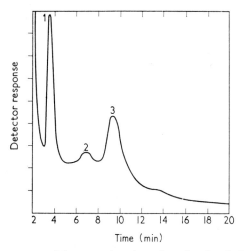

Fig. 20. Chromatogram of the noncarbonyl portion of authentic Tahiti vanilla bean extract on Carbowax 1500 at 200°C. (Burchfield and Prill, 1959a.)

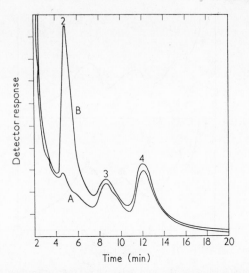

Fig. 21. Effect of alkali used during extraction on the pattern obtained from Bourbon third beans. (*A*) Beans extracted without alkali. (*B*) Beans extracted in the presence of KOH. (Burchfield and Prill, 1959a.)

When vanilla beans were extracted with a menstruum containing alkali instead of the standard alcohol extraction, peak 2 increased and became the predominant peak in the chromatographic pattern (Fig. 21). This is an effective method for the determination of the addition of alkali during the

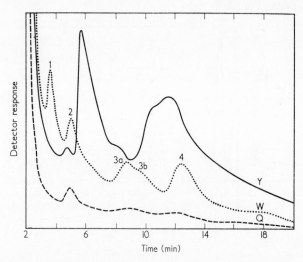

Fig. 22. Chromatograms of the noncarbonyl portion of commercial tenfold vanilla extracts on Carbowax 1500 at 200°C. (Burchfield and Prill, 1959a.)

extraction procedure. The retention volumes for peak 1 of Tahiti extract and peak 2 of this alkali-extracted vanilla are sufficiently different so that they are resolved when chromatographed in admixture.

Often foreign botanicals in vanilla extract can also be detected by gas chromatography. The presence of adulteration in commercial tenfold vanilla extracts was shown by comparison with the chromatograms of authentic extracts (Fig. 22). Tenfold W gave a pattern similar to a type B chromatogram with peak 1 abnormally high, while tenfolds Y and Q gave chromatograms which do not resemble those of any of the authentic extracts.

Vanilla extracts have been examined directly with the hydrogen flame detector (Anon., 1961). The extract is normally made up in ethanol–water. Ethanol, being volatile, passes through the chromatograph rapidly and does not interfere with the vanilla peaks. Water would interfere with most detecting systems. However, the hydrogen flame detector is insensitive to it, so its presence does not interfere in the chromatography of the extract (Fig. 23).

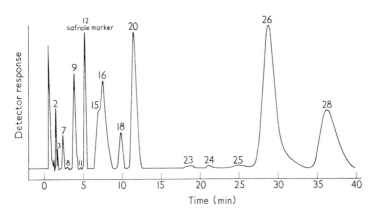

FIG. 23. Chromatogram of Mexican vanilla extract on Carbowax 20M at 200°C, made with a hydrogen flame detector. (Anon., 1961; courtesy of Wilkens Instrument and Research.)

Carbowax 20M at 200°C was used to obtain this chromatogram of Mexican vanilla. Castorwax, which is hydrogenated castor oil, has also been used successfully. Retention times of components are often different on this packing, since it differs in polarity from Carbowax, so additional separations can be obtained. This also aids in the identification of components.

Both Tahitian vanilla extract and imitation vanilla have been chromatographed on these liquids, and typical patterns obtained. For Mexican vanilla, peak 26 is the predominant peak in the extract, and peak 28, vanillin, represents only 13% of the vylatile components (Table VI). Tahitian vanilla

TABLE VI

SEPARATION OF COMPONENTS FROM VANILLA EXTRACTS ON CARBOWAX 20M AT 200°C

Peak	Mexican vanilla		Tahitian vanilla		Imitation vanilla	
	Relative retention time	Per cent	Relative retention time	Per cent	Relative retention time	Per cent
1			0.03	2.04		
2	0.04	9.24	0.04	0.51		
3	0.047	2.84				
4			0.05	1.23		
5					0.056	0.04
6						
7	0.07	3.94				
8	0.08	0.16				
9	0.10	2.76	0.10	1.02	0.10	0.15
10			0.12	5.62		
11	0.13	0.06				
12	0.14	b	0.14	b	0.14	b
13						
14			0.17	2.69		
15	0.19	2.43			0.19	0.17
16	0.21	6.40	0.21	2.17	0.21	0.07
17						
18	0.27	1.56	0.26	0.32	0.28	0.41
19			0.30	13.40		
20	0.32	8.62			0.33	1.35
21					0.37	0.08
22			0.41	29.15		
23	0.52	0.23	0.51	1.21	0.53	0.01
24	0.58	0.19				
25	0.69	0.79			0.72	0.17
26	0.79	48.00	0.79	1.34	0.82	3.40
27					0.90	7.60
28	1.00	12.78	1.00	39.30	1.00	86.55
Total volatiles (μg):		4.9		1.3		36.7

[a] From Anon. (1961).
[b] Safrole, secondary reference.

shows different relative amounts of these two components. Peak 28 comprises 86.5% of the total volatiles, whereas peak 26 contains only 3.4%. There are other striking differences in this extract, thus the peaks numbered 10, 19, and 22 are large and not present in the other extracts. Imitation vanilla also shows differences in numbers and areas of peaks.

*a. Preparation of Carbonyl-Free Extract for Chromatography
(Burchfield and Prill, 1959a)

A 100-ml sample of vanilla extract in 50% ethanol is diluted with an equal volume of water. Three milliliters of 1:1 HCl, 0.8 gm of crystalline 2,4-dinitrophenylhydrazine, and 4 ml of dichloromethane are added. The mouth of the flask is closed with Saran wrap, and the flask is shaken on a rotary shaker for 4 hours. A small portion is removed, filtered, and tested with 2,4-dinitrophenylhydrazine solution to assure that all the carbonyl compounds are bound. If the reaction is complete and no precipitate is formed, 2 ml of dinitrophenylhydrazine reagent is added to the flask, and the flask is shaken for an additional 2 hours with the cover removed to permit the dichloromethane to evaporate. The material from the flask is transferred without filtering to a liquid–liquid extractor and extracted with isopentane for 24 hours at a rate of about 20 ml/min. The isopentane is then carefully evaporated from the extract containing noncarbonyl compounds. The residue is dissolved in 80 μl of AR-grade acetone and is ready for chromatography.

b. Conditions for Chromatography

*1. Of the Noncarbonyl fraction on Carbowax 1500 (Burchfield and Prill, 1959a)

Chromatograph	Perkin-Elmer Vapor Fractometer 154C.
Column dimensions	100 × 0.66-cm o.d. copper U tube.
Solid support	C = 22 firebrick (40/60 U. S. mesh).
Stationary phase	Carbowax 1500 (20:80).
Temperature	200°C. throughout
Carrier gas	Helium at 100 ml/min. Inlet pressure: 15 psig. Outlet pressure: atmospheric.
Detector	Thermistor T/C cell at 8 volts.
Recorder	Leeds and Northrup, 5 mv; 1 second, 30 in./hr.
Sample size	25 μl.
Analysis time	20 minutes.

2. Of the Whole Extract on Carbowax 20M with a Hydrogen Flame Detector (Anon., 1961)

Chromatograph	Aerograph A-100-C.
Column dimensions	⅛-inch × 5-foot stainless steel.
Solid support	C-22 firebrick.
Stationary phase	Carbowax 20M (20:100).
Temperature	200°C.
Carrier gas	Nitrogen at 17.7 ml/min. Hydrogen at 17.7 ml/min.
Detector	Hydrogen flame.
Recorder	Brown, 1.0 mv; 1.0 second per speed.
Sample size	1 μl.
Analysis time	40 minutes.

G. Separation and Fingerprinting of Essential Oils of Angiospermae—Dicotyledoneae

I. CHROMATOGRAPHY OF MYRICACEAE

a. Eucalyptus and Niaouli

The main constituent of the oil of eucalyptus is 1,8-cineole (eucalyptol). This monoterpenoid inner ether is present in 70% and more in many eucalyptus oils from different regions. This oil has been analyzed by GLC, and quantitative measurements of the cineole content have been made on silicone oil at 160°C (Domange and Longuevalle, 1958; Longuevalle, 1960). Niaouli oil has also been chromatographed under the same conditions. Gas chromatography has been found to be superior to the o-cresol method for determination of cineole in oils derived from both genera.

*1. Chromatography on Silicone Oil (Domange and Longuevalle, 1958)

Chromatograph	Griffin and George.
Column dimensions	170 × 0.8 cm.
Solid support	Johns-Manville Celite 545 (120 B. S. mesh).
Stationary phase	E301 silicone (30:70).
Temperature	160°C.
Carrier gas	Nitrogen at 1 liter/min. Inlet pressure: 360 mm Hg. Outlet pressure: 145 mm Hg.
Detector	Katharometer.
Recorder	Honeywell type 153.
Sample size	2 μl.
Analysis time	6 minutes to eucalyptol.

II. CHROMATOGRAPHY OF CANNABINACEAE (HOPS)

a. Humulus

The essential oil of hops consists of about five major components which include a monoterpene hydrocarbon, myrcene, several sesquiterpenes including humulene and caryophyllene, and the oxygenated compound methyl nonyl ketone. There are many minor components also contributing to the flavor of the oil, as well as α-resin acids. The chromatography of these resin acids is discussed in Chapter 6.

The oxygenated fraction of the essential oil comprises roughly 30% of the oil. This fraction contributes more to the flavor and aroma of the oil then the hydrocarbon fraction. Prior to GLC these fractions are often separated by methods such as liquid–solid chromatography on silicic acid (see Section A.II.a). When the silicic acid slurry technique is used, it has been found that the two fractions are not completely separated (Rigby and

Bethune, 1957). Some methyl nonyl ketones and other ketones, not adsorbed on the silicic acid were found in the hydrocarbon fraction. The column method of silicic acid separation (Section A.II.a.1) is preferable, but even here the conditions for elution have to be carefully controlled.

The oxygenated fraction has been chromatographed on Apiezon M at 185°C. This substrate also separates components of the oxygenated fraction obtained from the distillation of hop oil. Substances giving rise to three of the peaks were isolated, the first peak being tentatively identified as the isobutyric ester of 2-methylbutanol.

Polar liquids stable at temperatures from 150° to 200°C should be useful for the separation of the oxygenated fraction also.

The hydrocarbon fraction is sometimes isolated prior to GLC. Mono- and sesquiterpenes are present in this fraction and are found to vary from variety to variety in a characteristic way, some varieties showing as many as nineteen peaks when chromatographed on Apiezon M (Howard and Slater, 1957). Some of the compounds in the hydrocarbon fraction have been separated by GLC and identified (Cassuto, 1960). Among the compounds were myrcene, α-pinene, limonene, a caryophyllene compound, and humulene. Methyl nonyl ketone appeared in this fraction also, indicating again that the silicic acid separation of the hydrocarbon and oxygenated components must be carefully controlled if complete separations are to be obtained.

The complete oil of hops has been chromatographed on both polar and nonpolar substrates. Apiezon M at 170°C has been used by Harold *et al.* (1960) to obtain chromatograms of hop oil for comparison and identification of constituents from beer (Fig. 24). Five components were identified. Hop

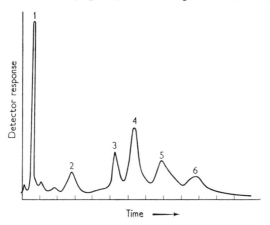

Fig. 24. Chromatogram of Late Grape hop oil on Apiezon M at 170°C. (1) Myrcene(?). (2) Methyl nonyl ketone. (3) Caryophyllene. (4) Humulene. (5) Isocaryophyllene. (6) Farnesene. (7) Oxygenated sesquiterpenes. (Harold *et al.*, 1960.)

oil volatiles have been separated nicely on poly(butanediol succinate) at 145°C. Thirty components were separated in this fingerprint of the oil (Fig. 25) (Anon., 1959b). Silicone separated twenty-one peaks, and asphalt

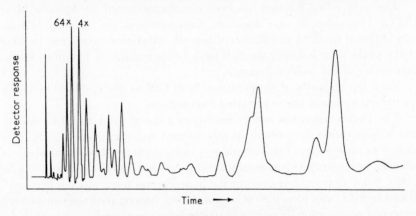

FIG. 25. Chromatogram of hop oil on poly(butanediol succinate) at 145°C. (Anon., 1959b); courtesy of Wilkens Instrument and Research.)

twenty-five. Polar substrates stable in this region of 140° to 150°C will probably separate more components than less polar stationary phases such as the Apiezons and silicones, whether the complete oil, oxygenated, or hydrocarbon fractions are chromatographed.

1. *Chromatography of the Oxygenated Fraction.* See Section C.VII.a for methods which could be adapted to this fraction.

2. *Chromatography of the Hydrocarbon Fraction.* See Sections B.I and B.II for methods which could be adapted to the separation of this fraction.

*3. *Chromatography of the Complete Essential Oil on Poly(butanediol Succinate)* (Anon., 1959)

Chromatograph	Aerograph Model A-110-C.
Column dimensions	300 × 0.635-cm o.d. coiled stainless-steel column.
Solid support	Johns-Manville C-22 firebrick (30/85 U. S. mesh).
Stationary phase	Poly(1,4-butanediol succinate) (20:80).
Temperature	Injector: 260°C. Detector: 145°C. Column: 145°C.
Carrier gas	Helium at 45 ml/min. Inlet pressure: 1200 mm Hg. Outlet pressure: atmospheric.
Detector	Four-filament hot-wire (W) T/C cell at 250 ma.
Recorder	1 mv; 1 second; 0.85 cm/min.
Sample size	1 μl.
Analysis time	60 minutes.

III. Chromatography of Rosaceae (Rose Oils)

a. Rosa

Rose oil is obtained from the fresh flowers of three species of the family: *Rosa damascena* Mill forma *triginitipetala* Dieck, *Rosa alba* L., and *Rosa centifolia* L. Most oil is produced in Bulgaria, Turkey, and North Africa, and some in France.

The principal components of the oil are rhodinol, geraniol, and nerol. Smaller amounts of many other components are also present such as phenylethyl alcohol, linalool, and citrals. In addition, Turkish and Bulgarian rose oils are reported to contain methoxy terpenoid derivatives. Gas chromatography is an excellent method for separating rose oil components for qualitative and quantitative determinations of constituents (Naves, 1958b). It is also the best tool for the separation of rhodinol for the determination of rose oil adulteration. Rhodinol is levorotatory β-citronellol and is a rather uncommon naturally occurring substance. Synthetic citronellol is sometimes added as an adulterant. However, its use can often be detected, since dihydrocitronellol is present as an impurity in the synthetic product and can be resolved by GLC (Fig. 26). When chromatographed on a silicone liquid packing, nerol and rhodinol are eluted together, but adulteration can still

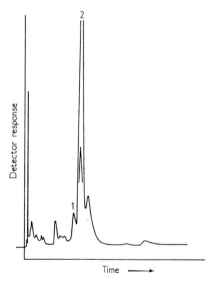

Fig. 26. Chromatogram of Bulgarian rose oil adulterated by addition of synthetic citronellol containing dihydrocitronellol on D.C. 550 silicone at 160°C. (1) Dihydrocitronellol. (2) Rhodinol, nerol, and citronellol. (Naves, 1958b.)

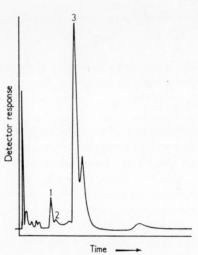

FIG. 27. Chromatogram of authentic Bulgarian rose oil on D.C. 550 silicone at 160°C. (1) n-Nonanal. (2) Phenylethyl alcohol. (3) Rhodinol and nerol. (Naves, 1958b.)

be detected even if the proportions of the major rose oil peaks are the same as those of the natural oil. The nerol–rhodinol peak can be collected and the rotatory power of the rhodinol measured to determine whether it is present in the proper ratio. In authentic rose oils, whether from Bulgaria, Turkey, or Morocco, the ratio of geraniol to nerol ranges from 1 to 1.3, and the ratio

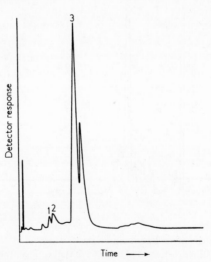

FIG. 28. Chromatogram of authentic Turkish rose oil on D.C. 550 silicone at 160°C. (1) n-Nonanal. (2) Phenylethyl alcohol. (3) Rhodinol and nerol. (Naves, 1958b.)

of rhodenol to geraniol plus nerol ranges from 3 to 4. Characteristic chromatograms of different rose oils are shown in Figs. 27, 28, and 29. Bulgarian

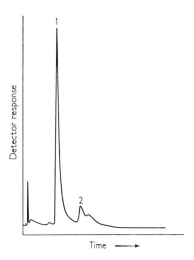

FIG. 29. Chromatogram of distillate of a rose *de mai* absolute from Provence, on D.C. 550 silicone at 160°C. (1) Phenylethyl alcohol. (2) Rhodinol and nerol. (Naves, 1958b.)

rose oil is rich in *n*-nonanal (peak 1) and poor in phenylethyl alcohol (peak 2) compared to Turkish oil where the peaks are about equivalent. The *rose de mai* absolute from Provence shows a different chromatogram with phenylethyl alcohol the predominant peak and the terpene alcohols as minor components.

Chromatograms of Bulgarian rose oil have been obtained on a mixed stationary liquid composed of Silicone S.F. 96 and poly(diethylene glycol succinate) (DEGS) (Broderick, 1961) (Fig. 30). Good fingerprints are obtained with resolution of citronellol, nerol, and geraniol.

*1. *Chromatography on D.C. 550 Silicone* (Naves, 1958b)

Chromatograph	Consolidated Electrodynamics type 26.201
Column dimensions	6-foot × 0.2-inch o.d. coiled glass tubing.
Solid support	Celite.
Stationary phase	D.C. 550 silicone (30:70).
Temperature	160°C.
Carrier gas	Hydrogen at 30 to 40 ml/min measured at exit at atmospheric pressure.
Detector	Katharometer.
Recorder	Philips, 3 mv; 0.5 second.
Sample size	1 to 2 μl.
Analysis time	30 minutes.

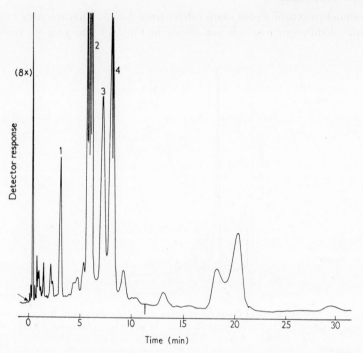

FIG. 30. Chromatogram of Bulgarian rose oil on silicone–DEGS at 171°C. (1) Linalool. (2) Citronellol. (3) Nerol. (4) Geraniol. Attenuation 2× unless otherwise marked. (Broderick, 1961; courtesy of Wilkens Instrument and Research.)

*2. *Chromatography on Silicone–DEGS* (Broderick, 1961)

Chromatograph	Aerograph A-90-C.
Column dimensions	10 feet × ¼ inch.
Solid support	C-22 firebrick.
Stationary phase	Poly(diethylene glycol succinate) (15:85); Silicone S.F. 96, (2.5:97.5); sodium bicarbonate, (1:99).
Temperature	171°C.
Carrier gas	Helium at 55 ml/min measured at outlet. Inlet pressure: 15 psig. Outlet: atmospheric.
Detector	T/C cell (hot wire) at 250 ma.
Recorder	Brown, 1.0 mv; 1.0 second.
Sample size	2 μl.
Analysis time	45 minutes.

IV. CHROMATOGRAPHY OF GERANEACEAE (GERANIUM)

a. *Pelargonium*

Geranium oil is obtained from various species of *Pelargonium*. The main constituents of the oil are the aliphatic alcohols geraniol and citronellol.

Good chromatograms of geranium oil have been obtained on the same mixed packing of silicone–DEGS as used for rose, with a column temperature of 155°C (Fig. 31) (Broderick, 1961). This oil also has been chromatographed

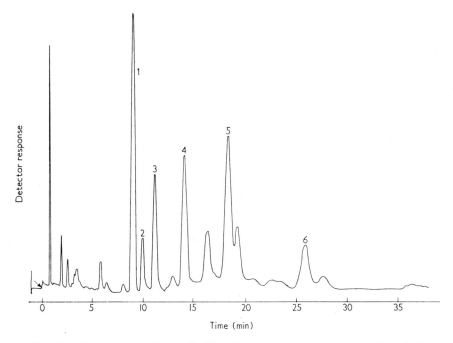

FIG. 31. Chromatogram of the oil of Bourbon geranium on silicone–DEGS at 155°C. (1) Linalool. (2) Menthone. (3) Isomenthone. (4) Citronellyl formate. (5) Citronellol. (6) Geraniol. (Broderick, 1961; courtesy of Wilkens Instrument and Research.)

on Silicone C–lithium capronate (9:1) at 156°C and at 187°C (Bayer *et al.*, 1958). Good resolution of peaks was not obtained under the conditions employed. The major components were found to be citronellol, geraniol, isomenthone, menthone, citronellyl formate, and linalool.

This oil contains oxygenated terpenoids as the major components, and good separations should be obtained at around 130° to 160°C on polar packings stable at high temperatures.

*1. *Chromatography on Silicone–DEGS* (Broderick, 1961)

Chromatograph	Aerograph A-90-C.
Column dimensions	20 feet × ¼ inch.
Solid support	C-22 firebrick.
Stationary phase	Poly(diethylene glycol succinate) (15:85); Silicone S.F. 96, (2.5:97.5); sodium bicarbonate, (1:99).

Temperature	155°C.
Carrier gas	Helium at 46 ml/min. Inlet pressure: 25 psig. Outlet pressure: atmospheric.
Detector	T/C cell (hot wire) at 250 ma.
Recorder	Brown, 1.0 mv; 1.0 second.
Sample size	2 μl.
Analysis time	30 minutes.

V. CHROMATOGRAPHY OF RUTACEAE (CITRUS OILS)

a. Citrus

The oxygenated terpenoids are minor constituents of citrus oils, although they are major contributors to the flavor and aroma of the oils. In lemon oil, for instance, the oxygenated fraction comprises only 4% of the total oil. Preliminary separation of this important fraction is usually necessary before the best chromatographic separations can be obtained for quality control analysis. Methods for preliminary separation of fractions are described in Sections A.II.a and A.II.b. This is a complex oil, and GLC separations are rather tricky. Care must be taken at all times to avoid decomposition and formation of artifacts on the column.

Several stationary phases have been found to give good separations of oxygenated components, including poly(diethylene glycol adipate) partially cross-linked with pentaerythritol (LAC-2-R446), poly(diethylene glycol succinate) (LAC-4-R777 or DEGS), and phenyl diethanolamine succinate (Clark and Bernhard, 1960b; Broderick, 1961). One-year-old raw cold-pressed lemon oil without preservatives added was chromatographed on LAC-2-R446, with thirty major peaks separated (Fig. 32). Many components

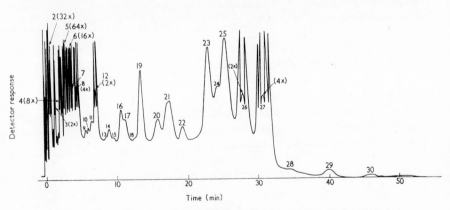

FIG. 32. Chromatogram of the oxygenated fraction of a cold-pressed California lemon oil on LAC-2-R446 at 150°C. For peak identities see Table VII. (Clark and Bernhard, 1960b.)

were identified tentatively by comparisons with the relative retention volumes of known compounds chromatographed under the same conditions (Table VII), and also by an enrichment procedure whereby known compounds were added one at a time to the lemon oil sample, the sample then being rechromatographed.

TABLE VII

RELATIVE CORRECTED RETENTION VOLUMES OF THE COMPONENTS
IN THE OXY FRACTION OF LEMON OIL[a]
(Stationary phase: LAC-2-R446. n-Decanal = 1.00)

| Peak | V_R/V_R^0 | | Compound |
	Unknown	Known	
1	0.065	—	—
2	0.090	—	—
3	0.148	0.148	α-Pinene
4	0.224	0.227	β-Pinene
5	0.289	0.298	Limonene
6	0.354	0.351	Cineole
	—	0.358	γ-Terpinene
7	0.397	—	—
8	0.433	0.435	p-Cymene
9	0.545	0.537	3-Hexen-1-ol
10	0.574	0.571	Methyl heptenone
11	0.617	0.621	Linalyl acetate
12	0.675	0.676	n-Nonanal
13	0.809	—	—
14	0.845	0.840	Octyl acetate
15	0.910	—	—
16	1.00	1.00	n-Decanal
17	1.06	1.06	Linalool
18	1.18	1.18	Citronellyl acetate
19	1.25	—	—
20	1.47	1.47	n-Undecanal
21	1.62	1.61	Geranyl formate
22	1.79	—	Decyl acetate
23	2.13	2.17	n-Dodecanal
24	2.25	2.23	n-Decanol
	—	2.28	α-Terpineol
25	2.35	2.38	Citronellol; neral
26	2.58	2.61	Geranyl acetate
27	2.85	2.89	Citral
28	3.15	3.10	D-Carvone
29	3.68	3.63	$trans$-Carveol
30	4.22	4.24	Geranyl butyrate

[a] From Clark and Bernhard (1960b).

The terpeneless oil of lemon has been chromatographed on phenyldiethanolamine succinate polyester (PDEAS), a column packing that has given good resolution of peaks and has not caused rearrangements of components (Fig. 33) (Broderick, 1961). Since lemon oil is such a complex mixture of compounds, it is difficult to chromatograph it well. The column temperature used here was 175°C, but the temperature can be reduced to as low as 140°C. The time for chromatography is lengthened, but the resolution of some components is more complete. Around eighteen major components were separated at 175°C; at 147°C, twenty-eight peaks were separated (Fig. 34). As with the other chromatograms of "terpeneless" essential oil fractions, the terpenes are not completely removed and are probably represented by the early peaks.

The hydrocarbon fraction of raw expressed lemon oil also was examined by Clark and Bernhard (1960a). It was separated from the oxygenated fraction by the silicic acid slurry technique (Section A.II.a.2). Here again, the substrate poly(diethylene glycol adipate) partially cross-linked with pentaerythritol (LAC-2-R446) was found to give the largest number of peaks (Fig. 35 and Table VIII), with twelve fractions separated. Poly(di-

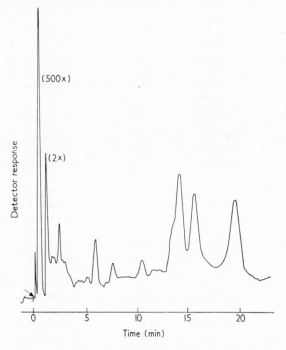

FIG. 33. Chromatogram of the oxygenated fraction of a cold-pressed California lemon oil on PDEAS at 175°C. Attenuation 2× unless otherwise marked. (Broderick, 1961; courtesy of Wilkens Instrument and Research.)

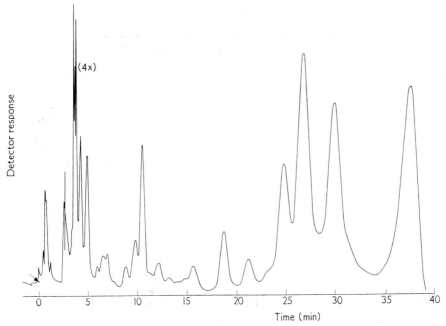

Fig. 34. Chromatogram of the oxygenated fraction of a cold-pressed California lemon oil on PDEAS at 147°C. Attenuation 2× except where marked. (Broderick, 1961; courtesy of Wilkens Instrument and Research.)

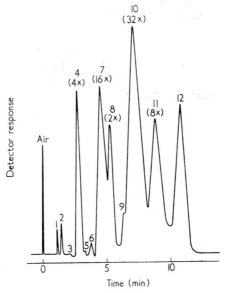

Fig. 35. Chromatogram of the terpene fraction of California lemon oil on LAC-2-R446 at 100°C. For peak identities see Table VIII. (Clark and Bernhard, 1960a.)

TABLE VIII

RELATIVE RETENTION VOLUMES OF THE COMPONENTS IN THE
HYDROCARBON FRACTION OF LEMON OIL[a]
(Stationary phase: LAC-2-R446. α-Pinene $= 1.00$)

Peak	$V_R{}^0/V_R{}^0$		Compound	Per cent composition
	Unknown	Known		
1	0.380	—	—	0.04
2	0.504	—	—	0.03
3	0.732	—	—	0.02
4	1.00	1.00	α-Pinene	2.52
5	1.22	—	—	0.05
6	1.37	1.37	Camphene	0.08
7	1.67	1.67	β-Pinene	20.69
8	1.98	1.96	Myrcene	1.28
9	2.35	2.36	Terpinolene	0.14
10	2.60	2.64	d-Limonene (β-phellandrene)	66.59
11	3.26	3.28	γ-Terpinene	6.88
12	3.99	4.01	p-Cymene	1.68

[a] From Clark and Bernhard (1960a).

ethylene glycol adipate) (LAC-1-R296) separated eleven fractions, and methyl abietate separated eight. The majority of peaks were identified by comparison to retention values of known compounds chromatographed on the same columns under identical conditions as well as by an enrichment procedure in which known terpenes were added one at a time to fresh portions of the terpene fraction and re-examined by GLC.

The unfractionated oil of expressed lemon has been examined as well (Broderick, 1961; Bernhard, 1960). However, more complete resolution of components of this complex oil is obtained by preliminary separations of the hydrocarbon and oxygenated portions of the oil. Figure 36 shows a chromatogram obtained on the complete expressed oil of lemon on PDEAS. This can be compared with Fig. 33, when the terpeneless fraction was chromatographed under the same conditions. With the unfractionated oil, the monoterpene fraction is eluted very rapidly and is not well resolved. The oxygenated portion is fairly well resolved, although there are some sesquiterpenes present which mask oxygenated peaks. To chromatograph the complete oil with good resolution of both the monoterpenes and the oxygenated terpenoids, either temperature programming or two different column temperatures should be employed.

Forty stationary liquid phases were compared for use in the separation

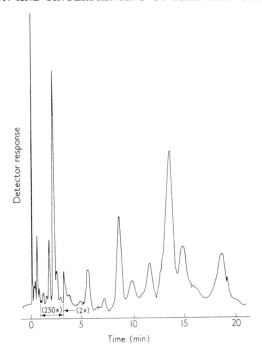

FIG. 36. Chromatogram of the complete cold-pressed California lemon oil on PDEAS at 175°C. Attenuation 2× except where marked. (Broderick, 1961; courtesy of Wilkens Instrument and Research.)

of raw unfractionated cold-pressed lemon oil components, the most extensive systematic survey published up to the present time on comparisons of substrates for essential oil chromatography (Table IX) (Bernhard, 1960). Materials were applied to Sil-O-Cel C-22 firebrick in the amount of 25% by weight.

Several stationary phases were found to give good separations. Again, as with the oxygenated and hydrocarbon fractions, poly(diethylene glycol adipate) cross-linked with pentaerythritol (LAC-2-R446) gave the best separations under the conditions employed, with thirty-two distinct peaks resolved (Fig. 37). Some of these are minor peaks and are not numbered in this chromatogram. Poly(diethylene glycol succinate) (LAC-4-R777) separated twenty-nine fractions, and poly(diethylene glycol adipate) (LAC-1-R296) separated twenty-two. Poly(ethylene glycol adipate) and poly(ethylene glycol succinate) also gave good separation of constituents, with twenty-seven and twenty-two peaks, respectively, being obtained. Glycerol gave fairly good separation, with twenty peaks resolved. Artifacts arising from decomposition of the oil may have occurred on some of these packings, since it has

TABLE IX

STATIONARY LIQUID PHASES EXAMINED FOR USE IN THE SEPARATION
OF UNFRACTIONATED COLD-PRESSED LEMON OIL[a]

Compounds	Source	Relative separation efficiency
Amines		
Triethanolamine	Eastman Kodak Co., Rochester, New York	−
Esters		
Di-*n*-butyl phthalate	Eastman Kodak Co., Rochester, New York	+
Di-*n*-octyl phthalate	Eastman Kodak Co., Rochester, New York	+
Dinonyl phthalate	K & K Laboratories, Inc., Long Island City, New York	++
Di-isodecyl phthalate	Ohio Apex Co., Los Angeles, California	+
Didecyl phthalate	Ohio Apex Co., Los Angeles, California	+
Didecyl adipate	Ohio Apex Co., Los Angeles, California	+
Di-*n*-octyl sebacate	Eastman Kodak Co., Rochester, New York	+
Methyl abietate	Eastman Kodak Co., Rochester, New York	++
Tri(2,6,8-trimethyl-4-nonyl) borate	U. S. Borax and Chemical Corp., Los Angeles, California	−
Sucrose acetate isobutyrate (SAIB)	Eastman Chemical Products, Inc., Kingsport, Tennessee	+
Tricresyl phosphate	Ohio Apex Co., Los Angeles, California	+
Tween 20 (polyoxyethylene sorbitan monopalmitate)	Atlas Powder Co., Wilmington, Delaware	+
Tide	Procter & Gamble Co., Cincinnati, Ohio	−
Craig polyester adipate	Wilkens Instrument and Research, Inc., Walnut Creek, California	+++
Craig polyester succinate	Wilkens Instrument and Research, Inc., Walnut Creek, California	+++
LAC-1-R296	Wilkens Instrument and Research, Inc., Walnut Creek, California	++
LAC-2-R446	Wilkens Instrument and Research, Inc., Walnut Creek, California	++++
LAC-4-R777	Wilkens Instrument and Research, Inc., Walnut Creek, California	++++
Beeswax (chiefly esters of C_{26} and C_{28} acids)		+

TABLE IX (*Continued*)

Compounds	Source	Relative separation efficiency
Glycols		
Glycerol		+++
Silver nitrate in glycerol (saturated solution)		−
Silver nitrate in ethylene glycol (saturated solution)		−
Ethylene glycol		−
Polypropylene glycol	Wilkens Instrument and Research, Inc., Walnut Creek, California	+
Carbowax 400	Union Carbide Chemicals Co., New York, New York	++
Carbowax 600	Union Carbide Chemicals Co., New York, New York	++
Carbowax 1500	Union Carbide Chemicals Co., New York, New York	++
Hydrocarbons		
Mineral oil		+
Squalene	Eastman Kodak Co., Rochester, New York	−
Apiezon L	James G. Biddle Co., Philadelphia, Pennsylvania	+
Apiezon M	James G. Biddle Co., Philadelphia, Pennsylvania	+
Apiezon N	James G. Biddle Co., Philadelphia, Pennsylvania	+
Silicones		
S.F. 96 (40 centistokes)	General Electric Co., Schenectady, New York	+
S.F. 96 (100 centistokes)	General Electric Co., Schenectady, New York	+
D.C. 550	Dow Corning Co., Midland, Michigan	+
Dow 710	Wilkens Instrument and Research, Inc., Walnut Creek, California	+
D.C. high-vacuum grease	Dow Corning Co., Midland, Michigan	+
Miscellaneous		
Flexol Plasticizer 8N8	Beckman Instruments Co., Fullerton, California	+

[a] From Bernhard (1960).

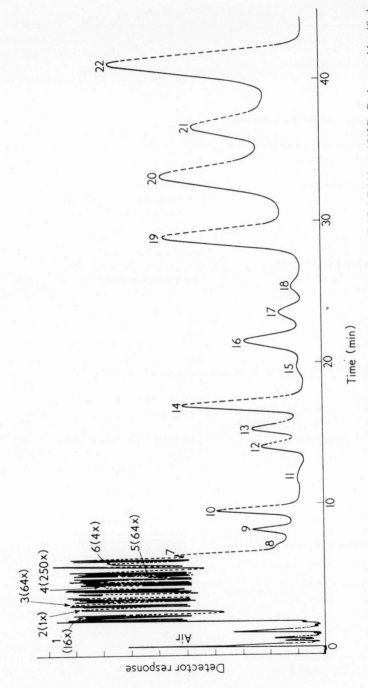

Fig. 37. Chromatogram of an unfractionated cold-pressed California lemon oil on LAC-2-R446 at 150°C. Peaks not identified. (Bernhard, 1960.)

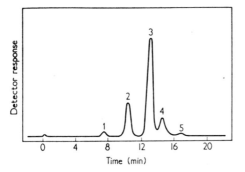

Fɪɢ. 38. Chromatogram of unfractionated cold-pressed lemon oil on Carbowax 600 at 177°C. Peaks not specifically identified. (Bernhard, 1958.)

been found that terpenoid compounds are unstable under some conditions of chromatography (see Section H).

A typical lemon oil chromatogram on a polyethylene glycol (Carbowax 600) column is shown in Fig. 38 (Bernhard, 1958). Fingerprints of twelve authentic domestic oils and nine foreign oils were compared under identical column conditions and the peak height ratios were compared to peak 1 which was adjusted to a peak height value of 1. The variation in peak height ratios for the various authentic samples was about twofold (Figs. 39 and 40).

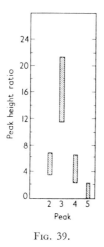

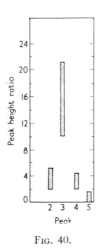

Fɪɢ. 39.   Fɪɢ. 40.

Fɪɢ. 39. Distribution of peak height ratios for twelve authentic samples of domestic lemon oil, compared to peak 1. (Bernhard, 1958.)

Fɪɢ. 40. Distribution of peak height ratios for nine authentic samples of foreign lemon oil, compared to peak 1. (Bernhard, 1958.)

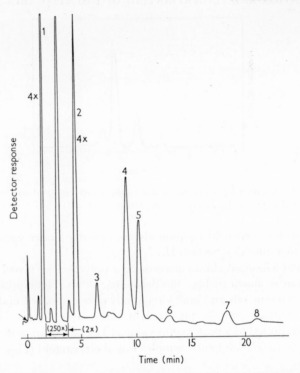

FIG. 41. Chromatogram of cold-pressed Florida orange oil on DEGS at 147°C. (1) Limonene. (2) C_8 aldehyde. (3) C_9 aldehyde. (4) C_{10} aldehyde. (5) Linalool. (6) C_9 alcohol. (7) C_{12} aldehyde. (8) Terpineol. Attenuation $2\times$ except where marked. (Broderick, 1961; courtesy of Wilkens Instrument and Research.)

Adulteration or fortification showed up either as additional peaks or as unusual peak height ratios.

D.C. 550 silicone has been used for the chromatography of citrus oils (Liberti and Cartoni, 1958b). Since this is a relatively nonpolar substrate, not many peaks were separated. However, typical chromatograms were obtained for both lemon and bergamot oils, allowing for easy identification.

Other citrus oils have been chromatographed, and typical fingerprints obtained. These oils are generally not so complex as lemon oil, and the unfractionated essential oil has been used. The expressed oils of Florida orange, Florida grapefruit, and Dominican bitter orange have been chromatographed at 147°C on DEGS (Figs. 41, 42, and 43) (Broderick, 1961). From fifteen to eighteen peaks are resolved, with others partially resolved under the conditions employed. Here again the monoterpenes are a major portion of the oil. Since most interest is in the oxygenated portion, conditions for the best separations of these components are used. Differences in com-

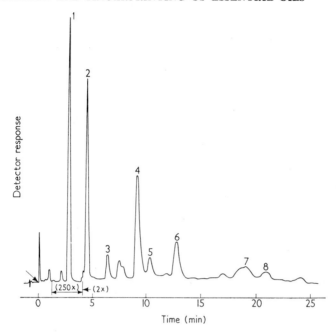

FIG. 42. Chromatogram of cold-pressed Florida grapefruit oil on DEGS at 147°C. (1) Limonene. (2) C_8 aldehyde. (3) C_9 aldehyde. (4) C_{10} aldehyde and C_8 alcohol. (5) Linalool. (6) C_9 alcohol. (7) C_{12} aldehyde. (8) Terpineol. Attenuation $2\times$ except where marked. (Broderick, 1961; courtesy of Wilkens Instrument and Research.)

ponents, and in the relative concentrations of components, are evident from comparisons of these chromatograms.

Oil of lime is usually distilled rather than expressed. This is a rather complex oil, and good fingerprints have been obtained on silicone–DEGS at 150°C (Fig. 44) (Broderick, 1961). The major component is α-terpineol.

The oil of Bigarde neroli is an enfleurage of bitter orange flowers, used in perfumes. When chromatographed on silicone–DEGS it gives a typical chromatogram (Fig. 45) (Broderick, 1961). This cannot be compared directly with the chromatogram for the expressed oil of bitter orange, since the column packings and temperatures are different.

Fingerprints of bergamot oil on Carbowax 1540 have been used to show the presence of foreign adulterants and also the dilution of the oil with terpene constituents already present in natural oil (Theile *et al.*, 1960). Percentage area measurements were used to allow direct comparisons between materials. The ratios of α-pinene to *d*-limonene are particularly critical for detection of dilution of the natural oil, since the addition of lemon oil terpenes lowers the α-pinene values or raises the limonene values (Figs. 46

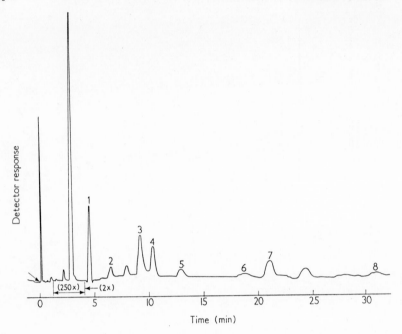

FIG. 43. Chromatogram of cold-pressed Dominican bitter orange oil on DEGS at 147°C. (1) C_8 aldehyde. (2) C_9 aldehyde. (3) C_{10} aldehyde. (4) Linalool. (5) C_9 alcohol. (6) C_{12} aldehyde. (7) Terpineol. Attenuation $2\times$ except where marked. (Broderick, 1961; courtesy of Wilkens Instrument and Research.)

and 47). The area percentage range for the four main components of natural bergamot oil are given in Table X, compared with the chromatographic results obtained on two suspect samples, X and Y.

TABLE X

AREA PERCENTAGE RANGE FOR THE MAIN COMPONENTS OF NATURAL BERGAMOT OIL[a]

Component	Sample X	Sample Y	Authentic oil
α-Pinene	2.1	5.7	7–10
d-Limonene	40.4	37.6	38–46
Linalool	24.1	10.1	17–24
Linalyl acetate	27.3	25.2	22–32
Unknown alcoholic contaminant	—	9.9	None

[a] From Thiele et al. (1960).

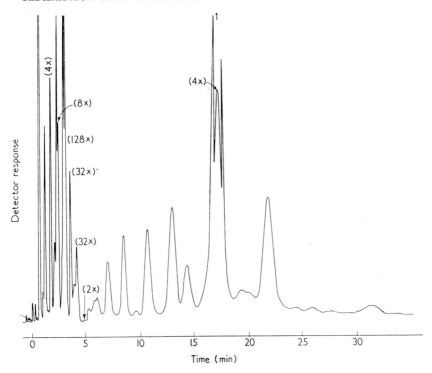

Fig. 44. Chromatogram of distilled oil of Cuban lime on silicone–DEGS at 150°C. (1) α-Terpineol. Attenuation 2× except where marked. (Broderick, 1961; courtesy of Wilkens Instrument and Research.)

*1. *Chromatography of the Oxygenated Fraction of Complete Lemon Oil on PDEAS* (Broderick, 1961)

Chromatograph	Aerograph A-90-C.
Column dimensions	20 feet × ¼-inch o.d.
Solid support	C-22 firebrick.
Stationary phase	Phenyldiethanolamine succinate polyester
Temperature	175°C.
Carrier gas	Helium at 75 ml/min measured at outlet. Inlet pressure: 25 psig. Outlet pressure: atmospheric.
Detector	T/C cell (hot wire) at 250 ma.
Recorder	Brown, 1.0 mv; 1.0 second.
Sample size	20 μl in dichloromethane.
Analysis time	25 minutes.

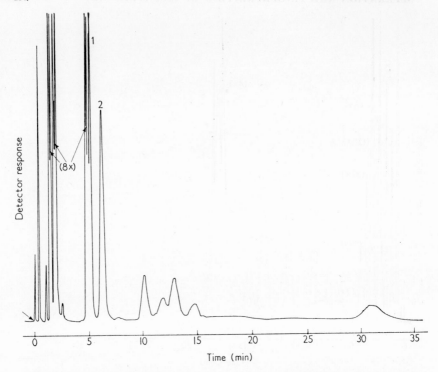

FIG. 45. Chromatogram of Bigarde neroli oil on silicone–DEGS at 150°C. (1) Linalool. (2) Linalyl acetate. Attenuation 2✕ except where marked. (Broderick, 1961; courtesy of Wilkens Instrument and Research.)

*2. *Chromatography of the Oxygenated Fraction of Lemon Oil on LAC-2-R446* (Clark and Bernhard, 1960b)

Chromatograph	Aerograph A-90-C.
Column dimensions	10 feet ✕ ¼-inch o.d.
Solid support	Sil-O-Cel C-22 (30/60 mesh).
Stationary phase	Poly(diethylene glycol adipate) cross-linked with pentaerythritol (20:80).
Temperature	150°C.
Carrier gas	Helium at 90 ml/min. Outlet pressure: atmospheric.
Detector	Four-filament hot-wire T/C cell.
Recorder	1 mv; 30 inches/hour.
Sample size	10 μl.
Analysis time	About 50 minutes.

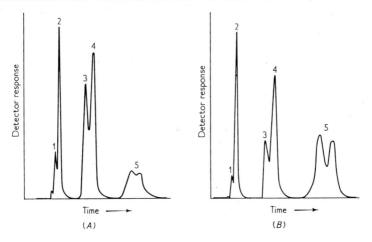

FIG. 46. Chromatograms of bergamot oil on Carbowax 1540 at 175°C. *A*, natural bergamot oil. *B*, bergamot oil reinforced with constituents already present in natural bergamot. (1) α-Pinene. (2) *d*-Limonene. (3) Linalool. (4) Linalyl acetate. (5) Unknown sesquiterpenes. (Theile *et al.*, 1960.)

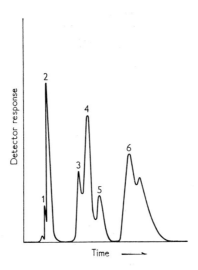

FIG. 47. Chromatogram of bergamot oil adulterated with methyl carbitol. Chromatographed on Carbowax 1540 at 175°C. (1) α-Pinene. (2) *d*-Limonene. (3) Linalool. (4) Linalyl acetate. (5) Methyl carbitol. (6) Unknown sesquiterpenes. (Theile *et al.*, 1960.)

*3. *Chromatography of the Hydrocarbon Fraction of Lemon Oil on LAC-2-R446*
(Clark and Bernhard, 1960a)

Chromatograph	Aerograph A-90-C.
Column dimensions	9-foot × ¼-inch o.d. stainless steel.
Solid support	Sil-O-Cel C-22 (30/60 mesh).
Stationary phase	Poly(diethylene glycol adipate) cross-linked with penta-erythritol (25:75).
Temperature	100°C.
Carrier gas	Helium at 145 ml/min.
Detector	Four-filament hot-wire T/C cell.
Recorder	1 mv.
Sample size	10 μl.
Analysis time	About 12 minutes to *p*-cymene.

*4. *Chromatography of the Complete Essential Oil of Lemon on LAC-2-R446*
(Bernhard, 1960)

Chromatograph	Aerograph A-90-C.
Column dimensions	10 feet × ¼-inch o.d.
Solid support	Sil-O-Cel C-22 firebrick (30/60 mesh).
Stationary phase	Poly(diethylene glycol adipate) cross-linked with penta-erythritol (25:75).
Temperature	150°C.
Carrier gas	Helium at 60 ml/min.
Detector	Four-filament hot-wire T/C cell.
Recorder	1 mv; 30 inches/hour.
Sample size	20 μl.
Analysis time	About 50 minutes.

*5. *Chromatography of the Complete Oil of Orange, Grapefruit, and Bitter
Orange on DEGS* (Broderick, 1961)

Chromatograph	Aerograph A-90-C.
Column dimensions	20 feet × ¼ inch.
Solid support	Celite C-22 firebrick.
Stationary phase	Poly(diethylene glycol succinate) (15:85) and 1% sodium bicarbonate.
Temperature	147°C.
Carrier gas	Helium at 50 ml/min measured at outlet. Inlet pressure: 25 psig. Outlet pressure: atmospheric.
Detector	T/C cell (hot wire) at 250 ma.
Recorder	Brown, 1.0 mv; 1.0 second.
Sample size	15 to 20 μl.
Analysis time	30 minutes.

*6. *Chromatography of the Complete Essential Oil of Lime and Neroli on Sili-
cone–DEGS* (Broderick, 1961)

Chromatograph	Aerograph A-90-C.
Column dimensions	10 feet × ¼ inch.
Solid support	C-22 firebrick.

Stationary phase	Poly(diethylene glycol succinate) (15:85); Silicone S.F. 96, (2.5:97.5); sodium bicarbonate, (1:99).
Temperature	150°C.
Carrier gas	Helium at 65 ml/min. Inlet pressure: 15 psig. Outlet pressure: atmospheric.
Detector	T/C cell (hot wire) at 250 ma.
Recorder	Brown, 1.0 mv; 1 second.
Sample size	1 to 5 μl.
Analysis time	35 minutes.

*7. *Chromatography of the Complete Essential Oil of Bergamot on Carbowax 1540* (Theile *et al.*, 1960)

Chromatograph	Perkin-Elmer Model 154.
Column dimensions	365 × 0.64-cm o.d. aluminum tubing.
Solid support	Chromosorb W (Johns-Manville).
Stationary phase	Carbowax 1540 (30:70).
Temperature	175°C.
Carrier gas	Helium. Inlet pressure: 25 psig. Outlet pressure: atmospheric.
Detector	T/C cell.
Recorder	Leeds and Northrup Speedomax, 5 mv; 1 second.
Sample size	5 μl.
Analysis time	10 minutes.

VI. Chromatography of Oleaceae

a. Jasmin

Jasmin absolutes have been examined by GLC on Silicone D.C. 550 at 160°C, and some of the constituents have been identified (Naves, 1959b). This oil is found to contain benzyl acetate as the major component, with around 70 to 85% of the essence composed of this compound. Linalool is also present as a major constituent, 15 to 25% being present in the oil. Benzyl alcohol is present in small amounts. Linalyl acetate was not detected, although this component was commonly thought to be present in the essence. Many other components such as geraniol, nerol, α-terpineol, and eugenol are found as minor constituents of the oil.

*1. *Chromatography on D.C. 550 Silicone* (Naves, 1959b)

Chromatograph	Consolidated Electrodynamics type 26.201.
Column dimensions	185 × 0.45-cm o.d. coiled glass tubing.
Solid support	Celite.
Stationary phase	D.C. 550 silicone oil (30:70).
Temperature	160°C.
Carrier gas	Hydrogen at 50 to 52 ml/min.
Detector	T/C cell.
Recorder	3 mv; 0.5 second.
Sample size	2 to 3 μl.
Analysis time	About 17 minutes.

VII. CHROMATOGRAPHY OF LABIATAE

a. Salvia (Sage)

The leaves of Salvia officinalis L., Dalmatian sage, contain an essential oil which is an important flavor for seasoning sausages and meat. This oil has been chromatographed on silicone at 190°C, and fifteen peaks have been separated (Fig. 48) (Brieskorn and Wenger, 1960). The bicyclic ketone

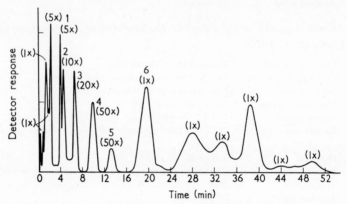

FIG. 48. Chromatogram of Dalmation sage on silicone at 190°C. (1) α-Pinene. (2) β-Pinene. (3) Cineole (linalyl acetate). (4) Thujone. (5) Camphor and borneol. (6) Bornyl acetate. Attenuation of peaks indicated in parentheses. (Brieskorn and Wenger, 1960.)

thujone (peak 4) constitutes about 50% of this oil. Cineole (peak 3), camphor and borneol (peak 5), and α-pinene (peak 1) are also present in amounts of more than 5% each. The attenuations used in obtaining the chromatogram are given in parentheses above each peak.

*1. Chromatography on Silicone (Brieskorn and Wenger, 1960)

Chromatograph	Beckman GC-2.
Column dimensions	180 cm.
Solid support	Kieselguhr.
Stationary phase	D.C. 550 silicone (ratio not given).
Temperature	190°C.
Carrier gas	Hydrogen at 20 psig.
Detector	T/C cell operated at 300 ma.
Recorder	1 mv; 1 second; 1.27 cm/min.
Sample size	30 μl.
Analysis time	About 40 minutes.

b. Thymus (Thyme)

The essential oil of thyme (genus Thymus) contains thymol and carvacrol as the main constituents. These compounds with phenolic structures can be

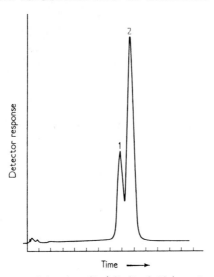

Fig. 49. Chromatogram of the phenolic (alkali-soluble) portion of thyme oil on Reoplex 100 at 200°C. (1) Thymol. (2) Carvacrol. (Naves, 1959a.)

separated from the nonphenolic fraction by extraction with strong alkalis (sodium or potassium hydroxide) (see Section A) and can then be converted to methyl ethers and separated from acids (see Chapter 4, Section B).

This portion of the essential oil has been chromatographed on Reoplex

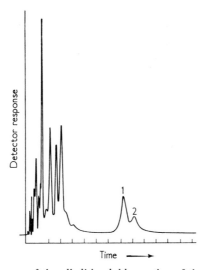

Fig. 50. Chromatogram of the alkali-insoluble portion of thyme oil on Reoplex 100 at 200°C. (1) Thymol. (2) Carvacrol. (Naves, 1959a.)

100 at 200°C, and carvacrol and thymol have been separated (Naves, 1959a) (Fig. 49). The separation factor was 1.1, and resolution was not complete under the conditions employed. Quantitative measurements of the components could be made. Essences from both France and Spain were chromatographed.

The oil fraction not soluble in alkali was chromatographed under the same conditions (Fig. 50). A relatively small percentage of thymol and carvacrol was found in this fraction, peaks 1 and 2, plus other unidentified compounds.

*1. *Chromatography on Reoplex 100* (Naves, 1959a)

Chromatograph	Consolidated Electrodynamics type 26.201.
Column dimensions	200 × 0.48-cm o.d. coiled glass tubing.
Solid support	Celite.
Stationary phase	Reoplex 100 (30:70).
Temperature	200°C.
Carrier gas	Hydrogen at 80 ml/min.
Detector	Katharometer.
Recorder	3 mv; 0.5 second.
Sample size	2 to 3 μl.
Analysis time	About 22.5 minutes to carvacrol.

c. Mentha (Peppermint and Spearmint)

Peppermint oil is a product of considerable commercial importance in many countries. In the United States only the oil from varieties of *Mentha piperita* can be designated as peppermint oil, by a ruling of the U. S. Department of Agriculture. However, some other countries use other species as the source of peppermint oil, and in Japan, China, and Brazil *M. arvensis* is grown commercially. The oils of the different species of peppermint as well as peppermint of the same species grown in different geographical locations can be identified by gas chromatography. Subtle adulteration of the oils also can be detected by this method.

Peppermint oil contains the monoterpenoid alcohol menthol as the major component, with other oxygenated compounds such as menthone, menthofuran, menthyl acetate, and cineole also present, and with terpene hydrocarbons as minor constituents. Menthofuran is of importance in determining the quality of *M. piperita* oil. American oils of the best quality contain 2 to 3% of this constituent, and this small amount is desirable. Some oils contain as much as 10 to 20% menthofuran, resulting in a product of poor quality and flavor.

Menthofuran is well separated from other terpenoid derivatives of naturally occurring peppermint oil on a 2:1 mixture of tetrakis(2-hydroxy-propyl)ethylenediamine (Quadrol) and sucrose diacetate hexaisobutyrate

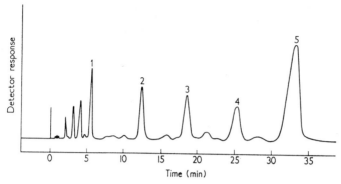

Fig. 51. Chromatogram of the oil of peppermint, American, on Quadrol–SAIB at 140°C. (1) Eucalyptol. (2) Menthofuran. (3) Menthone. (4) Menthyl acetate. (5) Menthol. (Anon., 1960; courtesy of Wilkens Instrument and Research.)

(SAIB) (Fig. 51) (Anon., 1960). Quantitative analysis of components can be made by using the methods for measuring peak area discussed in Chapter 1, and the quality of the oil can be determined. Other column packings have also been used to obtain separations of constituents of this oil. Some of these are listed in Table XI, and the relative retention times of the various components are compared.

TABLE XI

Comparisons of Separations of Peppermint Oil Constituents on Different Column Packings; Relative Retention Time[a]

Compound	Quadrol–SAIB, 140°C	DEGS, 155°C	Quadrol, 144°C	SAIB, 150°C	PDEAS, 125°C
Eucalyptol	0.176	0.219	0.162	0.256	0.200
Menthofuran	0.376	0.694	0.344	0.606	0.566
Peak 15.8	0.478	—	—	—	—
Menthone	0.564	0.755	0.546	0.716	0.758
Peak 21.2	0.653	—	—	—	—
Menthyl acetate	0.770	0.805	0.676	1.090	0.850
Peak 28.3	0.858	—	—	—	—
Menthol	1.000	1.000	1.000	1.000	1.000

[a] From Anon. (1960).

Sucrose diacetate hexaisobutyrate (SAIB) has been used as the liquid substrate at a column temperature of 170°C to obtain chromatograms of dif-

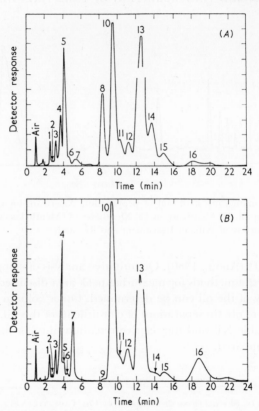

Fig. 52. Chromatogram of (*A*) oil of *Mentha piperita* from the United States—Yakima, and (*B*) oil of *Mentha arvensis* from Japan, chromatographed on SAIB at 170°C. (1) α-Pinene. (2) Camphene. (3) β-Pinene. (4) Limonene. (5) Cineole. (6) *p*-cymene(?). (7) Octanol-3. (8) Menthofuran. (9) Linalool. (10) Menthone. (11) Isomenthone. (12) Neomenthol. (13) Menthol. (14) Menthyl acetate. (15) Pulegone. (16) Piperitone. (Smith and Levi, 1961.)

ferent peppermint oils (Fig. 52) (Smith and Levi, 1961). The percentage composition of components was calculated from peak areas by the method described in Chapter 1, Section H.IV.a.3. The areas of partially resolved peaks can be calculated by this method also.

From these data, the ratios of certain constituents are calculated, which, when plotted against each other, yield information on the identity of species, the ecological conditions under which they are grown, maturity at harvest, and the process of manufacture. Thus the difference between *M. piperita* and *M. arvensis* oils is shown most strikingly by plotting the limonene/cineole ratio versus the menthofuran/"menthone-related constituents"(menthone,

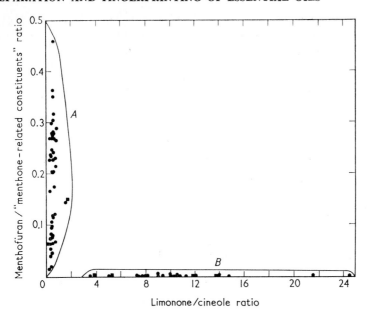

FIG. 53. Identification of (A) M. *piperita* and (B) M. *arvensis* oils. (Smith and Levi, 1961.)

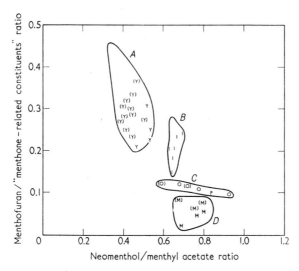

FIG. 54. Identification of M. *piperita* oils grown in different areas. (A) United States—Yakima. (B) Italy. (C) Unites States—Oregon. (D) United States—Midwest. (Smith and Levi, 1961.)

isomenthone, and menthofuran) ratio (Fig. 53). This identification procedure surpasses in reliability the classical chemical identification tests.

Oil of *M. piperita* grown in different geographical areas can be identified by plotting the ratio of neomenthol/menthyl acetate versus mentho-
furan/"menthone related constituents" (Fig. 54). Yakima, Midwestern, and
Oregon oils as well as Italian oils are differentiated.

M. arvensis oils can be classified by plotting the ratio of piperitone/"liquid-oxygenated constituents" (octanol-3, menthone, isomenthone, neomenthol, pulegone, and piperitone) versus menthyl acetate/"liquid-oxygenated
constituents" (Fig. 55). Formosan, Brazilian, Chinese and Japanese oils are
very well separated.

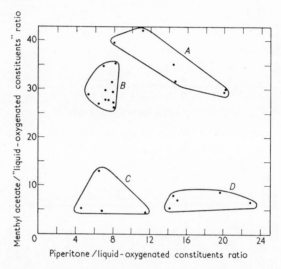

FIG. 55. Identification of *M. arvensis* grown in different areas. (*A*) Formosa. (*B*) Brazil.
(*C*) China. (*D*) Japan. (Smith and Levi, 1961.)

Adulteration can be recognized readily with these same procedures, one
possible exception being the adulteration of authentic *M. arvensis* oils with
small amounts of synthetic menthol. Whether adulteration with menthol
can be detected depends on the original menthol content of the sample.

The addition of *M. arvensis* to *M. piperita* oil also can be detected by comparing the ratios used for the identification of *M. piperita* varieties. The addition of 20 to 30% *M. arvensis* to the Yakima variety of *M. piperita* was detected easily.

This method shows promise for the analysis of other types of essential oils
also, and gas chromatography provides more information about them than
any other technique.

Quality of peppermint oil has also been determined on poly(propylene glycol sebacate) (Lund, 1961). For comparison of commercial oils and detection of adulteration, a temperature of 116°C was used, and a packing ratio of 10% substrate on Celite.

Spearmint oil is also produced commercially, although it is of less importance than the oil of peppermint. It is obtained from *Mentha specata* Huds. varieties. This plant sometimes becomes established in fields of peppermint. Even minor amounts of this oil in peppermint oil greatly reduce its quality. Spearmint oil contains carvone as a major constituent, whereas naturally occurring peppermint oil contains only about 1% of this constituent. This compound is easily separated by gas chromatography, and less than 1% of spearmint oil in peppermint can be detected by GLC (Anon. 1959a). In this case, poly(diethylene glycol succinate) was as the liquid substrate at 200°C.

Fingerprints of Scotch, native, and Midwest varieties of spearmint oil are shown in Figs. 56, 57, and 58 (Broderick, 1961). DEGS at column temperatures of 155°C and 165°C was used to obtain these separations. The

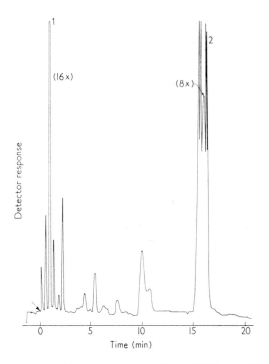

FIG. 56. Chromatogram of Scotch spearmint oil on DEGS at 165°C. (1) Limonene. (2) Carvone. Attenuation 2× except where marked. (Broderick, 1961; courtesy of Wilkens Instrument and Research.)

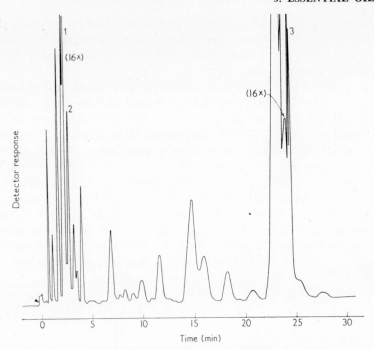

FIG. 57. Chromatogram of native spearmint oil on DEGS at 155°C. (1) Limonene. (2) Cineole. (3) Carvone. Attenuation 2× except where marked. (Broderick, 1961; courtesy of Wilkens Instrument and Research.)

chromatograms show carvone to be the major component of all three oils, although the amounts of other constituents vary.

*1. *Peppermint Oil on SAIB* (Smith and Levi, 1961)

Chromatograph	Burrell K-2 Kromo-Tog equipped with separate heating baths for column and detector.
Column dimensions	7 feet × 0.5-cm i.d.
Solid support	Chromosorb W (60/80 mesh), acid-washed.
Stationary phase	Sucrose diacetate hexaisobutyrate (20:80).
Temperatures	Column: 170°C. Detector: 200°C.
Carrier gas	Helium at 80 (±10) ml/min.
Detector	Hot wire, 200-ma current.
Recorder	½ inch/min.
Sample size	2 to 5 μl.
Analysis time	About 24 minutes.

*2. *Peppermint Oil on Quadrol–SAIB* (Anon., 1960)

Chromatograph	Aerograph A-110-C.
Column dimensions	300 × 0.635-cm o.d. coiled stainless-steel column.

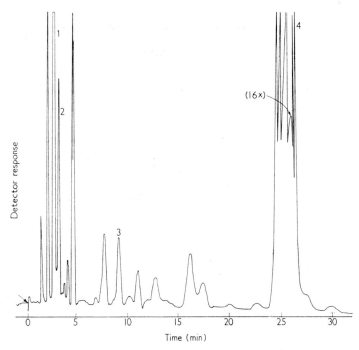

Fig. 58. Chromatogram of Midwest spearmint oil on DEGS at 155°C. (1) Limonene. (2) Cineole. (3) Menthone. (4) Carvone. Attenuation 2✕ except where marked. (Broderick, 1961; courtesy of Wilkens Instrument and Research.)

Solid support	Johns-Manville C-22 firebrick (60/80 U. S. mesh).
Stationary phase	2:1 mixture of tetrakis(2-hydroxypropyl)ethylenediamine and sucrose diacetate hexaisobutyrate (15:85).
Temperatures	Injector: 260°C. Detector: 140°C. Column: 140°C.
Carrier gas	Helium at 100 ml/min. Inlet pressure: 1200 mm Hg. Outlet pressure: atmospheric.
Detector	Four-filament hot-wire (W) T/C cell at 250 ma
Recorder	0 to 1 mv; 1 second; 0.85 cm/min.
Sample size	1 μl.
Analysis time	About 35 minutes.

*3. *Peppermint Oil on DEGS for Detection of Spearmint* (Anon., 1959a)

Chromatograph	Aerograph A-110-C.
Column dimensions	300 ✕ 0.635-cm o.d. coiled stainless-steel column.
Solid support	Johns-Manville C-22 firebrick (60/80 U. S. mesh).
Stationary phase	Poly(diethylene glycol succinate) (15:85).
Temperatures	Injector: 260°C. Detector: 200°C. Column: 200°C.
Carrier gas	Helium at 50 ml/min. Inlet pressure: 1200 mm Hg. Outlet pressure: atmospheric.

Detector	Four-filament hot-wire (W) T/C cell at 200 ma.
Recorder	0 to 1 mv; 1 second; 0.85 cm/min.
Sample size	1 μl.
Analysis time	Less than 12 minutes.

*4. *Peppermint Oil on Poly(propylene Glycol Sebacate)* (Lun, 1961)

Chromatograph	Laboratory-built.
Column dimensions	Four 400 × 1.0-cm o.d. U-shaped glass tubes.
Solid support	Celite 545 (60/80 British mesh).
Stationary phase	Poly(propylene glycol sebacate) (10:90).
Temperatures	116°C throughout.
Carrier gas	Argon at 75 ml/min. Inlet pressure: 1140 mm Hg. Outlet pressure: atmospheric.
Detector	Argon ionization detector supplied by Gas Chromatography Ltd.
Recorder	0 to 3 mv; 1 second.
Sample size	0.2 μl.
Analysis time	90 minutes.

d. Lavendula (*Lavender and Lavandin*)

Three species of the genus *Lavendula* are commonly used as commercial sources of essential oils. They are (1) *Lavendula officinalis chaix* (lavender), (2) *Lavendula latifolia* Vill. (spike lavender), and (3) *Lavendula hybrida* Reverchon, commonly called lavandin, which is a cross between the other two species. These species all contain linalool and linalyl acetate as the main constituents of the oil, although the ratio of the two varies with the species. Lavender oil of highest quality contains about 50% linalyl acetate; the oil of lavandin contains a higher percentage of linalool; and spike lavender contains linalool as the major component with very little linalyl acetate.

The constituents of these essential oils have been separated by GLC. The complete essential oil is usually chromatographed. The oils can be identified easily from comparisons of fingerprints of the three types. Adulteration as well as quality of the oil can be detected in the same way.

Components of the essential oils of both lavender and lavandin are well separated on Quadrol–SAIB (2:1) at 136°C (Broderick, 1960). No decomposition occurs, and linalool and linalyl acetate are completely resolved under the conditions employed (Fig. 59). Camphor and cineole are well separated, and other minor constituents are resolved as well.

Naves (1958a) has compared the oils of lavender and of lavandin on D.C. 550 silicone at 160°C (Fig. 60). He found the same components in each oil, with linalyl acetate the major fraction, but the percentage composition of compounds in the two oils differed. There is a striking difference in the amount of camphor (peak 3). Lavandin contains this compound as a major component, while it is present if at all as a very minor constituent in

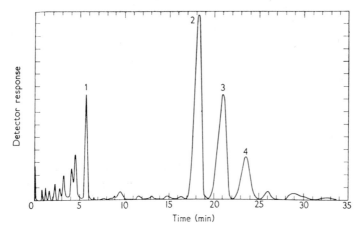

FIG. 59. Chromatogram of lavandin on Quadrol–SAIB at 136°C. (1) Cineole. (2) Linalool. (3) Linalyl acetate. (4) Camphor. (Broderick, 1960; courtesy of Wilkens Instrument
and Research.)

the oil of lavender and is seen only as a small shoulder on the peak representing borneol and α-terpineol. The linalool content of two oils also differs
considerably (peak 1), a much higher per cent being present in the lavandin.

When these oils are compared on squalane, camphor is not detected in
lavender oil, although it is present in the oil of lavandin (Naves, 1959c). It

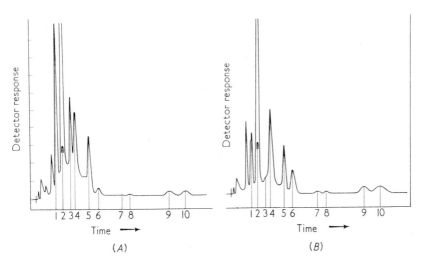

FIG. 60. Chromatograms of (A) lavandin and (B) lavender on Silicone D.C. 200 at
160°C. (1) Linalool. (2) Linalyl acetate. (3) Camphor. (4) Borneol and terpineol. (5) Geraniol. (6) Bornyl acetate. (7) Terpenyl acetate. (8) Geranyl acetate. (Naves, 1958a.)

is also established that true oils of lavender and lavandin contain no bornyl acetate, although they do contain more than 1.8% of the free alcohol borneol. Bornyl acetate is often present in commercial oils.

Other polar substrates stable at temperatures up to about 140° to 150°C should give good separations of lavender and lavandin oils—substrates such as poly(diethylene glycol succinate) (LAC-2-R446), poly(ethylene glycol adipate), and others discussed in Sections C and G.V.a.

*1. *On Quadrol–SAIB* (Broderick, 1960)

Chromatograph	Aerograph A-110-C.
Column dimensions	300 × 0.635-cm o.d. coiled stainless-steel tubing.
Solid support	Johns-Manville C-22 firebrick (60/80 U. S. mesh).
Stationary phase	2:1 mixture of N,N,N^1,N^1-tetrakis(2-hydroxypropyl)-ethylenediamine and sucrose diacetate hexaisobutyrate (15:85).
Temperatures	Injector: 260°C. Detector: 140°C. Column: 140°C.
Carrier gas	Helium at 100 ml/min. Inlet pressure: 1200 mm Hg. Outlet pressure: atmospheric.
Detector	Four-filament hot-wire (W) T/C cell at 250 ma.
Recorder	1 mv; 1 second; 0.85 cm/min.
Sample size	1 μl.
Analysis time	35 minutes to menthol.

*2. *On D.C. 550 Silicone* (Naves, 1958a)

Chromatograph	Consolidated Electrodynamics type 26.201.
Column dimensions	180 × 0.45-cm o.d. coiled glass tubing.
Solid support	Celite.
Stationary phase	D.C. 550 Silicone oil (30:70).
Temperature	160°C.
Carrier gas	Hydrogen at 30 ml/min.
Detector	Katharometer.
Recorder	3 mv; 0.5 second.
Sample size	2 μl.
Analysis time	35 minutes.

H. Rearrangements of Terpenoid Compounds during Gas Chromatography

Many components of essential oils are unstable and easily undergo catalytic dehydration or isomerization at elevated temperatures. These reactions most often take place at acid centers on the solid support or on the walls of the column itself. "Acid centers" have been reported even in some liquid phases. As the temperature is raised, these reactions take place much more readily than at lower temperatures. Thus, in chromatographing these unstable compounds the temperatures should be kept as low as possible, and special precautions must be taken.

Chemical rearrangements can take place in the thermal conductivity cell or exit heater if these are heated to temperatures higher than the column, or if a hot-wire detector is used (Howard and Stevens, 1960; Naves, 1958c). However, unless samples are collected for further work, decomposition after separation on the column will not affect the chromatographic data obtained. A gas density balance held at column temperature would avoid decomposition at the detector, and, if the exit line is also kept at column temperature, samples could be collected with no decomposition occurring beyond the column exit.

Many solid supports such as crushed firebrick and diatomaceous earth contain active acid sites unless specially treated. It has been shown that these are centers for decomposition of terpenes and oxygenated terpenoids (Mitzner and Jacobs, 1960; Zubyk and Conner, 1960; Vilkas and Abraham, 1959).

When untreated C-22 firebrick was coated with silicone and used to chromatograph pure β-pinene at 125°C, complete isomerization of the monoterpene took place (Vilkas and Abraham, 1959) (Fig. 61, curve A). α-Pinene,

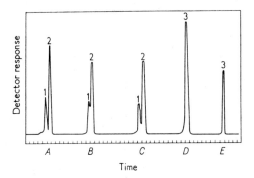

FIG. 61. Decomposition of β-pinene on solid supports. Chromatographed at 125°C on: (A) C–22 firebrick coated with silicone. (B) Used C–22 firebrick–silicone column. (C) Celite–silicone column. (D) Used Celite–silicone column. (E) C–22 firebrick–polyethylene glycol column. (1) α-Pinene and camphene. (2) Limonene. (3) β-Pinene. (Vilkas and Abraham, 1959.)

camphene, and limonene were obtained. Celite gave the same results (curve C). After 100 hours of use, however, the active sites on the Celite column were apparently deactivated, and chromatographs of β-pinene gave only one peak, corresponding to the unchanged compound (curve D). When a polar substrate, polyethylene glycol, was coated on C-22 firebrick, the acid centers were deactivated, probably by hydrogen bonding with the liquid substrate, and β-pinene was chromatographed without decomposition on the column. A large amount of pure β-pinene was passed through a column containing untreated C-22 firebrick or Celite at 125°C. The decomposition mixture was then chromatographed on the polar polyethylene glycol substrate supported on firebrick, which in this case was deactivated by the stationary phase (Fig. 62). The components separated were α-pinene (30%),

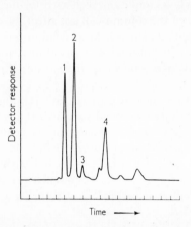

FIG. 62. Chromatogram of decomposition products of β-pinene chromatographed on polyethylene glycol at 125°C. (1) α-Pinene. (2) Camphene. (3) β-Pinene. (4) Limonene. (Vilkas and Abraham, 1959.)

camphene (40%), limonene (15%), β-pinene (5%), and four unidentified constituents (10%). Zubyk and Conner (1960) found that β-pinene and α-pinene also will decompose on many substrates. When β-pinene was chromatographed on active substrates, α-pinene, camphene, dipentene, and α-terpinene were formed. When α-pinene was chromatographed, several new peaks appeared.

Terpenoid alcohols are dehydrated when active acid sites are present on the support, and precautions must be taken similar to those used for prevention of isomerization in order to forestall dehydration (Mitzner and Jacobs, 1960)

"Acid centers" have been reported in some liquid substrates (Zubyk and Conner, 1960). Some samples of didecyl phthalate, for example, were found to possess sufficient acidity to isomerize α- and β-pinene.

Acid sites on the solid support can be deactivated by washing the support with sodium carbonate prior to coating (Vilkas and Abraham, 1959; Mitzner and Jacobs, 1960). Another alternative is to add a small amount of a basic material to the stationary liquid, such as diethanolamine (Mitzner and Jacobs, 1960). When polar packings are used, they often form hydrogen bonds with the active sites on the solid support, thus deactivating them (Vilkas and Abraham, 1959).

Another alternative is to use supports that do not contain active sites.

Certain chromosorbs have been found to be inactive, such as Chromosorb C-48560, a flux calcined aggregate (Zubyk and Conner, 1960), and Chromosorb W. Ground unglazed white tile is another support found to be inert (Lukeš et al., 1960). This support is made by crushing unglazed tile, screening to 0.2 to 0.3 mm, washing with water, drying, and igniting at 300°C. Other supports that have been tried are quartz sand and sodium chloride (Naves, 1958c). One disadvantage to these materials—the unglazed white tile, sand, and sodium chloride—is that they are less porous than other types of support and do not retain as much of the liquid phase. Thus sodium chloride retains only 5% silicone grease, and ground unglazed tile retains a maximum of 18% of the liquid substrate. The optimum concentration of tricresyl phosphate on this latter support is 7 to 10% for the best separation of a mixture of monoterpenes (Lukeš et al., 1960). The resolution is the same as for 20% tricresyl phosphate on Sterchamol at the same column temperature (Table XII).

TABLE XII

COMPARISON OF GROUND UNGLAZED TILE AND STERCHAMOL AS SOLID SUPPORTS FOR GLC[a]

Support	Tricresyl phosphate (%)	TP^b for Δ^3-Cacene	Column resolution[c] A	B	Pressure in column (mm Hg) Inlet	Outlet
Ground unglazed tile	5	1536	1.25	0.58	446	193
	7	2270	1.41	0.94	401	207
	10	1025	1.12	0.82	670	455
	13	868	0.98	0.73	416	210
	18	712	0.88	0.64	671	359
Sterchamol	20	1745	1.53	0.93	671	621

[a] From Lukeš et al. (1960).

[b] Calculated by the method recommended by the Committee of the 1st Symposium on Vapour Phase Chromatography, London, 1956.

[c] A, calculated by the method recommended by the Committee of the 2nd Symposium on Gas Chromatography, Amsterdam, 1958. B, calculated by the method of Struppe.

Another possible location of catalytic decomposition of essential oils is the wall of the chromatographic column itself (Zubyk and Conner, 1960). Glass and stainless-steel columns are inert, but copper columns, when filled with a nonisomerizing packing, cause isomerization of α- and β-pinene.

Capillary columns present several advantages for the analysis of trace quantities of materials in essential oils, but here also it has been found that decomposition of compounds takes place unless precautions are used. With capillary columns the wall itself is coated with the liquid substrate and is the support for the substrate. It has been found that dehydration of terpenoid alcohols takes place quantitatively on some commercially prepared stainless-steel capillary columns (Mitzner and Jacobs, 1960). There are "acid centers" present on the inner wall of the tubing that must be deactivated before use. One partially successful method of remedying this is to pass a small amount of amine through a coated column to deactivate the acid sites. A more successful method is to clean the column prior to coating to remove all traces of flux residues that might be present. A cleaning procedure has been developed with detergents, alkali, and various organic solvents. This procedure is given in detail in Chapter 1.

In summary, many of the unsaturated and oxygen-containing terpenoids found in essential oils are chemically unstable at high temperatures. Special precautions must be taken to remove all possible catalytic centers of decomposition in the chromatographic system, and temperatures should be kept as low as possible. "Acid centers" are sites of catalytic breakdown and are found on many untreated supports as well as on the column itself. These must be removed or deactivated before chromatography.

References

Anon. 1959a. Spearmint contamination in peppermint oil. Aerograph Research notes, Form 30. Wilkens Instr. and Research, Inc., Walnut Creek, California.

Anon. 1959b. Hop oil—volatiles. Aerograph Research Notes, Spring Issue. Wilkens Instr. and Research, Inc., Walnut Creek, California.

Anon. 1960. Oil peppermint, American. Aerograph Research Notes, Winter Issue. Wilkens Instr. and Research, Inc., Walnut Creek, California.

Anon. 1961. Aromatics of vanilla. Aerograph Research Notes, Spring Issue. Wilkens Instr. and Research, Inc., Walnut Creek, California.

Bayer, E., G. Kupfer, and K.-H. Reuther. 1958. Anwendung der Gaschromatographie zur Analyse künstlicher und natürlicher Aromastoffe. Z. anal. Chem. 164: 1–10.

Bernhard, R. A. 1958. Examination of lemon oil by gas partition chromatography. Food Research 23: 213–216.

Bernhard, R. A. 1960. Stationary liquid phases for use in gas-liquid chromatography suitable for the separation of essential oils. Food Research 25: 531–537.

Bernhard, R. A. and A. G. Marr. 1960. The oxidation of terpenes. I. Mechanism and reaction products of D-limonene autoxidation. Food Research 25: 517–530.

Brieskorn, C.-H. and E. Wenger. 1960. Analyse des ätherischen Salbeiöles mittels Gas- und Dünnschicht-Chromatographie. II. Mitteilung über die Inhaltsstoffe von Salvia off. L. Arch. Pharm. 293: 21–26.

Broderick, J. J. 1960. Linalool and linalyl acetate. Aerograph Research Notes, Fall Issue. Wilkens Instr. and Research, Inc., Walnut Creek, California.

Broderick, J. J. 1961. Personal communication.

Burchfield, H. P. and E. A. Prill. 1959a. Characterization of the noncarbonyl volatiles of vanilla by gas chromatography. Contribs. Boyce Thompson Inst. 20: 217–230.

Burchfield, H. P. and E. A. Prill. 1959b. Characterization of vanilla and other plant extracts by paper chromatography. *Contribs. Boyce Thompson Inst.* **20:** 251–264.

Carruthers, W. and R. A. W. Johnstone. 1960. Some phenolic constituents of cigarette smoke. *Nature* **185:** 762–763.

Cartoni, G. P. and A. Liberti. 1960. Gas chromatography of oxygen-containing terpenes. *J. Chromatog.* **3:** 121–124.

Cassuto. 1960. Vapor chromatography applied to the resins and essential oils of hops. *Brasserie* **15:** 40–45, 64–70.

Clark, J. R. and R. A. Bernhard. 1960a. Examination of lemon oil by gas-liquid chromatography. II. The hydrocarbon fraction. *Food Research* **25:** 389–394.

Clark, J. R. and R. A. Bernhard. 1960b. Examination of lemon oil by gas-liquid chromatography. III. The oxygenated fraction. *Food Research* **25:** 731–738.

Clements, R. L. 1958. Low temperature chromatography as a means of separating terpene hydrocarbons. *Science* **128:** 899–900.

Crisler, R. O. and C. L. Benford. 1959. Analysis of ionones and methylionones by gas-liquid partition chromatography. *Anal. Chem.* **31:** 1516–1518.

Cvrkal, H. and J. Janák. 1959. Anwendung der Gaschromatographie zur Identifizierung einiger Terpene aus ätherischen Ölen von Nadelbäumen (*Coniferae*). *Collection Czechoslov. Chem. Communs.* **24:** 1967–1974.

Domange, L. and S. Longuevalle. 1958. Dosage de l'eucalyptol dans les essences d'eucalyptus et de niaouli par chromatographie de partage gaz-liquide. *Ann. pharm. franç.* **16:** 557–561.

Harold, F. V., R. P. Hildebrand, A. S. Morieson, and P. J. Murray. 1960. Influence of hop oil constituents on the flavour and aroma of beer. *J. Inst. Brewing* **66:** 395–398.

Holness, D. 1959. The determination of linalool: a comparative study of the Glichitch and Fiore methods by gas-liquid partition chromatography. *Analyst* **84:** 3–10.

Holness, D. 1961. Personal communication.

Howard, G. A. and C. A. Slater. 1957. Evaluation of hops. VII. Composition of the essential oil of hops. *J. Inst. Brewing* **63:** 491–506.

Howard, G. A. and R. Stevens. 1960. The thermal isomerization of methyl geranate and dihydromyrcene. *J. Chem. Soc.*, pp. 161–163.

Kelkar, N. C. and B. S. Rao. 1934. Studies in Indian essential oils. VI. Essential oil from the rhizomes of *Acorus calamus*, Linn. *J. Indian Inst. Sci.* **17A:** 25–31.

Kirchner, J. G. and J. M. Miller. 1952. Preparation of terpeneless essential oils. A chromatographic process. *Ind. Eng. Chem.* **44:** 318–321.

Lamparsky, D. 1959. Die Anwendung der Gaschromatographie in der Analyse der ätherischen Öle. *Riechstoffe u. Aromen* **9:** 241–245.

Langenau, E. E. 1948. The examination and analysis of essential oils, synthetics, and isolates. *In* "The Essential Oils" (E. Guenther), Vol. I, pp. 229–367. Princeton, New Jersey, Van Nostrand.

Liberti, A. and G. P. Cartoni. 1958a. Cromatografia in fase gassosa degli idocarburi terpenici. *Ricerca sci.* **28:** 1192–1198.

Liberti, A. and G. P. Cartoni. 1958b. Analysis of essential oils by gas chromatography. *In* "Gas Chromatography." (D. H. Desty, ed.), pp. 321–328. New York, Academic Press.

Longuevalle, S. 1960. "Chromatographie de partage gaz-liquide: Applications au contrôle des médicaments," 125 pp. Paris, Société d'éditions d'enseignement supérieur.

Lukeš, V., R. Komers, and V. Herout. 1960. Ground unglazed tile—a new support for gas-liquid chromatography. *J. Chromatog.* **3:** 303–307.

Lund. N.A. 1961. Personal communication.

Mitzner, B. M. and M. Jacobs. 1960. The application of capillary column gas chromatography to the essential oil industry. Abstr. of Papers, 137th Am. Chem. Soc. meeting, April: No. 34B, 35B.

Motl, O., V. Herout, and F. Sorm. 1960. On terpenes. CXII. The composition of the oil from *Juniperus oxycedrus* L. berries. *Collection Czechoslov. Chem. Communs.* 25: 1656–1661.

Naves, Y.-R. 1958a. Sur les distinctions analytiques entre essence de lavande et essence de lavandin. *Compt. rend. acad. sci.* 246: 2163–2165.

Naves, Y.-R. 1958b. On the analysis of rose oils by vapourphase partition chromatography and by infra-red spectroscopy. *Perfumery Essent. Oil Record* 49: 290–296.

Naves, Y.-R. 1958c. Some remarks on the nature of the fixed phase or of the carrier in gas-liquid partition chromatography of essential oils and aromatics. *J. Soc. Cosmetic Chemists* 9: 101–103.

Naves, Y.-R. 1959a. Analyse d'essences de thym par la chromatographie de partition vapeurs-liquide. *France et ses parfums*, February issue, pp. 23–27.

Naves, Y.-R. 1959b. Etude sur les matières végétales volatiles. CLV. Sur la composition de l'essence absolue de jasmin. *Helv. Chim. Acta* 42: 1237–1238.

Naves, Y.-R. 1959c. Etudes sur les matières végétales volatiles. CLXIII. Présence de bornéol et de camphre, mais non d'acétate de bornyle dans les huiles essentielles de lavande et de lavandin. *Helv. Chim. Acta* 42: 2744–2746.

Naves, Y.-R. and A. Odermatt. 1958. Sur l'analyse des huiles essentielles par la chromatographie vapeurs-liquide, en général, et sur celle des huiles essentielles de citronelle et de lemongrass en particulier. *Compt. rend. acad. sci.* 247: 687–689.

Naves, Y.-R., P. Ardizio, and L. Favre. 1958. Etude sur les matières végétales volatiles. 150. Isolément et charactérisation du *cis*-anéthole. *Bull. soc. chim. France*,. 566–569.

Ofner, A., W. Kimel, A. Holmgren, and F. Forrester. 1959. Synthetisches Nerolidol und verwandte C₁₅-Alkohole. *Helv. Chim. Acta* 42: 2577–2584.

Paul, A., A. S. Bawdekar, R. S. Joshi, G. H. Kulkarni, A. S. Rao, G. R. Kelkar, and S. C. Bhattacharyya. 1960. Terpenoids XX. Examination of costus root oil. *Perfumery Essent. Oil Record* 51: 115–120.

Petrowitz, H. J., F. Nerdel, and G. Ohloff. 1960. Zur Gasverteilungschromatographie stereoisomerer Menthole. *J. Chromatog.* 3: 351–358.

Popják, G. and R. H. Cornforth. 1960. Gas-liquid chromatography of allylic alcohols and related branched-chain acids. *J. Chromatog.* 4: 214–221.

Rigby, F. L. and J. L. Bethune. 1957. Analysis of hop oil by gas-liquid partition chromatography. *J. Inst. Brewing* 63: 154–161.

Rogers, J. A., Jr. 1959. Instrumental evaluation of citronella oils and palmarosa oil-geraniol, citronellol and other constituents. *Proc. Sci. Sect. Toilet Goods Assoc.* 32 (Dec.): 9–13.

Rogers, J. A., Jr. 1961. Personal communication.

Runeberg, J. 1960a. The chemistry of the natural order cupressales. XXVII. Heartwood constituents of *Juniperus utahensis* Lamm. *Acta Chem. Scand.* 14: 797–804.

Runeberg, J. 1960b. The chemistry of the natural order *Cupressales*. XXVIII. Constituents of *Juniperus virginiana* L. *Acta Chem. Scand.* 14: 1288–1294.

Smith, D. M., J. C. Bartlet and L. Levi. 1960. Sucrose acetate isobutyrate as a new ester liquid phase for gas-liquid partition chromatography. *Anal. Chem.* 32: 568–569.

Smith, D. M. and L. Levi. 1961. Treatment of compositional data for the characterization of essential oils. Determination of geographical origins of peppermint oils by gas chromatographic analysis. *J. Agr. Food Chem.* 9: 230–244.

Stahl, E. and L. Trennheuser. 1960. Gasphasenchromatographie von Terpen- und Hydroxyphenylpropankörpern. *Arch. Pharm.* **293:** 826–837.

Stanley, W. L., R. M. Ikeda, S. H. Vannier, and L. A. Rolle. 1961. Determination of the relative concentrations of the major aldehydes in lemon, orange and grapefruit oils by gas chromatography. *J. Food Sci.* **26:** 43–48.

Sterrett, F. S. 1949. The preparation of derivatives of essential oil constituents. 1949. *In* "The Essential Oils" (E. Guenther), Vol. II, pp. 771–833. Princeton, New Jersey, Van Nostrand.

Tagaki, W. and T. Mitsui. 1960. Analysis of isomeric menthols by gas chromatography. *Bull. Agr. Chem. Soc. Japan* **24:** 217–218.

Theile, F. C., D. E. Dean, and R. Suffis. 1960. A modern approach to the evaluation of bergamot oil. *Am. Perfumer Aromat.* **75:** 103–107.

Vilkas, M. and N. A. Abraham. 1959. Sur un cas d'isomérisation en chromatographie gazeuse. *Bull. soc. chim. France;* 1651–1652.

von Rudloff, E. 1960. The separation of some terpenoid compounds by gas-liquid chromatography. *Can. J. Chem.* **38:** 631–640.

Zubyk, W. J. and A. Z. Conner. 1960. Analysis of terpene hydrocarbons and related compounds by gas chromatography. *Anal. Chem.* **32:** 912–917.

Chapter 6

Resin Acids

General Introduction

This chapter includes two types of compound, both of which are commonly called resin acids. The resin acids from pine rosin are diterpenoid carboxylic acids of the abietic and pimaric types and are analyzed by gas chromatography as their methyl esters. The resin acids from hops do not have a carboxyl group but do have an enolic OH group and therefore are acidic. They are composed of two general types of compound, the humulones and lupulones. They have isoprenoid side chains, and their biosynthesis probably is related to that of some of the simpler terpenoid constituents of hops. For analysis by gas chromatography, the acyl side chain is split off, and the volatile acids resulting are chromatographed either as the free acids or as the esters.

Since these two groups of resin acids are unrelated and are isolated and chromatographed differently, they will be treated entirely separately in two different sections in this chapter.

A. Resin Acids from Rosin

I. INTRODUCTION

These resin acids are monocarboxylic acids of alkylated hydrophenanthrene structures, separated into two types, the abietic and the pimaric acid classes. They have the general structures shown, the abietic type acids

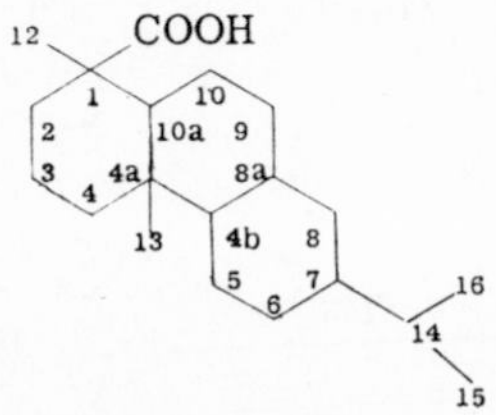

Abietic type 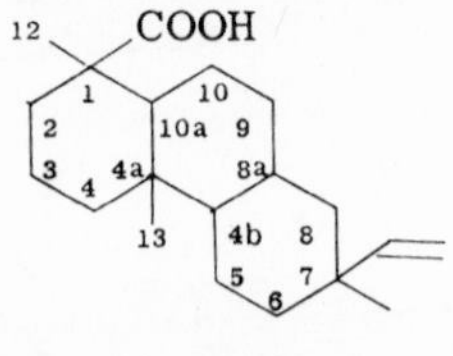   Pimaric type

having an isopropyl or isopropylidene group at the 7-position, and the pimaric type acids a methyl and a vinyl group, both at the 7-position. These acids vary in the positions and numbers of double bonds. In the abietic series, abietic, levopimaric, neoabietic, and palustric acids are positional isomers containing two double bonds; dehydroabietic acid contains three

476

double bonds in an aromatic ring; dihydroabietic and dihydropalustric acids contain one double bond; and tetrahydroabietic acid is the completely saturated compound. The same general structural relationships hold in the pimaric series, so that pimaric and isopimaric acids are stereo isomers containing two double bonds; dihydropimaric and dihydroisopimaric acids contain one double bond; and tetrahydropimaric and tetrahydroisopimaric acids are saturated stereo isomers.

The accurate analysis of individual resin acids has been difficult and time-consuming up to the present because of similarities in structure and the large numbers of isomers. The methyl esters of these acids have sufficiently high vapor pressures to be chromatographed at temperatures ranging from 225° to 270°C, so GLC is a promising tool for their quantitative separation and identification.

II. Isolation of Resin Acids from Rosin

The isolation of rosin and the separation of the resin acid fraction are commercial processes that will not be covered in detail here. The rosin is obtained by solvent extraction of pine stump wood, by wounding the living tree and collecting the exudate, or by separation from tall oil.

Tall oil is a product of increasing commercial importance in this country since the start of production in 1937. It is obtained from the kraft process of wood pulp manufacture by using resinous wood such as pine. In this process the resin from the wood is solubilized in the hot, spent alkaline liquor. On cooling, it is floated on top, removed, acidified, and separated as crude tall oil. About 90% of this is acidic material, consisting of approximately equal portions of fatty and resin acids. Tall oil is usually separated into its two main fractions for most effective use. This is accomplished most often by fractional distillation at reduced pressure. With this method there is as little as 3% cross-contamination of fractions. The fatty acid fraction distills over first, with the possibility that a small percentage of volatile pimaric-type resin acid may distill over with it. The resin acids have lower vapor pressures and will distill last. This tall oil rosin is commercially competitive with gum and wood rosins. Other methods of separation include fractional esterification of the fatty acids followed by distillation from the resin acids, and total esterification followed by selective saponification of the fatty acid esters and extraction. These methods are applicable because the carboxyl groups of the resin acids are relatively unreactive, since they are attached to tertiary carbon atoms and are closely surrounded by other groups.

Gum rosin is obtained from the oleoresin of living pine. The tree is wounded, and the exudate collected. This oleoresin consists mainly of rosin and turpentine, and the turpentine is removed easily by distillation.

Wood rosin is derived from aged virgin pine stumps which have remained in the ground for about ten years. The wood is extracted with solvents, yielding a high percentage of rosin.

III. Chromatography of Abietic and Pimaric Resin Acids

Both abietic and pimaric resin acids have been chromatographed as their methyl esters on polar and nonpolar packings at temperatures ranging from 225° to 270°C (Hudy, 1959). Poly(oxyalkalene adipate) (Reoplex 400), poly(diethylene glycol adipate) partially cross-linked with pentaerythritol (Resoflex 446), poly(1,4-butanediol succinate), and Apiezon N have been used as substrates for the separation of a series of sixteen resin acid esters, both naturally occurring and synthetically derived (Table I).

The doubly unsaturated pimaric type acid methyl esters are completely

TABLE I

Retention Volumes of the Resin Acid Methyl Esters Relative to Methyl Palmitate on Apiezon N and Polyester Columns[a]

		Stationary phase		
Methyl ester	Reoplex 400 (225°C)	Resoflex 446 (225°C)	Poly(1,4-butanediol succinate) (225°C)[b]	Apiezon N (270°C)
Palmitate	1.00	1.00	1.00	1.00
Δ-4b,8a-Isopimarate	—	4.50	4.64	3.10
Dihydropimarate	4.78	4.95	4.88	3.95
Tetrahydropimarate	—	—	4.95	3.99
Tetrahydroabietate[c]	4.92	5.11	5.16	4.18
Pimarate	5.00	5.20	5.28	3.53
Tetrahydroisopimarate	5.00	—	5.30	4.32
Dihydroabietate	5.85	6.10	5.91	4.48
Tetrahydroabietate[c]	5.85	6.14	6.00	4.83
Dihydropalustrate	5.96	6.20	5.80	4.37
Dihydroisopimarate	6.36	6.60	6.65	4.58
Palustrate[d]	6.36	6.63	6.60	4.00
Δ-8a,8-Isopimarate	6.86	7.20	7.16	4.30
Dehydroabietate	9.70	10.1	9.80	4.40
Abietate	9.70	10.1	9.80	5.17
Levopimarate[d]	9.70	—	9.80	4.37
Neoabietate	10.6	—	11.1	6.00

[a] From Hudy (1959).
[b] 2.5-meter column on Chromosorb P.
[c] Previously unseparated isomers present in standard.
[d] Main peak indicated, sample partially isomerized.

separated on both the polar and nonpolar substrates. The mono-unsaturated pimaric type acid esters are more retarded on the Apiezon N column and less retarded on the polyester columns than the dienes, as would be expected, since the dienes are more polar compounds. The completely saturated tetrahydroisopimaric ester gave much lower retention values on both polar and nonpolar substrates than would be expected for the loss of the final double bond, indicating that the compound might be the more volatile configuration of two isomers (Hudy, 1959).

The separation of methyl abietate and methyl dehydroabietate is accomplished on the nonpolar Apiezon N but, surprisingly, not on the polyester columns. The abietate is a diene, whereas the dehydroabietate contains an aromatic ring. Apparently the increased polarity of the aromatic ring offsets exactly the difference in vapor pressure so that the retention volumes are the same (Hudy, 1959).

Isomerization and disproportionation of some of the abietate-type compounds occur. For example, methyl palustrate is partially isomerized to methyl abietate, and methyl levopimarate is converted to methyl abietate and methyl dehydroabietate on the columns.

The mono-unsaturated abietic acid esters are retained for a shorter time than the dienes on the polar columns as expected, since they are less polar compounds. However, methyl dihydroabietate also is retained for a shorter time on the nonpolar Apiezon column, which would not be predicted. Because of this, methyl dihydroabietate and methyl dehydroabietate are not resolved on the nonpolar packing.

When the logarithms of retention volumes of the resin acid methyl esters on poly(1,4-butanediol succinate) are plotted against similar results obtained on the nonpolar Apiezon N column, a family of curves is obtained, each curve representing a series of methyl esters differing in polarity (Fig. 1). Thus, the completely saturated tetrahydro compounds are retained for the shortest period of time on the polar packing relative to the nonpolar packing (curve I). The dihydro compounds containing one double bond form a series (curve II) with relatively longer retention on the polar relative to the nonpolar column. The dienes (curve III) are more polar than the compounds in series I and II; therefore these compounds are retained longer on the polar substrate relative to the retention on the nonpolar packing. And the aromatic resin acid methyl ester (IV) is the most polar, as would be expected. Thus by chromatographing the methyl esters of unknown resin acids on both polar and nonpolar substrates and comparing them in this way, the degree of unsaturation can be determined by reference to curves obtained on known compounds. If the logs of the retention values for the methyl ester of an unknown resin acid are plotted and the point falls on curve III, for instance, the polarity of the unknown will be comparable to

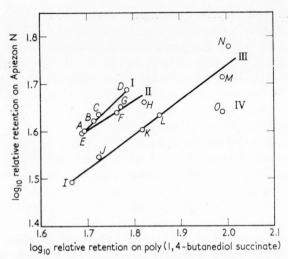

FIG. 1. Relationship between relative retention values (methyl palmitate = 100) on Apiezon N and poly(1,4-butanediol succinate) for some abietic- and pimaric-type methyl esters. These are the methyl esters of (A) tetrahydropimarate, (B) tetrahydroabietate, (C) tetrahydroisopimarate, (D) tetrahydroabietate, (E) dihydropimarate, (F) dihydropalustrate, (G) dihydroabietate, (H) dihydroisopimarate, (I) Δ-4b,8a-isopimarate, (J) pimarate, (K) palustrate, (L) Δ-8a,8-isopimarate, (M) abietate, (N) neoabietate, and (O) dehydroabietate. (Data from Hudy, 1959.)

the dienes, and the unknown probably is a doubly unsaturated compound. No correlation between the positions of the double bonds or the side chain in relation to the relative retentions can be seen. Thus in the diene series, compounds of the abietic type with conjugated double bonds are eluted both before and after the nonconjugated pimaric-type dienes. Neoabietic acid methyl ester is the one abietic acid derivative with a double bond in the isopropyl side chain. This is conjugated with a double bond in the ring. It is retained for the longest period on both packings. In the p-menthadiene series of monoterpene hydrocarbons (see Chapter 5), the dienes with one double bond in the isopropyl side chain also were retained for the longest period on polar and nonpolar packings, indicating that the double bond outside the ring had more effect on retention than the double bond within.

The whole tall oil acid fraction has been methylated and fingerprints obtained (Fig. 2) (Anon., 1959). Poly(1,4-butanediol succinate) was used at 245°C to give the separations shown. The acid fraction of tall oil includes not only resin acids of the abietic and pimaric types but also fatty acids. These can be separated, and commercially this is usually done as described in Section A.II. More complete chromatographic separations of components will be obtained if the tall oil is fractionated first. In this figure when the

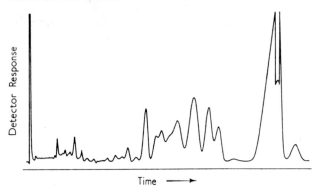

FIG. 2. Chromatogram of tall oil methyl esters on poly(1,4-butanediol succinate) at 245°C. (Anon., 1959; courtesy of Wilkens Instrument and Research, Inc.)

whole acid fraction is chromatographed, a typical fingerprint is obtained. This could be useful to the commercial tall oil producer for assessing tall oil quality, although preliminary separation of fatty acids from the resin acids will yield more information on component identities.

a. Conditions for Chromatography

*1. On Poly(1,4-butanediol Succinate) (Hudy, 1959)

Chromatograph	Laboratory-built.
Column dimensions	366 × 0.4-cm i.d. spiral copper tubing.
Solid support	Chromosorb W (60/100 U. S. mesh) untreated.
Stationary phase	Poly(1,4-butanediol succinate) (28.4:71.6).
Temperatures	Injection port: 300°C. Column: 225°C. Exit tubing and detector: 260°C.
Carrier gas	Helium at 100 ml/min. Inlet pressure: 24 psig. Outlet pressure: atmospheric.
Detector	Gow-Mac TR-2-B stainless-steel T/C cell, filament current 150–200 ma.
Recorder	Not given.
Sample size	100–200 μg of resin acid esters.
Analysis time	About 70 minutes.

*2. On Apiezon N (Hudy, 1959)

Chromatograph	Laboratory-built.
Column dimensions	366 × 0.4-cm i.d. spiral copper tubing.
Solid support	Chromosorb W (60/100 U. S. mesh) untreated.
Stationary phase	Apiezon N (28.4:71.6).
Temperatures	Injection port: 300°C. Column: 270°C. Exit tubing and detector: 260°C.
Carrier gas	Helium at 100 ml/min. Inlet pressure: 20 psig. Outlet pressure: atmospheric.

Detector	Gow-Mac TR-2-B stainless-steel T/C cell, filament current 150–200 ma.
Recorder	Not given.
Sample size	100–200 μg of resin acid esters.
Analysis time	About 45 minutes.

B. Resin Acids from Hops

I. INTRODUCTION

Resin acids from hops are important in imparting the characteristic bitterness to beer. They also are important in inhibiting the growth of undesirable organisms in the wort. The resin is located in small glands at the base of each petal in the female hop blossom. Two general types of acidic compound are present in the resin, the α- and β-acids. The α-acids consist of a group of analogues, chief of which are cohumulone, humulone, and adhumulone (I, Fig. 3) with R = a, b, and c, respectively. These acids generally are considered to be the important fraction in the brewing of beer. The β-acids consist of colupulone, lupulone, and adlupulone (II, Fig. 3) with R = a, b, and c, respectively, for the three related compounds.

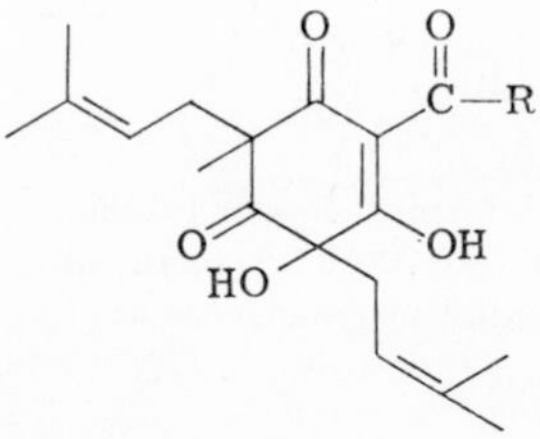

(I) 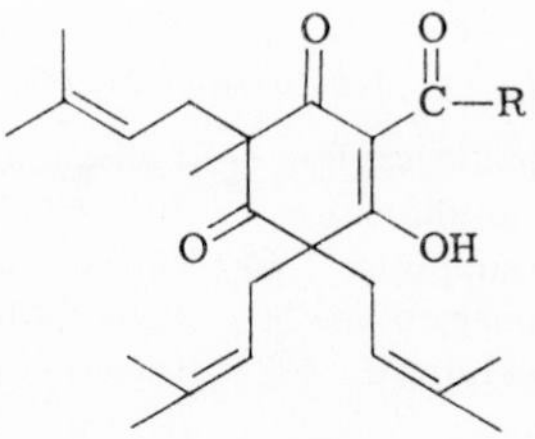   (II)

FIG. 3. (I) Humulone basic structure. (II) Lupulone basic structure. R = (a) CH(CH₃)₂, (b) CH₂CH(CH₃)₂, (c) CH(CH₃)CH₂CH₃.

The resin acids contain 3-methyl-2-butenyl side chains apparently derived from isoprene units, thereby indicating a possible relationship of these compounds with the terpenes. It has been found that a high proportion of the terpene hydrocarbon myrcene generally accompanies a low proportion of both cohumulone in the α-acids and colupulone in the β-acids (Howard and Slater, 1957). A high proportion of myrcene also generally indicates a low proportion of the sesquiterpene humulene. There appears to be a relationship between these two terpene hydrocarbons and colupulone and cohumulone content, indicating that the biosynthesis of these compounds may be interrelated.

II. Isolation and Separation of α- and β-Acids from Hops

a. Isolation Procedure

*1. By Solvent Extraction (Howard and Tatchell, 1956). A sample (15 to 20 gm) of whole hop cones is ground and extracted exhaustively with peroxide-free ether in a soxhlet. The ether is evaporated at a low temperature, and the residue is taken up in methanol to give a final volume of 100 ml and then filtered.

b. Separation of α- and β-Acids

*1. By Precipitation of α-Acids (Howard and Tatchell, 1956). A 60-ml portion of extract from the isolation procedure (II.a.1 above) is titrated against methanolic lead acetate (2% w/v) to the sulfide end point as in the method of Ford and Tait (1932). The lead salts of the α-acids are filtered off with the aid of kieselguhr (1 gm), washed with methanol, and dried. The combined filtrate and washings from lead salt precipitation are diluted with 1% aqueous sodium chloride and extracted exhaustively with petroleum ether. The petroleum ether extract is then partitioned with $2 N$ NaOH (1 × 15-ml and 1 × 5-ml portions), and the alkaline extracts are washed with chloroform. The β-acids are in the alkaline layer.

III. Chromatography of the α- and β-Acids

The hop resin acids have not been chromatographed directly by GLC. However, a measure of the relative amounts of the several homologues in both the α- and β-acid fractions can be obtained by gas chromatography of the isobutyric, isovaleric, and 2-methylbutyric acids (or their esters) derived from the acyl side chains (see Fig. 3, a, b, and c) on decomposition of the molecules.

Both the α- and β-acids (the α-acids being first liberated from their lead salts by hydrogen sulfide) can be oxidized with alkaline hydrogen peroxide with the production of the volatile acids in the form of their salts (Howard and Tatchell, 1956). The alkaline solution from the oxidation is passed through a column of anhydrous potassium hydrogen sulfate to liberate the volatile acids, which are then chromatographed.

Volatile acids such as these are difficult to handle without loss; tailing may occur when they are chromatographed; and the 2-methylbutyric acid is not well separated from isovaleric acid under the conditions employed. The lead salts of the α-acids can be pyrolyzed to liberate the volatile acids coming from the acyl side chains. The isopropyl esters of these acids can be formed and chromatographed (Rigby et al., 1960). Symmetrical peaks result, and good separations of the isovaleric and 2-methylbutyric esters can be obtained on several column packings. Liberation of the volatile acids by pyrolysis may not be quantitative, but the relative amount liberated is proportional to the amount of α-acid. Peak area from chromatography of the esters gives the same result as countercurrent distribution of the α-acids.

The lead salts of the α-acids are pyrolyzed in a sealed ampoule. The liberated volatile acids are distilled to the cool end of the ampoule which is shaped like an inverted V. The ampoule then is broken, and a mixture of isopropanol and H_2SO_4 is added to the free acids. This portion of the tube is resealed, and the acids are esterified by placing it in boiling water for $1\frac{1}{2}$ hours. The esters are extracted into petroleum ether, and an aliquot of this extract is chromatographed.

The pyrolysis produces some nonacidic substances which distill over also. These produce additional peaks on the chromatograms of the esterified acids unless they are removed. This can be done before esterification. The distillate is neutralized with alkali to form salts of the acids, and the neutral components are extracted into petroleum ether. The aqueous layer then is acidified, and the organic acids are extracted with diethyl ether. These volatile acids are then esterified. Results obtained without removal of the neutral substances are reliable if the isobutyrate peak is corrected as shown in Fig. 4B. Figure 4 shows chromatograms of the esterified acids obtained

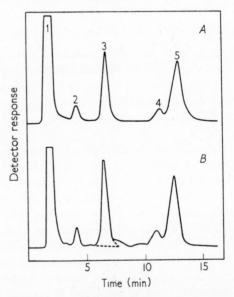

FIG. 4. Chromatograms of pyrolysis distillate of α-acid lead salts after esterification with isopropyl alcohol: A, neutral substances removed from distillate; B, neutral substances not removed; (1) solvent; (2) isopropyl alcohol; (3) isopropyl isobutyrate; (4) isopropyl 2-methylbutyrate; (5) isopropyl isovalerate. Ucon column at 50°C. (Rigby et al., 1960.)

from a pyrolysis distillate with and without removal of the neutral substances. Figure 5 shows the separation of these three acids as methyl and isopropyl esters. As methyl esters, isovaleric acid and 2-methylbutyric acid were not resolved on the polar Ucon packing, but the isopropyl esters showed different retention volumes and almost complete resolution of peaks under the conditions employed.

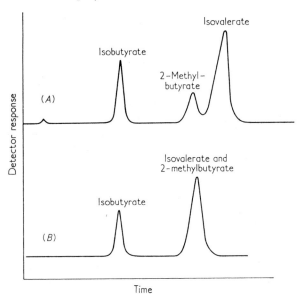

Fig. 5. Chromatograms of esters of isobutyric, 2-methylbutyric, and isovaleric acids: A, isopropyl esters; B, methyl esters. Ucon column at 50°C. (Rigby *et al.*, 1960)

This method cannot be applied to the β-acids directly, since insoluble lead salts are not formed when they are treated with methanolic lead acetate. The free acids can be obtained as described in method B.III.a.1 below, and esterification might be carried out by modifications of the flash esterification procedure described in Chapter 3 C.II., or of the method mentioned above.

a. Preparation of Derivatives for Chromatography

*1. *Volatile Acids from Oxidation of α-Acids with Hydrogen Peroxide* (Howard and Tatchell, 1956). The α-acid lead salt is ground in a mortar until homogeneous. A portion (about 400 mg of lead salt) is suspended in methanol (40 ml) and decomposed with hydrogen sulfide. The lead sulfide precipitate is filtered off and washed with methanol, and the combined filtrate and washings are evaporated to dryness under reduced pressure. The residue is dried for 1 hour at 1 mm Hg and oxidized as follows.

The regenerated α-acids are dissolved in $2N$ NaOH (about 20 ml). Aqueous hydrogen peroxide (30% w/v) is added at 0°C. This addition and the total volume of solution are so adjusted that the final solution contains about 10 mg/ml of α-acids and about 7% (w/v) of hydrogen peroxide. The solution is allowed to stand at 0°C until oxidation is complete (around 2 hours). Excess hydrogen peroxide is destroyed by heating for 1 hour in a boiling-water bath.

An aliquot (2 ml) of the solution is pipetted onto a column (1.5-cm diameter) of powdered anhydrous potassium hydrogen sulfate (15 gm). The liberated acids are eluted with 50 to 70 ml of anhydrous ether, and the eluate is dried for not less than 10 minutes and not more than 15 minutes over anhydrous potassium hydrogen sulfate. The dried solution is evaporated, with care to prevent losses, to 2 to 3 ml in a round-bottomed flask in a hot-water bath. Aliquots of this solution can be injected into the chromatograph.

*2. *Volatile Acids from Oxidation of β-Acids with Hydrogen Peroxide* (Howard and Tatchell, 1956). The alkaline solution of the β-acids as obtained in method B.II.b is similarly treated with hydrogen peroxide to obtain the volatile acids arising from the acyl side chains.

*3. *Isopropyl Esters of Volatile Acids from α-Acids* (Rigby et al., 1960). A Pyrex tube 20 cm × 7 mm is sealed at one end. A portion (about 250 mg) of the α-acid lead salt (see Section B.II.b) is placed in the tube so that it settles at the closed end. The tube then is heated at the center, drawn out slightly, and bent into a V shape (Fig. 6A). The open arm is heated gently until any lead salt adhering to the walls disappears. This end then is sealed.

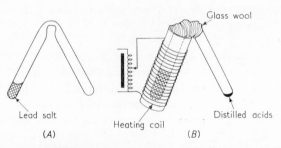

Fig. 6. Apparatus for pyrolysis of lead salts of α-acids and distillation of liberated volatile acids. (Rigby et al., 1960)

The tube is wrapped at the bend with a small amount of glass wool (Fig. 6B), and the arm of the tube containing the lead salt is placed inside a porcelain tube wound on the outside with electrical heating wire. The heating element is connected to a variable transformer adjusted to maintain a temperature of 400°C.

Pyrolysis is complete after 10 minutes at 400°C, and the liberated acids distill rapidly and collect in the cool arm of the tube. The tube is allowed to cool, wrapped in a cloth, and broken at the bend. Care must be taken at this step, since pressure develops in the tube, and it may shatter when broken.

Esterification of the liberated acids is carried out by adding 0.1 ml of isopropanol–H_2SO_4 (2.5 ml of concentrated H_2SO_4 in 100 ml of isopropanol) to about 50 mg of the acids in the ampoule, which is sealed and placed in boiling water for $1\frac{1}{2}$ hours. The tube is cooled and opened, and 0.2 ml of water and 0.1 ml of petroleum ether are added. The esters are extracted into the organic layer by shaking. An aliquot of the petroleum ether extract is used for chromatography.

b. Conditions for Chromatography

1. *Volatile Acids from the Oxidation of Resin Acids.* See Chapter 3, Section C for methods of chromatography.

*2. *Isopropyl Esters of Volatile Acids from the Pyrolysis of α-Acid Lead Salts* (Rigby et al., 1960)

Chromatograph	Burrell Kromo Tog, Model K-2.
Column dimensions	250 cm.
Solid support	Acid-washed Celite (30/60 mesh).
Stationary phase	Ucon lubricant 5OHB2000.
Temperature	50°C.
Carrier gas	Helium at 40 ml/min at the inlet.
Detector	T/C cell.
Recorder	Brown, 1 mv, 1 second.
Sample size	5 μl.
Analysis time	About 15 minutes.

References

Anon. 1959. Tall oil—volatiles. Aerograph Research Notes, Spring Issue. Wilkens Instrument and Research Corp., Walnut Creek, California.

Ford, J. S. and A. Tait. 1932. Gravimetric estimation of the preservative value of hops. *J. Inst. Brewing* **38**: 351–352.

Howard, G. A. and C. A. Slater. 1957. Evaluation of hops VII. Composition of the essential oil of hops. *J. Inst. Brewing* **63**: 491–506.

Howard, G. A. and A. R. Tatchell. 1956. Evaluation of hops: new approach to the detailed analysis of hop resins. *J. Inst. Brewing* **62**: 20–27.

Hudy, J. A. 1959. Resin acids. Gas chromatography of their methyl esters. *Anal. Chem.* **31**: 1754–1756.

Rigby, F. L., E. Sihto and A. Bars. 1960. Rapid method for detailed analysis of the α-acid fraction of hops by gas chromatography. *J. Inst. Brewing* **66**: 242–249.

Chapter 7

Lipids

General Introduction

Lipids are a heterogeneous group of compounds derived from biological systems, characterized by their solubility in organic solvents and insolubility in water. They are separated into constituent fractions by auxiliary methods before gas chromatography. Lipids are of relatively high molecular weight and have low vapor pressures. Therefore they must often be converted to more volatile derivatives before they can be chromatographed. The following lipids are structurally modified before injection-glycerides, phospholipids, sterol esters, higher fatty acids, O-alkyl glycerols, and higher fatty aldehydes. Sterols and higher fatty alcohols may be chromatographed either unchanged or as derivatives. Hydrocarbons are chromatographed unchanged. Fatty amines and higher fatty nitriles do not occur naturally, but members of both series are prepared from naturally occurring lipids.

A number of conventions commonly used for abbreviating the structures of lipids are employed in this chapter to simplify the tabulation of data. The number of carbon atoms in the long chain is given in arabic numerals, followed by the number of double bonds, the two being separated by a colon. The positions of the double bonds, if known, are indicated by superscripts. The configuration around the double bond is indicated by placing the word *cis* or *trans* after the number of bonds. If the positions and/or configurations of the bonds are unknown, these designations are omitted. If the number of double bonds is also unknown, unsaturation is indicated by the abbreviation "un" after the number of carbon atoms.

In this notation, the symbol $16:3^{7,10,13}$ signifies that the longest chain contains 16 carbon atoms and has three double bonds at positions 7, 10, and 13, numbering beginning with the carbon atom of the functional group. The symbol $18:1^9$ *cis* represents a chain containing 18 carbon atoms with a single double bond in the 9 position having *cis* configuration.

Branching near the end of the long chain is indicated by the following abbreviations

$$CH_3-CH-CH_2- \qquad CH_3-CH_2-CH- \qquad CH_3-\overset{\overset{\displaystyle CH_3}{|}}{\underset{\underset{\displaystyle CH_3}{|}}{C}}-$$

$$\underset{\displaystyle CH_3}{|} \qquad\qquad\qquad \underset{\displaystyle CH_3}{|}$$

iso   anteiso   neo

If the point of branching is unknown, it is abbreviated as "br." Chain branching, if known, is indicated by placing the appropriate abbreviation

488

before the numeral signifying the number of carbon atoms. Thus iso 16:0 represents a saturated compound containing 16 carbon atoms in the long chain with a methyl group substituted on the next to the last carbon atom of the chain.

A. Methods of Isolation and Separation

I. Isolation of Total Lipids

Total lipids can be extracted from tissues by using various solvent combinations. Diethyl ether–95% ethanol 1:3 (v/v) is sometimes used (Bloor, 1928; James, 1960; Insull and Ahrens, 1959), although phospholipids are not completely extracted.

Dimethoxymethane (methylal)–methanol 4:1 (v/v) is a satisfactory solvent combination (Fillerup and Mead, 1953; Lakshminarayana et al., 1960) which extracts lipids more completely than diethyl ether–ethanol. With either of these solvents, the extract is evaporated and the lipids are removed from the residue with petroleum ether.

Petroleum ether is used for the Soxhlet extraction of total lipids from dried leaf material (Zirm et al., 1955). Owens (1960) uses a series of solvents in the extraction of fungus spores. These consist of 80% ethanol, ethanol–ether 1:1, ether, and chloroform, in that order.

The most widely applicable solvent combination is chloroform–methanol 2:1 (v/v). It is used for the extraction of animal tissues, plant tissues, and blood (Folch et al., 1957; Lewin and Wagenknecht, 1960; Böttcher et al., 1959; Wren and Mitchell, 1959). Folch et al. have developed a method for washing the extract free of nonlipid materials by adding water. Böttcher has made a detailed study of the extraction of total lipids and has developed a method for the thorough extraction of lipids from aorta tissue that is generally applicable.

a. Extraction with Chloroform–Methanol

*1. *Homogenized Tissue* (Folch et al., 1957). *Extraction.* The tissue is homogenized (usually 3 minutes will suffice) with chloroform–methanol 2:1 (v/v) to a final dilution 20-fold the volume of the tissue sample for 1 gm of tissue or less. For amounts greater than 1 gm the tissue is homogenized with a 17-fold volume of solvent mixture. The balance of solvent mixture required to dilute the homogenate to final volume is used to ensure the quantitative transfer of the homogenate into a volumetric flask. After temperature equilibration and final volume adjustment, the homogenate is filtered through a fat-free paper into a glass-stoppered vessel.

Washing of crude extract. The lipid extract is thoroughly mixed with one-fifth its volume of water, and the mixture is allowed to separate into two phases without interfacial fluff, either by standing or by centrifugation. As much of the upper phase as possible is carefully removed by siphoning. A small amount of an equilibrated upper-phase rinse solvent is added carefully so as not to disturb the lower phase, and as much as possible is siphoned off. This is repeated two times more. Finally the lower phase and the rinsing fluid remaining after siphoning are made into one phase by the careful addition of methanol. The solution may be diluted to any desired final volume by the addition of chloroform–methanol 2:1.

Upper-phase rinse solvent. Chloroform, methanol, and water are mixed in a separatory funnel in the proportions 8:4:3 by volume and allowed to stand. The upper phase is an equilibrated rinse solvent and is stored in glass-stoppered bottles.

2. *Lyophilized Tissue* (Böttcher *et al.*, 1959). *Extraction.* The tissue is cut in small pieces and lyophilized for 8 hours before extraction. Lipids may also be extracted quantitatively with fresh tissue by this procedure, but the amounts of nonlipid material extracted are much greater. The tissue is transferred to chloroform–methanol 2:1 (v/v) and stirred for 3 hours at room temperature. It is filtered and re-extracted with chloroform–methanol with stirring for 24 hours. This is repeated, and the tissue is finally extracted for 3 hours in a Soxhlet apparatus with chloroform–methanol 2:1 containing 1 mg of hydroquinone to prevent oxidation of unsaturated acids. Ninety-five per cent of the total lipids are extracted at room temperature, and the remaining 5% in the Soxhlet apparatus. The extracts are combined and evaporated under nitrogen at 50°C in the absence of direct sunlight to a small volume.

Removal of nonlipid fraction. The lipids are separated from nonlipid materials on a powdered cellulose column as follows: Whatman standard-grade powdered cellulose is made into a slurry with chloroform–methanol 2:1 (v/v) and packed into a 2 × 30-cm column. It is washed with the solvent (about 200 ml) until no further fines are eluted. Not more than 500 mg of lipid is placed on the column in a maximum of 5 ml of chloroform–methanol. The lipids are eluted with about 250 ml of solvent. The eluate is evaporated almost to dryness, and residual methanol is removed by twice adding small amounts of petroleum ether and evaporating almost to dryness. Petroleum ether is added to make the extract up to a volume of about 15 ml.

b. *Extraction with Dimethoxymethane (Methylal)–Methanol*

1. *Serum or Homogenized Tissue* (Lakshminarayana *et al.*, 1960). One volume of serum (or tissue homogenate) is added dropwise to 15 volumes of dimethoxymethane–methanol 4:1 (v/v) and stirred at room temperature for 30 minutes. The mixture is brought to a boil, cooled, and filtered through a sintered-glass funnel under reduced pressure. The precipitate is washed four times with large amounts of the solvent mixture. The filtrate is taken

to dryness at 40°C in a rotary vacuum evaporator. Absolute ethanol is added at the final evaporation stage to remove water. The residue is dissolved in hexane, evaporated, redissolved in hexane, filtered through a sintered-glass funnel, concentrated, and diluted to a suitable volume.

c. Extraction with a Solvent Series

*1. *Fungus Spores* (Owens, 1960). One volume of fungus spores is extracted with 20 volumes of 80% ethanol for 30 minutes and filtered through a Büchner funnel with suction. The filter cake is transferred to fresh solvent, and the procedure is repeated twice more. The spores are then extracted successively with 20 volumes of ethanol–ether 1:1 (v/v), twice with peroxide-free ether, and twice with chloroform. The extracts are combined and evaporated under nitrogen with the addition of a small amount of hydroquinone to retard oxidation. The residue is wet with a minimum amount of water and extracted with 3 × 25-ml portions of petroleum ether, the lipids extracting into the petroleum ether layer.

II. Separation of Lipid Fractions

The total lipid extract may be saponified, with the cleavage of ester linkages. The free fatty acids thus liberated are then separated from unsaponifiable lipids such as hydrocarbons, higher fatty alcohols, and sterols. The lipids in the unsaponifiable portion may then be fractionated by liquid–solid chromatography or through the formation of urea clathrates followed by chromatography.

The total lipids may also be separated without saponification by liquid–solid chromatography on silicic acid or by stepwise separation of phospholipids and free fatty acids, followed by liquid–solid chromatographic separation of the sterol esters and glycerides.

Unsaponified lipids can also be separated according to class by thin layer chromatography on silica gel (Malins and Mangold, 1960). The active solid is 250-mesh silica gel containing 1% plaster of Paris coated on glass in a layer 250 to 275 μ thick. The lipid mixture is applied to the bottom of the Chromatoplate and resolved by development with a 90:10:1 mixture (vv) of petroleum ether (b.p. 60° to 70°C), diethyl ether, and acetic acids. About 40 minutes is required for the separation. The positions of the lipid fractions are located by spraying the plates with a 0.2% solution of 2′,7′-dichlorofluorescein in ethanol. All lipids yield bright yellow-green fluorescent spots when treated in this way and viewed under ultraviolet light. Highly polar compounds such as monoglycerides, glyceryl ethers, and phospholipids do not migrate under these conditions. These can be separated from one another by developing the Chromatostrip with a 30:70:1 mixture (v/v) of petroleum ether, diethyl ether, and acetic acid. Compounds within homologous series (triglycerides, for example) are separated slightly from each other, but usually not enough to interfere with the separation of classes. After separation, the lipid classes are isolated by scratching the active solid from the plate and eluting it with a suitable solvent. Diethyl ether is satisfactory for the recovery of most compounds, but phospholipids require methanol and removal is not complete. This method is said to give separations that are more discrete and more rapid than those obtainable by column chromatography. However, at the time of writing, insufficient data were given to warrant inclusion of details.

a. Separation of Components of the Total Lipid Fraction without Preliminary Saponification

1. *On Silicic Acid Column* (Fillerup and Mead, 1953). Thirteen grams of 100-mesh silicic acid are packed into a 2-cm glass column to a height of 7 cm. The column is then washed with 40 ml of absolute methanol followed by 40 ml of acetone, 40 ml of anhydrous peroxide-free ether, and 40 ml of petroleum ether (see comments in method 2 below). About 50 mg of the lipid fraction (in petroleum ether) is added to the top of the column. The lipid fractions are then eluted as shown in Table I. Two hundred to three

TABLE I

CHROMATOGRAPHIC SEPARATION OF AN ARTIFICIAL LIPID MIXTURE[a]

Fraction (in order of elution)	Compounds used	Solvent mixture eluting fraction	Column volume of eluate	Per cent recovery
1. Sterol ester	Cholesterol palmitate, cholesterol oleate	1% ether in petroleum ether	20	98.4–100
2. Triglyceride	Tripalmitin, triolein	4% ether in petroleum ether	20	96–100
3. Sterol	Cholesterol	10% ether in petroleum ether	15	99–100
4. Acid	Stearic, oleic	50% ether in petroleum ether	15	97
5. Phospholipid	Lecithin	25% methanol in ether	15	100

[a] From Fillerup and Mead (1953).

hundred milliliters each of 1% ether in petroleum ether, 4% ether in petroleum ether, 10% ether in petroleum ether, 50% ether in petroleum ether, and 25% methanol in ether are used in this order for the elution of various fractions. Owens has found that phospholipids from *Neurosporasitophila* spores are not eluted quantitatively with 25% methanol in ether. He adds 1% 10 N HCl to the mixture to elute them, but some phospholipids are hydrolyzed by this procedure.

2. *By Stepwise Separation of Fractions* (Böttcher *et al.*, 1959). Phospholipids are separated from the lipid fraction by dialysis, the free fatty acids by extraction with potassium hydroxide, and the sterol esters, sterols, and glycerides by liquid–solid chromatography on silicic acid. A rubber membrane is used for the dialysis of the petroleum ether extract to separate the phospholipids in the residue from the remainder of the lipid fraction in the dialyzate. The membrane is the finger of a surgical glove which is first extracted with diethyl ether and then with petroleum ether for 3 hours each in a Soxhlet apparatus. The petroleum ether solution of lipids is added to the dialysis sac and placed in a larger vessel containing petroleum ether. The contents of the dialysis sac are stirred constantly with a glass rod shaped to keep the sac expanded. The outer vessel has a constant-level device allowing continuous replenishment of solvent and removal of dialyzate. The extract is dialyzed for 24 hours, after which time the receiver is changed. The dialyzate is collected every hour and evaporated to dryness until not more than 0.2 mg of material per hour appears in the dialyzate fraction. Estimations of phosphorus (Allen, 1940) and cholesterol (Sperry and Webb, 1950) are made, and, if the phosphorus content is more than 0.05% in the dialyzate, or the cholesterol content more than 2% in the residue, the dialysis is repeated.

Free fatty acids are removed from neutral material by extraction with potassium hydroxide. One hundred milliliters of the petroleum ether solution is extracted with 2 × 10-ml portions of 0.05 N aqueous KOH. The fatty acids are extracted into the aqueous layer. This is washed with 3 × 10-ml of petroleum ether and centrifuged. If necessary, ethanol is added to form two clear layers. The petroleum ether extract is washed with water and dried over anhydrous sodium sulfate, and the water washings are added to the alkaline layer. This is then acidified with HCl and the fatty acids are extracted with 3 × 25-ml portions of petroleum ether. This extract is dried over sodium sulfate.

The neutral dialyzate containing sterol esters, sterols, and glycerides is separated by liquid–solid chromatography. Silicic acid (100 mesh) is prepared by drying at 120° to 125°C for at least 4 hours. Böttcher obtains more reproducible results when the silicic acid is dried, rather than by the washing procedure of Fillerup and Mead, since the water content of the solvents varies.

Fourteen grams of the dried silicic acid is suspended in at least 100 ml of petroleum ether and boiled briefly under reduced pressure to remove air bubbles. This is packed in a column 3.3 cm in diameter to a height of 4 cm. Not more than 200 mg of lipids in a few milliliters of petroleum ether is applied to the column. The sterol esters are eluted with 200 to 300 ml of petroleum ether–benzene 7:3 (v/v). The remainder of the lipids, containing glycerides and sterols, is eluted with ether–methanol 20:1 (v/v).

b. Saponification of Oils, Fats, and Waxes

The procedure chosen for the saponification of fatty acids depends on the nature of the fatty material. Highly unsaturated liquid oils require less drastic treatment than do high-melting fats and waxes. Unsaturated acids are liable to undergo isomerization and polymerization when heated for prolonged periods of time in the presence of alkalis. Hydroxy acids may form etholides when free fatty acids are isolated. Therefore the calcium salts are formed and converted directly to methyl esters.

1. *Saponification of Unsaturated Liquid Oils—Cold Process* (Paech and Tracey, 1955). Ten grams of oil is added, with vigorous stirring, to a solution of potassium hydroxide (2.6 gm) in 2.5 ml of water. Ethanol (0.1 ml) is added, and an exothermic reaction occurs. The solution is allowed to stand overnight. The soaps are diluted with water and extracted in a separatory funnel with diethyl ether or petroleum ether. A continuous extractor may be preferable if bad emulsions are formed by shaking in the separatory funnel. The soaps remain in the aqueous layer, and unsaponifiable materials are extracted into the organic solvent.

The soaps are acidified with 25% sulfuric acid. If the free acids formed are solid, the mixture is warmed gently until the fatty acids melt and form a layer on the aqueous solution. The mixture is cooled and the fatty acids are extracted with peroxide-free ether. The water layer is re-extracted several times with ether to remove the lower fatty acids completely. The ether extract is filtered and dried over Na_2SO_4, and the solvent is evaporated.

2. *Saponification of Fats.* The fat (10 gm) is added to a flask together with 3.9 gm of potassium hydroxide and 50 ml of 95% ethanol. A condenser is attached to the flask, and the mixture is refluxed gently for 2 to 3 hours with occasional swirling. The mixture is diluted with water and extracted with ether or petroleum ether as described above.

3. *Saponification of Fats Containing Hydroxy Acids* (Downing et al., 1960). Fats containing esters of hydroxy acids are saponified with aqueous KOH–ethanol as described above (method 2) and extracted four times with hot hexane to remove unsaponifiable fractions. The acids are isolated as their calcium salts. The procedure is as follows: The hexane extracts are washed with 30% alcohol in water. All aqueous layers are combined and treated with 10% calcium chloride solution (50 ml) to precipitate the calcium salts of the fatty acids. The salts are obtained in granular form by evaporation of most of the liquid. The salts are washed with water, dried, and crushed. They are then refluxed with acetone twice for periods of 1 hour to extract the

remaining unsaponifiable fractions. These fractions are combined with the main fraction isolated by hexane extraction. The calcium salts of the acids are then converted directly to methyl esters as described in Section G.III.

4. *Saponification of Waxes* (Chibnall *et al.*, 1934). The wax (10 gm) is dissolved in hot benzene (300 ml), and a 10% solution of ethanolic potassium hydroxide is added (200 ml). The mixture is refluxed for 12 hours, after which a 25:45 (w/v) solution of calcium chloride in 95% ethanol (450 ml) is added. Boiling is continued for an additional 2½ hours, and the mixture is then filtered hot through a heated funnel. The calcium salts of the fatty acids on the funnel are washed with 3 × 450-ml portions of boiling 95% alcohol followed by 450 ml of boiling acetone. The crude alcohols separate out when the filtrates are cooled.

These filtrates are resaponified by dissolving them in hot benzene, adding sodium ethoxide solution (2 gm of sodium in 48 ml of absolute ethanol), and refluxing for 2 hours. Calcium chloride solution (3 gm in 25 ml of 95% ethanol) is added, and the boiling is continued for another 2 hours. The mixture is filtered hot, and the insoluble calcium salts are extracted with 3 × 100 ml of boiling 95% ethanol followed by 3 × 100 ml of boiling acetone. The filtrates are combined and cooled, whereon the fatty alcohol fraction separates out. These may be purified by digestion with hot acetone and filtration through a heated funnel. This is repeated five times, and the alcohols separate from the filtrates on cooling.

c. *Prefractionation of Unsaponifiable Lipids*

The hydrocarbons, higher fatty alcohols, and sterols, constituents of the unsaponifiable fraction, must be separated before they can be chromatographed successfully. This can be accomplished by treating the unsaponifiable fraction with urea in hot alcohol solution (von Rudloff, 1951). On cooling, the urea forms crystalline clathrate compounds with fatty alcohols and hydrocarbons. The sterols remain in the supernatant solution. When the clathrates are digested with water, the fatty alcohols and hydrocarbons are released. Downing *et al.* (1960) further separated this material into hydrocarbon, monohydric alcohol, and dihydric alcohol fractions by liquid–solid chromatography on alumina. Alternatively, the unsaponifiable lipid fraction can be separated by direct chromatography on alumina without resorting to a prefractionation with urea (MacKenna *et al.*, 1952). The crude alcohol fraction can then be separated into monohydric alcohols, α,ω-diols, and α,β-diols by rechromatographing on alumina, with different solvent combinations for elution.

*1. *Liquid-Solid Chromatographic Method* (MacKenna *et al.*, 1952). A sample of the unsaponifiable material (1 gm) dissolved in 100 ml of petroleum ether is applied to a 1.4 × 10-cm chromatographic column packed with grade II alumina (Brockman and Schodder, 1941). The column is then successively eluted with 100- to 200-ml portions of light petroleum ether (40° to 60°C), 5% chloroform in petroleum ether, 10% chloroform in petroleum ether, chloroform, methanol, and acetic acid. The compositions of the various fractions are shown in Table II. Hydrocarbons are found in fraction 1, wax alcohols in fraction 2b, cholesterol in fraction 3b, and other sterols in fraction 4. The fractions were not completely identified, and only 89% of the unsaponifiable lipids were recovered.

TABLE II

CHROMATOGRAPHIC FRACTIONATION ON ALUMINA OF THE UNSAPONIFIABLE MATERIAL FROM A BULKED SAMPLE OF HUMAN FOREARM SEBUM[a]

Fraction	Eluent	Percentage of total unsaponifiable matter	Appearance	Nature
1	Light petroleum	37.5	Soft white solid	Hydrocarbons
2a	5% CHCl₃–light petroleum (first 100 ml)	0.4	Yellow wax	—
2b	5% CHCl₃–light petroleum	20.6	Yellow wax	Wax alcohols
3a	10% CHCl₃–light petroleum (first 200 ml)	3.9	Yellow wax	—
3b	10% CHCl₃–light petroleum	13.7	White crystalline solid	Cholesterol
4	CHCl₃	3.6	Brown-yellow oil	Other sterols
5	Methanol	6.4	Gray wax	—
6	Acetic acid	3.0	Gray-yellow viscous liquid	—
	Total recovered	89.1		

[a] From Boughton and Wheatley (1959).

*2. *Urea Clathrate Method* (von Rudloff, 1951; Downing et al., 1960). The unsaponifiable fraction (10 gm) is placed in a flask with urea (5.5 parts) and ethanol (75 volumes). The mixture is heated to reflux temperature and allowed to cool. The insoluble complex which precipitates is filtered off and washed with cold ethanol. Urea (4 gm) is added to the filtrate, and the mixture is reheated and cooled to obtain a second crop of crystals. A third crop is obtained by reducing the volume of the second filtrate. Aliphatic hydrocarbons and alcohols without extensive branching are isolated by this method. The combined complex is recrystallized from ethanol and decomposed by stirring with a mixture of water and ether. The lipids are extracted into the ether layer and are recovered by evaporating the solvent. The residue is dissolved in petroleum ether and chromatographed on activated alumina. Petroleum ether (60° to 80°C) elutes saturated hydrocarbons. Monohydric alcohols are eluted with chloroform–benzene 1:2 and α,β-diols by chloroform–ethanol. To purify this fraction, the α,β-diols are then dissolved in acetone containing a trace of sulfuric acid to form ketals. These are chromatographed on alumina and eluted with petroleum ether. The α,β-diols are recovered from their acetals by hydrolysis. The diol fractions are analyzed by GLC after conversion to the corresponding hydrocarbons.

A portion of the unsaponifiable fraction not forming adducts with urea is separated by chromatography on alumina. A nonvolatile oil is eluted with petroleum ether, and sterols with benzene and chloroform.

III. Subtraction Methods (Farquhar et al., 1959)

Unsaturation in hydrocarbons, higher fatty alcohols, and methyl esters of fatty acids may be determined by two methods using GLC. The double bonds can be brominated, thus lowering the volatility of the compounds so that they will not be eluted from the chromatographic column. Unsaturated compounds can also be hydrogenated to form saturated derivatives of equivalent carbon number, thus shifting the retention volumes to those of the saturated compounds. By chromatographing mixtures before and after bromination or hydrogenation, the unsaturated components can be identified and quantified.

*a. Bromination

A 0.5- to 5.0-mg sample of material is dissolved in a small amount of diethyl ether in a conical centrifuge tube. The tube is cooled to $-10°C$ by placing it in a dry ice–ethanol bath. Liquid bromine, 2% in diethyl ether, is added to the solution dropwise until the yellow color persists, indicating complete bromination. The solvent is then evaporated at less than 30°C under a stream of air or nitrogen. The brominated compounds tend to crystallize out. The supernatant solution is chromatographed.

*b. Hydrogenation

The sample (0.5 to 20 mg) is dissolved in 5 ml of absolute ethanol in a 25-ml flask, and 10 mg of platinum oxide is added. The flask is attached over the magnetic stirrer in the hydrogenation apparatus shown in Fig. 1, in which all joints are greased. Hydrogen is introduced through stopcock A with stopcocks B and C closed, the water in the burette being forced below the zero mark. After stopcock A is closed, B is opened to allow water to fill the burette again. This flushing of the system is repeated six to ten times.

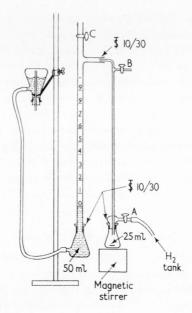

Fɪɢ. 1. Apparatus for microhydrogenation of lipids. (Farquhar *et al.*, 1959.)

Finally, with the water level at about zero, all stopcocks are closed and the magnetic stirrer is switched on. Hydrogen uptake is shown by a rising water level in the burette. The reaction is complete when this level remains constant, at which point the catalyst begins to form long strands. The supernatant clear fluid is freed of catalyst by filtration, and the ethanol is evaporated at 15 mm Hg and 40°C or less.

B. Higher Aliphatic Hydrocarbons

I. Introduction

Small amounts of hydrocarbons are present in many naturally occurring fats and waxes. They have been isolated from palm wax, carnauba wax, beeswax, and other vegetable and insect waxes. Beeswax has been shown to contain hentriacontane ($C_{31}H_{64}$), together with pentacosane ($C_{25}H_{52}$), heptacosane ($C_{27}H_{56}$), and nonacosane ($C_{29}H_{60}$). Cuticle wax from apples consists mostly of hydrocarbons, chiefly pentatriacontane ($C_{35}H_{72}$) together with smaller amounts of *n*-heptacosane. Indian sugar cane wax contains a small amount of pentatriacontane, and *Eucalyptus* wax contains heptacosane and nonacosane in quantity. Most of the hydrocarbons that have been reported on in the past are straight-chain saturated compounds, but branched unsaturated compounds are also found; squalene ($C_{30}H_{50}$), for example, is an important constituent of the unsaponifiable fraction of Elasmobranchii liver oils. The presence of hydrocarbons of different chain lengths in such a variety of materials incites interest as to their origin. Perhaps studies of their distribution by carbon number in related taxonomic species may help to answer such questions.

II. ISOLATION

Hydrocarbons are found in the unsaponifiable fraction of fats and waxes together with sterols, higher fatty alcohols, and vitamin A. They may also be obtained in admixture with fatty alcohols, by stripping cuticular waxes from plants with solvents such as petroleum ether (Huelin and Gallop, 1951). Hydrocarbons can be separated from fatty alcohols by liquid–solid chromatography on alumina (Downing et al., 1960). They are readily eluted by petroleum ether, whereas the alcohols require more polar solvents for removal from the column (Section A.II). The hydrocarbons can be purified further by treating them with urea in warm methanol (Section A.II). Clathrates are formed from which the hydrocarbons can be released by digestion with water. Urea yields complexes with n-alkanes and their linear derivatives, but with most branched and cyclic compounds it does not (Zimmerschied et al., 1950). The formation of adducts with n-alkane chains occurs up to a carbon number of at least 50.

Saturated hydrocarbons can be separated from unsaturated hydrocarbons by chromatography on silica gel. The saturated fraction can be further divided into normal paraffins and isoparaffins by selective adsorption on molecular sieve type 5A (O'Connor and Norris, 1960). Normal hydrocarbons, C_5 through C_{28}, are adsorbed quantitatively, whereas isohydrocarbons are not. As will be seen below, normal hydrocarbons can be subtracted from iso and anteiso compounds during the course of GLC by including a column of molecular sieve in the gas stream. This may be used as a precolumn (Whitham, 1958) or inserted between the analytical column and the detector (Downing et al., 1960).

III. CHROMATOGRAPHIC METHODS

Carruthers and Johnstone (1959) isolated the hydrocarbon fractions of green leaf wax of tobacco, fermented tobacco wax, and cigarette wax. Chromatography on E 301 silicone grease at a temperature of 288°C and a carrier gas flow rate of 1.6 liters of N_2 per hour revealed the presence of eleven hydrocarbons with chain lengths varying from C_{24} to C_{34}. All the even- or odd-numbered members of the series were present in one sample or the other. Hentriacontane was the predominant compound in all three samples, but the peak representing it was not resolved from that of a slightly branched hydrocarbon. Dotriacontane and tritriacontane were also present in fairly large amounts. Several of the peaks represent both normal and iso compounds, the presence of the latter being demonstrated by mass spectrometry (Table III). The occurrence of isohydrocarbons in plant and animal waxes has been reported elsewhere (Barbezat, 1958). Carruthers and Johnstone, as well as Downing (vide infra), purify the hydrocarbon fractions by complexing with urea, a procedure which is supposed to eliminate highly branched chains. In view of the fact that both groups of workers detect isohydrocarbons in the purified products, a careful study of this process is needed to determine the degree of branching in proportion to chain length necessary to prevent inclusion of such hydrocarbons in the clathrates. It may be that chromatograms obtained on such preparations are not representative of the naturally occurring materials.

TABLE III

Gas–Liquid Chromatographic Analysis of Paraffin Waxes[a]
(Percentage Area)

Paraffin	Green leaf wax	Fermented tobacco wax	Cigarette smoke wax
$n\text{-}C_{24}$	—	—	0.1
$n\text{-}C_{25}$	0.5	—	0.6
$n\text{-}C_{26}$	0.3	0.3	0.4
$n\text{-}C_{27}$	7.5	4.4	6.3
$n\text{-}C_{28}$	0.6	1.0	1.1
$n\text{-}C_{29}$	8.8[b]	9.2[b]	7.4
$n\text{-}C_{30}$	3.9[c]	7.1	3.8[c]
$n\text{-}C_{31}$	47.0[b]	46.5[b]	43.4[b]
$n\text{-}C_{32}$	12.5	16.0	13.0
$n\text{-}C_{33}$	18.9[b]	15.5[b]	22.8[b]
$n\text{-}C_{34}$	—	—	1.1

[a] From Carruthers and Johnstone (1959).

[b] These peaks were composed of two unresolved peaks. The results given include both peaks. The impurity is probably a very slightly branched paraffin.

[c] These peaks were probably due to $n\text{-}C_{30}$ paraffins, but this was not fully confirmed.

Downing et al. (1960) chromatographed the naturally occurring hydrocarbons isolated from wool wax, as well as the hydrocarbons obtained by reducing fatty alcohols and acids isolated from the wax. They used a silicone column and programmed the temperature between 100° and 265°C so that peaks representing both low-boiling and high-boiling homologues would be well separated (Fig. 2). Peaks representing thirty-seven components were resolved or partly resolved including normal, isohydrocarbons and anteisohydrocarbons. Normal and isohydrocarbons with the same carbon number were resolved. Isohydrocarbons have slightly shorter retention times than anteiso compounds with the same carbon number, but the difference is not great enough to differentiate between them chromatographically. However, in most cases no difficulty was experienced in separating iso and anteiso compounds, since the former were always of even carbon number and the latter always of odd carbon number.

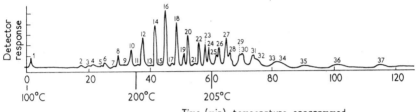

Time (min), temperature-programmed

FIG. 2. Hydrocarbons which occur naturally in wool wax chromatographed on a silicone elastomer E 301 stationary phase with the temperature programmed from 100°C to 265°C. i. = iso; a.i. = anteiso. (1) Air. (2) 13:0. (3) 14:0, i. (4) 14:0. (5) 15:0, a.i. (6) 15:0. (7) 16:0, i. (8) 16:0. (9) 17:0, a.i. (10) 17:0. (11) 18:0, i. (12) 18:0. (13) 19:0, a.i. (14) 19:0. (15) 20:0, i. (16) 20:0. (17) 21:0, a.i. (18) 21:0. (19) 22:0, i. (20) 22:0 (21) 23:0, a.i. (22) 23:0. (23) 24:0, i. (24) 24:0. (25) 25:0, a.i. (26) 25:0. (27) 26:0, i. (28) 26:0. (29) 27:0, a.i. (30) 27:0. (31) 28:0, i. (32) 28:0. (33) 29:0, a.i. (34) 29:0 (35) 30:0. (36) 31:0. (37) 32:0. (Downing et al., 1960.)

It was possible to distinguish between the peaks representing the normal hydrocarbons and those of the branched hydrocarbons by passing the sample through a column containing preconditioned Linde molecular sieve (type 5A) before it entered the analytical column. This selectively subtracted the normal hydrocarbons so that a chromatogram was obtained showing peaks for branched chains only (Fig. 3). In the example shown here, the hydrocarbons were obtained by reduction of the corresponding fatty acids. Figure 3B contains peaks representing the branched chains only, and shows clearly the alternation of iso and anteiso compounds with carbon number.

The completeness of elution of the hydrocarbon fraction obtained by reduction of fatty acids was tested by comparing total peak area with that obtained on a sample known to be eluted completely, where identical amounts of the two materials were injected into the chromatograph. It was found that only 30% of the charge was eluted up to a carbon number of 33. This indicates that most of the hydrocarbon fraction was not sufficiently volatile to be eluted at temperatures up to 270°C. It is possible that this material could be swept through the chromatograph at higher column and detector temperatures. Commercial instruments are now available that pro-

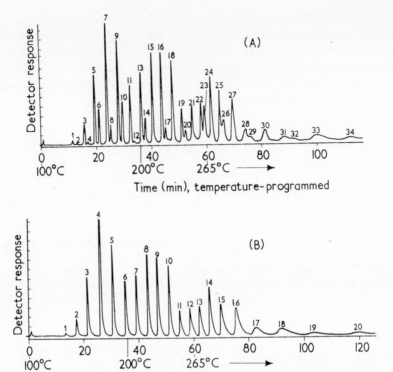

Time (min), temperature-programmed

F_{IG.} 3. Hydrocarbons derived from nonhydroxylated acids of wool wax chromatographed on silicone elastomer E 301 with the temperature programmed from 100°C to 265°C. i. = iso; a.i. = anteiso. *A*, original sample. (1) 12:0, i. (2) 12:0. (3) 13:0, a.i. (4) 13:0. (5) 14:0, i. (6) 14:0. (7) 15:0, a.i. (8) 15:0. (9) 16:0, i. (10) 16:0. (11) 17:0, a.i. (12) 17:0. (13) 18:0, i. (14) 18:0. (15) 19:0, a.i. (16) 20:0, i. (17) 20:0. (18) 21:0, a.i. (19) 22:0, i. (20) 22:0. (21) 23:0, a.i. (22) 24:0, i. (23) 24:0. (24) 25:0, a.i. (25) 26:0, i. (26) 26:0. (27) 27:0, a.i. (28) 28:0, i. (29) 28:0. (30) 29:0, a.i. (31) 30:0, i. (32) 30:0. (33) 31:0, a.i. (34) 32:0, i. *B*, after subtraction of normal hydrocarbons on molecular sieve. (1) 12:0, i. (2) 13:0, a.i. (3) 14:0, i. (4) 15:0, a.i. (5) 16:0, i. (6) 17:0, (7) 18:0, i. (8) 19:0, a.i. (9) 20:0, i. (10) 21:0, a.i. (11) 22:0, i. (12) 23:0, a.i. (13) 24:0, i. (14) 25:0, a.i. (15) 26:0, i. (16) 27:0, i. (17) 28:0, i. (18) 29:0, a.i. (19) 30:0, i. (20) 31:0, a.i. (Downing *et al.*, 1960.)

vide for programming temperatures linearly up to 500°C.[1] Highly conditioned silicone gum rubber can be used as a stationary phase. Preliminary results on normal paraffins showed that peaks up to C_{40} are eluted and can be easily identified from data on pure compounds. There are a sufficient

---

[1] F&M Scientific Corp., Avondale, Pennsylvania, for example.

number of peaks with longer retention times to account for the elution of compounds up to carbon number 75, if it is assumed that both even and odd members of the homologous series are present. This extended temperature range should make possible the chromatography of most hydrocarbons of biochemical interest.

Hydrocarbons isolated from sugar cane wax and those derived from other lipids present in the wax have been chromatographed under isothermal conditions with E301 silicone grease at 270°C (Kranz *et al.*, 1960). The C_{34} compound comes off the column in 60 to 70 minutes.

a. Procedures (Downing *et al.*, 1960)

*1. *Preparation of Subtraction Column.* A copper tube 8 inches in length with a 0.17-inch bore is packed with Linde molecular sieve, type 5A (44/60 B.S.S. mesh), and installed in the oven of the chromatograph at the outlet of the column. When first used at 270°C, the column totally absorbs singly branched iso- and anteisohydrocarbons. This capacity for binding branched hydrocarbons is destroyed by passing 5-μl samples of branched hydrocarbons through the tube until they are no longer retained. Thereafter the packing retains only the normal compounds.

*2. *Conditions for Chromatography*

Chromatograph	Laboratory-built, temperature-programmed air bath.
Column dimensions	8-foot × 0.17-inch i.d. coiled copper tube.
Solid support	Water-washed Celite 545 (60/85 B.B.S. mesh).
Stationary phase	Silicone Elastomer E 301 (10:90).
Temperatures	Column: 100° to 270°C linear. Injection port: 280°C above column. Detector: 260°C.
Carrier gas	Nitrogen. Inlet pressure: 500 mm Hg. Outlet pressure: atmospheric.
Detector	Martin gas density meter (Murray, 1959).
Recorder	Brown-Honeywell, 100 mv; 4-second response.
Sample size	2.5 μl.
Analysis time	160 minutes to anteiso C_{33} hydrocarbons.

IV. Summary

Higher aliphatic hydrocarbons can be isolated from the unsaponifiable fraction of lipids by liquid–solid chromatography on alumina or by formation of urea clathrates. Saturated hydrocarbons can be separated from unsaturated hydrocarbons by liquid–solid chromatography on silica gel, and the normal saturated fraction can be adsorbed on molecular sieve and thus separated from the isoparaffins. Normal and isohydrocarbons from C_{12} to C_{33} can be separated on a silicone column with the temperature programmed from 100° to 270°C.

C. Higher Fatty Alcohols

I. INTRODUCTION

Higher fatty alcohols are found in the unsaponifiable fraction of plant and animal fats together with hydrocarbons and sterols. They are also major components of the plant waxes cutin and suberin, and of insect waxes. In general, the plant waxes consist of esters of the higher fatty acids and higher fatty alcohols, along with free acids, hydrocarbons and alcohols. Some plant waxes may also contain fatty acid esters of carotenols, and free and combined sterols. It is necessary to liberate the bound alcohols by saponification and to separate them from the other components of the lipid fraction prior to chromatography.

II. METHODS OF ISOLATION AND PREPARATION

Fats, oils, and waxes are saponified by methods described in Section A. The unsaponifiable fraction contains the higher fatty alcohols as well as hydrocarbons and sterols. The crude alcohol fraction may be separated from the other unsaponifiable fractions in several ways, and the monohydric and dihydric alcohols are then separated by liquid–solid chromatography of the crude alcohol fraction. Mixtures of higher fatty alcohols may be separated from the saponification of waxes by precipitating the fatty acids as their calcium salts. The fatty alcohols separate from the cooled filtrate and are purified by digestion with hot acetone (Chibnall et al., 1934).

The crude alcohol fraction can also be separated by liquid–solid chromatography on alimina (MacKenna et al., 1952). Urea clathrate compounds can also be formed with the higher fatty alcohols and hydrocarbons from the unsaponifiable fraction (Downing et al., 1960). The monohydric and dihydric alcohols from the crude fractions of any of these methods may then be separated by liquid–solid chromatography on alumina (Downing et al., 1960).

Pure fatty alcohols for use as chromatographic standards can be ob-obtained by reducing the corresponding fatty acid methyl esters with lithium aluminum hydride. The crude products are purified by chromatography on alumina (Link et al., 1959a).

*a. Synthesis of Fatty Alcohols (Link et al., 1959a)

1. *Reduction of Fatty Ester.* Ethyl ether is refluxed over lithium aluminum hydride and distilled into a second flask containing twice the theoretical amount of lithium aluminum hydride needed for the reduction. (See Section G.IX for details of handling.) After the reagent dissolves, the methyl ester of the fatty acid is added slowly, and the solvent is refluxed gently for 30

minutes, care being taken to exclude atmospheric moisture at all times. Aqueous 10% sulfuric acid is added to decompose the complex, and the ether layer is evaporated to recover the fatty alcohol.

2. *Purification of Alcohol.* The crude alcohol is dissolved in a minimum of carbon tetrachloride, and the solution is added to the top of a 2.5 × 12-cm chromatographic column packed with activated alumina. The unreacted fatty acid ester is then removed from the column by washing with carbon tetrachloride. The fatty alcohol is eluted from the column with methanol and recovered by evaporation of the solvent.

III. Chromatography as Alcohols

The higher fatty alcohols are not so polar as the analogous fatty acids having the same carbon number and so can be chromatographed directly. Nevertheless they are sufficiently polar so that serious tailing occurs when separations are made on nonpolar stationary phases coated on incompletely deactivated solid supports. As with the lower alcohols, symmetrical peaks can be obtained by using the specially deactivated supporting media described in Chapter 1, Section C.III.

Dijkstra *et al.* (1955) first separated the fatty alcohols from C_8 to C_{16} on a Dow Corning silicone high-vacuum grease–Celite 545 (10:100) packing at a column temperature of 220°C. The peaks were asymmetrical, and the C_{11} alcohol was incompletely resolved from the C_{10} and C_{12} homologues. Cropper and Heywood (1957) used GLC for the quantitative determination of stearyl alcohol in technical palmityl alcohol, and for small amounts of lauryl and palmityl alcohols in technical myristyl alcohol. They first employed a Dow Corning high-vacuum silicone grease–Celite 545 (40:60) packing. At an inlet pressure of 400 mm Hg and an outlet pressure of 20 mm Hg a column temperature of 265°C was required. This resulted in slight charring of each sample put on the column, with a resultant build-up of decomposition products, and a concomitant loss in column efficiency. By using sodium chloride (30/60 **B.S.** mesh) coated with 5% of its weight of silicone grease as the column packing, the inlet pressure was reduced to 40 cm Hg, and the temperature for chromatography could be lowered by about 60°C. It now seems likely that the lower temperature was occasioned as much by the low liquid-to-support ratio necessitated by the meager capacity of the salt for holding liquid, as it was by the fact that the chromatograph was operated at reduced pressures. In any event, it is possible to obtain good separation of the fatty alcohols at temperatures ranging from 197°C to 232°C by using conventional packings (about 25:100) with the outlet at atmospheric pressure.

Boughton and Wheatley (1959) chromatographed the fatty alcohols on Apiezon M at 197°C. Alcohols containing from 6 to 20 carbon atoms were separated from an isolate from human sebum. The peaks were asymmetric and very broad at high retention times (Fig. 4), isoeicosanol being eluted between 250 and 290 minutes. A total of 28 peaks were recorded, representing normal, iso, highly branched, mono-unsaturated, and di-unsaturated monohydric alcohols.

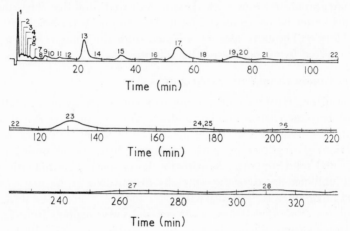

Fig. 4. Chromatogram of wax alcohols isolated from human forearm sebum run on Apiezon M at a temperature of 197°C. i. = iso; br. = branched. (1) Air. (2) 6:0. (3) 8:0. (4) 9:0, i. (5) 9:0. (6) 10:0. (7) 11:0, br. (8) 11:0. (9) 12:0. (10) 13:0, br. (11) 13:0. (12) 14:0, i. (13) 14:0. (14) 15:0, br. (15) 15:0. (16) 16:0, i. (17) 16:0. (18) 17:0, br. (19) and (20) 17:0, i., +17:1. (21) 17:0. (22) 18:0, i. (23) 18:0. (24) and (25) 19:0, i., +19:1. (26) 19:0. (27) 20:0, i. (28) 20:0. (Boughton and Wheatley, 1959.)

The saturated and unsaturated alcohols were distinguished from one another by a subtraction technique used earlier by James and Martin (1956) to differentiate saturated and unsaturated fatty acid esters. The sample is chromatographed in its original condition, after which a portion of it is brominated and rechromatographed. The di- and tetrabromo derivatives derived from monoenes and dienes, respectively, are much less volatile than the parent alcohol and are not eluted from the column under the expeirmental conditions employed. Consequently, the peaks that disappear on bromination are those representing the unsaturated alcohols.

Mixtures of saturated fatty alcohols containing 8 to 18 carbon atoms can be analyzed quantitatively on Apiezon L (method C.III.b.1). Tailing is avoided, and symmetrical peaks are obtained by using a specially deactivated solid support. Acid-washed Chromosorb W (40/60 mesh) is poured into a solution of methanolic potassium hydroxide. After the solvent is removed, the support is impregnated with stationary liquid in the usual way. Alcohols up to C_{12} are chromatographed at 180°C, and alcohols up to C_{18} at 230°C. This procedure is useful for the quantitative analysis of commercial mixtures. It is advantageous in that the Apiezon packing can be used at elevated temperatures for prolonged periods without encountering base-line drift arising from bleeding. Moreover, the percentage composition of the sample is related directly to peak area, whereas this is not the case with some polar packings.

Link et al. (1959a) chromatographed higher fatty alcohols ranging from C_{10} to C_{20} on a Carbowax 4000 monostearate column at 226°C. Stearyl alcohol was eluted under these conditions in 16 minutes, compared to 130 minutes by the method of Boughton and Wheatley. Peak symmetry was also greatly improved, probably because the more polar packing deactivated the solid support. However, the peaks for arachidyl and behenyl alcohols were so broad that accurate area measurements were difficult to make. Much better resolution of these two compounds was obtained on a silicone column at 230°C, the retention time of behenyl alcohol being 80 minutes under these conditions.

Attempts to resolve alcohol mixtures with the same chain lengths but varying degrees of unsaturation met with only limited success on these column packings. An alcohol mixture derived from soybean oil showed only 5 peaks when run on a 15-inch Carbowax (Wilkens No. 3) column at 217°C. The C_{18} peak was partly resolved, indicating the probable presence of stearyl, oleyl, linoleyl, and linoleyl alcohols in the mixture. Separation of the saturates from the unsaturates is not good enough for quantitative or qualitative analysis. However, the amount of stearyl alcohol and the total unsaturates could be determined by subtracting the latter by bromination.

a. Subtraction Method

The bromination of unsaturated compounds is described in Section A.III.

b. Conditions for Chromatography

*1. On Nonpolar Liquid with Deactivated Support (Link and Morrissette, 196 0)

Chromatograph	Beckman CG-2.
Column dimensions	63 × 0.655-cm o.d. coiled stainless steel tubing.
Solid support	Acid-washed Chromosorb W (40/60 U. S. mesh) impregnated with KOH (10:100).
Stationary phase	Apiezon L (20:100).
Temperatures	Injection: 350°C. Detector and column: 180°C for C_8 through C_{12}; 230°C for C_8 through C_{18}.
Carrier gas	Helium at 63 ml/min at 180°C or 70 ml/min at 230°C, measured at 25°C and 760 mm. Inlet pressure: 1050 mm Hg. Outlet pressure: atmospheric.
Detector	Four-filament hot-wire T/C cell operated at 250 ma.
Recorder	1 mv; 1 second; 0.5 inch/min.
Sample size	1.5 to 4 μl.
Analysis time	About 23 minutes to C_{18} at 230°C.

*2. *On a Polar and a Nonpolar Liquid* (Link *et al.*, 1959a)

Chromatograph	Beckman GC-2.
Column dimensions	1.5-foot × ¼-inch o.d. stainless steel.
Solid support	C-22 firebrick (30/60 mesh).
Stationary phase	(I) Carbowax 4000 monostearate (for alcohols up to C_{18}).
	(II) Silicone grease (32:68) for higher alcohols.
Temperatures	(I) 226°C. (II) 232°C.
Carrier gas	(I) Helium at 67 ml/min and 30 psig. (II) Helium at 85 ml/min.
Detector	Hot-wire T/C cell operated at 250 ma.
Recorder	1 mv.
Sample size	10 to 15 μl.
Analysis time	(I) 16 minutes to C_{18}. (II) 80 minutes to behenyl alcohol.

IV. CHROMATOGRAPHY AS ACETATES

To obtain better separation of saturated from unsaturated alcohols having the same carbon number, Link *et al.* (1959b) converted the alcohols to their corresponding acetates and employed a polyester column at a temperature of 228°C. They based their reasoning on the fact that unsaturated fatty acid esters move through polyester columns more slowly than their saturated analogues, with retention times being proportional to degree of unsaturation. They believed that the same results could be achieved by converting the alcohols to acetates by reaction with acetic anhydride and chromatographing them on Resoflex 446. Excellent separation of the C_{18} monoene, diene, and triene, was obtained, the latter being eluted in about 48 minutes (Fig. 5). However, stearyl and oleyl acetates were not completely resolved. This might be accomplished on a column with a larger number of theoretical plates. In any event, the oleyl alcohol could be subtracted from the mixture by a preliminary bromination step.

Link *et al.* (1959b) made quantitative analyses of a number of known

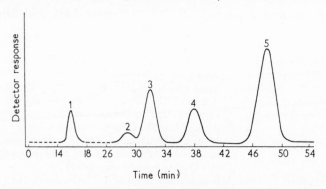

FIG. 5. Linseed alcohol acetates chromatographed on Resoflex 446 at 228°C. (1) 16:0. (2) 18:0. (3) 18:1. (4) 18:2. (5) 18:3. (Link *et al.*, 1959b.)

mixtures of alcohol acetates using the peak area–internal normalization method for calculating the results (Table IV). High results were obtained consistently for stearyl acetate even in the absence of oleyl acetate. The reasons for this are unexplainable but are apparently associated with the amount of saturated compound present. When the amount of saturated compound was decreased, the difference between weight per cent and area per cent also decreased. Despite this limitation the method is at least as reliable as the ultraviolet spectrophotometric technique for measuring unsaturates.

TABLE IV

ANALYSIS OF KNOWN MIXTURES OF ALCOHOL ACETATES[a]

Mixture	Component	Present (%) weight	Run:	Found area (%) 1	2	3	Avg.
1	Stearyl	25.3		28.0	28.4	28.7	28.4
	Oleyl	25.0		24.9	24.7	24.5	24.7
	Linoleyl	24.9		23.9	23.7	23.2	23.6
	Linolenyl	24.8		23.2	23.2	23.6	23.3
2	Oleyl	26.2		27.9	27.6		27.8
	Linoleyl	31.2		29.9	30.3		30.1
	Linolenyl	42.6		42.2	42.1		42.1
3	Stearyl	28.5		31.2	30.2		30.7
	Linoleyl	29.4		27.4	27.9		27.6
	Linolenyl	42.1		41.4	41.9		41.6

[a] From Link et al. (1959b).

Meyer zu Reckendorf (1960) has chromatographed the free alcohols on a similar column packing (Reoplex 400). Good resolution by carbon number was obtained, but unfortunately no unsaturated alcohols were included.

a. Procedures (Link et al., 1959b)

1. *Acetylation.* The alcohols are converted to their acetates by refluxing them with an equal weight of acetic anhydride. The excess reagent is hydrolyzed by adding water. The product is washed with warm water, dried in a vacuum oven at 60°C, and stored under nitrogen at 0°C.

2. *Deactivation of Support.* Chromosorb W is washed with concentrated hydrochloric acid, 10% sodium hydroxide, and water, in that order. It is then heated at 200°C for 2 hours. Some tailing still occurs. It should be possible to reduce this by using the inert supports described in Chapter 1, Section C.III.

b. Conditions for Chromatography

*1. On Resoflex 446 (Link et al., 1959b)

Chromatograph	Beckman Model GC-2.
Column dimensions	9-foot × ¼-inch o.d. stainless steel.
Solid support	Chromosorb W (60/80 mesh) deactivated by washing as described above.
Stationary phase	Resoflex 446 (15:85).
Temperature	228°C.
Carrier gas	Helium at 42 ml/min (25°C). Column pressure: 30 psig.
Detector	Hot-wire T/C cell operated at 200 ma.
Recorder	1 mv.
Sample size	2 μl.
Analysis time	70 minutes to C_{20} acetate.

V. CHROMATOGRAPHY AS HYDROCARBONS

Mixtures of monohydric alcohols and α,β-diols containing from 12 to 33 carbon atoms can be separated by GLC after conversion to their corresponding hydrocarbons (Downing *et al.*, 1960). This permits the analysis of alcohols possessing higher carbon numbers than any other procedure developed thus far and also makes possible the determination of the highly polar diols. However, it is first necessary to separate the diols from the monohydric alcohols by liquid–solid chromatography before reduction, since many of the hydrocarbon chains are common to both groups. After this is done, the alcohol fractions are converted to iodo alkanes by treatment with iodine and red phosphorus. The iodides are then reduced to hydrocarbons with lithium aluminum hydride. An alternative procedure is to convert the alcohol fractions to tosylates before reduction.

Downing *et al.* (1960) chromatographed hydrocarbons derived from the monohydric alcohol fraction of wool fat on a silicone column with the temperature programmed between 100°C and 270°C. Twenty-nine compounds were resolved or partly resolved. It was possible to distinguish between peaks representing the normal hydrocarbons and peaks representing the branched-chain hydrocarbons by subtracting the former with a column of molecular sieve (type 5A) connected into the gas stream of the chromatograph (see Section B.III.a).

It was found that isohydrocarbons have slightly shorter retention times than anteisohydrocarbons with the same carbon number, but the difference is not great enough to make it possible to distinguish between them. In practice, no difficulty was experienced in telling iso from anteiso compounds, since the former were always of even carbon number, and the latter always of odd carbon number.

During fractionation of the unsaponifiable material from the wool wax, the α,β-diols became divided into two parts: those which formed complexes with urea, and those which did not form complexes with urea. The two fractions were reduced separately to hydrocarbons and examined by GLC. As might be expected, the longer chains were more easily complexed by urea. However, iso and anteiso compounds were found in the urea adduct together with normal hydrocarbons, indicating once more that urea fractionation does not give a clean-cut separation of the straight and branched-chain members of the series (see Section B). The composition of the α,β-diols was calculated from the combined figures for the two fractions. Normal compounds formed only a small portion of the fraction.

a. Procedures

1. *Preparation of a Molecular Sieve Column.* Preparation of a column for subtracting n-hydrocarbons and conditions for chromatography are described in Section B.III.a.

*2. *Conversion to Hydrocarbons* (Downing et al., 1960). The fatty alcohols are mixed with iodine (twofold excess) and red phosphorus (20% of the weight of iodine) and heated at 100°C for 1 hour. The remaining iodine is removed under reduced pressure at 100°C. The residue is dissolved in petroleum ether, the solution is washed with water and dried over anhydrous sodium sulfate, and the solvent is evaporated. The alkyl iodides that are formed in this step are dissolved in ether (A.R. grade) and an excess of lithium aluminum hydride is added (see Section G.IX for details of handling). The mixture is permitted to stand overnight before ethyl acetate is added, to destroy the excess reagent. The solution is next washed with dilute sulfuric acid, and the solvent is evaporated. The residue is refluxed for 30 minutes with 0.5 N ethanolic potassium hydroxide to hydrolyze any unreduced iodides which might be present. The solution is next acidified with aqueous acid and extracted with petroleum ether. The ether extract is dried, the volume reduced, and the extract percolated through a chromatographic column packed with alumina (Brockman activity I). The column is washed with petroleum ether to remove the hydrocarbons, which are then recovered from the eluate by evaporating the solvent.

VI. SUMMARY

Fatty alcohols can be isolated from the unsaponifiable fraction of lipids by complexing with urea and/or liquid–solid chromatography on alumina. They can be separated by GLC as alcohols, as acetates, or as the parent hydrocarbons. The best resolution of the C_{18} saturate and unsaturates is obtained by chromatographing the acetates on a polyester column. Dihydric alcohols and the alcohols of carbon number greater than 20 are best separated by previously converting them to the corresponding hydrocarbons.

D. *O*-Alkyl Glycerols

I. INTRODUCTION

Fatty acid esters of monoalkyl ethers of glycerol are major components of the liver and muscle lipids of several groups of lower Elasmobranchii and are found to some extent among the Teleostei and in other phyla, including Mammalia and Echinodermata. The carbon number of the long-chain part of the molecule is known to vary from 12 to 22, and the chain may be saturated, or it may contain from one to three double bonds. The compounds most thoroughly investigated include chimyl (*n*-hexadecanyl), batyl (*n*-octadecyl), and selachyl (*n*-octadecenyl) alcohols.

II. ISOLATION FROM LIPID FRACTION

The *O*-alkyl glycerols are separated from other unsaponifiable fractions by the same general procedures used for the higher fatty alcohols (Section C.II). Karnovsky and Brumm (1955) isolated batyl alcohol from the unsaponifiable fraction of starfish diverticulum fat by forming a urea complex with it (Section A.II), the sterols remaining in the supernatant solution. On decomposition of the complex with water and recrystallization from ethyl acetate, products melting at 68° to 70°C were obtained. These were mostly batyl alcohol, possibly contaminated with some other alkyl glycerol. Fatty alcohols, if present, would also be in this fraction. The alkyl glycerols can also be isolated by liquid–solid chromatography on activated alumina. Hallgren and Larsson (1959) eluted the hydrocarbons with light petroleum ether, the sterols with dichloromethane, and the alkyl glycerols with 10% methanol in dichloromethane. Swain (1948) eluted the hydrocarbons with petroleum ether, cholesterol, and vitamin A with benzene or dichloromethane, and the dihydric alcohols (selachyl, etc.) and alkyl glycerols with ethyl ether.

Alkyl glycerols can also be separated from other lipids by thin-layer chromatography (Malins, 1960). Silicic acid is deposited on 20 × 20-cm glass plates in a layer 250 to 275 μ thick. Liver oil (about 20 mg) dissolved in diethyl ether is applied to the plate about 2 cm from the edge, and separation and isolation are effected with 90:10:1 petroleum ether (b.p. 30° to 60°C)–diethyl ether–acetic acid.

III. METHODS OF CHROMATOGRAPHY

The alkyl glycerols found in Elasmobranchii liver oil contain from 12 to 22 carbon atoms and two hydroxyl groups. Because of their high molecular weights and polarities it is not practical to chromatograph them directly in the gas phase. They must first be converted to derivatives with higher vapor pressures. Hallgren and Larsson (1959) accomplish this by methylating the two free hydroxyl groups with diazomethane in the presence of boron tri-fluoride. The yield is only 70 to 80% and may be lower in individual cases (Müller and Rundel, 1958). The methylated derivatives were chromato-graphed on silicone grease at a column temperature of 265°C, and on Reoplex 400 at a column temperature of 247°C. Good separation by carbon number was obtained on the silicone column, but, as usual, the saturated and the unsaturated fractions were not resolved. On Reoplex 400, the fraction containing 18 carbon atoms in the long chain was resolved into a small peak representing the saturated ether, a large peak representing the ether with a single double bond, and another small peak arising from the presence of monoöctadecadienyl dimethyl ether (Fig. 6). Eleven glyceryl derivatives

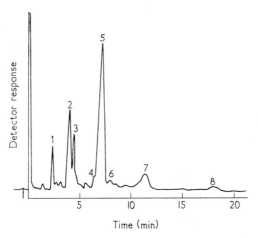

FIG. 6. Chromatogram of the dimethyl ethers of O-alkyl glycerols isolated from liver oil of *Squalus acanthias* run on Reoplex 400 at 247°C. The figures below define the long-chain part of the molecule. (1) 14:0. (2) 16:0. (3) 16:1. (4) 18:0. (5) 18:1. (6) 18:2. (7) 20:1. (8) 22:1. (Hallgren and Larsson, 1959.)

were isolated in measurable amounts and three in trace amounts with selachyl alcohol being the major component in the liver oil of three species of Elasmobranchii (Table V). Straight-line relationships were obtained between $\log_{10}$ retention times relative to methyl behenate on Reoplex 400 and the number of carbon atoms in the long alkyl chain of the glyceryl ether for both the saturated and the unsaturated compounds. The lines for the saturated and the unsaturated ethers were parallel, and they were all parallel to the line relating the logarithm of the retention time to carbon number of the methyl esters of the fatty acids.

Blomstrand and Gürtler (1959) converted the monoalkyl ethers of glycerol to diacetates before separating them by GLC. A mixture of acetic

TABLE V

PERCENTAGE COMPOSITION (WEIGHT) OF THE ALKOXY GLYCEROLS FROM LIVER OILS[a]
(The carbon number of the long chain is given.)

Alkoxy glycerol		Gray dogfish (Squalus acanthias)	Greenland shark (Somniosus microcephalus)	Ratfish (Chimaera monstrosa)
C_{12}		Trace	Trace	Trace
C_{14}	n-Tetradecanyl	5.7	2.0	1.7
C_{15}		1.9	0.7	1.1
C_{16}	n-Hexadecanyl (chimyl)	13.2	9.1	10.4
C_{16}	n-Hexadecenyl	10.6	10.8	9.1
C_{17}		3.0	3.6	4.7
C_{18}	n-Octadecanyl (batyl)	3.4	2.8	6.7
C_{18}	n-Octadecenyl (selachyl)	47.8	59.4	53.6
C_{18}	Octadecadienyl	2.4	1.6	2.5
C_{18}	Octadecatrienyl	Trace	?	?
C_{19}	n-Nonadecenyl	1.2	1.5	2.4
C_{20}	n-Eicosenyl	3.0	6.2	6.4
C_{21}		Trace	?	?
C_{22}	n-Docosenyl	2.7	2.2	1.0

[a] From Hallgren and Larsson (1959).

anhydride and pyridine was the reagent, but a mixture of acetic anhydride, acetic acid, and boron trifluoride might be more effective, since it has been used for acetylating compounds which resist esterification by the former procedure (Shoppee and Prins, 1943). If the volatilities of the lower glycols are any criterion, acetylation should be less effective than methylation for preparing these compounds for chromatography, for the boiling point of ethylene glycol is 197°C, compared to 186°C for its diacetate and 82.3°C for the dimethyl ether. Thus the increase in vapor pressure achieved by methylation is considerably greater than that achieved by acetylation. Nevertheless, Blomstrand and Gürtler (1959) were able to chromatograph chimyl, batyl, and selachyl alcohols as their diacetates on a polyester column at 218°C, a temperature considerably below the ones used for separation of the corresponding dimethyl ether derivatives. However, the retention time for batyl alcohol diacetate was 49 minutes compared to about 6 to 7 minutes for the dimethyl ether of batyl alcohol on Reoplex 400 at 247°C. Thus, either method seems satisfactory for separating these compounds. The separation factor for batyl (saturated) and selachyl (one double bond) diacetates was 1.11, a value slightly less than that usually obtained for the separation of the methyl esters of stearic and oleic acids on polyester succinate columns (Lipsky and Landowne, 1959).

Derivatives more volatile than either the esters or the ethers might be prepared by converting the alkyl glycerol to allyl ethers. This might be accomplished by mesylating them with methanesulfonyl chloride and converting the resulting dimesyl intermediates to alkyl allyl ethers by refluxing them with sodium iodide in anhydrous acetone. It is also possible to analyze O-alkyl glycerols by first converting them to aldehydes by oxidation with lead tetraacetate or periodic acid (Malins, 1960). The crude aldehydes are then purified by thin-layer chromatography on silica gel with a 95:5 mixture of petroleum ether and diethyl ether. The aldehydes are chromatographed on an 1.8-meter or 3.1-meter column packed with poly(ethylene glycol succinate) on siliconized Chromosorb (20:80) at 185°C and a flow rate of 120 to 130 ml of argon per minute.

a. Synthesis of Derivatives

1. *Preparation of Ethers* (Müller and Rundel, 1958). The sample is dissolved in dry ether, the solution is chilled to 0°C, and 10 mole % of boron trifluoride etherate is added. A threefold excess of *freshly distilled*[2] diazomethane in ether is cooled to 0°C and added (DeBoer and Backer, 1956). Alternatively, gaseous diazomethane is passed through the solution until the yellow color persists. After standing at room temperature for about 30 minutes the solution is warmed on a water bath to remove excess diazomethane. It is then washed with aqueous sodium bicarbonate solution, dried over anhydrous sodium sulfate, and the solvent evaporated. The yield of ether varies, depending on the nature of the alcohol, but it is generally around 70 to 80%. *Caution:* Diazomethane is very toxic and should be used with extreme care. *See Appendix 4.*

*2. *Separation of Dimethyl Ethers on Activated Alumina* (Hallgren and Larsson, 1960). *Pretreatment of aluminum oxide.* One kilogram of aluminum oxide is suspended in 2 liters of distilled water, and HCl is added so that the pH is maintained at 2 for 10 minutes. The aluminum oxide is washed with distilled water several times until neutral. The alumina is dried and activated at 110°C for 24 hours. The particles passing a 120 U. S. mesh sieve are used for chromatography.

Liquid–solid chromatography. The dimethoxy derivatives of the glyceryl ethers are separated from the monomethoxy derivatives and unchanged glyceryl ethers by chromatography on activated alumina. A column containing 1 gm of alumina per 20 mg of sample is packed with light petroleum

[2] The diazomethane must be freshly distilled, or artifacts may be produced on chromatography.

ether (b.p. 40° to 60°C). The dimethoxy derivatives are applied to the column in this solvent and eluted with a solution of diethyl ether in petroleum ether (10:90) which has been previously dried over sodium.

3. *Preparation of Acetates.* The sample is dissolved in about five times its weight of pyridine, and an equal volume of acetic anhydride is added. The mixture is refluxed gently for 12 hours, cooled, and quenched with ice water. The precipitate is taken up in ether, and the ether layer is washed repeatedly with dilute hydrochloric acid to remove the pyridine. The solution is dried over anhydrous sodium sulfate, and the solvent is evaporated. The residue is dissolved in ethyl acetate, and a suitable aliquot is injected into the chromatographic column.

b. Conditions for Chromatography

*1. *Chromatography of Dimethyl Ethers on Silicone Grease* (Hallgren and Larsson, 1959)

Chromatograph	Perkin-Elmer Model 116 modified with a separate heating wire to increase the injection temperature. No thermostat.
Column dimensions	200 × 0.60-cm o.d. W-shaped aluminum tubing.
Solid support	Johns-Manville C-22 firebrick (60/80 U. S. mesh) washed with concentrated HCl, then neutralized with NaOH soln, washed with water, and dried at 200°C.
Stationary phase	Dow Corning high-vacuum silicone grease (30:100). The column filling was heated for 2 weeks at 320° to 330°C in an oxygen-free stream of nitrogen.
Temperatures	Injection: 300°C. Detector and column: 265°C (measured with thermocouple).
Carrier gas	Helium at 70 ml/min. Inlet pressure: 900 mm Hg. Outlet pressure: atmospheric.
Detector	Thermistors, detector voltage: 8 volts.
Recorder	2.5 mv; 1 second; 1.74 cm/min.
Sample size	3 to 7 μl of a concentrated solution.
Analysis time	12 to 13 minutes.

*2. *Chromatography of Dimethyl Ethers on Reoplex 400* (Hallgren and Larsson, 1959)

Chromatograph	Perkin-Elmer Model 116 modified with a separate heating wire to increase the injection temperature. No thermostat.
Column dimensions	(I) 200 × 0.60-cm. o.d. W-shaped aluminum tubing. (II) 100 × 0.60-cm o.d. U-shaped aluminum tubing.
Solid support	(I) Kieselguhr 098–1504 (Perkin-Elmer, Ueberlingen) (80/100 U. S. mesh) treated with concentrated HCl–NaOH solution and washed with water until neutral. (II) The same as (I), but 60/80 U. S. mesh.

Stationary phase	(I and II) Reoplex 400, a polar polyester supplied by The Geigy Company (30:100).
Temperatures	Injection: 280°C. Detector: 247°C. (I and II) 247°C (measured with thermocouple).
Carrier gas	(I and II) Helium at 50 ml/min. Inlet pressure: 990 mm Hg. Outlet pressure: atmospheric.
Detector	Thermistors, detector voltage, 8 volts.
Recorder	5 mv; 1 second; 1.46 cm/min. A Hewlett-Packard 425-amp DDC amplifier was used to amplify the detector voltage before recording. Full-scale response about 1 mv.
Sample size	1 to 1.5 μl of a concentrated solution.
Analysis time	18 minutes.

3. Chromatography of Diacetates (Blomstrand and Gürtler, 1959)

Chromatograph	Pye argon.
Column dimensions	4 feet.
Solid support	Celite (100/400 mesh), acid-washed, alkali-treated.
Stationary phase	Poly(diethylene glycol adipate) (LAC-IR-296).
Temperature	218°C.
Carrier gas	Argon at 20 ml/min. Inlet pressure: 720 mm Hg.
Detector	Beta ionization detector at 1250 volts.
Recorder	Not given.
Sample size	Not given.
Analysis time	About 49 minutes.

IV. SUMMARY

O-Alkyl glycerols can be separated from other unsaponifiable fractions by the formation of urea clathrates or by liquid–solid chromatography on activated alumina. They have been chromatographed as dimethyl ethers or as acetates and probably could be chromatographed as allyl ethers. The glycerol ethers have been separated on silicone grease or Reoplex 400, and the diacetates on LAC-IR-296 polyester.

E. Steroids

I. INTRODUCTION

Steroids are widely distributed in the plant and animal kingdoms. Their basic structure consists of four fused rings, three of which are 6-membered, and the remaining one 5-membered. Thus they are derivatives of cyclopentanoperhydrophenanthrene.

Many steroids have now been separated by GLC at column temperatures ranging from 220° to 290°C. These include sex hormones, adrenal cortical hormones, and bile acids. Vitamins D_2 and D_3 have also been chromatographed, but they undergo thermal cyclization when flash-evaporated. Many steroids are stable under the conditions used for separation.

Steroids are usually chromatographed without prior chemical modification, the main exception being the bile acids. These are first converted to methyl esters by methods described in Section G.III.

II. Methods of Isolation

Steroids are found in the unsaponifiable lipid fraction of tissues. They can be separated from other unsaponifiable lipids such as hydrocarbons and higher alcohols by liquid–solid chromatography on alumina. The steroids eluted from the alumina column are further purified by precipitation as steroid digitonides (Boughton and Wheatley, 1959) before separation by gas chromatography. They also may be separated from the total lipid fraction by liquid–solid chromatography on silicic acid (see Section A.IIa.1.).

a. Experimental Method

1. *Digitonin Procedure* (Boughton and Wheatley, 1959). The unsaponifiable lipids from a tissue extract are chromatographed on alumina as described in Section A.II.c. The steroid fractions are eluted with 10% $CHCl_3$ in petroleum ether and $CHCl_3$ alone, and the solvent is evaporated. A sample of residue (100 mg) is dissolved in 5 ml of 90% ethanol at 60°C. Five milliliters of 90% ethanol containing 300 mg of digitonin is added. The mixture is allowed to stand overnight at room temperature. A white precipitate is formed which is filtered and washed with 90% ethanol. The filtrate and washings are combined and evaporated to a small volume. A small amount of digitonin in 90% ethanol is again added at 60°C, and the process is repeated. The precipitates are combined. This is the sterol digitonide fraction. Other steroids not precipitated are recovered from the mother liquor by quenching of the solutions with water and extraction with ether.

The sterol digitonide is decomposed by dissolving the precipitate in 2 ml of pyridine at 70°C. The solution is allowed to stand at room temperature overnight. An excess of ether is added, and the digitonin precipitates. This is centrifuged, and the steroids are recovered from the supernatant.

III. Chromatography

Steroids have relatively low vapor pressures, so most of the early work on their separation was done at high column temperatures. They can be chromatographed on silicone oil at 287°C with some success, but retention volumes are large (Beerthuis and Recourt, 1960). A polar substrate, poly(ethylene glycol isophthalate), has also been used which gives shorter retention volumes at 270°C. However, these methods do not separate all steroids investigated, and they suffer the additional disadvantage of requiring high column temperatures at which some of the compounds are unstable.

The most promising method yet developed for the separation of steroids is through use of a methyl-substituted silicone gum (General Electric Co. SE-30). Good resolution of many hydrocarbons, sterols, ethers, and acetyl esters can be obtained. Column temperatures and retention volumes are kept low by using a small percentage of liquid on the solid support. With low liquid–solid ratios, chromatograms can be obtained at temperatures as much as 250°C below the boiling points of the materials being analyzed, since even at these temperatures many compounds have vapor pressures sufficiently high to pass through columns.

The steroids are separated at a temperature of 222°C on a column packing composed of 2 to 3% silicone SE-30 coated on treated Chromosorb W. The retention time of cholesterol is about 35 minutes under these conditions (Fig. 7). Symmetrical peaks are obtained except for ketone derivatives which

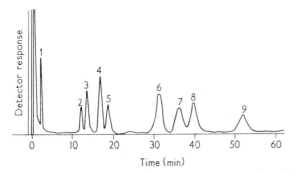

FIG. 7. Separation of steroids on SE-30 silicone gum at 222°C. (1) Androstane. (2) Pregnan-3,20-dione. (3) Allopregnan-3,20-dione. (4) Coprostane. (5) Cholestane. (6) Stigmastone. (7) Cholesterol. (8) Cholestan-3-one. (9) Stigmasterol. (VandenHeuvel et al., 1960.)

show slight tailing. All materials investigated were stable at this temperature. Neither cholesterol and cholestanol nor their methyl ethers or acetates were well separated (Table VI). However, stereoisomers were separated, coprostane giving a relative retention value of 0.90 compared to a value of 1.00 for cholestane. Hydroxy compounds were eluted before the corresponding ketones, and the retention times of the methyl ethers were slightly less than either the corresponding hydroxy compounds or ketones. The column can handle only a small sample load, since there is such a thin coating of liquid substrate on the solid support. Therefore a sensitive detector such as a flame or ionization instrument is required.

a. Conditions for Chromatography

*1. *On a Nonpolar Packing* (Beerthuis and Recourt, 1960)

Chromatograph   Laboratory-built.
Column dimensions   90 × 0.4 cm i.d.

TABLE VI

RELATIVE RETENTION TIMES OF STEROIDS ON SE-30 SILICONE GUM[a]

Compound	Temperature	
	260°C[b]	222°C[c]
Androstane	0.17	0.11
Androstan-17-one	0.30	0.22
Androstan-3,17-dione	0.56	0.47
4-Androsten-3,17-dione	0.68	0.57
Pregnan-3,20-dione	0.74	0.67
Allopregnan-3,20-dione	0.82	0.74
Allopregnan-3β,20β-diol		0.70
Allopregnan-3,11,20-trione	1.05	0.99
Coprostane		0.90
Cholestane	1.00[d]	1.00[e]
Cholestanyl methyl ether	1.58	1.78
Cholesteryl methyl ether	1.47	1.72
Cholestan-3-one	2.00	2.17
4-Cholesten-3-one	2.37	2.72
Cholestanol	1.70	1.99
Cholesterol	1.21 (broad)	1.98
Cholestanyl acetate	1.15 (very broad)	2.84
Cholesteryl acetate	1.18 (broad)	2.81
β-Sitosterol	1.82 (very broad)	3.26
β-Sitosterol acetate		4.62
Stigmastane		1.65
Stigmasterol	1.62 2.29	2.84

[a] From VandenHeuvel et al. (1960).
[b] Pressure, 20 psig; 7/100 SE-30 on Chromosorb W, 80/100 mesh.
[c] Pressure, 10 psig; 2–3/100 SE-30 on Chromosorb W, 80/100 mesh.
[d] Time, 19.3 minutes.
[e] Time, 17.6 minutes.

Solid support	Celite 545 (80/100 mesh, Bureau of Standards) treated with acid, screened, and treated with dichlorodimethyl silane.
Stationary phase	Midlands silicone No. 550 residue of molecular distillation at 200°C and 2 μ of pressure (20:80).
Temperature	287°C (conditioned at this temperature for 2 days).
Carrier gas	Nitrogen at 24 ml/min. Inlet pressure: 53 cm Hg. Outlet pressure: atmospheric.
Detector	Gas density balance at column temperature.
Recorder	Sunvac DC amplifier with Evershed ammeter.
Sample size	2 to 4 mg.
Analysis time	225 minutes to cholesteryl valerate. 105 minutes to stigmasterol.

*2. *On a Polar Liquid* (Sweeley and Horning, 1960)

Chromatograph	Barber Coleman Model 10.
Column dimensions	100 × 0.2-cm glass U tube.
Solid support	Acid-washed Celite 545 (60/80 U. S. mesh).
Stationary phase	Poly(ethylene glycol isophthalate) (20:80) conditioned at 200°C.
Temperature	Column: 220° to 280°C.
Carrier gas	Argon at 50 to 100 ml/min. Inlet pressure: 25 psig. Outlet pressure: atmospheric.
Detector	Argon ionization, 600 volts, radium source.
Recorder	Wheelco, 50 mv; 1 second.
Sample size	10 to 50 μg in a 1 to 2% solution.
Analysis time	Less than 30 minutes for most steroids at 270°C. 18.5 minutes for 4-androstene-3,17-dione.

3. *On SE-30 at Low Packing Ratio* (VandenHeuvel *et al.*, 1960)

Chromatograph	Pye argon.
Column dimensions	6 feet × 4 mm i.d.
Solid support	Treated Chromosorb W (80/100 mesh).
Stationary phase	Methyl-substituted gum rubber (General Electric Co.) SE-30 (2 to 3%).
Temperature	222°C.
Carrier gas	Argon. Inlet pressure: 10 psig. Outlet pressure: atmospheric.
Detector	Ionization.
Recorder	Not given.
Sample size	5 to 10 μg.
Analysis time	55 minutes to stigmasterol.

IV. Summary

Steroids can be isolated from the unsaponifiable fraction of lipids by liquid–solid chromatography on alimina, or from the total lipid fraction by chromatography on silicic acid. Some can be purified by precipitation as steroid digitonides.

They are separated by GLC most effectively on a silicone SE-30 stationary phase with a low liquid-to-solid packing ratio, a relatively low temperature, and a small sample size.

F. Higher Fatty Aldehydes

I. Introduction

Higher fatty aldehydes such as octanal, nonanal, and dodecanal occur in small amounts in many plant oils and undoubtedly contribute to their characteristic odors. Their separation and chromatography are discussed in Chapter 5. Normally aldehydes do not occur in the free state in unsaponified fats except as products of oxidation. However, they may be produced from unsaturated fatty acids by cleavage of the hydrocarbon chains with ozone. This technique is important in organic structure determination. Fatty aldehydes may also be produced by mild acid hydrolysis of members of a class of phospholipids called plasmalogens. These compounds are vinyl ethers with the following general structure:

$$
\begin{array}{l}
\overset{\displaystyle O}{\overset{\displaystyle \|}{}} \\
CH_2-O-C-R_1 \\
| \\
CH-O-CH=CH-R_2 \\
| \\
CH_2-O-PO\cdot(OH)-O-CH_2-CH_2-NH_2
\end{array}
$$

On rupture of the ether linkage, the alkylvinyl alcohol reverts to the tautomeric aldehyde.

II. ISOLATION

The isolation of plasmalogens is complicated, so a general outline only will be given here. The reader is referred to papers by Gray and Macfarlane (1958) and Gray (1958) for details. The plasmalogens are normally found in the phospholipid fraction isolated from the unsaponified fats by chromatography on silica gel. However, in the presence of the glyceride fraction they tend to be partly hydrolized on the column, the free aldehydes appearing in the fat fraction. Hydrolysis can be reduced or eliminated by running two lipid extracts in succession through the same column. Breakdown occurs in the first but not in the second run, presumably because the column is deactivated.

Hydrolysis can also be reduced by extracting the tissue in such a way that the phospholipids are obtained essentially free of fats (Pangborn, 1945). The tissue is dehydrated and defatted by treatment with acetone. The phospholipids are then extracted with methanol, and barium chloride solution is added to precipitate acidic phospholipids. Phospholipids which form ether-soluble barium salts are found in the supernatant. These fractions are purified further, and the phospholipids are recovered. Plasmalogens are isolated from the fraction by chromatography on silica gel. Aldehydes are liberated from them, and residual fatty acids are removed as described in Section G.

III. CHROMATOGRAPHY

Aldehydes up to C_{13} can be chromatographed on a Reoplex 400 column at 150°C (Meyer zu Reckendorf, 1960). However, at higher temperature they are likely to undergo aldol condensations and ultimately form polymers. To avoid this, Gray (1960a) converted the higher fatty aldehydes to dimethyl acetals by treatment with methanolic hydrochloric acid prior to chromatography. The acetals are more stable than the parent aldehydes and, according to Gray, more volatile. This latter statement is not correct for the lower aldehydes, since acetaldehyde boils at 21.5°C and its dimethyl acetal at 64.5°C, whereas hexanal boils at 131°C and its dimethyl acetal at 158°C. As usual, the values tend to converge as the carbon number increases.

The acetals were as stable as the corresponding fatty acid methyl esters at 190°C on Apiezon L, and more stable on Reoplex. Evidently a small amount of transesterification can take place between the esters and the polar packing, but this is not possible with the acetals. However, for some unknown reason, the acetals were unstable on a polyester adipate column. It was also impossible to subtract unsaturated acetals from saturated ones by bromination, since peaks representing both groups of compounds were removed by the treatment. This should not be surprising, since the α-hydrogens of

TABLE VII

Retention Volumes of Known Aldehyde Dimethyl Acetals Relative to Stearaldehyde Dimethyl Acetal[a,b]

		Stationary phase	
Aldehyde, familiar name	Shorthand[c] designation	Apiezon L at 190°C	Reoplex 400 at 190°C
Capryl	10:0	0.028	0.064
Undecanoic	11:0	0.043	0.089
Lauryl	12:0	0.067	0.124
Tridecanoic	13:0	0.106	0.177
Myristoleic	14:1	0.150	0.280
Myristyl	14:0	0.167	0.254
Pentadecanoic	15:0	0.263	0.364
Palmetoleic	16:1	0.364	0.570
Palmityl	16:0	0.412	0.506
Heptadecanoic	17:0	0.640	0.715
Oleic	18:1	0.84	1.12
Linoleic	18:2	0.79	1.34
Linolenic	18:3	0.79	1.68
Stearyl	18:0	1.0	1.0
Nonadecanoic	19:0	1.56	1.41

[a] From Gray (1960a).

[b] All retention volumes were measured from the middle of the air peak.

[c] Evolved by Ahrens and co-workers to designate compounds by number of carbon atoms, number of double bonds, and presence of chain branching; e.g., br. 16:1 represents a branched-chain mono-unsaturated C_{16} compound. See introduction of this chapter for details.

acetals readily undergo substitution reactions with bromine in the cold (Pinner, 1872). Therefore it was necessary to hydrogenate the mixtures to identify peaks arising from unsaturated compounds. This was done in ethyl alcohol solution at a concentration of 1% by volume with platinum oxide as a catalyst. It was sometimes necessary to add up to 20% by volume of chloroform to keep the acetals in solution.

The acetals were chromatographed on Reoplex 400 and Apiezon L at 190°C. The acetals had slightly better separation factors on Apiezon L than the methyl esters of the fatty acids, but on Reoplex 400 resolution within the two groups of compounds was about the same. The retention volumes of the acetals were higher than those of the corresponding fatty acid esters on the nonpolar (Apiezon) column and lower on the polar (Reoplex) column, showing that dimethyl acetals are less polar than esters.

Saturated and unsaturated acetals containing up to 19 carbon atoms in the long chain were separated by these procedures (Table VII). The retention time of the C_{18} derivative was about 30 to 35 minutes on Reoplex 400 and greater than 210 minutes on Apiezon L. Saturates were resolved from unsaturates, the separation factor for the stearyl and oleyl derivatives being 1.12, or about the same as was obtained on the alkyl glycerol analogues

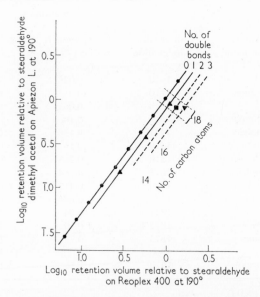

FIG. 8. Log_{10} relative retention volumes of dimethyl acetals of higher fatty aldehydes on Apiezon L plotted against relative retention volumes on Reoplex 400. ●, straight-chain saturated aldehyde dimethyl acetals. △, mono-unsaturated aldehyde dimethyl acetals. ■, di-unsaturated aldehyde dimethyl acetals. ▽, tri-unsaturated aldehyde di-methyl acetals. (Gray, 1960a.)

(Section D.III). It is interesting that the acetals can be separated according to relative polarity on Reoplex even though they do not have an ester group, a requirement that was postulated by Link *et al.* (1959a) (Section C) to be necessary for the resolution of saturates from unsaturates on these packings.

Straight lines were obtained when $\log_{10}$ retention volumes were plotted against carbon number for both packings. A similar result was obtained when the logarithms of the retention volumes on Apiezon L and Reoplex 400 were plotted against each other (Fig. 8). Parallel straight lines for the saturated and unsaturated series were obtained, with the former lying somewhat below the latter. With this grid it is possible to identify tentatively the unknown compounds by finding out on which line they lie when the two retention volumes are plotted against one another. This is identical to the technique used for the identification of amines, and for fatty acids.

Gray (1960a) separated acetals derived from ox spleen choline plasmalogen by this technique. He found peaks corresponding to C_{13} to C_{18} vinyl esters, all the members of the series with odd carbon numbers being represented. He was able to classify them according to carbon number, degree of chain branching, and number of double bonds, by relative retention volumes on the polar and nonpolar packings coupled with subtraction of the peaks arising from unsaturated compounds by hydrogenation.

a. Sample Preparation

*1. *Hydrolysis of Plasmalogens* (Gray, 1960b). A sample of phospholipid containing plasmalogen is dissolved in 90% (v/v) acetic acid (10 mg of phosphorus per milliliter) and incubated at 38°C for 18 hours. The solution is cooled, neutralized with NaOH, and then shaken with an equal volume of chloroform–methanol 2:1 (v/v). The phases are separated by centrifugation, and the upper aqueous methanol layer is removed. The chloroform layer is washed three times with 0.2 volume of 0.5 M NaCl. The presence of NaCl is necessary to keep emulsion formation to the minimum. The chloroform solution is dried over anhydrous Na_2SO_4, filtered, and evaporated at 35°C *in vacuo;* the residue is redissolved in a known volume of chloroform–methanol 49:1 (v/v).

The solution containing phospholipids and free aldehydes is chromatographed on silicic acid (1 gm/mg of phosphorus) in chloroform–methanol 49:1 (v/v). Development is continued with this solvent, and the free aldehydes are rapidly eluted from the column. All the phospholipids are retained by the column in this solvent. The fractions containing the aldehydes are bulked, and the solvent is evaporated under reduced pressure.

*2. *Preparation of Acetals* (Gray, 1960a). The aldehydes (1 gm) are refluxed for 2 hours with 2% anhydrous methanolic hydrochloric acid (20 ml). The solution is allowed to cool, and the acid is neturalized by adding a slight excess of anhydrous sodium carbonate. The acetals are then extracted from the methanol with petroleum ether (b.p. 40° to 60°C), and the ether layer is shaken with saturated sodium metabisulfite solution to remove unreacted aldehyde. The petroleum ether layer is washed with water until neutral and dried over anhydrous sodium sulfate, and the solvent is removed under reduced pressure. The residue contains the dimethy acetals of the aldehydes, together with small amounts of the methyl esters of fatty acids carried over during the isolation from plasmalogens. These latter are removed as their sodium salts by refluxing for 2 hours with 0.5 M methanolic sodium hydroxide solution (20 ml). The solution is cooled, diluted with water, and extracted with petroleum ether. The ether layer is washed with water until free of alkali and then dried over anhydrous sodium sulfate, and the solvent is removed under reduced pressure.

*b. Conditions for Chromatography

1. On Apiezon and Reoplex (Gray, 1960a)

Chromatograph	Laboratory-built, incorporating commercial amplifier by W. G. Pye & Co.
Column dimensions	4 feet × 0.4-cm i.d. glass.
Solid support	(I) Celite (100/120 B.S. mesh) deactivated with methanolic alkali (James et al., 1952). (II and IIa) Celite (100/120 B.S. mesh).
Stationary phase	(I) Apiezon L (18:70). (II) Reoplex 400 (21:70).
Temperature	(I and II) 190°C. (IIa) 170°C.
Carrier gas	Argon. Inlet pressure: (I and II) 725 mm Hg. (IIa) 517 mm Hg. Outlet pressure: atmospheric.
Detector	Argon ionization.
Recorder	(I) Sunvic, 0 to 10 mv; 1.0-second response, 8 inches, or (II) Evershed, 0 to 1 ma; 12 inches/hour.
Sample size	100 μg.
Analysis time	(I) 220 minutes. (II) 40 minutes. (IIa) 90 minutes.

IV. Summary

Higher fatty aldehydes, occasionally occurring free in plant oils, may be produced by cleavage of unsaturated fatty acids by ozone, or by rupture of the ether linkage in plasmalogens. They can be chromatographed unchanged up to C_{13} on a polyester column, but the higher homologues are unstable at the higher temperatures necessary for chromatography and therefore are converted to dimethyl acetals. The acetals may be chromatographed on polyester columns other than polyester adipate and also on Apiezon grease.

G. Fatty Acids

I. INTRODUCTION

James and Martin (1952) first described the gas chromatographic separation of fatty acids from formic through dodecanoic. Serious tailing was encountered on silicone columns because of concentration-dependent molecular association of the solutes in the partition liquid. Peak symmetry was improved by including stearic acid in the stationary phase so that the acids would tend to associate with the column packing rather than dimerize. However, this approach is untenable for the higher fatty acids, since the stearic acid would bleed from the column at temperatures required for chromatography. Infrared studies (Beerthuis *et al.*, 1959) have shown that degree of association of acids in paraffin solution is dependent on both temperature and concentration, and that it is possible to obtain them almost entirely as monomers by heating them to 200°C and keeping the molar concentration below 0.007. This makes it possible to separate free fatty acids from C_{12} to C_{18} on Apiezon L at 276°C. However, the peaks are markedly asymmetric. This is reduced but not eliminated by raising the temperature to 300°C. Therefore the method does not give good enough separations to make it possible to detect fatty acids with odd carbon numbers or to resolve saturated and unsaturated compounds having the same carbon number. A recent approach to the analysis of free fatty acids has been reported (Metcalfe, 1960), whereby a polyester treated with phosphoric acid is the liquid phase. Well-defined symmetrical peaks are obtained with C_4 to C_{22} acids by using poly(diethylene glycol adipate) partially cross-linked with pentaerythritol (LAC-2-R-446) and containing 2% phosphoric acid (85% acid) as the stationary phase. This is coated on 60/80 mesh Celite 545, and the separations are made at a column temperature of 220° to 235°C. Stearic and oleic acids are not completely separated under the conditions employed, although a C_{18} acid with two double bonds is separated, as well as several unsaturated C_{16} acids. A larger sample of free fatty acids is required to give the same detector response with a hot-wire detector as the methyl esters of the same acids, and quantitative recoveries do not agree too well, possibly owing to differences in thermal conductivities between free acids and the esters, indicating that calibration of detector response would be required. A number of workers have experienced difficulties with this procedure.

Cropper and Heywood (1953) introduced a more fruitful approach by converting the acids to methyl esters prior to chromatography. These are more volatile than the free acids and, moreover, do not dimerize. They were able to separate C_{12} to C_{22} acids on the basis of carbon number, but resolution was not good enough to detect differences in unsaturation. Since then, other workers have improved the method through the introduction of more sensitive detectors and new column packings, so that now chromatography of the fatty acids as their methyl esters is the only technique that will be considered. Gas chromatographic techniques have been used more extensively in this field than in any other single area of biochemical research. Consequently, the methods have gained a degree of acceptance and maturity not found elsewhere in this book. They are rapidly replacing older methods such as paper chromatography and alkaline isomerization because of greater speed, accuracy, and versatility. Nevertheless, sharp differences of opinion on techniques still exist, and new developments are moving ahead rapidly, particularly in the field of capillary chromatography.

II. Isolation Methods

Free fatty acids may be separated from total lipids, methylated, and analyzed by GLC. The total lipids may also be separated into glyceride, phospholipid, and sterol ester fractions. The fatty acids in these fractions may then be methylated by interesterification, or by saponification and methylation, and analyzed by GLC (See Section A.I.b).

The volatile fatty acids (up to C_8 to C_{10}) are discussed in Chapter 3 and may be separated from the higher fatty acids by procedures described in Section A of that chapter. This separation is not necessary if only the long-chain materials are of interest, since at the high column temperatures used to separate them the short-chain substances are eluted rapidly and are not resolved. Consequently, they do not interfere with the separation of the methyl esters of the long-chain acids.

III. Methylation Methods

The methyl esters of fatty acids may be formed by interesterification of glycerides, phospholipids, and sterol esters, by methylation of the salts of the acids, or by direct methylation of the free fatty acids.

Interesterification prevents structural changes involving double bonds which may occur during saponification. Stoffel et al. (1959) have developed a micromethod for interesterification with anhydrous methanol–HCl. The methyl esters are then isolated from nonsaponifiable contaminants by extraction into petroleum ether and microsublimation. Other workers have also interesterified with the same reagents (Johnston and Kummerow, 1960; Rowe, 1959). The esters are separated from the filtrates by means of organic solvents such as petroleum ether or diethyl ether.

Interesterification can also be accomplished with methanol and sodium or potassium methoxide (Luddy et al., 1960). The methyl esters are separated from other petroleum ether-soluble materials on a silicic acid column. Both of these methods interesterify phospholipids and sterol esters quantitatively as well as the more easily esterified glycerides.

The three-membered ring of epoxy acids opens when these compounds are interesterified by means of acid catalysts. However, if a minimum amount of sodium methoxide is used, these acids can be methylated without ring opening.

Salts of the fatty acids may be converted directly to methyl esters. This avoids the formation of etholides (linear esters) from hydroxy acids which occurs when the free acids are isolated. Downing *et al.* (1960) saponify the lipids and form the calcium salts of the acids and methylate by refluxing with methanol, benzene, and a small amount of concentrated H_2SO_4. Gehrke and Goerlitz (1960,) form the insoluble silver salts of the free acids. These are washed and caused to react with methyl iodide to form the methyl esters and are then free from contamination from unsaponifiable lipids.

Free fatty acids may be methylated with anhydrous methanol–HCl by the procedure of Stoffel *et al.* (1959) for interesterification of lipids. Hornstein *et al.* (1960) employ this reagent for methylation of naturally occurring fatty acids from unsaponified lipids after preferentially adsorbing them on a strong anion-exchange resin. The fatty acids are converted to the methyl esters directly on the resin. Sammons and Wiggs (1960) saponify the lipids and adsorb free fatty acids on activated alumina. They then form the methyl esters on the alumina by using methanol–HCl. Free fatty acids may also be esterified with diazomethane (Schlenk and Gellerman, 1960). This method is good for small quantities of acids, but the diazomethane must be freshly distilled, and it is very toxic and explosive if not handled properly. Boron trifluoride has been used as a catalyst to methylate free fatty acids (Metcalfe and Schmitz, 1961). The acids are esterified in about 2 minutes by boiling in methanol–BF_3. The solution is then quenched with water, and the esters either are extracted with petroleum ether for the higher fatty acids, or are separated physically from the water layer for the lower fatty acids (less than C_{10}) where losses on evaporation would occur. This reagent has been utilized successfully for saturated fatty acids as well as for oleic and linoleic acids. It also has been used to methylate dicarboxylic (azeleic and pimelic) acids. Care must be taken when handling BF_3 gas, since it is very toxic, but the methanol–BF_3 solution is stable and may be stored for periods of at least 4 months.

a. Interesterification Methods

*1. *Anhydrous Methanol–HCl* (Stoffel *et al.*, 1959). *Interesterification.* "The esters or acids to be methylated (1 to 10 mg) are dissolved in 4 ml of 5% hydrochloric acid in superdry methanol and 0.5 ml of dry benzene in a 15 ml microsublimation tube to which a condenser with a calcium chloride moisture trap is connected. The mixture is refluxed . . . at 80° to 100°C for 2 hours, with frequent shaking at the start to dissolve the lipide mixture. After cooling to room temperature, two volumes of water are added, and the methyl esters are extracted three times with 3 ml of petroleum ether. The pooled extracts are simultaneously neutralized and dried over sodium sulfate–sodium bicarbonate mixture for 1 hour. The esters are then quantitatively transferred with petroleum ether to a second microsublimation tube and the solvent is evaporated to dryness at reduced pressure in a 40°C water bath.

"*Microsublimation.* After the microsublimation tube is fitted to the cold finger, a vacuum of 0.2 ± 0.15 mm of mercury is produced. The tube is then lowered into a . . . bath at $60° \pm 2°C$ for 60 minutes. The assembly is disconnected after cooling, and the sublimed methyl esters are rinsed off [the cold finger] with petroleum ether into a glass-stoppered tube. After evaporation of solvent, the preparation is now ready for application to the gas-liquid chromatography column.

"The sublimation technique is described for use with 1 to 5 mg of methyl esters. If greater quantities are sublimed, an increased sublimation time may be required. Use of a manifold permits several sublimations to be carried out simultaneously."

Apparatus. "Microinteresterification assembly, 19/38, consisting of round-bottomed test tubes, Liebig condensers, cold fingers, and six-place manifold, with nitrogen inlet. (Available *in toto* from Metro Industries . . . , catalog No. ME-517, or piecemeal)."

2. *Methanol–Sodium or Potassium Methoxide* (Luddy *et al.*, 1960). Apparatus, reagents, and sample must be kept dry, and exposure to atmospheric moisture must be avoided.

Preparation of sodium or potassium methoxide. Standard solutions in absolute methanol are prepared. Metallic sodium or potassium is cut into small bright pieces under petroleum ether and added, a piece at a time, to a known volume of anhydrous methanol. A slight excess is added, an aliquot is titrated, and methanol is added to the solution to adjust the concentration to $0.4\ N$.

Methanolysis. Ten to fifty milligrams of lipid is added to a small round-bottomed flask with a standard taper joint and condenser. The sample is dissolved in 5 ml of petroleum ether ($40°$ to $55°C$), and 60 ml of $0.4\ N$ sodium or potassium methoxide is added. Oxygen-free dry nitrogen is bubbled slowly through the mixture through the condenser by means of a glass capillary, and the mixture is refluxed for $1\frac{1}{2}$ hours. While the reaction mixture is still warm, a $0.5\ N$ sulfuric acid solution in methanol is added through the condenser in slight excess of the amount needed to neutralize the methoxide. The cooled reaction mixture is transferred to a 100-ml separatory funnel, and the flask is rinsed with 2×15-ml portions of petroleum ether. Twenty milliliters of water is added, and the mixture is shaken. The petroleum ether layer is removed and saved, and the water layer is re-extracted with 20 ml of petroleum ether. The petroleum ether extracts are combined and washed with 15-ml portions of water until the washings are neutral to Congo Red paper. The extract is dried over anhydrous sodium sulfate and evaporated to a small volume on a water bath at 45°C with a stream of nitrogen.

Purification of methyl esters by silicic acid liquid–solid chromatography. The column is prepared as follows: A silicic acid–filter aid mixture (80:20) is spread in a ½-inch layer in a crystallizing dish and heated for 2 hours at 100°C. Then it is cooled in a desiccator without drying agent. Water equal to 4% of the weight of the silicic acid–filter aid mixture is added to the bottom of the desiccator, and the gel is equilibrated with it overnight. The mixture is then transferred to an airtight bottle, shaken, and stored. Ten grams of this adsorbent is made into a slurry with petroleum ether and packed into a chromatographic column.

Liquid–solid chromatography. The sample of crude methyl esters is transferred quantitatively to the top of the column. Three hundred milliliters of petroleum ether–diethyl ether 1:99 (v/v) is added to a separatory funnel attached to the column, and the solvent is forced through it under a constant pressure of nitrogen adjusted so that the flow rate is about 225 ml/hour. The methyl esters are eluted when at least 300 ml of eluate is obtained. Sterols and other unsaponifiable materials are retained on the column.

The eluate is evaporated to a small volume on the steam bath. The concentrate is transferred quantitatively to a tube drawn out to a closed capillary at one end, and the remaining solvent is removed by warming under a gentle stream of oxygen-free nitrogen. The methyl esters of the fatty acids are now ready for injection into the gas chromatograph.

b. Methylation of the Salts of Acids

1. Calcium Salts Methylated with Methanol–Benzene–H_2SO_4 (Downing et al., 1960). The calcium salts of the free fatty acids are made by using aqueous calcium chloride as described in Section A.II. The dried, crushed salts are refluxed for 3 hours with AR methanol–AR benzene–concentrated sulfuric acid 10:10:0.5 (v/v). The calcium sulfate is removed by filtration, and the filtrate containing the methyl esters is washed five times with 25% aqueous ethanol. The benzene is distilled, the last trace being evaporated at 100°C and 100 mm of pressure.

2. Silver Salts Methylated with Methyl Iodide–Pentane (Gehrke and Goerlitz, 1960). After the lipid fraction is saponified with alcoholic KOH, the alcohol is removed by steam distillation. The basic aqueous solution is titrated with standard aqueous hydrochloric acid, adjusted to pH 2 with phosphoric acid, and the free acids are extracted with ether. The ether is removed, and an excess of KOH is added. The solution of the potassium salts is warmed on a steam bath, and an excess of silver nitrate is added. Water is removed from the precipitated silver salts, first under vacuum and finally in a vacuum oven at 40°C. Methyl iodide in *n*-pentane and acid-washed dry sand are added to the dried salts, and the mixture is stirred with a magnetic stirrer for 1 hour in a tightly stoppered flask. The mixture is allowed to stand for 8 hours to ensure complete reaction. Methyl heptanoate is used as an internal standard for quantitative analysis. Aliquots of the methyl esters are then analyzed by injection into the gas chromatograph. This method is applicable for the determination of polycarboxylic and hydroxy acids in biological materials.

c. Methylation of Free Fatty Acids

*1. *On Anion Exchange Resin with Methanol–HCl* (Hornstein *et al.*, 1960). Pretreated Amberlite IRA-400 anion-exchange resin is used to adsorb naturally occurring fatty acids. The fatty acids are then methylated on the resin.

Resin pretreatment. Ten grams of Amberlite IRA-400 is stirred for 5 minutes with 25 ml of 1 *N* NaOH. The supernatant is discarded, and the resin is washed with several portions of distilled water, 3 × 35 ml of anhydrous ethanol, and 3 × 25 ml of petroleum ether.

Separation of fatty acids from total lipids. A 0.1-gm lipid sample is dissolved in 40 to 50 ml of petroleum ether. This is stirred for 5 minutes with 10 gm of pretreated resin in a 250-ml Erlenmeyer flask. The resin is allowed to settle, and the supernatant is decanted. The resin is washed free of lipids other than free fatty acids by stirring with 3 × 25 ml of petroleum ether and decanting the supernatant.

Methyl ester preparation. Twenty-five milliliters of anhydrous methanol–HCl is added to the resin and stirred with a magnetic stirrer for 25 minutes. The supernatant is decanted through a rapid filter paper into a separatory funnel. The resin is washed with 2 × 15 ml of anhydrous methanol–HCl with stirring for 5 minutes. The methanol–HCl solutions are combined, and 10 ml of distilled water is added. The methyl esters are extracted from the aqueous layer with 50 ml of petroleum ether. The aqueous layer is then washed with 2 × 20 ml of petroleum ether. The petroleum ether extracts are combined and washed with 50-ml portions of water until free of acid. The extract is then dried over anhydrous Na_2SO_4 and evaporated to a small volume on a water bath, under a stream of dry nitrogen.

Quantitative estimation. Prior to analysis, a known amount of *n*-heptadecanoic acid, usually 10 to 25 mg, is added to the original sample. Quantitative estimation of free fatty acids present is based on the recoveries of this C_{17} acid.

*2. *Diazomethane Method* (Schlenk and Gellerman, 1960). *Reagents.* The diazomethane is generated from *N*-methyl-*N*-nitroso-*p*-toluenesulfonamide

(MNSA). This compound is available commercially under the trade name Diazald (Aldrich Chemical Co.). Its storage stability is improved by re-crystallization. 2-(β-Ethoxyethoxy)ethanol (Carbitol) which has been purified by heating to 110°C for 1 hour with 5% KOH followed by distillation at approximately 90°C and 12 mm of Hg is used as the reaction solvent. After such treatment, the solvent does not turn yellow in the presence of alkali, thereby making it possible to observe the formation of diazomethane visually. Peroxide-free ether dried over sodium is used. Diazomethane is generated from MNSA with a solution containing 6 gm of potassium hydroxide in 10 ml of water.

Apparatus. The apparatus consists of three test tubes with side arms connected in series. A stream of nitrogen is saturated with ether in the first tube (16 × 150 mm) and carries diazomethane generated in the second tube into a third tube where esterification takes place. The dimensions of the latter tubes are 15 × 85 mm. The side arms (0.7 cm o.d.) of the tubes are bent downward, and each almost reaches the bottom of the following tube. The ends are drawn out to about 1 mm o.d. Rubber stoppers are used for connections.

Procedure. The flow of nitrogen through the ether contained in tube 1 is adjusted to 6 ml/min. Carbitol (0.7 ml), ether (0.7 ml), and 1 ml of a solution of 6 grams of KOH in 10 ml. of water are placed in tube 2. The fatty acids are dissolved in 2 to 3 ml of ether containing 10% methanol and placed in tube 3. MNSA (2 meq per 1 meq of fatty acid) dissolved in 1 ml of ether is added to tube 2. The tubes are connected immediately, and the diazomethane generated in tube 2 is swept into tube 3. As soon as a tinge of yellow appears in tube 3 when it is viewed against a white background, it is disconnected and the slight excess of reagent is destroyed by adding a dilute solution of acetic acid in ether. Alternatively, the diazomethane can be removed in a stream of nitrogen. The procedure requires 10 to 12 minutes. *Diazomethane is very toxic and must be handled with caution (see Appendix 4).* Artifacts are produced if old ether solutions of it are used for methylation.

3. BF₃–Methanol Method (Metcalfe and Schmitz, 1961). *Preparation of reagent.* One liter of reagent grade methanol, in a 2-liter flask, is weighed and cooled in an ice bath. Boron trifluoride is bubbled through a glass tube into the methanol until 125 gm is taken up. The flask should be kept in the ice bath during this procedure. *Precautions:* A good fume hood should be used for this operation, and the BF₃ should be bubbled slowly enough so that no white fumes emerge from the flask. If a cylinder of BF₃ is used, gas should flow through the glass tube before it is put in and until it is taken out of the methanol, to prevent liquid from being drawn into the cylinder valve.

Esterification procedure. Three milliliters of the BF₃–methanol reagent is added to a test tube containing 100 to 200 mg of fatty acids. The solution is boiled on a steam bath for 2 minutes. If the esters are more than 10 carbon atoms in chain length, they may be extracted with petroleum ether. Twenty milliliters of water is added to the BF_3–methanol solution, and this is extracted with 30 ml of petroleum ether in a separatory funnel. The petroleum ether layer is drained through filter paper and evaporated on a 60°C water bath.

Esters having less than 10 carbon atoms will be lost during evaporation of the petroleum ether. However, if large amounts of esters are present, they may be separated physically by adding water (20 ml) to the BF_3–methanol solution. The esters will separate and form a layer on top from whence they can be removed with a pipette. Then they are centrifuged to remove small amounts of water.

IV. Handling and Storage

Certain general precautions should be taken when handling and storing fatty acids and fatty acid esters. These materials may be stored safely for several months in dilute solutions in petroleum ether at 4°C or lower in the dark. The solvent is removed by evaporating slowly with a stream of nitrogen at 60° to 70°C. The last traces of solvent are removed under reduced pressure at 25°C, or at room temperature under a stream of nitrogen. Screw-top bottles with plastic caps and aluminum foil liners can be used for storage, but cork or rubber stoppers are to be avoided. They may be stored solvent-free only if sealed in ampoules in an atmosphere of nitrogen.

V. Chromatography on Nonpolar Liquids

The chromatographic separation of the methyl esters of the higher fatty acids on nonpolar liquids has been described by a number of authors, including James, Insull, Lipsky, and Beerthuis. The preferred partition medium is Apiezon L or Apiezon M high-vacuum grease coated on size-graded Celite. These greases will withstand temperatures up to 300°C without extensive cracking or loss. James (1959) used a packing prepared from Apiezon L and alkali-treated Celite (100/210 mesh) for the separation of C_{10} to C_{18} fatty acid methyl esters derived from fecal lipids. At a temperature of 197°C and a column inlet pressure of 760 mm Hg above atmospheric, stearic acid methyl ester was eluted in about 65 to 70 minutes. Higher temperatures must be employed to elute the fatty acid methyl esters up to carbon number 30 in a reasonable time with conventional column packing ratios. Beerthuis *et al.* (1959) used a column containing Apiezon L on Celite 545 in a 10:90 ratio. At a temperature of 270°C and a flow rate of 29 ml of N_2 per minute, triacontanoic acid was eluted in about 100 to 120 minutes (Fig. 9). The C_{26} to C_{30} saturated fatty acid esters were cleanly resolved. Beerthuis *et al.* used a modification of this technique for chromatographing methyl

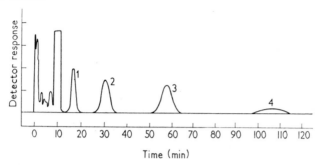

FIG. 9. Separation of methyl esters of fatty acids up to C_{30} on Apiezon L at 270°C. (1) 24:0. (2) 26:0. (3) 28:0. (4) 30:0. (Beerthuis *et al.*, 1959.)

esters derived from oil of *Ximenia caffra*, since this substance has long been known to contain high-molecular-weight fatty acids. At a temperature of 274°C, fatty acids up to and including C_{28} were detected (Fig. 10). However,

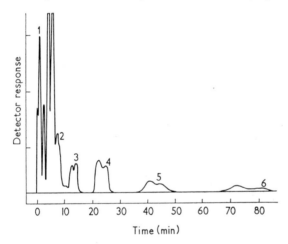

FIG. 10. Separation of methyl esters derived from oil of *Ximenia caffra* on Apiezon L at 274°C. (1) Air. (2) 20:0. (3) 22:0. (4) 24:0. (5) 26:0. (6) 28:0. (Beerthuis *et al.*, 1959.)

C_{30} and higher acids were not found, even when the column was overloaded. Each peak representing a saturated fatty acid was preceded by a companion peak from which it was incompletely resolved. On hydrogenation, these pre-peaks shifted to the saturated series, thus proving they originated from un-saturated fatty acids. It was possible to separate these same materials at a column temperature of 231°C. However, the retention time for the saturated C_{28} methyl ester was about 180 minutes compared to 80 minutes at the higher temperature.

Nonpolar stationary phases such as Apiezon L give excellent resolution of the C_{10} to C_{30} fatty acid esters by carbon number when used at temperatures between 197°C and 286°C, the lower range for compounds up to and including C_{18}, and the higher range for esters up to C_{30}. With Apiezon L grease at temperatures above 240°C, small amounts of volatile products bleed from the column. However, if the packing is preconditioned at 300°C and 10 mm Hg in a nitrogen atmosphere for 5 hours, this can be eliminated. A well-prepared column of this type will have an efficiency of 1000 or more theoretical plates per foot.

Saturated fatty acid esters are eluted from Apiezon L in order of increasing carbon number, the retention volume increasing by a factor of 1.56 for each additional methylene group. Thus when log_{10} of the retention volume is plotted against carbon number, a straight line results (Fig. 11). A single

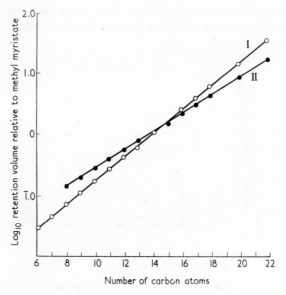

Fig. 11. Log_{10} relative retention volumes (methyl myristate = 1) of methyl esters of saturated fatty acids in relation to number of carbon atoms in the long chain. (I) On Apiezon L at 197°C. (II) On poly(ethylene glycol adipate) at 180°C. (James, 1959.)

methyl side chain reduces van der Waals binding between the solute and partitioning liquid, so that the compound moves ahead of the corresponding straight-chain saturated acid by a factor of about 0.9.

The introduction of a double bond into the solute molecule increases its polarity and concomitantly decreases its affinity for the nonpolar substrate. As a result, the unsaturated compound moves ahead of the saturated analogue. For example, the retention volume of oleic acid on Apiezon M at 197°C is 0.815 relative to 1.00 for stearic acid (Farquhar *et al.*, 1959). The separation factor for this combination is 1.23, which permits easy resolution of the two compounds by chromatography on this liquid. The introduction of a second isolated double bond, as in linoleic acid, increases rate of travel through the column still further, so that the retention volume is 0.792 relative to stearic acid. However, the separation factor for the oleic–linoleic combination is only 1.03. The addition of a third isolated double bond, as in linolenic acid, results in no further change in retention volume, linoleic and linolenic acids being eluted as a single peak.

Tetraenes move ahead of the corresponding saturated esters by a factor of 0.6 but are not resolved from pentaenes, while hexaenes move ahead of the tetraene–pentaene peak. Conjugation of the double bonds in polyunsaturated esters causes the peaks to move ahead of those representing the unconjugated isomers. The peaks representing unsaturated compounds can be located by brominating a portion of the ester mixture and rechromatographing it. The brominated esters are not sufficiently volatile to be eluted from the column, so the peaks representing the unsaturated esters are subtracted entirely (Section A.III). An alternative procedure is to reduce the double bonds by catalytic hydrogenation before chromatographing the sample a second time (Section A.III). This not only subtracts the peaks arising from unsaturated compounds but also gives the total composition of the mixture in terms of carbon number, since the unsaturated peaks are added to the corresponding saturated peaks. Thus nonpolar substrates such as the Apiezons will separate homologous series of compounds by carbon number and when used in conjunction with subtraction techniques (bromination and hydrogenation) will give some information on the distribution of unsaturates.

Gas-liquid chromatography on nonpolar substrates will also yield information on the position of double bonds and orientation about them. In general, long-chain esters containing double bonds in the 9,10 position are

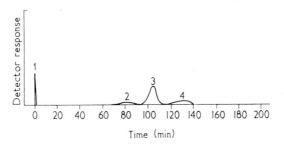

Fɪɢ. 12. Chromatogram of alkali-isomerized 9-*cis*,12-*cis*-linoleic acid esters on Apiezon L at 197°C (1) Air. (2) Unconverted *cis,cis* isomer. (3) Conjugated *cis,trans* isomer. (4) Conjugated *trans,trans* isomer. (Beerthuis *et al.*, 1959.)

eluted from Apiezon columns more rapidly than when the double bond is located elsewhere in the molecule. Also, *trans* isomers elute less rapidly than the corresponding *cis* isomers, oleic acid, for example, having a retention volume of 2.03 relative to palmitic acid compared to a value of 2.12 for elaidic acid. This phenomenon makes it possible to study rearrangements of double bonds produced by the isomerization of polyenes with alkali at high temperatures. Thus pure 9-*cis*,12-*cis*-linoleic acid shows three chromatographic peaks when it is isomerized with alkali prior to methylation and chromatography (Beerthuis *et al.*, 1959). One of these (Fig. 12, peak 2) represents unconverted *cis,cis* isomer, a second peak (3) represents a conjugated *cis,trans* isomer, and the third peak (4) arises from a conjugated *trans,trans* isomer. Configuration about the double bonds was established by collecting fractions and obtaining infrared curves on them.

a. Conditions for Chromatography

1. *On Apiezon L for Esters up to C_{18}* (James, 1959)

Chromatograph	Laboratory-built.
Column dimensions	4-foot × 0.4- to 0.5-mm straight glass tubes.
Solid support	Alkali-treated Celite (100/200 mesh) prepared according to method of James *et al.* (1952).
Stationary phase	Apiezon L (20:80).
Temperature	197°C.
Carrier gas	Argon. Inlet pressure: 760 mm Hg. Outlet pressure; atmospheric.
Detector	Beta-ray ionization.
Recorder	Not given.
Sample size	80 μg in 0.5 μl of petroleum ether.
Analysis time	65 minutes to stearic acid.

*2. *On Apiezon L for C_{22} to C_{30} Esters* (Beerthuis *et al.*, 1959)

Chromatograph	Laboratory-built with combustion tube.
Column dimensions	115 × 0.4-cm i.d.
Solid support	Size-graded Celite 545. Fines removed by sedimentation.
Stationary phase	Apiezon L (20:80).
Temperatures	Column: 270°. Detector: room temperature.
Carrier gas	Nitrogen at 25 ml/min. Inlet pressure: 290 mm Hg. Outlet pressure: atmospheric.
Detector	Sample combusted and CO_2 detected with gas density balance.
Recorder	Sunvic DC amplifier with Evershed ammeter.
Sample	2 mg.
Analysis time	About 110 minutes to C_{30}.

VI. CHROMATOGRAPHY ON POLAR LIQUIDS

Under optimum conditions it is possible to obtain good separations of methyl stearate from methyl oleate, and partial resolution of methyl oleate

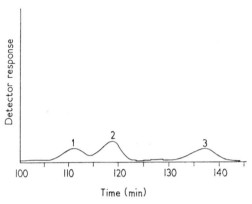

Fɪɢ. 13. Separation of fatty acid methyl esters on Apiezon L according to degree of unsaturation. (1) 18:2. (2) 18:1. (3) 18:0. (Orr and Callen, 1959.)

from methyl linoleate with Apiezon L as the partition liquid (Fig. 13). In no case, however, has it been possible to resolve methyl linoleate and methyl linolenate on this medium. To accomplish this, it is necessary to use a polar liquid as the stationary phase. Up to the present, the best materials for this purpose are polyesters obtained by condensing dibasic acids with dihydric alcohols. The simplest example is the condensation product of ethylene glycol with succinic acid:

$$(-O-CH_2CH_2-O-CO-CH_2CH_2-CO-)_n$$

Higher polymers can be obtained by cross-linking the chains by means of a small amount of polyhydric alcohol such as pentaerythritol. Details on the synthesis of these materials are supplied in Chapter 1, Section C.II.a.

Polyesters differ from the Apiezons in the following respects in their capacities for separating methyl esters of the fatty acids. (1) The polyesters are much more polar. In consequence, the passage of all fatty esters through columns packed with them is faster at equivalent temperatures because of reduced van der Waals interactions between solute and solvent. This makes it possible to chromatograph samples in shorter times, or, better, reduce column temperatures and still elute higher esters in reasonable times. (2) On increasing the chain length by a single CH_2 group, the retention volume increases by a factor of 1.46 compared to 1.56 for Apiezon L at 200°C. Thus polyesters can separate members of homologous series by boiling point, but they are not quite so efficient for this purpose as nonpolar liquids. (3) Unsaturated compounds are retained longer on polyester columns than their saturated analogues because of higher solute–solvent interactions between the more polar solute and polyester. Consequently, retention volumes for elution from polyester packings decrease in the order trienes > dienes >

monoenes > saturated. By contrast, retention volumes on Apiezon L decrease in the order saturated > monoenes > dienes = trienes. It should be
noted that the order of elution is inverted, and also that dienes and trienes
can be separated from one another on polyesters but not on Apiezons. In
addition, hexaenes, pentaenes, and tetraenes can be separated on polyesters,
while certain pairs of these compounds pentaenes and tetraenes for example,
have the same retention volumes on Apiezon grease. (4) No change in retention volume on a polyester column is produced when a double bond is
moved from the 9,10 position to some other position in the hydrocarbon
chain. Similarly there is no difference in retention volumes between *cis* and
trans isomers. Oleic and elaidic acids, for example, are eluted from polyester
columns together. The introduction of a methyl side chain reduces retention
volumes by about 10% compared to the straight-chain ester with the same
carbon number. In this respect the polyester and Apiezon columns are
similar.

The condensation products of dibasic acids with diols often consist of a
mixture of polymers having a broad molecular-weight range, since it is difficult to drive these reactions to completion. Consequently, most commercial
polymers contain small amounts of monomers and lower polymers having
sufficiently high vapor pressures to bleed from the column. Therefore it is
necessary to precondition them by passing a stream of nitrogen or helium
through them at a temperature above operational temperature until a steady
base line is obtained. Even when properly conditioned, polyester columns
tend to bleed when used much above 200°C, owing to thermal cracking, the
life of a Reoplex 400 column being only a few weeks even at the low temperature range. Column life can be prolonged by including a drying tube
between the gas cylinder and the injection port to remove moisture from the
carrier gas, and by making sure that carrier gas flows continuously when the
column is hot. The packing of worn-out columns often shows considerable
darkening for the beginning few inches indicating that its life might be
prolonged by using a pre-column containing a polyester in advance of the
analytical column and the injection port, to scrub the carrier gas further.

Thermal instability also arises in part from the basic structure of the
polymer. Esters prepared from branched-chain glycols such as 1,2-dipropyl-
ene glycol are less stable than polymers made from linear glycols such as
diethylene glycols. Furthermore, Pohl (1951) has shown that the ether linkage in diethylene glycol contributes to instability. Acting on this information,
Craig and Murty (1959) evaluated poly(ethylene glycol succinate) and
poly(1,4-butanediol succinate) as stationary liquids. Both gave a marked
improvement in thermal stability. The ethylene glycol-based polymer gave
the same separations as the diethylene glycol polymer, while the 1,4-butane-
diol condensation product was equivalent to the adipate–succinate polyester

except that resolution of stearic and oleic acids was better. Wilkins Instrument and Research Inc. supply a polyester based on 1,4-butanediol and succinic acid which is said to withstand temperatures up to 225°C.

Orr and Callen (1959) used a commercial plasticizer, Reoplex 400, for the separation of fatty acid methyl esters. This material is said to be a poly(oxyalkalene adipate). Good separations were obtained, but the complete composition of the packing has not been disclosed, and it is thermally unstable when used for prolonged periods at 200°C.

James (1958) chromatographed a mixture of methyl esters on a 4-foot column containing a stationary phase composed of poly(ethylene glycol adipate) on Celite. At a column temperature of 175°C and an inlet pressure of 650 mm Hg above atmospheric, linolenic acid (14) was eluted in less than 100 minutes. It was cleanly resolved from linoleic acid, (13) which in turn was resolved from oleic acid (12) (Fig. 14). Slight overlap occurred between the oleic

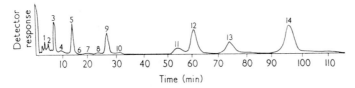

Fig. 14. Chromatogram of methyl esters of fatty acids on poly(ethylene glycol adipate) at 175°C. br = branched. (1) 10:0. (2) 11:0. (3) 12:0. (4) 13:0. (5) 14:0. (6) 14:1. (7) 15:0. (8) 16:0, br. (9) 16:0. (10) 16:1. (11) 18:0. (12) 18:1. (13) 18:2. (14) 18:3. (James, 1958.)

and stearic acid peaks because of the comparatively small separation factor (1.13) obtainable for these two compounds on this partition fluid (Table VIII). The column efficiency was 3500 theoretical plates. Lipsky *et al.* (1959b) sepa-

TABLE VIII

VARIATION IN SEPARATION FACTORS OF C_{18} FATTY ACID ESTERS
WITH POLAR STATIONARY LIQUIDS

Stationary liquid	Temperature	Oleate — Stearate	Linoleate — Oleate	Linoleate — Linolenate
Polyvinyl acetate	205°C	1.13	1.12	1.17
Reoplex 400	200°C	1.11	1.19	1.24
Poly(diethylene glycol succinate)	203°C	1.18	1.23	1.18
Poly(ethylene glycol adipate)	180°C	1.13	1.15	1.30

rated these compounds on a poly(diethylene glycol succinate) packing (LAC-4-R-777) of molecular weight 4450. The separation factor for oleate–stearate was 1.17, and the column efficiency was 1400 theoretical plates calculated for the stearate peak. At a column temperature of 158°C and a flow rate of 60 ml of argon per minute, linoleate, linolenate, and oleate were resolved (Fig. 15). Some overlap occurred between the oleate and stearate peaks, but

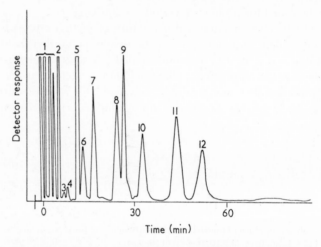

FIG. 15. Separation of fatty acid methyl esters at 158°C and 60 ml of argon per minute on a 9-foot packed column containing poly(diethylene glycol succinate) as the partition liquid. (1) 8:0 to 13:0. (2) 14:0. (3) 14:1. (4) 15:0. (5) 16:0. (6) 16:1. (7) 17:0. (8) 18:0. (9) 18:1. (10) 18:2. (11) 18:3. (12) 20:0. (Lipsky et al., 1959b.)

it was not serious enough to interfere with accurate quantitative analysis. At a temperature of 190°C and a flow rate of 180 ml/min, resolution of stearate and oleate was better, but linolenate was incompletely resolved from the C_{20} peak. The time required for elution of the C_{20} peak was about 15 minutes under these conditions, compared to about 50 minutes at 158°C and 60 ml of argon per minute.

Lipsky and Landowne (1959) analyzed a standard mixture of methyl esters on a poly(diethylene glycol succinate) column at 203°C (Table IX). All eight components of the mixture were resolved, and the differences between the amounts of each component found and the amounts present were within experimental error. It should be noted that, despite the fact that the contents of stearate, oleate, and linoleate together comprised 43% of the total mixture, the separation of each from the other was practically complete. Gross contamination between stearate and oleate amounted to less than 1.0% as calculated from the Glueckauf equation.

TABLE IX

ANALYSIS OF A STANDARD MIXTURE OF METHYL ESTERS
OF LONG-CHAIN FATTY ACIDS ON A SUCCINATE POLYESTER
OF DIETHYLENE GLYCOL AT 203°C[a]

	Percentages		
	Weighed	Found	Difference
Methyl palmitate	13.9	15.1	+1.2
Methyl palmitoleate	3.0	3.3	+0.3
Methyl stearate	15.6	16.5	+0.9
Methyl oleate	20.6	21.0	+0.4
Methyl linoleate	15.9	16.4	+0.5
Methyl linolenate	11.3	9.6	−1.7
Methyl arachidate	10.6	9.6	−1.0
Methyl behenate	9.1	8.5	−0.6
	100.0		

[a] From Lipsky and Landowne (1959).

James (1960) prefers to carry out analyses slowly, at low temperatures and flow rates to prevent crowding of peaks with low retention volumes. Other workers contend that long residence times in columns lead to peak broading due to longitudinal diffusion of the vapors comprising the peaks during transit. Farquhar et al. (1959) state that it may be desirable to operate at higher than optimum flow rates if the time saved warrants the reduction in column efficiency that occurs. However, they state that it is rarely wise to lower the flow below the optimal rate, since column efficiency declines rapidly under conditions which permit longitudinal diffusion of the solute within the column. As usual, a compromise must be sought which best answers the demands of the specific problem at hand.

Selection of an optimum operating temperature is critical, since polyesters contain volatile components and are thermally unstable at temperatures in the range of 200° to 250°C. Moreover, they may undergo interesterification with the solutes. Columns packed with this material can be used continuously for 2 to 3 months at 200°C before deterioration occurs. Column efficiency is said to be about 200 to 300 theoretical plates per foot for newly packed columns, but this will decline with time.

Thermal cracking of the column packing is not the only factor that mitigates against the use of polyesters at high temperatures. As mentioned above, interesterification reactions between the polyesters and the solute esters may occur. The extent to which this will take place depends on the temperature and on the residence time of the solute in the column. James (1960) has compiled data from various sources showing the importance of these factors (Table X). In all the cases illustrated, results were calculated by the peak area–internal normalization method, so results on components with low retention times tend to be high to compensate for losses of components with long retention times. Thus at 240°C the loss of slower components such as linoleate and oleate results in an apparent increase in stearate and palmitate content, the errors amounting to as much as 40% in extreme cases. Even at 200°C there is still appreciable loss if retention times are very long. Therefore it is advisable to use high carrier gas flow rates if high temperatures are needed. In other cases it may be preferable to reduce the temperature to a point where interesterification reactions do not occur to an appreciable extent, and settle for a longer analysis time with some broadening of the peaks for components having high retention volumes. James (1958, 1959, 1960) prefers a temperature of 175° to 180°C for polyester adipate columns. As seen above, satisfactory peak resolution and reasonably rapid elution can be obtained at temperatures as low as 158°C with polyester succinate packings at a 10:90 liquid-to-support ratio. Optimum resolution with a minimum of artifacts can probably be attained with small liquid-to-solid support ratios coupled with low temperatures, high flow rates, small samples, and sensitive detection systems.

TABLE X

ERRORS INTRODUCED BY TRANSESTERIFICATION IN POLYESTER COLUMNS[a]
(In per cent: + = high; − = low)

Methyl ester	Column temperature		
	240°C	200°C	203°C
Palmitate	+43.5	+22	+8.6
Palmitoleate	—	—	—
Stearate	+4.4	+2.1	+5.8
Oleate	−10	+4.2	+1.0
Linoleate	−37.6	−8.7	+3.4
Linolenate	—	−6.9	−17
Arachidate	—	—	−9.4
Behenate	—	—	−6.6

[a] From James (1960).

Hornstein et al. (1959) have introduced a new type of polar packing which gives about the same separations obtainable with the polyesters (Table XI). This is polyvinyl acetate of molecular weight 1500, the structure of which is represented by

$$\left[\begin{array}{c} -CH_2-CH- \\ | \\ CH_3COO \end{array}\right]_n$$

The authors used this material coated on Chromosorb (15:85) for the separation of the C_{18} fatty esters by unsaturation at a column temperature of 205°C. Good resolution was obtained in all cases. Polyvinyl acetate yields acetic acid on thermal cracking. The yield is less than 0.1 mg of acid per hour at 195°C, and 1.5 mg/hour at 230°C. The rate of acetic acid evolution decreases with time without impairing the efficiency of the column. In all studies the base-line drift was less than ±0.02 mv. Infrared spectra of the products collected over a period of 12 hours indicated the presence of acetic acid only. Although some thermal cracking occurs, this type of column offers some advantages when it is necessary to collect fractions for optical analysis, since acetic acid, the only possible contaminant, is easily removed.

TABLE XI

SEPARATION OF METHYL ESTERS OF FATTY ACIDS ON A
POLYVINYL ACETATE POLYMER, MOLECULAR WEIGHT 1500,
COATED ON CHROMOSORB 30/60 MESH (15:85), 205°C[a]

Compound	Retention volume (ml)[b]
Methyl palmitate	1080
Methyl stearate	1860
Methyl oleate	2100
Methyl linoleate	2350
Methyl linolenate	2750
Methyl arachidonate	5230

[a] From Hornstein et al. (1959).
[b] Retention volumes calculated for a flow rate of 83 ml/min and measured from the time of emergence of the solvent phase.

a. Conditions for Chromatography

1. On Poly(ethylene Glycol Adipate) (James, 1958, 1959)

Chromatograph	Laboratory-built.
Column dimensions	4-foot × 0.4- to 0.5-cm straight glass tubes.
Solid support	Celite (100/210 mesh).
Stationary phase	Poly(ethylene glycol adipate) (25:80).
Temperature	175° to 180°C.
Carrier gas	Argon. Inlet pressure: 570 mm Hg. Outlet pressure: atmospheric.
Detector	Argon ionization detector.
Recorder	Not given.
Sample size	80 μg in 0.5 μl of petroleum ether.
Analysis time	About 72 minutes to linoleic acid.

*2. On Poly(*diethylene Glycol Succinate*) (Lipsky *et al.*, 1959a)

Chromatograph	Barber-Colman Model 10.
Column dimensions	9-foot × 0.6-cm glass U tube.
Solid support	Acid-washed Celite 545 (60/80 mesh).
Stationary phase	Poly(diethylene glycol succinate, mol. wt. 4450 (10:90).
Temperatures	Column: 158° or 168°C. Detector bath: 225°C. Injection port: 300°C.
Carrier gas	Argon at 60 or 70 ml/min at outlet.
Detector	Argon β-ray ionization, Sr^{90} source.
Recorder	Wheelco 8000 series, 1 to 10 mv.
Sample size	0.1 mg.
Analysis time	About 80 minutes to C$_{22}$ at 168°C and 70 ml of argon per minute.

*3. On Polyvinyl Acetate (Hornstein *et al.*, 1959)

Chromatograph	Beckman Model GC-2.
Column dimensions	250 × 0.63-cm o.d. coiled copper tubing.
Solid support	Johns-Manville Chromosorb R or W (30/60 U. S. mesh) washed with concentrated HCl, followed by 1 N NaOH, dried at 130°C, treated with vapors of dichlorodimethyl silane, washed with methanol, and vacuum-dried at 80°C.
Stationary phase	Polyvinyl acetate polymer (Vinylite AYAC), mol. wt. 1500 (15:85).
Temperatures	Injection: 270°C. Detector: 205°C. Column: 205°C.
Carrier gas	Helium at 83 ml/min measured at outlet. Inlet pressure: 1550 mm Hg. Outlet pressure: atmospheric.
Detector	Four-filament hot-wire T/C cell at 300 ma.
Recorder	0 to 1 mv; 1 second; 1.27 cm/min.
Sample size	5 to 20 μl of approximately 5% (w/v) solution.
Analysis time	Approximately 30 minutes to linolenate.

VII. IDENTIFICATION OF HIGHER FATTY ACID ESTERS

The Apiezon and the polyester columns supplement rather than replace one another in the analysis and identification of fatty acid esters. The Apiezons and similar liquids are good boiling-point separators and in addition distinguish between *cis* and *trans* configurations about double bonds, and between different positions of the double bond in the hydrocarbon chain. The polyesters afford separations by carbon number, but their main attribute is their capacity for separating saturated esters, monoenes, dienes, trienes, etc., from one another. The unsaturated compounds are retarded by the packing more than saturated compounds having the same carbon number. Hence, when the sample contains polyenes, the peaks arising from them may overlap the saturated ester having the next highest carbon number. This can happen when the sample is derived from acids with even carbon number and is much more likely to happen when compounds with odd carbon numbers are present also. The former possibility is shown in Fig. 16, in

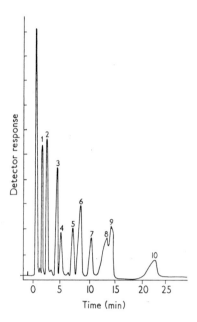

FIG. 16. Separation of fatty acid methyl esters at 190°C and a flow rate of 180 ml of helium per minute on an 8-foot packed column containing poly(diethylene glycol succinate) as the partition liquid. (1) 12:0. (2) 14:0. (3) 16:0. (4) 16:1. (5) 18:0. (6) 18:1. (7) 18:2. (8) 18:3. (9) 20:0. (10) 22:0. (Lipsky *et al.*, 1959b.)

which the peak arising from linolenate (8) is seen to overlap the arachidate peak (9). This situation can be circumvented by first running the sample on Apiezon L and collecting fractions by carbon number. Since the unsaturated members of any series, the C_{18} series for example, will run ahead of the saturated member, it is possible to collect the entire fraction without serious contamination from the series with the next highest carbon number, particularly if the latter does not contain highly unsaturated polyenes. The C_{18} fraction can then be rerun on a polyester column to obtain separation according to degree of unsaturation with minimal interference from higher homologues. Theoretically at least, samples could be re-collected and rerun once more on Apiezon to determine if the unsaturated fractions contained *cis,trans* or other isomers. Methods for sample collection and reintroduction are discussed in Chapter 1, Section I.

Data obtained independently on the two columns can be pooled to give information on the identity of fatty acid esters. It is first necessary to measure retention volumes of homologous series of known compounds containing zero, one, two, three etc., double bonds on Apiezon and on a polyester column. Log_{10} retention volume of Apiezon is plotted against log_{10} retention

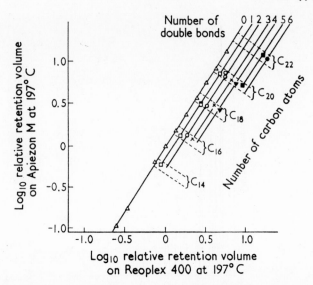

Fig. 17. Relation between $\log_{10}$ relative retention volume on Apiezon M and $\log_{10}$ relative retention volume on Reoplex 400 for methyl esters of saturated and unsaturated fatty acids. (James, 1960.)

volume of polyester. A family of parallel straight lines is obtained, one for each homologous series (Fig. 17). Thus the points on the upper line of the figure represent saturated fatty acid esters with different carbon numbers, the points on the second line down represent the homologous series containing one double bond, etc. The retention volumes of the unknown on Apiezon and polyester are then determined, and the logarithms of these values are plotted on the grid. The line on which the point falls reveals how many double bonds are in the molecule. The position of the point on the line tells how many carbon atoms are in the molecule. This latter value can be verified by reference to a graph of carbon number versus $\log_{10}$ retention volume for the specific homologous series to which the compound belongs. This method has been shown to be valid only for compounds in which the double bonds are unconjugated. If the peak is believed to arise from an unsaturated compound, this can be verified by hydrogenating the sample and rechromatographing it (Section A.III). If the peak in question is not recorded on the chromatogram in the second run, the compound originally giving rise to it can be presumed to be unsaturated. Bromination works equally well as a subtraction method if the reaction product is chromatographed on Apiezon. However, the bromination products of monoenes such as oleic acid may give rise to as many as three peaks when chromatographed on polyester columns (Landowne and Lipsky, 1958).

TABLE XII

RETENTION VALUES (16:0 = 1) OF FATTY ACID METHYL ESTERS ON POLAR LIQUIDS AT VARIOUS TEMPERATURES
(Data compiled from the literature.)

Common name of parent compound	Code	Poly(ethylene glycol adipate)				Poly(diethylene glycol succinate)			Reoplex 400 at 197°C
		173.5°C	180°C	184.5°C	197°C	200°C	203°C	220°C	
Caprylic	8:0	—	0.060	—	—	0.096	—	—	—
Pelargonic	9:0	—	0.082	—	—	0.136	—	—	—
Capric	10:0	—	0.134	—	—	0.181	—	—	0.179
	10:0 un	—	—	—	—	0.232	—	—	—
Hendecanoic	11:0	—	0.183	—	—	0.237	—	—	—
Lauric	12:0	0.245	0.261	0.261	0.300	0.322	—	—	0.232
Tridecanoic	13:0	0.355	0.362	0.378	0.404	0.412	0.36	—	0.286
	iso 13:0	—	—	—	—	0.373	—	—	0.388
Myristic	14:0	0.502	0.51	0.522	0.549	0.565	0.60	0.588	0.555
	iso 14:0	0.420	—	0.447	0.458	0.497	—	—	—
	14:1	0.600	0.615	0.607	0.624	—	—	—	0.634
	14:1 cis	—	—	—	—	—	—	—	—
	14:3	—	0.90	—	—	—	—	—	—
Pentadecanoic	15:0	0.705	0.705	0.714	0.729	0.704	—	—	0.754
	iso 15:0	0.635	—	0.656	0.667	0.644	—	—	—
	anteiso 15:0	—	—	—	—	0.689	—	—	—
Palmitic	16:0	1.00	1.00	1.00	1.00	1.00	1.00	1.00	1.00
	iso 16:0	0.855	—	0.862	0.858	0.881	—	—	—
	neo 16:0	0.705	—	0.716	0.731	—	—	—	—
	16:1 7 cis	—	1.15	—	—	1.18	1.17	—	1.13
	16:1 9 trans	—	1.15	—	—	—	—	—	—
	16:1 9	1.15	—	1.13	1.15	—	—	—	—
	16:1 8	1.15	—	1.13	1.15	—	—	—	1.13
	16:2 9,12	1.46	—	1.45	1.43	—	—	—	1.39
	16:2 6,9	1.46	—	1.45	1.43	—	—	—	1.28
	16:3 6,9,12	1.71	—	1.72	1.64	—	—	—	1.59
	16:3 7,10,13	1.71	—	1.72	1.64	—	—	—	—
	16:4 6,9,12,15	—	—	—	—	—	—	—	1.97
	17:0	1.41	1.40	1.37	1.33	1.29	—	—	1.32

TABLE XII (*Continued*)

Common name of parent compound	Code	Poly(ethylene glycol adipate)				Poly(diethylene glycol succinate)			Reoplex 400 at 197°C
		173.5°C	180°C	184.5°C	197°C	200°C	203°C	220°C	
	iso 17:0	—	—	—	—	1.18	—	—	—
	anteiso 17:0	1.29	—	—	—	1.22	—	—	—
	17:1	—	1.62	1.30	1.23	—	1.66	1.62	1.79
Stearic	18:0	1.99	1.97	1.92	1.82	1.75	—	—	1.95
	iso 18:0	1.71	—	1.69	1.56	1.57	—	—	—
	neo 18:0	1.41	—	1.39	1.32	—	—	—	—
Oleic	18:1^{9}	2.23	—	2.15	2.04	2.00	—	—	2.02
	18:1^{9} cis	—	2.21	—	—	1.96	1.93	—	—
	18:1^{9} trans	—	2.21	—	—	—	—	—	—
	18:1^{6} cis	—	2.22	—	—	—	—	—	—
Linoleic	18:2^{9,12}	2.70	—	2.60	2.44	2.45	—	—	2.32
	18:2^{6,9}	2.89	—	2.76	2.60	—	—	—	2.56
Linolenic	18:3^{9,12,15}	3.51	—	3.32	3.13	3.16	—	—	2.91
	18:3^{9,12,15} cis	—	3.51	—	—	—	—	—	2.95
	18:4^{6,9,12,15}	4.06	—	3.82	3.58	—	—	2.06	3.48
	19:0	2.81	—	2.65	2.46	2.27	—	—	2.32
	anteiso 19:0	2.55	—	2.42	2.26	—	—	—	—
	19:un	3.35	—	3.19	2.98	—	—	—	2.79
	20:0	3.96	3.87	3.63	3.31	3.11	—	2.70	3.15
	iso 20:0	3.37	—	3.19	2.89	—	—	—	—
	neo 20:0	2.79	—	2.67	2.46	—	—	—	—
	br 20:0	—	—	—	—	3.09	—	—	—
	20:1	4.30	—	4.01	—	—	—	—	3.57
	20:1^{11}	4.46	—	4.32	3.67	—	—	—	3.44
	20:un	—	—	—	—	—	—	—	—
	20:2	4.94	—	4.61	4.22	—	—	—	3.88
	20:2^{8,11}	—	—	—	4.46	—	—	—	3.93
	20:2^{11,14}	—	—	—	4.46	—	—	—	4.14
	20:2	5.29	5.96	4.84	—	—	—	—	—
	20:3	—	—	—	—	—	—	—	4.80
	20:3^{8,11,14}	6.02	—	5.53	5.02	—	—	—	4.70

TABLE XII (*Continued*)

Common name of parent compound	Code	Poly(ethylene glycol adipate)				Poly(diethylene glycol succinate)			Reoplex 400 at 197°C
		173.5°C	180°C	184.5°C	197°C	200°C	203°C	220°C	
Arachidonic	$20:4^{5,8,11,14}$	6.61	6.56	6.08	5.53	5.44	—	—	5.28
	$20:4^{8,11,14,17}$	—	—	—	—	—	—	—	5.35
	$20:un$	7.79	—	7.10	6.38	—	—	—	5.84
	$20:5^{5,8,11,14,17}$	8.63	8.5	7.83	7.00	—	—	—	6.64
	$20:un$	9.46	—	8.48	7.47	—	—	—	7.02
	$21:0$	—	—	4.91	4.47	4.12	—	—	—
anteiso	$21:0$	—	—	4.61	4.16	—	—	3.48	—
Behenic	$22:0$	—	—	—	5.95	5.55	4.67	4.65	6.8
iso	$22:0$	—	—	—	5.29	—	—	—	—
	$22:1$	—	8.15	—	—	6.36	—	—	—
	$22:1^{13}$	—	—	—	—	—	—	—	—
	$22:4$	12.29	—	11.04	9.64	—	—	—	8.79
	$22:5$	14.80	—	12.96	11.07	—	—	—	10.18
	$22:5$	16.24	—	14.32	12.00	—	—	—	11.05
	$22:5^{7,10,13,16,19}$	16.73	—	14.76	12.73	—	—	—	11.7
	$22:5^{5,8,11,16,17}$	—	—	—	—	—	—	—	12.2
	$22:6^{4,7,10,13,16,19}$	19.02	18.2	16.49	14.09	—	—	—	12.98
	$22:6^{6,7,10,13,16,19}$	—	—	—	—	—	—	—	13.5
	$23:0$	—	—	—	—	—	—	—	—
Lignoceric	$24:0$	—	—	—	11.16	7.75	—	5.93	—
iso	$24:0$	—	—	—	9.67	9.89	—	8.89	—
neo	$24:0$	—	—	—	8.22	—	—	—	—
	$26:0$	—	—	—	—	17.98	13.8	11.96	—

TABLE XIII

RETENTION VALUES (16:0 = 1) OF FATTY ACID METHYL ESTERS ON NONPOLAR LIQUIDS AT VARIOUS TEMPERATURES

(Data compiled from the literature.)

Common name of parent acid	Code	Apiezon M					Apiezon L, 197°C	Silicone grease, 200°C
		173.5°C	182.5°C	188°C	197°C	200°C		
Caprylic	8:0	—	—	—	—	0.029	0.030	0.053
Pelargonic	9:0	—	—	—	—	0.042	0.047	0.078
	anteiso 9:0	—	—	—	—	—	0.041	—
Capric	10:0	—	—	—	0.069	0.071	0.073	0.117
	iso 10:0	—	—	—	—	—	0.061	—
Hendecanoic	11:0	—	—	—	0.112	0.113	0.117	0.160
	anteiso 11:0	—	—	—	—	—	0.10	—
Lauric	12:0	0.145	0.150	0.160	0.18	0.176	0.18	0.238
	iso 12:0	—	—	—	—	—	0.15	—
Tridecanoic	13:0	0.232	0.246	0.254	0.267	0.269	0.250	0.340
Myristic	14:0	0.379	0.391	0.400	0.416	0.420	0.42	0.485
	iso 14:0	0.311	0.327	—	0.353	0.357	—	—
	br 14:00	0.316	—	0.343	0.37	—	—	—
	14:1	0.329	—	0.360	0.38	—	—	—
	14:1 cis	—	—	—	—	—	0.39	—
	14:3	—	—	—	—	—	0.291	—
	15:0	0.611	0.622	0.635	0.65	0.643	0.66	0.699
	iso 15:0	—	—	—	—	0.538	—	0.617
	anteiso 15:0	0.521	0.541	—	0.552	0.559	0.58	—
Palmitic	16:0	1.00	1.00	1.00	1.00	1.00	1.00	1.00
	iso 16:0	0.821	0.835	—	0.877	0.840	—	0.883
	neo 16:0	0.647	0.660	—	0.668	—	0.90	—
	16:1^9 cis	—	—	0.864	0.89	0.903	0.92	—
	16:1^9 trans	—	—	0.864	—	—	—	—
	16:1^9	0.847	—	—	0.89	—	—	—
	16:1^8	0.847	—	—	0.79	—	—	—
	16:2^{9,12}	—	—	—	0.86	—	—	—
	16:2^{6,9}	—	—	—	0.77	—	—	—
	16:3^{6,9,12}	0.732	—	0.760	—	—	—	—

TABLE XIII (*Continued*)

Common name of parent acid	Code	Apiezon M					Apiezon L, 197°C	Silicone grease, 200°C
		173.5°C	182.5°C	188°C	197°C	200°C		
	16:3^{7,10,13}	0.732	—	0.760	0.77	—	—	—
	16:4^{6,9,12,15}	0.750	—	0.726	0.744	—	—	—
	16:4^{4,7,10,13}	0.700	—	0.726	0.744	—	—	—
	17:0	1.62	1.60	1.58	1.55	1.46	1.51	1.41
iso	17:0	—	—	—	—	1.27	—	1.27
br	17:0	1.20	—	1.89	1.19	—	—	—
br	17:0	1.35	—	1.33	1.31	—	—	—
anteiso	17:0	1.38	1.39	—	1.34	—	1.38	—
	17:1	—	—	—	—	1.33	1.31	—
Stearic	18:0	2.63	2.54	2.47	2.39	2.31	2.36	2.05
iso	18:0	2.17	2.12	—	2.00	1.99	—	1.80
neo	18:0	1.71	1.69	—	1.61	—	—	—
Oleic	18:1^9	2.15	—	2.08	2.04	2.03	2.03	—
	18:1^9 cis	—	—	—	2.08	—	2.12	—
	18:1^9 trans	—	—	—	—	—	2.09	—
	18:1^{16} cis	—	—	—	—	—	2.22	—
	18:1^{14} trans	—	—	—	—	—	2.12	—
	18:1 cis	—	—	—	—	—	—	—
Linoleic	18:2^{9,12}	1.98	—	1.93	1.88	1.98	—	—
	18:2^{6,9}	—	—	—	1.81	—	—	—
	18:2^{9,12} cis,trans	—	—	—	—	—	2.56	—
	18:2^{10,12} trans,cis	—	—	—	—	—	2.56	—
	18:2^{9,11} trans	—	—	—	—	—	3.09	—
	18:2^{10,12} trans	—	—	—	—	—	3.09	—
Linolenic	18:3^{9,12,15}	1.98	—	1.93	1.88	1.85	—	—
	18:3^{6,9,12}	1.98	—	1.93	1.88	—	—	—
	18:3 trans	—	—	—	—	—	—	—
	18:3^{9,11,13} cis,cis,trans,trans	—	—	—	—	—	4.35	—
	18:3^{9,12,5}	—	—	—	1.84	—	3.82	—
	18:4^{6,9,12,15}	1.74	—	1.71	1.72	—	1.93	—
	19:0	4.26	4.04	—	3.70	3.63	—	2.97

TABLE XIII (*Continued*)

Common name of parent acid	Code	Apiezon M					Apiezon L, 197°C	Silicone grease, 200°C
		173.5°C	182.5°C	188°C	197°C	200°C		
	br 19:0	—	—	—	—	1.30	—	—
	anteiso 19:0	3.63	3.50	—	3.20	—	—	4.12
Arachidic	20:0	6.95	6.42	6.12	5.62	—	5.8	—
	20:0 iso	—	—	—	4.79	—	—	—
	neo 20:0	—	—	—	3.84	2.06	—	—
	br 20:0	—	—	—	—	—	—	—
	$20:1^{11}$	—	—	—	4.72	—	—	—
	20:1	—	—	—	4.75	—	—	—
	$20:2^{8,11}$	—	—	—	4.17	—	—	—
	$20:2^{11,14}$	—	—	—	4.38	—	—	—
	20:2	—	—	—	4.5	—	—	—
	$20:3^{8,11,14}$	—	—	4.05	3.89	—	3.65	—
	$20:3^{5,8,11}$	—	—	4.05	3.89	—	3.48	—
	20:3	—	—	—	3.92	—	—	—
Arachidonic	$20:4^{5,8,11,14}$	—	—	3.61	3.48	—	—	—
	$20:4^{8,11,14,17}$	—	—	3.61	3.48	—	3.48	—
	$20:5^{5,8,11,14,17}$	—	—	3.61	3.48	—	—	—
	21:0	—	—	—	8.72	—	—	—
	anteiso 21:0	—	—	—	7.53	—	—	—
Behenic	22:0	—	—	—	13.22	—	—	—
	iso 22:0	—	—	—	11.16	—	—	—
	22:1	—	—	—	—	—	10.9	—
	$22:5^{7,10,13,16,19}$	—	—	—	7.82	—	—	—
	$22:5^{5,8,11,16,17}$	—	—	—	7.88	—	—	—
	$22:6^{4,7,10,13,16,19}$	—	—	—	7.16	—	—	—
	$22:6^{6,7,10,13,16,19}$	—	—	—	7.15	—	7.15	—
Lignoceric	24:0	—	—	—	31.04	—	—	—
	iso 24:0	—	—	—	26.30	—	—	—
	neo 24:0	—	—	—	21.33	—	—	—

Relative retention values of methyl esters of fatty acids on various polar stationary liquids at several temperatures are shown in Table XII. Similar data on nonpolar liquids are given in Table XIII. These values can be of considerable assistance in identifying unknown materials.

A number of other methods have been used in conjunction with GLC for determining the structures of fatty acids, including ozonolysis, oxidative degradation (Murray, 1959), and reduction. However, these involve special techniques which are outside the scope of this chapter.

VIII. Separation on Capillary Columns

A large number of papers on the construction of ionization detectors and their use in conjunction with capillary columns have appeared within the past few years, but comparatively little material has been published on biochemical applications, particularly in the field of lipid research. Perhaps this can be traced to the fact that until recently it has not been possible to coat capillary tubes in such a way as to secure reproducible results from column to column. Furthermore, the small amounts of materials handled make it impossible to collect and analyze fractions by conventional methods. Lipsky *et al.* (1959b,c) have described the separation of mixtures of methyl esters of fatty acids on a 200-foot capillary column coated with Apiezon L. Chromatography was carried out at 240°C at argon pressure of 10 to 20 psig. The samples were introduced into a chamber heated at 300°C so that they would be volatilized immediately and swept into a split-stream system that would route about 1 μg of material into the column and vent the remaining 99.9% of the sample to the atmosphere. Column efficiency was 171,000 theoretical plates for methyl behenate. The number of theoretical plates increased with retention time except where an individual component of the mixture was present in amounts greater than 8%. When the columns were overloaded the peaks had leading fronts and sharp backs. This phenomenon was particularly evident with fatty acid esters but did not occur with hydrocarbons at loads 100 times as high. Peak asymmetry was eliminated almost entirely by increasing the sensitivity of the detector tenfold and decreasing the sample size proportionately.

The stearate peak was eluted from a 200-foot column at 240°C in about 78 minutes, compared to a retention time of 140 minutes on an 8-foot conventional packed column at 196°C. The peak was much sharper and well defined on the capillary chromatogram (Fig. 18). Methyl elaidate was separated from methyl oleate, and stearate and oleate were sharply resolved. However, linoleate was not separated from linolenate. These are about the same separations that would be expected on a packed column with Apiezon L as the partition fluid.

The lipid mixture was also chromatographed on a 100-foot capillary

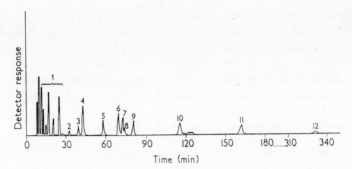

Fig. 18. Separation of a mixture of methyl esters of known acids at 240°C on a 200-foot capillary column coated with Apiezon L. (1) 8:0 to 14:0. (2) 15:0. (3) 16:1. (4) 16:0. (5) 17:0. (6) 18:2 + 18:3. (7) 18:1. (8) 18:1. (9) 18:0. (10) 20:4. (11) 20:0. (12) 22:0. (Lipsky *et al.*, 1959b.)

column coated with poly(diethylene glycol glutarate). At a temperature of 193°C and a carrier gas pressure of 28 psig of argon, linolenate was eluted in less than 20 minutes. Column efficiency was only 2800 theoretical plates for methyl behenate. The separation factor, α, for stearate and oleate was 1.13. This afforded excellent separation despite the low efficiency of the column. Resolution of linoleate from linolenate was excellent, as would be expected on a polyester column. Elaidate and oleate were not resolved, which also would be expected.

These preliminary results suggest that capillary columns may have great potential for the analysis of lipids, but this has not been realized yet. Separations were about as would be expected from packed columns except for sharper peaks at high retention times. Areas of future use will probably include the resolution of compounds with very small separation factors, and the analysis of mixtures with wide boiling-point ranges.

a. Conditions for Chromatography

*1. *On Apiezon L or Poly(diethylene Glycol Glutarate)* (Lipsky *et al.*, 1959b)

Chromatograph	Laboratory-built.
Column dimensions	100-foot and 200-foot × 0.010-inch stainless steel No. 316 seamless coils of 0.062 inch o.d.
Solid support	Column wall.
Stationary phase	(I) Apiezon L. (II) Poly(diethylene glycol glutarate).
Temperatures	(I) 240°C. (II) 193°C. Injection port: 300°C. Detector bath: 250°C.
Carrier gas	Argon at 0.5 to 1.5 ml/min. Inlet pressure: (I) 10 to 20 psig. (II) 28 psig. Outlet pressure: atmospheric.
Detector	Argon ionization detector with low effective volume. Sr^{90} source.
Recorder	Wheelco No. 8000 series, 0 to 10 mv.

Sample size	About 1 µg by split-stream method.
Analysis time	(I) About 330 minutes to behenate. (II) About 20 minutes to linolenate.

IX. Chromatography of Fatty Acids and Hydroxy Acids as Hydrocarbons

Hydroxy acids are sometimes found in admixture with higher fatty acids in materials of biological origin. Thus Barbier and Pain (1960) isolated a fraction from the mandible glands of bees with the same retention volume as 10-hydroxy-Δ^2-decenoic acid. In some instances hydroxy acids are dehydrated during GLC (Morris *et al.*, 1960). Methyl dimorphecolate is converted to a mixture of conjugated trienoates, and α-hydroxy monoenes emerge from the column as conjugated dienes. Hydroxy compounds not activated by adjacent unsaturation appear to be stable when analyzed by GLC.

Downing *et al.* (1960) describe an indirect procedure for the chromatography of mixtures of higher fatty acids and hydroxy fatty acids which appears to eliminate these artifacts. Fatty acids and hydroxy fatty acids are isolated from the saponifiable fraction of wool wax as their calcium salts. These are converted to methyl esters by refluxing them with a mixture of methanol, benzene, and concentrated sulfuric acid (Section A). The mixed esters are then reduced to the corresponding alcohols with lithium aluminum hydride (Section A). The reduction step yields a mixture of monohydric alcohols, α,ω-diols and α,β-diols. These fractions are cleanly resolved from one another by liquid-solid chromatography on activated alumina. The monohydric alcohols are eluted by a mixture of chloroform and benzene (1:2), the α,ω-diols by chloroform and ethanol (2:1), and the α,β-diols by further quantities of chloroform and ethanol. The α,β-diols are purified further by converting them to ketals through treatment with acetone containing a trace of sulfuric acid. The ketals are chromatographed on alumina and eluted with light petroleum ether. Hydrolysis yields a refined α,β-diol fraction.

The three fractions are converted separately to hydrocarbons as described in Section C. The hydrocarbons representing each fraction are separated by GLC on a silicone column with the temperature programmed between 100° and 165°C (Section B.III.a.).

a. Conversion to Alcohols (Nystrom and Brown, 1947)

An ether, or tetrahydrofuran solution or slurry, of lithium aluminum hydride, is used for the reduction of fatty acid esters to alcohols. Care must be taken to keep all equipment and reagents free from water and contaminants such as alcohols, ketones, and esters. A three-necked 2-liter flask equipped with a reflux condenser, a dropping funnel, and a mechanical stirrer is used for the reduction. Calcium chloride tubes are attached to all openings for protection against moisture until the completion of the reaction. The ether or tetrahydrofuran solution of the ester to be reduced is added with stirring to excess lithium aluminum hydride at a rate determined by the vigor of the reaction. The reaction is complete soon after the final addition of the ester solution. Water is added dropwise, with caution, the flask being cooled if necessary. The mixture is then poured into ice water, and 10% sulfuric acid is added to decompose the metal alcoholate and excess reagent. Hydrogen gas is formed in the hydrolytic decomposition of excess reagent, and sparkproof motors are recommended. The ether layer is removed, and the aqueous layer is washed with two portions of ether. The ether extracts (peroxide-free) are dried and evaporated. The alcohols are separated by liquid-solid chromatography, and the individual fractions are converted to hydrocarbons prior to analysis by GLC as described in Section C.

X. Summary

Fatty acids occur free or as esters in the lipids of tissues and are the main constituents of the saponifiable fraction. They are most often chromatographed as their methyl esters on polar and nonpolar stationary liquids. They are separated according to carbon number on nonpolar packings such as Apiezon grease, and according to degree of unsaturation on polar packings such as poly(ethylene glycol adipate). Retention volumes obtained on these two packings can often be used for identifying unknown compounds.

Many fatty acid esters are stable at column temperatures. However, some compounds, notably conjugated trienoates and esters of vicinally unsaturated hydroxy derivatives, undergo isomerization or dehydration on the column. Therefore, the possibility of artifact formation should always be considered in chromatographing complex mixtures of unknown compounds, particularly at high column temperatures.

H. Glyceryl Esters

I. Introduction

Monoglycerides and diglycerides are produced through partial hydrolysis of triglycerides by pancreatic amylase. The reaction proceeds stepwise. α,β-Diglycerides are formed first, after which the second ester linkage is broken to yield β-monoglycerides. Thus the nature of the fatty acids present in the β-position of triglycerides can be determined by isolating β-monoglycerides from the reaction mixture and finding out what fatty acid components they contain. Therefore, the chromatographic separation of the monoglycerides, and to a lesser extent of the diglycerides, is of interest because of the information it will yield on the structure of fats.

Triglycerides are the major components of all fats and oils of animal or vegetable origin. In the past, it has been customary to analyze them by first interesterifying with methanol, and chromatographing the methyl esters of the fatty acids. However, it is now possible to elute triglycerides through tristearin from GLC columns without prior chemical modification.

II. Chromatographic Methods

Huebner (1959) found that monoglycerides and diglycerides could not be eluted as such from chromatographic columns. However, by first converting them to corresponding diacetates and monoacetates by treatment with acetyl chloride, he was able to separate them on high-vacuum silicone grease at temperatures of 284° to 317°C. It was necessary to condition the columns at 340° to 370°C for several days prior to use. Monoglycerides up to monoarachidin and diglycerides up to myristopalmitin were separated in this way. A small extraneous peak appeared before most of the major peaks, indicating that chemical changes of some sort took place on the column. The monoglyceride diacetate of molecular weight 358 was eluted in a little over 4 minutes, and the diglyceride monoacetate of molecular weight 625 in about 28 to 30 minutes. However, some of the lower diglyceride monoacetates were eluted in less than 4 minutes, so the two groups of compounds overlap to some extent (Fig. 19). The α-glyceride diacetates were eluted slightly faster than the β-isomers, separate straight lines being obtained for each group of compounds when $\log_{10}$ retention time was plotted against molecular weight. Similarly, the α,α-diglyceride monoacetates were eluted slightly faster than the α,β derivatives. Huebner employed this method for the analysis of a synthetic mixture containing nineteen components at concentrations ranging from a few tenths of a per cent to over 30%. At 305°C it was possible to detect fifteen of these. Two of the lower-molecular-weight compounds, α-monocaprin diacetate and β-monolaurin diacetate, were missing from the chromatograms, presumably because they were eluted too fast. They could be detected by running the column at a lower temperature. Two of the higher-molecular-weight compounds, dipalmitin monoacetate and diolein monoacetate, also were not detected, but they were present in comparatively small amounts. The major component of the mixture, trilaurin, could be detected at 305°C and 298°C, but not at 284°C. This is a preliminary report in which no data are given on the separation of fat hydrolyzates. Nevertheless, it seems evident that many of the monoglycerides and some of the lower-molecular-weight diglycerides can be detected in this manner.

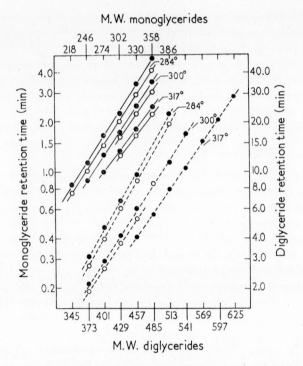

M.W. monoglycerides

FIG. 19. Log$_{10}$ retention time on high-vacuum silicone grease at various temperatures versus molecular weight for acetates of monoglycerides and diglycerides. ——— Monoglycerides. – – – – Diglycerides. ● α or α,α Components. ○ β or α,β Components. (Huebner, 1959.)

McInnes *et al.* (1960) have developed a method which is specific for the monoglycerides. Both the α- and the β-glycerides are converted to the allyl esters of the corresponding fatty acids by mesylating them with methanesulfonyl chloride and treating the products with sodium iodide in anhydrous acetone.

Triglycerides cannot be mesylated at all. Diglycerides can be mesylated in one position, but the products cannot react further with sodium iodide to yield the allyl ester. Therefore, these materials can be eliminated from the chromatographs by running the column at a temperature too low to elute them (240°C) but satisfactory for the more volatile allyl esters.

The same products are formed from the α- and β-monoglycerides. Hence, this technique alone cannot be used to distinguish between the fatty acid residues contained in them. This can be accomplished by treating the mixed isomers with periodic acid prior to chromatography. This cleaves the α-isomer, since it has vicinal hydroxyl groups. The hydroxy groups of the β-isomer are not vicinal, so this compound does not react. Consequently, the allyl ester peaks obtained when the reaction product is chromatographed arise from the β-isomer alone. The identities of the fatty acid residues in the α-monoglycerides can be determined by comparing chromatographs obtained on the original sample and on the periodate-treated sample.

The over-all yield of allyl esters from both the α- and β-isomers determined either separately or in mixtures is 96 to 98% of theory, and differentiation between the isomers in an α,β mixture is absolute. The presence of free fatty acids, diglycerides and triglycerides does not interfere with the reactions.

The allyl esters were separated on an Apiezon M column at 240°C, the retention time of the C_{18} ester being 60 minutes. The logarithms of the retention times varied linearly with carbon number, but the peak areas were proportional to sample weight. To show that no structural changes occurred during chromatography of the allyl esters, samples of synthetic allyl esters were collected from the effluent gas stream. Iodine values and infrared spectra were identical to those of the original samples.

McInnes et al. (1960) also chromatographed the isopropylidine derivatives of the α-monoglycerides. This is a good separation technique, since the β-isomers cannot form cyclic acetals of this type. Good separation of these

$$
\begin{array}{l}
\quad\quad\quad \overset{\displaystyle O}{\overset{\|}{}} \\
CH_2O-C-R \\
| \\
CHO \quad\quad CH_3 \\
| \quad\quad \diagdown \diagup \\
\quad\quad\quad C \\
| \quad \diagup \diagdown \\
CH_2O \quad\quad CH_3
\end{array}
$$

compounds was obtained up to C_8 on an Apiezon M column at 198°C. The higher esters required a temperature of 240°C, and even then the C_{18} derivative had a retention time of 130 minutes. Chromatography of the allyl esters seems more practical. Furthermore, the isopropylidine method will detect only the α-isomers, and it is the β-isomers that are of greater biochemical interest.

Triglycerides need not be modified chemically prior to chromatography, since they are already nonpolar. However, because of their high molecular weights, very high injection and column temperatures are required to elute them from conventional packings. Tributyrin, tricaproin, and tricaprylin can be separated on a 200-foot capillary column at 250°C with Apiezon L as the stationary liquid (Patton, 1960). The time required for elution is 500 minutes at 30 psig argon. Esters of higher molecular weight cannot be analyzed under these conditions. However, it is possible to separate tributyrin through tripalmitin on a short (18-inch) polyester column operated at

250°C (Fryer *et al.*, 1960). This is beyond the upper temperature limit where polyesters are stable; consequently it is necessary to employ a more heat-resistant liquid to extend the range of analysis. A fraction isolated from Dow Corning high-vacuum silicone grease is satisfactory for this purpose. Triglycerides through tristearin can be eluted from an 18-inch column packed with this material at temperatures in the range of 300° to 350°C. Recoveries are almost quantitative from tributyrin through trimyristin, but losses occur when higher glycerides are chromatographed. The main problem in obtaining good results on higher homologues is in vaporizing the oil without thermal decomposition. For compounds up to trimyristin, this can be done by using high injection block temperatures. However, this does not work so well for the higher homologues; thus increased flow rates must be combined with higher temperatures to obtain elution of the compounds. Even so, good peaks are not obtained for compounds having molecular weights above 800.

This method can be applied to vegetable and animal oils containing a preponderance of glycerides of low-molecular-weight fatty acids without serious problems arising from degradation. Butter oil, for example, shows seventeen peaks when chromatographed under these conditions, all of them reasonably symmetrical, and coconut oil shows fifteen.

a. Chemical Modification of Glycerides

*1. *Conversion to Acetates* (Huebner, 1959). The sample (1 ml) is treated with acetyl chloride (1 ml), and the mixture is refluxed for 45 minutes. The excess reagent is removed under reduced pressure.

2. *Conversion to Allyl Esters* (McInnes *et al.*, 1960). The monoglyceride or lipid sample (100 mg) is dissolved in alcohol-free anhydrous chloroform (1 ml) and anhydrous pyridine (0.1 ml) contained in a dry glass-stoppered test tube. The solution is chilled to 0°C, and redistilled methanesulfonyl chloride (0.1 ml) is added. The contents of the tube are thoroughly mixed and allowed to stand at 0°C overnight. The reaction mixture is quenched in 100 ml of ice water, and the test tube is rinsed several times with water. The water–chloroform mixture is placed in a 250-ml separatory funnel and extracted with 3 × 50-ml portions of chloroform. The combined chloroform extracts are dried over anhydrous sodium sulfate, and the solvent is removed in a rotary evaporator at 35°C.

The residue is dried in a vacuum desiccator over phosphorus pentoxide for 2 hours, dissolved in anhydrous acetone, and the solution is placed in a 22 × 0.6-cm Pyrex glass tube sealed at one end. The volume of the solution is reduced to 1 ml by evaporating some of the solvent in a stream of dry nitrogen. A 25% solution of sodium iodide in anhydrous acetone (1 ml) is then added, and the tube is sealed and heated at 100°C for 2 hours. The tube is cooled, and the contents are washed into a 250-ml separatory funnel with several portions of water and ether. Free iodine is reduced by adding 10% aqueous sodium thiosulfate solution until the brown color disappears. The water layer is extracted with 3 × 50 ml of ethyl ether, and the combined ether extracts are dried over anhydrous sodium sulfate. The solvent is removed in a rotary evaporator at 35°C, and the residue is redissolved in a standard volume of cyclohexane. Aliquots of this solution are injected into the chromatograph.

3. *Oxidation of α-Monoglycerides* (McInnes *et al.*, 1960). The reagent for oxidizing the α-glycerides is prepared by dissolving 12 gm of periodic acid in water and diluting to 100 ml. A portion of this stock solution (5 ml) is then diluted to 100 ml with methanol. The stock solution is stable, but the methanol solution should not be kept more than 4 or 5 days.

Procedure. A mixture of α- and β-monoglycerides containing not more than 100 mg of the α-isomer is dissolved in 25 ml of chloroform. Periodate-in-methanol reagent (25 ml) is added, and the solution is heated to boiling. After cooling for 30 minutes, it is poured into a separatory funnel containing 30 ml of water. The chloroform layer is washed with 3 × 50-ml portions of water to remove iodic and periodic acids. The solution is dried over anhydrous sodium sulfate, and the solvent is removed in a rotary evaporator at 35°C. The unchanged β-monoglycerides are converted to allyl esters as described above.

b. Conditions for Chromatography

*1. Chromatography as Acetates (Huebner, 1959)

Chromatograph	Conventional design.
Column dimensions	2-foot × 0.35-mm i.d. stainless steel.
Solid support	Acid-washed Celite 545 (40/70 mesh).
Stationary phase	High-vacuum silicone grease (23:77).
Temperatures	Column: 284°, 298°, 300°, 305°, and 317°C.
Carrier gas	Helium at 35 ml/min. Inlet pressure: 35 psig. Outlet pressure: atmospheric.
Detector	Hot wire (Pt) T/C cell.
Recorder	1 mv.
Sample size	2 to 20 μl.
Analysis time	Monoglycerides: about 4 minutes to mol. wt. 358 at 284°C. Diglycerides: about 30 minutes for mol. wt. 625 at 317°C.

2. *Chromatography as Allyl Esters* (McInnes *et al.*, 1960)

Chromatograph	Podbielniak Chromacon No. 9475-3V.
Column dimensions	122 × 0.4-cm i.d. glass.
Solid support	Celite 545.
Stationary phase	Apiezon M (10:40).
Temperature	240°C.

Carrier gas	Helium. Flow rate not given.
Detector	T/C cell.
Recorder	Not given.
Sample size	2 to 20 μl.
Analysis time	About 60 minutes to allyl stearate.

*3. *Separation of Triglycerides on Silicone Grease* (Fryer *et al.*, 1960)

Chromatograph	Specially built oven with a thermal conductivity bridge copied after the Aerograph.
Column dimensions	35- to 90-cm stainless-steel columns, 5 mm i.d.
Solid support	Chromosorb W, acid-washed (30/60 U. S. mesh).
Stationary phase	Ethyl acetate-soluble fraction of Dow Corning high-vacuum silicone grease (30:70 and 15:85).

		Optimum*	Range
Temperatures	Injection:	365°C	300°–520°C
	Column:	310°C	229°–350°C
	Detector:	Slightly above column, 2 to 5°C.	
	* After 2- to 3-week conditioning.		

Carrier gas	Helium at 40 to 200 ml/min. Outlet: atmospheric pressure.
Detector	Gow-Mac TE III Model 9230, four filament (W) T/C cell operated at 200 ma and 12 volts DC.
Recorder	Sargent Model SR, 1.25-mv full scale.
Sample size	1 to 8 μl.
Analysis time	15 to 60 min. dependent upon conditions.

III. SUMMARY

Monoglycerides and diglycerides up to a molecular weight of 625 can be chromatographed at temperatures in the neighborhood of 300°C by first converting them to acetates. The retention times of the β-isomers of the monoglycerides are slightly longer than those of the α-isomers, but not enough so for good resolution. More effective separation of the isomers from each other, can be obtained by selectively oxidizing the α-isomer with periodate. The β-isomer is then converted to the allyl ester of the corresponding fatty acid and chromatographed.

Triglycerides up to a molecular weight of 800 can be chromatographed on a short (18-inch) silicone-packed column operated at 350°C. Tristearin can be eluted, but losses occur, probably because of thermal decomposition of part of the sample in the injection block.

I. Synthetic Compounds Derived from Lipids

I. INTRODUCTION

Fatty amines with carbon number greater than 6 do not occur commonly in biological systems, but they can be obtained synthetically by the reaction of fatty alcohols with ammonia and have been used for the preservation of vitamin A in food. Amides are easily reduced to amines with lithium aluminium hydride, and the resulting amines may then be chromatographed. Higher fatty nitriles also do not occur in nature but are readily obtained from the reaction of the corresponding alkyl halide with an alkali metal cyanide or by the dehydration of amides. Since members of both these series are prepared from naturally occurring lipids, their separation by GLC will be described briefly here.

II. HIGHER FATTY AMINES

The analysis of mixtures of fatty amines, as well as of fatty alcohols, has been hampered by the fact that asymmetrical peaks are obtained which interfere with peak resolution and area measurements. This asymmetry is caused by leading, tailing, or both, and occurs frequently when polar compounds are chromatographed on columns containing incompletely deactivated solid supports. James *et al.* (1952) noted this effect in the gas chromatographic separation of ammonia and methylamines, and deactivated their solid support with methanolic sodium hydroxide, but with only partial success. More recently, Nelson and Milun (1960) have obtained satisfactory chromatograms of fatty amines with Dow Corning high-vacuum silicone grease on sodium chloride. They also got satisfactory resolution of the C_8 to C_{18} amines on a column packed with Dow Corning 550 silicone oil on Chromosorb W which was previously deactivated with methanolic potassium hydroxide. The peaks were symmetrical, and it was possible to obtain a quantitative measurement of alkyl chain length distribution in mixtures of primary amines (Table XIV). Results were calculated by the peak area–internal normalization method. Agreement between the amounts actually present and the amounts found is quite good, considering the large differences in the amounts of the various components that were present.

TABLE XIV

WEIGHT PERCENTAGES OF PRIMARY AMINES FOUND IN
A SYNTHETIC MIXTURE BY GAS CHROMATOGRAPHY
ON SILICONE OIL–CHROMOSORB W

Fraction	Present (%)	Found (%)
C_{12}	0.6	0.9
C_{14}	7.5	8.8
C_{16}	30.0	27.7
C_{18}	62.0	62.6

Link *et al.* (1960) suggest two packings for the resolution of fatty amines. One of these is Apiezon L on deactivated Chromosorb W, and the other is silicone grease on deactivated Chromosorb. Excellent resolution of even-numbered C_8 to C_{18} fatty amines is obtained without appreciable tailing. Quantitative results on the analysis of known mixture of amines are comparable to those reported by Nelson and Milun. They also report that fatty alcohols give symmetrical peaks when chromatographed on these packings, but no data are given.

Link *et al.* (1960) determined the responses of the thermal detectors used in the analyses and found that peak area per unit weight of amine decreases with increasing molecular weight. Thus, on doubling chain length in going from C_8 to C_{16}, detector response per unit weight decreases from 1.13 to 1.00. The data show that the relative response per gram among the fatty amines is a linear function of molecular weight, a conclusion that is in agreement with data on other homologous series of fatty compounds.

a. Conditions for Chromatography

*1. Silicone Grease–NaCl Method (Nelson and Milun, 1960)

Chromatograph	Podbielniak Model 9475 V.
Column dimensions	114 × 0.4-cm i.d. stainless steel.
Solid support	Sodium chloride (40/60 mesh).
Stationary phase	Dow Corning high-vacuum silicone grease (5:95).
Temperatures	Column: 204°C. Injection port: 330°C. Detector: 204°C.
Carrier gas	Helium at 23 ml/min. Inlet pressure: 83 mm Hg. Outlet pressure: atmospheric.
Detector	Four-filament hot-wire (W) T/C cell at 200 ma.
Recorder	0.2 to 2.0 mv; 2 seconds.
Sample size	1.2 μl.
Analysis time	20 minutes to octadecylamine.

*2. Silicone Oil–Chromosorb W Method (Nelson and Milun, 1960)

Chromatograph	Podbielniak Model 9475 V.
Column dimensions	127 × 0.4-cm i.d. stainless steel.
Solid support	Alkali-treated Chromosorb W prepared as in Chapter 1, Section C.III.
Stationary phase	Dow Corning 550 silicone oil (35:100).
Temperatures	Column: 200°C. Injection port: 340°C. Detector: 200°C.
Carrier gas	Helium at 45 ml/min. Inlet pressure: 230 mm Hg. Outlet pressure: atmospheric.
Detector	Four-filament hot-wire (W) TlC cell at 200 ma.
Recorder	0.2 to 2.0 mv; 2 seconds.
Sample size	1.2 μl.
Analysis time	24 minutes to octadecylamine.

*3. *Apiezon L–Chromosorb W Method* (Link *et al.*, 1960)

Chromatograph	Beckman GC-2 chromatograph.
Column dimensions	2-foot × ¼-inch o.d. stainless steel.
Solid support	Alkali-treated Chromosorb W prepared according to procedure in Chapter 1, Section C.III.
Stationary phase	Apiezon L (18:82).
Temperature	225°C.
Carrier gas	Helium at 55 ml/min.
Detector	T/C cell at 200 ma.
Recorder	1 mv; 1 sec; 0.5 in./min.
Sample size	2 to 5 μl.
Analysis time	20 minutes to C_{18} amine.

*4. *Silicone Grease–Chromosorb Method* (Link *et al.*, 1960)

Chromatograph	Podbielniak Chromacon, Model 9580.
Column dimensions	4-foot × ¼-inch o.d. copper tubing.
Solid support	Alkali-treated Chromosorb prepared according to procedure in Chapter 1, Section C.III.
Stationary phase	Dow Corning high-vacuum silicone grease (50:100).
Temperature	177°C.
Carrier gas	Helium at 58 ml/min.
Detector	T/C cell at 245 ma.
Recorder	1 mv; 1 sec; 0.5 in./min.
Sample size	1 μl or less.
Analysis time	12 minutes to C_{18} amine.

III. HIGHER FATTY NITRILES

Fatty nitriles containing even-numbered carbon atoms from C_8 to C_{20} can be successfully resolved on 18-inch Carbowax 4000 monostearate columns at 226°C (Link *et al.*, 1959a). Figure 20 shows the chromatograms of a

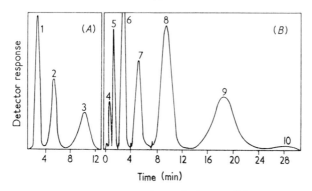

FIG. 20. Separation of higher fatty nitriles on Carbowax 4000 monostearate at 226°C. *A*, coconut nitriles. *B*, mixture of pure nitriles. (1) 12:0. (2) 14:0. (3) 16:0. (4) 8:0. (5) 10:0. (6) 12:0. (7) 14:0. (8) 16:0. (9) 18:0. (10) 20:0. (Link *et al.*, 1959a.)

known mixture of pure nitriles, and of a mixture synthesized from coconut oil. Good resolution is obtained of all the components of the mixture, and the peaks are symmetrical. This method can be used for the quantitative analysis of complex mixtures of nitriles. Nitriles also can be separated on polyester columns according to both chain length (C_6 to C_{20}) and degree of unsaturation. Conditions employed are similar to those for fatty acid methyl esters, or the acetates of fatty alcohols.

Gas chromatography of nitriles may be a potentially useful method for the analysis of biologically important amides, since these can be dehydrated to yield nitriles in good yield. The gain in volatility would be considerable, as shown by the fact that acetamide boils at 220°C compared to 82°C for acetonitrile.

a. Chromatographic Method

*1. *Separation of Fatty Nitriles on Carbowax* (Link et al., 1959a)

Chromatograph	Beckman Model GC-2.
Column dimensions	1.5-foot × 0.25-inch o.d. stainless steel.
Solid support	C-22 firebrick (30/60 mesh).
Stationary phase	Carbowax 4000 monostearate (35:65).
Temperature	226°C.
Carrier gas	Helium at 52 ml/min. Inlet pressure: 25 psig. Outlet pressure: atmospheric.
Detector	T/C cell.
Recorder	1 mv; 1 sec; 0.5 in./min.
Sample size	15 μl.
Analysis time	28 minutes to C_{20} nitrile.

IV. SUMMARY

Higher fatty amines and nitriles do not occur in nature, but they can be synthesized from naturally occurring lipids. The higher amines are chromatographed on nonpolar stationary liquids coated on specially deactivated solid supports. Good resolution of C_8 to C_{20} fatty nitriles can be obtained on Carbowax 4000 monostearate.

References

Allen, R. J. L. 1940. The estimation of phosphorus. *Biochem. J.* **34**: 858–865.

Barbezat, S. 1958. *J. recherches centre nat. recherche sci., Labs. Bellevue (Paris)* **45**: 273. (Reference from Carruthers and Johnstone *Nature* **184**: 1131.)

Barbier, M. and J. Pain. 1960. Étude de la sécrétion des glandes mandibulaires des reines et dds ouvrières d'abeilles (*Apis mellifica*) par chromatographie en phase gazeuse. *Compt. rend. acad. sci.* **250**: 3740–3742.

Beerthuis, R. K., D. Dijkstra, J. G. Keppler, and J. H. Recourt. 1959. Gas-liquid chromatographic analysis of higher fatty acids and fatty acid methyl esters. *Ann. N. Y. Acad. Sci.* **72**: 616–632.

Beerthuis, R. K. and J. H. Recourt. 1960. Sterol analysis by gas chromatography. *Nature* **186**: 372–374.

Blomstrand, R. and J. Gürtler. 1959. Separation of glycerol ethers by gas-liquid chromatography. *Acta Chem. Scand.* **13**: 1466–1467.

Bloor, W. R., 1928. The determination of small amounts of lipid in blood plasma. *J. Biol. Chem.* **77**: 53–73.

Böttcher, C. J. F., F. P. Woodford, E. Boelsma-Van Houte, and C. M. Van Gent. 1959. Methods for the analysis of lipids extracted from human arteries and other tissues. *Rec. trav. chim.* **78**: 794–814.

Boughton, B. and V. R. Wheatley. 1959. Studies of sebum. 9. Further studies of the composition of the unsaponifiable matter of human-forearm "sebum." *Biochem. J.* **73**: 144–149.

Brockmann, H. and H. Schodder. 1941. Aluminiumoxyd mit abgestuften Adsorptionsvermögen zur chromatographischen Adsorption. *Ber. deut. chem. Ges.* **74**: 73–78.

Carruthers, W. and R. A. W. Johnstone. 1959. Composition of a paraffin wax fraction from tobacco leaf and tobacco smoke. *Nature* **184**: 1131–1132.

Chibnall, A. C., A. L. Latner, E. F. Williams, and C. A. Ayre. 1934. The constitution of coccerin. *Biochem. J.* **28**: 313–325.

Craig, B. M. and N. L. Murty. 1959. Quantitative fatty acid analysis of vegetable oils by gas-liquid chromatography. *J. Am. Oil Chemists' Soc.* **36**: 549–552.

Cropper, F. R. and A. Heywood. 1953. Analytical separation of the methyl esters of the C_{12}–C_{22} fatty acids by vapour-phase chromatography. *Nature* **172**: 1101–1102.

Cropper, F. R. and A. Heywood. 1957. The analysis of fatty acids and fatty alcohols by vapour phase chromatography. *In* "Vapour Phase Chromatography" (D. H. Desty, ed.), pp. 316–328. New York, Academic Press.

DeBoer, T. J. and H. J. Backer. 1956. Diazomethane. *Organic Syntheses* **36**: 16–19.

Dijkstra, G., J. G. Keppler, and J. A. Schols. 1955. Gas-liquid partition chromatography. *Rec. trav. chim.* **74**: 805–812.

Downing, D. T., Z. H. Kranz, and K. E. Murray. 1960. Studies in waxes. XIV. An investigation of the aliphatic constituents of hydrolysed wool wax by gas chromatography. *Australian J. Chem.* **13**: 80–94.

Farquhar, J. W., W. Insull, Jr., P. Rosen, W. Stoffel, and E. H. Ahrens, Jr. 1959. The analysis of fatty acid mixtures by gas liquid chromatography: construction and operation of an ionization chamber instrument. *Nutrition Revs.* **17**: 1–30.

Fillerup, D. L. and J. F. Mead. 1953. Chromatographic separation of the plasma lipids. *Proc. Soc. Exptl. Biol. Med.* **83**: 574–577.

Folch, J., M. Lees, and G. H. S. Stanley. 1957. A simple method for the isolation and purification of total lipides from animal tissues. *J. Biol. Chem.* **226**: 497–509.

Fryer, F. H., W. L. Ormand, and G. B. Crump. 1960. Triglyceride elution by gas chromatography. *J. Am. Oil Chemists' Soc.* **37**: 589–590.

Gehrke, C. W. and D. F. Goerlitz. 1960. The quantitative determination of fatty acids by gas chromatography. Personal communication.

Gray, G. M. 1958. The structure of the plasmalogens of ox heart. *Biochem. J.* **70**: 425–433.

Gray, G. M. 1960a. The separation of long chain fatty aldehydes by gas-liquid chromatography. *J. Chromatog.* **4**: 52–59.

Gray, G. M. 1960b. The phospholipids of ox spleen with special reference to the fatty acid and fatty aldehyde compositions of the lecithin and kephalin fractions. *Biochem. J.* **77**: 82–91.

Gray, G. M. and M. G. Macfarlane. 1958. Separation and composition of the phospholipids of ox heart. *Biochem. J.* **70**: 409–425.

Hallgren, B. and S. O. Larsson. 1959. Separation and identification of alkoxyglycerols. *Acta Chem. Scand.* **13:** 2147–2148.

Hallgren, B. and S. O. Larsson. 1960. Personal communication.

Hornstein, I., L. E. Elliott, and P. F. Crowe. 1959. Gas chromatographic separation of long-chain fatty acid methyl esters on polyvinyl acetate. *Nature* **184:** 1710–1711.

Hornstein, I., J. A. Alford, L. E. Elliott, and P. F. Crowe. 1960. Determination of free fatty acids in fat. *Anal. Chem.* **32:** 540–542.

Huebner, V. R. 1959. Preliminary studies on the analysis of mono- and di-gylcerides by gas-liquid partition chromatography. *J. Am. Oil Chemists' Soc.* **36:** 262–263.

Huelin, F. E. and R. A. Gallop. 1951. Studies in the natural coating of apples. 1. Preparation and properties of fractions. *Australian J. Sci. Research, Ser. B* **4:** 526–532.

Insull, W., Jr. and E. H. Ahrens, Jr. 1959. The fatty acids of human milk from mothers on diets taken *ad libitum. Biochem. J.* **72:** 27–33.

James, A. T. 1958. The separation of long-chain fatty acids by gas-liquid chromatography. *Am. J. Clin. Nutrition* **6:** 595–600.

James, A. T. 1959. Determination of the degree of unsaturation of long chain fatty acids by gas-liquid chromatography. *J. Chromatog.* **2:** 552–561.

James, A. T. 1960. Qualitative and quantitative determination of the fatty acids by gas-liquid chromatography. *In* "Methods of Biochemical Analysis" (D. Glick, ed.), Vol. 8, pp. 1–60. New York, Interscience.

James, A. T. and A. J. P. Martin. 1952. Gas-liquid partition chromatography. The separation and micro-estimation of volatile fatty acids from formic acid to dodecanoic acid. *Biochem. J.* **50:** 679–690.

James, A. T. and A. J. P. Martin. 1956. Gas-liquid chromatography. The separation and identification of the methyl esters of saturated and unsaturated acids from formic acid to *n*-octadecanoic acid. *Biochem. J.* **63:** 144–152.

James, A. T., A. J. P. Martin, and G. H. Smith. 1952. Gas-liquid partition chromatography. The separation and micro-estimation of ammonia and the methylamines. *Biochem. J.* **52:** 238–242.

Johnston, P. V. and F. A. Kummerow. 1960. Gas-liquid chromatography of methyl esters of fatty acid from human and chicken brain lipids. *Proc. Soc. Exptl. Biol. Med.* **104:** 201–205.

Karnovsky, M. L. and A. F. Brumm. 1955. Studies on naturally occurring α-glycerol ethers. *J. Biol. Chem.* **216:** 689–701.

Kranz, Z. H., J. A. Lamberton, K. E. Murray, and A. H. Redcliffe. 1960. Sugar-cane wax. II. An examination of the constituents of sugar-cane cuticle wax by gas chromatography. *Australian J. Chem.* **13:** 498–505.

Lakshminarayana, G., F. A. Kruger, D. G. Cornwell, and J. B. Brown. 1960. Chromatographic studies on the composition of commercial samples of triolein–I[131] and oleic acid–I[131] and the distribution of the label in human serum lipids following oral administration of these lipids. *Arch Biochem. Biophys.* **88:** 318–327.

Landowne, R. A. and S. R. Lipsky. 1958. Retection of certain brominated long-chain fatty acid esters by gas-liquid chromatography. *Nature* **182:** 1731–1732.

Lewin, L. M. and A. C. Wagenknecht. 1960. An inositol phosphatide of peas. *Arch. Biochem. Biophys.* **87:** 239–246.

Link, W. E. and R. A. Morrissette. 1960. Gas-liquid chromatography of fatty derivatives. IV. Quantitative analysis of *n*-alcohols. *J. Am. Oil Chemists' Soc.* **37:** 668–671.

Link, W. E., H. M. Hickman, and R. A. Morrissette. 1959a. Gas-liquid chromatography of fatty derivatives. I. Separation of homologous series of α-olefins, *n*-hydrocarbons, *n*-nitriles and *n*-alcohols. *J. Am. Oil Chemists' Soc.* **36:** 20–23.

Link, W. E., H. M. Hickman, and R. A. Morrissette. 1959b. Gas-liquid chromatography of fatty derivatives. II. Analysis of fatty alcohol mixtures by gas-liquid chromatography. *J. Am. Oil Chemists' Soc.* **36:** 300–303.

Link, W. E., R. A. Morrissette, A. D. Cooper, and C. F. Smullin. 1960. Gas-liquid chromatography of fatty derivatives. III. Analysis of fatty amines. *J. Am. Oil Chemists' Soc.* **37:** 364–366.

Lipsky, S. R. and R. A. Landowne. 1959. Evaluation of a stationary phase for fatty acid analysis by gas-liquid chromatography. *Ann. N. Y. Acad. Sci.* **72:** 666–674.

Lipsky, S. R., R. A. Landowne, and M. R. Godet. 1959a. The effects of varying the chemical composition of the stationary liquid on the resolution of the long-chain saturated and unsaturated fatty acid esters by gas-liquid chromatography. *Biochim. et Biophys. Acta* **31:** 336–347.

Lipsky, S. R., R. A. Landowne, and J. E. Lovelock. 1959b. Separation of lipides by gas-liquid chromatography. *Anal. Chem.* **31:** 852–856.

Lipsky, S. R., J. E. Lovelock, and R. A. Landowne. 1959c. The use of high efficiency capillary columns for the separation of certain *cis-trans* isomers of long chain fatty acid esters by gas chromatography. *J. Am. Chem. Soc.* **81:** 1010.

Luddy, F. E., R. A. Barford, and R. W. Riemenschneider. 1960. Direct conversion of lipid components to their fatty acid methyl esters. *J. Am. Oil Chemists' Soc.* **37:** 447–451.

McInnes, A. G., N. H. Tattrie, and M. Kattes. 1960. Application of gas-liquid partition chromatography to the quantitative estimation of monoglycerides. *J. Am. Oil Chemists' Soc.* **37:** 7–11.

MacKenna, R. M. B., V. R. Wheatley, and A. Wormall. 1952. Studies of sebum. 2. Some constituents of the unsaponifiable matter of human sebum. *Biochem. J.* **52:** 161–168.

Malins, D. C. 1960. Fatty acids and glyceryl ethers in alkoxydiglycerides of dogfish liver oil. *Chem. & Ind. (London),* 1359–1360.

Malins, D. C. and H. K. Mangold. 1960. Analysis of complex lipid mixtures by thin layer chromatography and complementary methods. *J. Am. Oil Chemists' Soc.* **37:** 576–578.

Metcalfe, L. D. 1960. Gas chromatography of unesterified fatty acids using polyester columns treated with phosphoric acid. *Nature* **188:** 142–143.

Metcalfe, L. D. and A. A. Schmitz. 1961. The rapid preparation of fatty-acid esters for gas chromatographic analysis. *Anal. Chem.* **33:** 363-364.

Meyer zu Reckendorf, W. 1960. Polyester als stationäre Phasen in der Gaschromatographie. *Z. anal. Chem.* **175:** 350–355.

Morris, L. J., R. T. Holman, and K. Fontell. 1960. Vicinally unsaturated hydroxy acids in seed oils. *J. Am. Oil Chemists' Soc.* **37:** 323–327.

Müller, E. and W. Rundel. 1958. Verätherung von Alkoholen mit Diazomethan unter Borfluorid-Katalyse. *Angew. Chem.* **70:** 105.

Murray, K. E. 1959. A method for the determination of the structure of saturated branched-chain fatty acids. *Australian J. Chem.* **12:** 657–670.

Nelson, J. and A. Milun. 1960. Gas chromatography of high molecular weight fatty primary amines. *Chem. & Ind. (London)* 663–664.

Nystrom, R. F. and W. G. Brown. 1947. Reduction of organic compounds by lithium aluminum hydride. I. Aldehydes, ketones, esters, acid chlorides, and acid anhydrides. *J. Am. Chem. Soc.* **69:** 1197–1199.

O'Connor, J. G. and M. S. Norris. 1960. Molecular seive adsorption. Application to hydrocarbon type analysis. *Anal. Chem.* **32:** 701–706.

Orr, C. H. and J. E. Callen. 1959. Recent advances in the gas chromatographic separation of methyl esters of fatty acids. *Ann. N. Y. Acad. Sci.* **72**: 649–665.

Owens, R. G. 1960. Personal communication.

Paech, K. and M. V. Tracey, eds. 1955. "Modern Methods of Plant Analysis," Vol. II, 626 pp. Berlin, Springer.

Pangborn, M. C. 1945. A simplified preparation of cardiolipin, with a note one purification of lecithin for serologic use. *J. Biol. Chem.* **161**: 71–82.

Patton, S. 1960. Gas chromatographic analysis of milk fat. *J. Dairy Sci.* **43**: 1350–1354.

Pinner, A. 1872. Ueber einige Derivate des Acetals. *Ber. deut. chem. Ges.* **5**: 147–151.

Pohl, H. A. 1951. The thermal degradation of polyesters. *J. Am. Chem. Soc.* **73**: 5660–5661.

Rowe, C. E. 1959. The biosynthesis of phospholipids by human blood cells. *Biochem. J.* **73**: 438–442.

Sammons, H. G. and S. M. Wiggs. 1960. A method for the quantitative separation of fatty acids from unsaponifiable matter. *Analyst* **85**: 417–418.

Schlenk, H. and J. L. Gellerman. 1960. Esterification of fatty acids with diazomethane on a small scale. *Anal. Chem.* **32**: 1412–1414.

Shoppee, C. W. and D. A. Prins. 1943. Über Bestandteile der Nebennierenrinde und verwandte Stoffe. Über Umlagerungen von 17-Oxy-20-keto-steroiden in Poly-hydrochrysen-Derivate. Acelytierungen in Gegenwart von Borfluorid. *Helv. Chim. Acta* **26**: 201–223.

Sperry, W. M. and M. Webb. 1950. A revision of the Schoenheimer-Sperry method for cholesterol determination. *J. Biol. Chem.* **187**: 97–106.

Stoffel, W., F. Chu, and E. H. Ahrens, Jr. 1959. Analysis of long-chain fatty acids by gas-liquid chromatography. Micromethod for preparation of methyl esters. *Anal. Chem.* **31**: 307–308.

Swain, L. A. 1948. Chromatographic analysis of the unsaponifiable matter of marine animal oils. *Can. Chem. Process Inds.* **32**: 553–554; *Chem. Abstr.* **42**: 7069*g* (1948).

Sweeley, C. C. and E. C. Horning. 1960. Microanalytical separation of steroids by gas chromatography. *Nature* **187**: 144–145.

VandenHeuvel, W. J. A., C. C. Sweeley, and E. C. Horning. 1960. Separation of steroids by gas chromatography. *J. Am. Chem. Soc.* **82**: 3481–3482.

von Rudloff, E. 1951. Fatty alcohols from wool wax unsaponifiables by urea-complex formation. *Chem. & Ind. (London)*, pp. 338–339.

Whitham, B. T. 1958. Use of molecular sieves in gas chromatography for the determination of the normal paraffins in petroleum fractions. *Nature* **182**: 391–392.

Wren, J. J. and H. K. Mitchell. 1959. Extraction methods and an investigation of drosophila lipids. *J. Biol. Chem.* **234**: 2823–2828.

Zimmerschied, W. J., R. A. Dinerstein, A. W. Weitkamp, and R. F. Marschner. 1950. Crystalline adducts of urea with linear aliphatic compounds. A new separation process. *Ind. Eng. Chem.* **42**: 1300–1306.

Zirm, K. L., A. Pongratz, and W. Polesofsky. 1955. Beitrag zur Konstitution pflanzlicher Lipoide, im besonderen der Lipoidkomponente des Chloroplastins. *Biochem. Z.* **326**: 405–412.

Chapter 8

Nonvolatile Components of Tissues

General Introduction

Nonvolatile or slightly volatile compounds isolable from plant and animal tissues include amino acids, other organic acids, and sugars. Their vapor pressures must be increased and polarities reduced prior to GLC through removing or masking functional groups by oxidation, acylation, alkylation, or through other means. Once this is done, quite as much information can be gathered about these compounds by chromatography in the vapor phase as is obtainable on more volatile compounds. Furthermore, the compositions, and to a lesser extent the structures, of some of their condensation products, namely proteins, polysaccharides, and glycosides, can be worked out by using modifications of these techniques. As yet no papers have appeared on nucleotides and nucleic acids, but it is almost certain that GLC will prove invaluable for analyzing the phosphate and sugar moieties of these compounds, if not the nitrogenous bases.

A. Amino Acids

I. INTRODUCTION

Comparatively little work has been done on the separation and determination of amino acid derivatives by GLC despite the obvious advantages of such a procedure. Paper chromatographic and ion-exchange techniques currently in use are excellent, but they do not have the speed, adaptability to automation, or capacity for separating closely related compounds inherent in GLC. Thus, special solvents are needed to resolve the leucines by paper chromatography, and the complete analysis of a protein hydrolyzate by the Moore and Stein ion-exchange method takes 22 hours and requires specialized equipment useful mainly for this procedure. It should be possible to achieve the same results within an hour or so with a general-purpose gas chromatograph. Progress in the analysis of amino acids by this technique has been slow because they are not volatile, owing to their zwitterion structures. Thus alanine, with a molecular weight of only 89, melts at 297°C, and on more intense heating chars, leaving a carbonaceous residue. Obviously such compounds must be converted to derivatives in which the carboxyl group, the amino group, or both are removed or masked before they can be chromatographed in the gas phase. This will eliminate internal charges, reduce hydrogen bonding, and so render the molecules more volatile.

II. Isolation Procedures

Free amino acids along with proteins and other contaminants can be extracted from tissues with water, and the proteins removed by precipitation with trichloroacetic acid, phosphotungstic acid, perchloric acid, and a variety of other reagents. However, it is often simpler to extract the tissues with 80% ethanol. This dissolves the amino acids and other low-molecular-weight compounds. Most proteins will be precipitated, although some seed proteins and possibly others are soluble. The amino acids are then isolated on ion-exchange resins. In the procedure given below, amines and the basic amino acids are adsorbed on the ammonium form of Dowex 50 (a sulfonic acid type of ion-exchange resin), and the other amino acids are adsorbed on the hydrogen form. This allows a partial separation of amines from amino acids. If it is unnecessary to separate the amines and basic amino acids from the other amino acids, isolation on the hydrogen form of Dowex 50 alone will suffice.

Bound amino acids are obtained by isolating the protein fraction and hydrolyzing it with hydrochloric acid, hydrochloric–formic acid, sulfuric acid, trichloroacetic acid, or barium hydroxide (Block, 1958). Artifacts may be produced during hydrolysis, and care must be taken to avoid these. Tryptophan is often destroyed during acid hydrolysis, the presence of carbohydrates and metallic impurities being chiefly responsible. Heavy metal salts are also likely to result in degradation of other amino acids. Tryptophan can be obtained by alkaline hydrolysis, but many other amino acids are destroyed. Serine is degraded to pyruvic acid, alanine, glycine, and ammonia; cysteine to hydrogen sulfide, alanine, ammonia, etc.; therefore alkali is generally less useful than acid for the hydrolysis of proteins.

a. Extraction of Tissues

*1. *Ethanol Method* (Block et al., 1958). The chopped tissues are placed in a Waring blendor with sufficient absolute ethanol to make the final concentration, as estimated from the water content of the tissue, 80% by volume. The mixture is blended thoroughly and filtered with suction on a Büchner funnel. The precipitate is washed with 80% ethanol, and the filtrates are combined. Chloroform (3 volumes) is added to each volume of extract, and the mixture is shaken thoroughly. The aqueous (upper) layer containing the free amino acids is then concentrated to the volume required for separation on the ion-exchange resin.

*2. *Perchloric Acid Method* (Block et al., 1958). A sufficient quantity of 2 M (about 20%) perchloric acid is added to the aqueous tissue extract to bring the final concentration to 7%. The suspension is filtered, and the precipitate is washed with dilute acid. The *minimum* quantity of potassium acetate is added to the filtrate that will precipitate the perchlorate ion as insoluble potassium perchlorate. This precipitate is then removed by filtration and discarded, and the aqueous solution containing the amino acids is reduced to the desired volume. Removal of all the perchlorate ion can be very tedious, particularly if much concentration is required. In such cases it will be more convenient to extract the tissue with ethanol or trichloroacetic acid.

b. Purification of Free Amino Acids (Thompson *et al.*, 1959)

1. *Ion-Exchange Method.* Water which has been previously distilled or passed through a commercial water purifier is deionized by percolation through a column packed with Amberlite IRA-400 (2 parts) and Amberlite IR-120 (1 part).

Hydrogen form of Dowex resin. Dowex 50-X4 ion-exchange resin (200/400 mesh) is soaked in water overnight and stirred in a cylinder with an equal volume of water. The suspension is permitted to settle for 30 minutes after stirring, and the fines are decanted off. The process is repeated twice. The resin is then added to 1 N sodium hydroxide (2 volumes), and the mixture is heated at 100°C for 16 hours. The resin is poured into a column, drained, and washed with deionized water to free it from alkali. Next it is treated with 5 column volumes of 6 N hydrochloric acid, and the column is washed repeatedly with deionized water until the effluent is free of chloride ion.

Ammonium form of Dowex. The hydrogen form of Dowex 50-X4 is packed in a column and treated with 10 volumes of 2 N ammonium hydroxide prepared with deionized water. The column is washed with deionized water (10 to 20 column volumes) until the pH is reduced to between 8 and 9. The resin should be preserved with chloroform to prevent growth of microorganisms. If not used within a week, it should be rewashed just before use.

Apparatus. The columns for holding the resins are made of glass tubes (20 × 0.9 cm) with capillary tubes (10 × 0.2 cm) attached to the bottoms. A plug of glass wool is placed in each of two columns, and the hydrogen or the ammonium form of Dowex is added to a depth of 7 cm. The column containing the ammonium form of the resin is mounted directly above the column containing the hydrogen form of the resin so that the percolate from the upper column will pass directly into the lower column. If it is necessary to avoid the hydrolysis of amides such as glutamine and asparagine, the separations should be made at 0° to 6°C.

Procedure. An aqueous solution containing about 500 μg of amino nitrogen is adjusted to pH 7.0 ± 0.1 with ammonium hydroxide or hydrochloric acid and poured on the upper (ammonium) column. The percolate emerges from this column and passes through the lower (hydrogen) one. The resins are then rinsed with 4 × 10-ml portions of deionized water. Some plant extracts contain large amounts of polyphenols, in which case the column should be washed with additional 80% ethanol (about 100 ml) until the effluent gives a negative ferric chloride test.

The upper (ammonium) column is removed from tandem with the hydrogen column and eluted separately with 2 N ammonium hydroxide (80 ml). The eluate is dried in a carbon dioxide-free atmosphere at a temperature under 50°C. This fraction contains the basic amino acids and some of the amines. The column is washed free of excess ammonium hydroxide with deionized water (40 ml), followed with 0.50 ± 0.02 N hydrochloric acid (50 ml), the washings being discarded. The remaining amines are then eluted from the column with 6 N hydrochloric acid.

1-Amino-2-propanol, isobutylamine, tyramine, and histamine are eluted by the 2 N ammonium hydroxide, but recoveries of known amounts of compounds are not quantitative, possibly because some of them are lost in the evaporation step. Phenylethylamine, putrescine, cadaverine, and agmatine are eluted by the 6N hydrochloric acid, and recoveries are quantitative.

The lower (hydrogen) column is eluted with small portions of 2N ammonium hydroxide (cold if amides are to be recovered intact) until the effluent is just basic. A total of 8 to 10 ml is required. The column is then washed with cold deionized water (40 ml). The eluates are lyophilized rapidly or vacuum-distilled at 30°C to avoid the decomposition of labile compounds. This fraction contains the neutral and acidic amino acids.

c. Hydrolysis of Proteins

*1. *Hydrochloric Acid Method* (Block et al., 1958). A protein sample containing approximately 1.6 mg of nitrogen is refluxed with 6N hydrochloric acid (10 ml) for 20 hours. The excess acid is removed by evaporating the solution to dryness on the steam bath or at 35°C under reduced pressure. The amino acid hydrochlorides are then dissolved in warm water, the solution is filtered to remove humins, and the water is removed by evaporation.

*2. *Barium Hydroxide Method* (Block et al., 1958). A protein sample containing about 1.6 mg of nitrogen is heated with 14% barium hydroxide solution (10 ml) on an oil bath at 125°C. Refluxing is continued for 18 to 20 hours. The solution is cooled, and a slight excess of 1N sulfuric acid is added to precipitate the barium. The suspension is filtered, and the precipitate is washed with hot water containing a trace of acetic acid. The filtrate is concentrated to a small volume under reduced pressure, and the remaining water is removed in a desiccator over calcium chloride.

III. Chromatography of Esters

The simplest way to increase vapor pressures of amino acids is to convert them to methyl esters as was done by Fischer (1901) in his classic work on their separation by fractional distillation. This approach has been used by

Bayer (1958) with some success. He achieved the separation of the methyl esters of valine, norvaline, leucine, and norleucine on a silicone column at 138°C. On the same column at 191°C, he achieved good resolution of the methyl esters of glutamic acid and phenylalanine. In the methanolyzate of albumin, he was able to show the presence of esters of alanine, proline, valine, leucine, and isoleucine at 140°C, and of aspartic and glutamic acids at 187°C. The silicone grease used as the stationary phase contained 10% sodium caproate to reduce tailing. Bayer states that the esters of the aliphatic, acidic, aromatic, sulfur, and heterocyclic amino acids are well separated rapidly. This is certainly true in specific cases, but esters of many of them do not appear on the chromatograms. These are probably not volatile enough to be eluted at the column temperatures employed. Temperatures greatly exceeding the ones Bayer used might result in condensation of the amino acid esters with the elimination of methanol. Therefore, the most promising way by which a larger number of amino acid esters could be chromatographed is through the use of column packings containing a very small proportion of stationary liquid coated on a solid support such as glass beads. This technique has made it possible to chromatograph high-boiling compounds at comparatively low temperatures in a number of other instances. Another modification of the Bayer technique that might be useful would be to program the temperature so that aliphatic methyl esters are eluted at low temperatures, and aromatic and heterocyclic esters at higher temperatures. In view of the disparity in molecular weight between amino acids such as glycine and tryptophan, such a step would appear highly desirable, at least with packed columns.

Under certain specified conditions the Bayer technique can be used to separate alanine, proline, valine, leucine, isoleucine, methionine, phenylalanine, and aspartic and glutamic acids. Serine, threonine, lysine, arginine, tyrosine, hydroxyproline, and histidine are not accounted for. It is probable that additional esters could be recovered by modifying operating conditions. However, it is by no means certain that all of them could be chromatographed. Hence, the Bayer method, as well as some of the others discussed below, are useful only if a partial analysis of amino acids will satisfy the requirements of the specific problem.

More promising results have been obtained by converting amino acids to N-acetyl esters prior to GLC, thus masking the two main functional groups. Youngs (1959) used butyl esters, since he found that the N-acetyl ethyl ester of glycine tended to crystallize from mixtures so that homogeneous samples could not be taken. Johnson *et al.* (1961) investigated the suitability of the N-acetylated methyl, *n*-butyl, isobutyl, *n*-amyl, and isoamyl esters for this purpose and conclude that the N-acetyl-*n*-amyl esters give better separations than the other compounds tried.

Youngs chromatographed a synthetic mixture of the N-acetyl butyl esters of glycine, alanine, valine, leucine, isoleucine, and proline on hydrogenated safflower oil using a 1:4 ratio of liquid to solid support. Proline was eluted from the column in about 60 minutes at an oven temperature of 220°C. Glycine emerged before alanine. Peaks for leucine and isoleucine were not resolved. The same compounds were found in gelatin hydrolyzate, and in addition a number of unidentified peaks were observed beyond proline.

Johnson *et al.* (1961) were able to separate seventeen naturally occurring amino acids as their N-acetyl-n-amyl esters by chromatographing them on dual columns packed with Carbowax 1540 at different temperatures. The use of a low liquid/support packing ratio, an argon ionization detector, and a small sample size made it possible to achieve excellent separations at comparatively low temperatures. Two columns were employed at different packing ratios and temperatures to make it possible to chromatograph all the components of the mixture in a reasonable length of time. Of the amino acids derived from proteins, only derivatives of tryptophan, histidine, and arginine were not eluted under the conditions illustrated. Column I contained 1% Carbowax 1540 on Chromosorb W and was 8 feet long. With it, alanine, valine, isoleucine, and leucine derivatives were eluted in 20 to 25 minutes at 125°C. After the emergence of the leucine ester, the column temperature was raised rapidly to 148°C to elute derivatives of glycine, alanine, proline, threonine, serine, cysteine, methionine, phenylalanine, hydroxyproline, and aspartic acid in that order (Fig. 1). Less volatile esters were chro-

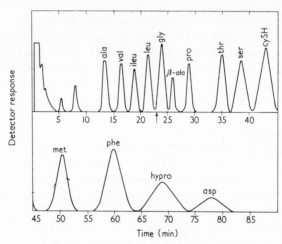

FIG. 1. Chromatogram of a mixture of N-acetyl-n-amyl esters of amino acids on 1% Carbowax 1540 on Chromosorb W. Temperature was advanced from 125°C to 148°C at the point indicated by the arrow. (Johnson *et al.*, 1961)

matographed on a 2-foot column containing 0.5% Carbowax 1540 on Chromosorb W at a temperature of 148°C. Derivatives through aspartate emerged within 10 minutes, and peaks representing glutamate, tyrosine, and lysine emerged in 15 to 30 minutes (Fig. 2). Thus with two columns at dif-

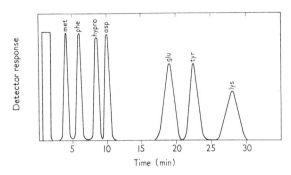

Fig. 2. Chromatogram of a mixture of *N*-acetyl-*n*-amyl esters of amino acids on a 2-foot column containing 0.5% Carbowax 1540 on Chromosorb W at a column temperature of 148°C. (Johnson *et al.*, 1961)

ferent packing ratios and temperatures, it is possible to chromatograph all but three of the important naturally occurring amino acids. It should be possible to achieve the same end, perhaps more conveniently, by programming the temperature continuously. Also, if the effluent gases were combusted to CO_2 it would simplify calibration and make possible the monitoring of C^{14}-labeled compounds with a very high degree of sensitivity.

This method has not been adapted yet for quantitative analysis, but it is probable that the per cent conversion of amino acid to *N*-acetyl-*n*-amyl derivatives is of the same order of magnitude for most of the amino acids, because the detector responses for derivatives prepared by the standard procedure are about the same. Moreover, the response is about 85% of that obtained with solutions of pure derivatives. Unfortunately, histidine and arginine are esterified in poor yield under the conditions employed, and acetylation does not proceed smoothly. Therefore it is probable that a modified procedure will be needed for the analysis of these amino acids. Better results have been obtained on them by reducing the heating period to 5 minutes during esterification, and by refluxing with acetic anhydride for 10 minutes. These derivatives have greater retention volumes than lysine on column II (Fig. 2). It might be practical to convert arginine to ornithine before esterification, since this derivative has a retention time of only 33 minutes on column I. The tryptophan derivative was not eluted under any of the conditions studied.

Amino acids also have been chromatographed as their trifluoroacetyl methyl esters on silicone grease and polyester columns used alternately or in series (Bayer, 1958; Weygand *et al.*, 1960). This method potentially is useful because of the relatively high vapor pressures of fluorine-containing compounds. However, it is not possible to compare results with those obtained on N-acetyl-n-amyl esters directly, since different stationary liquids at conventional packing ratios (Perkin-Elmer O and P columns) were used. Furthermore, retention times on the silicone column were unusually short (6 minutes to lysine), which resulted in crowding of early peaks. Derivatives of ten amino acids were eluted. These were valine, alanine, isoleucine, leucine, glycine, proline, aspartic acid, threonine, methionine, and phenylalanine. Leucine–isoleucine and glycine–alanine peaks were not resolved on silicone oil, and proline–aspartic acid peaks were only partly resolved. On the polyester column, the isoleucine and alanine derivatives were not separated. However, by using the two columns in series it was possible to obtain partial resolution of alanine, leucine, and isoleucine.

N-Trifluoroacetyl methyl esters of tyrosine and arginine yield four and two peaks, respectively, when chromatographed on poly(ethylene glycol isophthalate) at 220°C, indicating the presence of impurities or breakdown on the column (Saroff and Karmen, 1960). Derivatives of cystine, histidine, and tryptophan were not eluted under these conditions.

This method also has been used to separate simple peptides including derivatives of alanylglycine, glycylalanine, glycylglycine, leucylglycine, and glycylleucine. Therefore, it appears to have considerable potential for the sequential analysis of proteins, since both qualitative and quantitative data can be obtained in a relatively simple operation. It is interesting that it was possible to separate the diastereoisomeric pair, N-trifluoroacetyl-O-methyl-L-alanyl-L-phenylalanine from N-trifluoroacetyl-O-methyl-L-alanyl-D-phenylalanine by this technique (Weygand *et al.*, 1960).

N-Trimethylsilyl derivatives of amino acids also have been separated by gas chromatography (Rühlmann and Giesecke, 1961). These are prepared by treating amino acid salts with trimethylchlorosilane, or by the reaction of N-trimethylsilyldialkylamines with free amino acids. Both amino and carboxyl groups react, the products being trimethylsilyl esters of N-substituted amino acids. Derivatives of glycine, alanine, leucine, isoleucine, valine, glutamic acid, and phenylalanine can be separated at 165°C on a column (280 cm) packed with silicone oil on Sterchamol (30:70). The phenylalanine derivative is eluted after 28 to 30 minutes. Results are reproducible to within 0.5% by using the peak area method and a T/C cell for detection. It is stated that all available amino acids could be silylated almost quantitatively, but no data are given on the chromatography of high-molecular-weight compounds such as derivatives of tryptophan or histidine.

a. Preparation of Derivatives

*1. *Methyl Esters from Amino Acids* (Bayer, 1958). Amino acids are added to anhydrous methanol saturated with dry hydrogen chloride, and this mixture is refluxed for several hours. The hydrochloric acid is neutralized, and the hydrochlorides of the amino acid esters are converted to free bases by adding 2N sodium hydroxide. The free bases are extracted from the aqueous phase with ethyl ether. Aliquots of the ether layer are injected directly into the chromatograph, or the solvent can be evaporated and a portion of the residue injected.

*2. *Methyl Esters from Proteins* (Bayer, 1958). Esters are produced directly from proteins in a one-step reaction by suspending the protein in anhydrous methanol saturated with hydrogen chloride gas. This suspension is refluxed for 24 hours. The solution is neutralized by addition of 2N sodium hydroxide, and the amino acid esters are extracted from the aqueous phase with ether. A portion of the ether solution, or the residue obtained on evaporating it, is injected into the chromatograph.

*3. *N-Acetyl Butyl Esters* (Youngs, 1959). Free amino acids (100 mg) are suspended in butanol (50 ml), and the mixture is saturated with anhydrous hydrogen chloride. The liquid is distilled slowly at atmospheric pressure so that about one-half of the alcohol comes over during a period of 45 minutes. The remaining butyl alcohol is removed under vacuum, leaving the ester hydrochlorides as a viscous syrup. Acetic anhydride (25 ml) is added to the residue. After standing for an hour, excess reagent is removed by vacuum distillation. The viscous oil that remains is injected into the chromatograph.

*4. *N-Acetyl-n-amyl Esters* (Johnson et al., 1961). The amino acid (1 to 10 mg) is suspended in n-amyl alcohol, and the mixture is saturated with anhydrous hydrogen bromide. This procedure takes 2 to 4 minutes. The flask containing the mixture is placed in an oil bath at 165°C, and about one-half of the alcohol is removed by distillation at atmospheric pressure during a period of 30 minutes. The remaining alcohol is removed under vacuum at 60°C in a rotary evaporator. The residual material is mixed with 8 ml of acetic anhydride and allowed to stand at 26°C for 5 minutes. Next, the solution is evaporated under vacuum at 60°C to a syrup, which is dissolved in n-amyl alcohol or benzene and injected into the chromatograph. The preparation of samples by this procedure takes about an hour.

*5. *N-Trifluoroacetyl Methyl Esters* (Weygand et al., 1960). The amino acid (1 gm) is dissolved in concentrated hydrochloric acid (5 ml), and the solution is evaporated to form the hydrochloride. The residue is taken up in 0.2 N hydrochloric acid in anhydrous methanol (20 ml) and heated under reflux for 2 hours. The solvent is evaporated under vacuum, whereupon the methyl ester is redissolved in methanol (15 ml) and treated with triethylamine (2.3

ml) and methyl trifluoroacetate (5 ml). After standing for 2 hours at 20°C, the solvent is removed under reduced pressure, and the residue is partitioned between water and ethyl acetate. The *N*-trifluoroacetyl methyl ester is obtained by evaporating the organic layer under reduced pressure.

b. Conditions for Chromatography

*1. Separation of Methyl Esters (Bayer, 1958)

Chromatograph	Obtained from Rubarth u. Co., Hanover, Germany.
Column dimensions	2-meter × 0.8-cm stainless steel.
Solid support	Sterchamol (0.2 to 0.3 mm).
Stationary phase	Silicone high-vacuum grease containing 10% sodium caproate (30:100).
Temperatures	138° to 140°C for valine, leucine, isoleucine, alanine, and proline. 187° to 191°C for methionine, phenylalanine, glutamic acid, and aspartic acid
Carrier gas	Hydrogen at 43 to 100 ml/min.
Detector	Hot-wire (Pt) T/C cell.
Analysis time	90 minutes for phenylalanine at 191°C and 45 ml of hydrogen per minute.

*2. Separation of N-Acetyl Butyl Esters (Youngs, 1959)

Chromatograph	Beckman Model GC-2.
Column dimensions	183 × 0.64 cm o.d. coiled copper tubing.
Solid support	Johns Manville C-22 firebrick (20/40 U. S. mesh).
Stationary phase	Safflower oil hydrogenated to an iodine value of less than 1 (10:40).
Temperatures	Injection: 250°C. Detector: 220°C. Column: 220°C.
Carrier gas	Helium at 80 ml/min at outlet. Inlet pressure: 2820 mm Hg. Outlet pressure: atmospheric.
Detector	Four-filament hot-wire T/C cell at 250 ma.
Recorder	1 mv; 1 second; 0.8 cm/min.
Sample size	10 µl.
Analysis time	60 to 70 minutes to proline.

*3. Separation of N-Acetyl-n-amyl Esters on Alternate Columns (Johnson et al., 1961)

Chromatograph	Barber-Coleman No. 10 with dual columns.
Column dimensions	(I) 8 feet × 0.5 cm i.d. (II) 2 feet × 0.5 cm i.d. Glass U tubes.
Solid support	Acid-washed Chromosorb W (60/80 U. S. mesh).
Stationary phase	(I) Carbowax 1540 (1%). (II) Carbowax 1540 (0.5%).
Temperatures	Injection (flash heater): 250°C. Detector: 225°C. (I) 125°C to leucine; 148°C to cysteine. (II) 148°C.
Carrier gas	Argon at 60 ml/min.
Detector	Argon ionization.
Recorder	Wheelco 8000 series.
Sample size	Sensitive to 10^{-10} mole.
Analysis time	(I) 45 minutes. (II) 85 minutes.

*4. *Separation of N-Trifluoroacetyl Methyl Esters in Columns used Alternately or in Series* (Weygand et al., 1960)

Chromatograph	Perkin-Elmer Model 116H.
Column dimensions	(I) and (II) 2 meters. (A) and (B) 1 meter.
Solid support	Celite.
Stationary phase	(I) and (B) Silicone grease. (II) and (A) Reoplex.
Temperatures	(I) 204°C. (II) 209°C. (A) and (B) 200°C.
Carrier gas	Helium. (I) 100 ml/min. (II) 64 ml/min. (A) and (B) 107 ml/min.
Detector	Hot-wire T/C cell.
Recorder	10 mv (Siemens and Halske).
Sample size	0.03 to 0.7 mg in 2 to 5 μl of ethyl acetate.
Analysis time	(I) 6 minutes to lysine derivative. (II) 20 minutes to phenylalanine derivative. (A) and (B) 3.5 minutes to glycine derivative.

IV. CHROMATOGRAPHY OF OXIDATION PRODUCTS

The foregoing procedures rely on the synthesis of amino acid derivatives having higher molecular weights than their precursors, but with increased volatility owing to lower polarity. It is also possible to produce compounds amenable to gas chromatography through degradation reactions. Foremost among these is oxidation to an aldehyde having one less carbon atom. Deamination accompanies oxidation. The product formed from α-alanine, for example, is acetaldehyde. Langheld (1909) showed that this reaction could be carried out by treatment with alkaline hypochlorite. Bayer (1958) used this reagent to oxidize alanine, α-aminobutyric acid, norvaline, valine, norleucine, and leucine. He obtained good separation of the resulting aldehydes by chromatography on a dinonyl phthalate column at 92°C. Unfortunately, he found that acidic and sulfur-containing amino acids gave complex mixtures of volatile substances. Moreover, the same compounds were sometimes produced from different amino acids. This limits the usefulness of the method for the analysis of complex mixtures of amino acids.

α-Amino acids can also be oxidized by ninhydrin (triketohydrindene) to aldehydes having one less carbon atom. Virtanen and Rautanen (1946) developed a quantitative method for the analysis of amino acids in which the aldehydes liberated by treatment with this reagent are distilled into bisulfite solution and determined iodometrically. The procedure is applicable to the determination of valine, the leucines, phenylalanine, and methionine. Hunter et al. (1956) used a modification of this technique to prepare aldehydes derived from valine, leucine, isoleucine, and alanine. He also showed that 3-methylbutanal (from leucine) and 2-methylbutanal (from isoleucine) could be separated on a silicone–Celite column at a temperature of 69°C.

Bier and Teitelbaum (1959) describe a microprocedure for oxidizing α-aminobutyric acid, valine, and leucine prior to GLC. The amino acids are treated with ninhydrin in a sealed ampoule, and the products are extracted into a chlorinated hydrocarbon solvent. The solution containing the aldehydes is then analyzed on a silicone column at 78°C. For quantitative estimation of these amino acids, standard curves are prepared by chromatographing known concentrations of the corresponding aldehydes.

The ninhydrin technique has been mechanized by Zlatkis *et al.* (1960) for the automatic analysis of amino acids that form volatile aldehydes. These include leucine, isoleucine, norleucine, valine, norvaline, α-amino-*n*-butyric acid, and alanine. On oxidation glycine yields formaldehyde which polymerizes under the experimental conditions and cannot be detected. The aldehydes derived from phenylalanine and methionine would require higher column temperatures for elution than used in this work. Nevertheless, good resolution with slight tailing is obtained on the compounds studied, and leucine and isoleucine derivatives are separated from one another.

In the Zlatkis technique, two reactors are connected in series with a gas chromatograph, one before the column and the other between the column and detector (Fig. 3). The pre-column reactor (*A*) is filled with ninhydrin

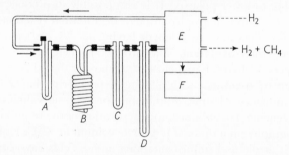

FIG. 3. Reactor gas unit for chromatography of aliphatic amino acids as their aldehydes. (Zlatkis *et al.*, 1960)

coated on firebrick, and the temperature is regulated at 140°C. The amino acids are converted to aldehydes and carbon dioxide *in situ*, and thus the need for collecting the aldehydes in a separate step is eliminated. To ensure complete reaction, the amino acids are given a preliminary treatment with ninhydrin reagent prior to injection into the apparatus. The aldehydes, carbon dioxide formed through oxidation, and water from the aqueous solution pass through a chromatographic column (*B*) loaded with a mixture of ethylene and propylene carbonates. The aldehydes and carbon dioxide are separated, while water passes through the column very slowly and does not interfere in the analysis.

On emergence from the chromatographic column, the fractions pass through a second reactor (*C*) filled with nickel–kieselguhr catalyst heated to 425°C (Zlatkis and Ridgway, 1958). This catalyst, in conjunction with the reducing power of the carrier gas (hydrogen), results in hydrocracking of the aldehydes to methane and water according to the equation

$$C_nH_{2n+1}CHO + (n + 2)H_2 \rightarrow (n + 1)CH_4 + nH_2O$$

The carbon dioxide produced in the ninhydrin reaction is also converted to methane and water.

The purpose of the second reactor is twofold. First, it makes it possible to dry the gas emerging from it with molecular sieves before the fractions enter the detector. This removes water formed during hydrocracking, as well as water injected with the amino acids. There is no convenient way to dry aldehydes, but methane can be dried this way without difficulty. Second, conversion to methane eliminates the need for calibrating the thermistor for individual aldehydes. However, the number of carbon atoms in each compound must be taken into account in the final calculations, since different aldehydes produce different amounts of methane in accordance with their carbon numbers, as shown in the above equation.

Zlatkis *et al.* (1960) applied this technique to known mixtures of amino acids. The concentration of each component could be determined with an accuracy of about 5%, and as little as 1 μg could be detected with a thermistor. It can be anticipated that the ultimate limit of detection would be several orders of magnitude less than this with an ionization detector. An analysis of casein hydrolyzate by this method showed four main peaks on the chromatogram, corresponding to alanine, valine, leucine, and isoleucine. Since norleucine, norvaline, and α-aminobutyric acid produce peaks with known retention times and are not found in proteins, it should be possible to use them as internal standards.

Amino acids also can be analyzed by first converting the aldehydes produced on ninhydrin oxidation to esters (Baraud, 1960). The volatile aldehydes are distilled into alkaline permanganate and oxidized to the corresponding carboxylic acids. These are recovered as their sodium salts and subsequently esterified. The esters are then separated by GLC on a poly(propylene glycol adipate) column at 150°C, and an N_2 flow rate of 10 ml/min. Methylthiopropionaldehyde, derived from methionine, is destroyed during oxidation, and the esters derived from leucine and isoleucine are not resolved from one another. Under the conditions of preparation, only amino acids that yield volatile aldehydes can be detected. Therefore the procedure is limited to the determination of alanine, valine, norvaline, leucine plus isoleucine, and phenylalanine. Conversion to esters prior to chromatography is advantageous in that they are more stable chemically than aldehydes. However, conversion to dimethylacetals might be preferable if a simple way could be found to obtain the aldehydes in an anhydrous condition.

a. In-Stream Oxidation with Reactor–Gas Unit (Zlatkis *et al.*, 1960)

1. *Equipment.* A Perkin-Elmer Fractometer is modified as shown in Fig. 3. The reactor for converting amino acids to aldehydes (*A*) is a 15 × 0.6-cm glass U tube containing 30% ninhydrin coated on C-22 firebrick. The packing in reactor *A* is effective for about five sample injections. The U tube is wrapped with heating tape and kept at a temperature of 140°C. Lower temperatures usually result in incomplete reactions. Component *B* is the chromatographic column and is described in detail under Conditions of Chromatography below. Component *C* is the reactor used to hydrocrack the aldehydes to methane and water. It consists of a 30 × 0.6-cm glass U tube filled with nickel–kieselguhr catalyst (30/60 mesh) and is heated to 425°C by a nichrome coil (Zlatkis and Ridgway, 1958). The catalyst retains its activity after the analysis of fifty samples. When operated at a lower temperature, considerable tailing of the chromatographic peaks occurs. Component *D* is the drying column for removing injection water and water of reaction from the gas stream. It is a 30 × 0.6-cm glass U tube filled with molecular sieve (10/30 U. S. mesh). The packing must be replaced after five runs. Component *E* is a thermal conductivity cell, and *F* is a recorder.

2. *Procedure.* A ninhydrin–amino acid solution is prepared by mixing 1 part of a saturated aqueous solution of ninhydrin with 1 part of a 0.28 *M* solution of amino acids. The mixture is kept in an ice bath until used. A 15-μl sample is injected into the reactor with a syringe.

3. *Conditions for Chromatography*

Chromatograph	Perkin-Elmer Vapor Fractometer, Model 154B, modified as described above.
Column dimensions	305 × 0.6-cm o.d. copper tubing.
Solid support	C-22 firebrick treated with aqua regia (Zlatkis *et al.*, 1960).
Stationary phase	50:50 mixture of ethylene and propylene carbonates (10:90).
Temperature	25°C.
Carrier gas	Hydrogen at 100 ml/min.
Detector	Thermistor.
Sample size	15 μl of a 0.14 *M* solution.
Analysis time	43 min to norleucine.

V. Miscellaneous Methods

Several other methods have been proposed for the gas chromatographic analysis of amino acids but they have not been evaluated as fully as the foregoing. According to Liberti (see Bayer, 1958, pp. 341–342), amino acids can be deaminated to hydroxy acids with sodium nitrite in acetic acid, and the sodium ion removed on a cation-exchange column. The hydroxy acids are then methylated with diazomethane, and the esters are chromato-graphed. The column is 1 meter in length and is packed with 30% D.C. 550 silicone on Sterchamol. The flow rate of carrier gas (type not specified) is 60 ml/min, and the temperature is programmed between 80° and 140°C. Under these conditions, the methyl esters of the hydroxy acids derived from glycine, valine, alanine, leucine, serine, aspartic acid, and glutamic acid are eluted in that order, the last peak coming off at 120 min. Experimental details are meager, and quantitative data are not given.

Amino acids also can be analyzed by converting them to the correspond-ing α-chloro compounds by treatment with a mixture of concentrated hydro-chloric and nitric acids (Melamed and Renard, 1960). The α-chloro acids are then converted to their methyl esters with diazomethane and chromato-graphed. The best separation of complex mixtures was obtained on a 2-meter polyethylene glycol column followed by a 2-meter silicone oil–stearic acid column. With this combination, derivatives of α-alanine, glycine, α-amino-butyric acid, valine, norvaline, leucine, isoleucine, and norleucine can be separated at a temperature of 130°C and a flow rate of 2.6 liters of hydrogen per hour.

Bier and Teitelbaum (1959) suggest that amino acids might be decarbox-ylated to primary amines either enzymatically, or by heating them in high-boiling solvents. These might be more amenable to GLC because of their relatively high vapor pressures. Thus tyramine boils at 220°C, whereas its precursor, tyrosine, cannot be distilled under any conditions. Bier and Teitelbaum (1959) obtained yields of amines ranging from 10 to 88% by heating various amino acids with diphenylmethane or p-dimethylamino-benzaldehyde. Evidently the decarboxylation step has not yet been worked out to the point where it can be used as the basis of a quantitative procedure. The authors also report poor detector sensitivity and severe tailing when the amines are chromatographed on a Perkin-Elmer Vapor Fractometer with dodecylphthalate, silicone oil, and poly(ethyleneglycol) as stationary liquids. In view of the highly sensitive detectors now available, and recent progress in the production of inert supporting media for the chromatography of highly polar compounds, these should not be serious problems if the details of the decarboxylation step can be worked out.

Mixtures of di-, tri-, and tetrapeptides can be analyzed by converting them to amino alcohols in advance of GLC (Biemann and Vetter, 1960). The N-acetyl ethyl esters are prepared first, and these are reduced by over-night treatment with lithium aluminum hydride. The peptides are chromato-graphed on a column containing Apiezon L coated on Chromosorb W (8:92) at a temperature of 260°C and a flow rate of 60 ml of helium per minute.

Wagner (1960) has presented a paper on the gas chromatographic separation and determination of amino acids, but details are not available at this time.

VI. Summary

Amino acids must be converted to volatile compounds before they can be separated by gas–liquid chromatography. Among derivatives that have been investigated for this purpose are methyl esters, N-acetyl alkyl esters, esters of their hydroxy acid analogues, and oxidation products formed by the action on ninhydrin. The most promising method is chromatography of the N-acetyl-n-amyl esters on two columns containing 0.5% and 1.0% Carbowax 1540 on Chromosorb W at temperatures of 125° and 140°C. Eighteen amino acids can be separated in this way, but derivatives of histidine, arginine, and tryptophan are not analyzed. The procedure has not been quantitated as yet.

Aliphatic amino acids derived from proteins, including alanine, valine, leucine, and isoleucine, can be determined satisfactorily by oxidation with ninhydrin and chromatography of the resulting aldehydes. None of the methods currently available is satisfactory for all the amino acids, but it is likely that this situation will improve in the near future.

B. Nonvolatile Acids

I. Isolation and Esterification

Compounds in this category include hydroxy acids, keto acids, and the di- and tricarboxylic acids of the Krebs cycle. Volatile fatty acids are discussed in Chapter 3, higher fatty acids in Chapter 7, and rosin acids in Chapter 6. The substances considered here are extracted from tissues with aqueous alkali or alcohol and ultimately recovered as free acids by solvent evaporation. The simpler nonvolatile acids are actually slightly volatile. Consequently significant losses may occur during isolation by these methods, particularly when small amounts of materials are involved. Recoveries of citric and succinic acids, for example, are excellent, but substantial losses of oxalic and furoic acids have been reported.

Nonvolatile acids are found in the percolate and washings from the Dowex 50-X4 column used to separate amino acids from tissue extracts (Section A.II.b). They can be separated from neutral compounds by passing these solutions through Dowex 1 in the formate form (Prill *et al.*, 1960). Anions are bound to the resin, and neutral molecules, including carbohydrates, appear in the percolate. The Dowex 1 column is then stripped with $6N$ formic acid, and the nonvolatile acids are recovered by evaporating the eluate to dryness under a current of clean dry air.

In situations where recovery of amino acids is not required, the tissue extract is filtered and passed directly through a column containing an acid-binding resin such as Dowex 1 in the carbonate form. The acids are stripped from the column with 1.5 N ammonium carbonate, and the eluate is heated at 70°C to decompose and drive off the reagent. This solution is next passed through a base-binding resin, and the percolate is evaporated to dryness. Mirocha and DeVay (1961) state that purification of extracts with ion-exchange resins is unnecessary in the analysis of fumarate in almond extracts by GLC.

Quin and Hobbs (1958) devised a procedure which utilizes differences in pK_a to separate nonvolatile from volatile acids by liquid–liquid extraction. This avoids any distillation of aqueous solutions of the free acids and thus reduces losses of slightly volatile components. Alkaline solutions containing salts of the acids are evaporated to dryness under reduced pressure to drive off volatile neutral and basic compounds. The residue is then partitioned between 4% aqueous acetic acid and diethyl ether. Weak acids and some nonvolatile neutrals go into the ether layer, while salts of the stronger oxygenated acids remain in the water layer. The water is then evaporated, and the acids are liberated from their salts by treatment with anhydrous hydrochloric acid dissolved in a mixture of ethanol and ether. This procedure gives excellent recoveries of lactic and malonic acids, but substantial losses of furoic and oxalic acids are still encountered. Separation of the acids from all other organic constituents is not so good as obtained by the ion-exchange method. Furthermore, amino acids (which were probably not present in the sample analyzed) would not be removed by this technique. Consequently it might be desirable to use a combination of the ion-exchange and solvent partition methods to reduce volatility losses and at the same time avoid high background and extraneous peaks on the chromatograms.

Oxygenated and oligobasic acids must be converted to esters prior to GLC to increase vapor pressure. Theoretically this can be accomplished by any of the methylation procedures used for the higher fatty acids (Chapter 7). However, in practice the use of diazomethane should be avoided unless the mixture consists solely of saturated, nonoxygenated acids such as succinic and glutaric. It has been observed, for example, that maleate and fumarate can be detected by GLC only when carefully methylated with a stoichiometric amount of reagent; when excess diazomethane is added, no peaks are obtained, probably because of the formation of nonvolatile pyrazoline by reaction at the double bonds of the acids. Tartaric, α-ketoglutaric, and several amino acids were also found to react with diazomethane, but no peaks could be obtained on gas chromatography of the products (Quin and Hobbs, 1958). House et al. (1960) have recently studied the reactions of diazomethane with a variety of ketones.

The methanol–hydrochloric acid method has proved satisfactory in the authors' laboratory for methylating a number of di- and tricarboxylic acids of the Krebs cycle. Metcalfe and Schmitz (1961) report yields of 60 to 70% on the esterification of azelaic and pimelic acids with methanol–boron trifluoride reagent. The products contained less than 0.5% free acids.

Mirocha and DeVay (1961) convert dicarboxylic acids to their ethyl esters by treatment with a 4% solution of sulfuric acid in absolute ethanol. The reaction mixture is quenched with water, and the esters are extracted with heptane. The over-all efficiency of the operation is 78%, based on comparisons of peak heights of known concentrations of diethyl fumarate with those of the ester produced from fumaric acid. However, when plant extracts were fortified with known amounts of fumarate, recoveries were 102 to 104% of theory. This is not explained but presumably arose from high background readings.

Esters of these acids are not so volatile as those of fatty acid esters of comparable carbon number. Nevertheless, their vapor pressures are appreciable, and losses can be quite severe unless the esters are handled carefully prior to injection into the chromatograph. Therefore evaporation steps should be avoided or carried out under controlled conditions. The flash-exchange technique developed by Ralls (Chapter 3, Section C) for the simultaneous esterification and injection of volatile fatty acids is worth consideration, but it should be kept in mind that yields may be low because of the need for methylating several carboxy groups in the same molecule simultaneously.

a. Sample Collection

1. *Extraction with Aqueous Alkali* (Resnik *et al.*, 1955). Plant tissue containing about 0.5 gm of organic acids is weighed out and placed in a Waring blendor. Water (500 ml) is added, and the mixture is homogenized for 10 minutes. Enough solid sodium hydroxide (about 200 mg) is added to bring the pH up to 8. The mixture is blended for an additional 10 minutes and filtered.

2. *Extraction with Hot Ethanol* (Bryant and Overell, 1953). Disks (1 × 80 mm) are cut from turgid carrots, rinsed in distilled water, and plunged into boiling 80% ethanol. The suspensions are refluxed for 90 minutes and then macerated in hot ethanol for 3 minutes in a Waring blendor. The mixture is filtered through sintered glass, and the residue is washed thoroughly with 80% ethanol. The filtrate plus washings are combined and evaporated to dryness on a steam bath. The residue is dissolved in water (250 ml), and this solution is passed through an ion-exchange column as described below.

*3. *Extraction with Cold Ethanol* (Mirocha and DeVay, 1961). Organic acids are extracted from leaves and hulls of almond by blending the tissues (1 gm dry weight) for 2 minutes in 70% ethanol (10 ml). The tissue is then re-extracted with 2 × 10-ml portions of 70% ethanol, and the extracts are combined and concentrated to a convenient volume (10 ml) at room temperature. The extract can be purified on an ion-exchange resin (method B.I.b.1), but satisfactory results can be obtained by ethylating the residue directly (method B.I.c.2) and chromatographing the products on a polyester column (method B.II.a.2).

*4. *Collection of Smoke Condensates* (Quin and Hobbs, 1958). Cigarettes (50) are smoked with an automatic smoking machine at the rate of one 35-ml puff per minute of 2 seconds duration (Bradford *et al.*, 1936). The smoke is condensed in a series of six traps in dry ice–ethanol baths. The traps and connecting tubing are washed with ether (50 ml) and then with 5 × 40-ml portions of 0.5% sodium hydroxide solution. The combined alkali solutions are extracted with 3 × 50-ml portions of ethyl ether, separated from the ether layer, and retained for analysis.

b. Separation from Neutral and Basic Compounds

1. *Ion-Exchange Method* (Bryant and Overell, 1953; Resnik *et al.*, 1955). *Preparation of anion-exchange column.* A piece of glass wool is placed in a 50-ml burette, and 2 gm (wet weight) of Dowex 1 (200/400 mesh) in the chloride form is washed into it. The column is backwashed with water, after which a piece of glass wool is placed on top of the resin to prevent its being disturbed during addition of eluants. The resin is washed with 2 N sodium carbonate until the eluate gives a negative test for chloride; 1.5 N ammonium carbonate (200 ml) is passed through the column, and the resin is washed exhaustively to remove excess carbonate. *Preparation of cation-exchange column.* Amberlite IR-112 (3 gm wet weight) is placed in a 1 × 20-cm column. The resin is washed with water until the eluate no longer gives an acid reaction when tested with Bromcresol purple. *Procedure.* Tissue extract containing approximately 25 mg of total acids in 100 ml of solution is passed through the Dowex 1 anion-exchange column at a rate of 1 ml/min. After the meniscus of the solution reaches the top of the resin, the column is washed thoroughly with water. The organic acids are then eluted with 1.5 N ammonium carbonate (100 ml). The eluate is heated at 70°C until the odor of ammonia can no longer be detected. The solution is next cooled to room temperature, and one-fourth of it is passed through the Amberlite IR-112 column at a rate of 1 ml/min to remove cations. The column is washed thoroughly with water, and the eluate and washings are evaporated to recover the nonvolatile acids. *Note:* The procedure states that one-fourth of the eluate from Dowex 1 is passed through Amberlite IR-112 A. Actually the entire eluate could be used if the exchange capacity of the Amberlite is not exhausted.

*2. *Solvent Partition of Smoke Condensate* (Quin, 1961). The sodium hydroxide solution obtained by method B.I.a.4 is treated with carbon dioxide gas for 1 hour to release phenols. The mixture is then extracted continuously for 2 days with ether. The aqueous solution is then acidified with conc sulfuric acid, and extraction with fresh ether is continued for 2 days. The ether extract is treated with a small excess of diazomethane,[1] dried overnight over sodium sulfate, and stripped to an exact volume of 3 ml. This solution is stored in the refrigerator until used for withdrawal of 20- to 50-μl aliquots for gas chromatography.

c. Esterification Methods

1. *Methylation.* See procedures in Chapter 7, Section G.

*2. *Ethylation* (Mirocha and DeVay, 1961). Aliquots (1 ml) of ethanol extracts of plant tissues obtained according to method B.I.a.3 are air-dried in 15-mm × 15-cm test tubes and treated with a 4% (v/v) solution of concentrated sulfuric acid in absolute ethanol (5 ml). The tube is capped with a glass marble, and the contents are refluxed for 1 hour at 90°C. The mixture is then concentrated to a volume of 2 ml and diluted with distilled water (4 ml). *n*-Heptane (0.5 to 1 ml) is shaken with the reaction mixture to extract the esters. During extraction, a black precipitate frequently forms at the interface of the heptane and water layers, making it difficult to obtain clear samples of the heptane solution. The *n*-heptane layer is clarified by transferring the entire mixture to a stoppered 6 × 100-mm tube and centrifuging for 15 minutes at 3000 × *g*. An aliquot of the upper layer is then injected into the chromatograph.

II. CHROMATOGRAPHY OF ESTERS

Quin and Hobbs (1958) chromatographed the methyl esters of nonvolatile acids isolated from cigarette smoke on a number of partition liquids. On dioctyl adipate at 138°C, eight peaks were observed, the order of elution of identified esters being: lactate–glycolate, oxalate, malonate, furoate, levulinate, and succinate. The boiling points of the methyl esters ranged from 144°C for methyl lactate to 193°C for dimethyl succinate. The identities of the peaks were established by comparing retention times on different columns with those of known compounds under the same conditions. For esters boiling above dimethyl succinate, Flexol R-2H was used at a temperature of 190°C. This liquid is a polyester supplied by Union Carbide Chemicals Co. Its vapor pressure is sufficiently low to permit sustained use for a few days, but significant volatilization occurs in time. The methyl esters of succinic, glutaric, adipic, and malic acids were eluted in the order given from this column. The highest-boiling compound examined was dimethyl phthalate (b.p. 282°C). It was eluted from a Flexol R-2H column in 16.7 minutes at a temperature of 192°C and a flow rate of 26 ml of helium per minute.

Methyl lactate could not be separated from methyl glycolate on dioctyl

---

[1] Note artifacts that are produced by diazomethane in Section B.I., above.

adipate or Flexol. However, it was possible to resolve these compounds on Carbowax 1500 coated on firebrick at a temperature of 122°C. At a flow rate of 20 ml of helium per minute, the retention time of methyl lactate was 15 minutes, and that of methyl glycolate was 22 minutes, on a 2-meter column. Other nonvolatile acids whose methylation products (diazomethane method) yielded single peaks on gas chromatography include citric, α-hydroxyisobutyric, pimelic, oxalacetic, and pyruvic acids.

Mirocha and DeVay (1961) chromatographed the diethyl esters of five dicarboxylic acids on poly(diethyleneglycol succinate) at 150°C. The order of elution was: malonate, fumarate, succinate, maleate, and malate (Table I). Similar results were obtained on poly(1,4-butanediol succinate).

TABLE I

RETENTION TIMES OF DIETHYL ESTERS OF DICARBOXYLIC
ACIDS ON POLAR STATIONARY LIQUIDS[a]

	Relative retention time on:	
Parent acid	Poly(1,4-butanediol succinate)	Poly(diethylene glycol succinate)
Malonic	1.00	1.00
Fumaric	1.48	1.30
Succinic	1.53	1.45
Maleic	2.06	2.04
Malic	—	6.81

[a] From Mirocha and DeVay (1961).

The cis-unsaturated ester (maleate) was eluted after succinate on both polyesters, in keeping with its more polar character. However, the trans (fumarate) isomer was eluted before succinate. This agrees with the general observation that trans isomers tend to be less soluble than cis isomers in most solvents. It is noteworthy that good separation of the two isomers was obtained on the polar packings, in view of the fact that nonpolar packings give better separation of such pairs in the higher fatty acid series.

Nowakowska et al. (1957) chromatographed a series of methyl esters of dibasic acids containing 3 to 9 carbon atoms in the long chain on D.C. 550 silicone oil. Separation of the C_3 to C_7 esters was obtained at 150°C, and separation of the C_6 to C_9 esters at 220°C. The entire range of esters was separated in a single run at 200°C (Table II). It is interesting to note that the usual plot of log_{10} retention time at 200°C versus carbon number does not give a straight line, the C_3 to C_6 esters forming a group with a steeper slope than the C_7 to C_9 compounds.

TABLE II

RETENTION TIMES OF DIMETHYL ESTERS OF DICARBOXYLIC ACIDS
ON D.C. 550 SILICONE GREASE AT A SERIES OF TEMPERATURES

	Retention time in minutes at flow rate of 13 ml of helium per minute				
Parent acid	150°C	170°C	180°C	200°C	220°C
Malonic	8.8	5.6	5.0	3.5	—
Succinic	13.4	8.6	7.5	5.4	—
Glutaric	20.7	12.1	10.0	—	—
Adipic	31.8	17.8	13.8	12.7	7.3
Pimelic	52.1	26.7	19.6	18.4	11.3
Suberic	—	—	—	24.5	14.8
Azelaic	—	—	—	33.8	19.8

ª From Nowakowska et al. (1957).

Tepe and Wesselman (1958), using a silicone column at 220°C, chromato-graphed a series of diethyl malonates substituted on the methylene carbon with one or two ethyl or isoamyl groups. Diethyl diisoamylmalonate was eluted in about 30 to 35 minutes. Bartsch et al. (1960) describe conditions for separating three aliphatic C_{10} dibasic acids and two C_9 monobasic acids by GLC on D.C. 550 silicone oil and a polyester at 236°C. Most of the com-pounds discussed in these last three papers do not occur in nature, but the procedures for chromatographing them may be of interest in setting up conditions for the analysis of mixtures of mono- and dibasic acids produced by ozonolysis and oxidation of unsaturated lipids.

Insufficient work has been done on gas chromatography of this group of compounds to uncover all the pitfalls that may trap the unwary. However, opportunities for creating artifacts both during sample preparation and GLC are great. The limitations of the diazomethane method for preparing methyl esters have already been pointed out. Interesterification of samples on poly-ester packings, followed by decarboxylation, is also a possibility. Ackman et al. (1960) found that the amount of dimethyl malonate relative to dimethyl succinate eluted from a poly(1,4-butanediol succinate) column decreased rapidly with temperature. At 140°C recovery was fair, but at 190°C the malonate peak was not recorded. Dimethyl oxalate also showed appreciable decomposition, but, as the retention time was comparatively short, the loss was less noticeable. On a silicone grease column, the recovery of malonate was temperature-independent. Evidently some interaction with the polar packing occurred, culminating in degradation. This can be minimized by using low temperatures and non-ester packings. Although no definitive findings have yet been published, it seems likely that similar reactions might occur on chromatography of the esters of oxaloacetic and possibly α-ketoglutaric acids, since these also are faily strong acids and contain labilizing carbonyl groups. Furthermore, they would have to be chromatographed at temperatures higher than those required for oxalate and malonate.

Another source of artifacts might be dehydration of hydroxy acids such as malic, tartaric, or citric to yield unsaturated compounds. Citric acid, for example, produces itaconic and citraconic anhydrides on dry distillation, with the intermediate formation of aconitic acid. It is known that malic and citric acids as their methyl esters can be chromatographed in the vapor phase without serious decomposition, yet the possibility of dehydration reactions occurring under some conditions cannot be ignored.

So far, conditions have not been published for chromatographing the full complement of Krebs cycle esters, together with allied compounds such as lactate, pyruvate, and malonate. However, it seems most likely that good results could be obtained by using a polyester stationary phase and programming the temperature from 120° to 190°C. This would allow separation of compounds having a wide boiling-point range and at the same time would minimize decomposition of compounds such as malonic esters. If necessary, it should be possible to decrease the temperature range required for chromatography by using a low ratio of liquid to solid support with a correspondingly small sample size.

a. Conditions for Chromatography

*1. *Esters Derived from Tobacco Smoke* (Quin and Hobbs, 1958). (*I*) *Conditions for Resolution of Lactate and Glycolate.* (*II*) *Conditions for Esters Boiling up to 193°C.* (*III*) *Conditions for Esters Boiling between 193°C and 282°C*

Chromatograph	Perkin-Elmer 154B Vapor Fractometer with heated vent line.
Column dimensions	2-meter × 0.6-cm o.d. copper or glass U tubes.
Solid support	C-22 firebrick (30/60 mesh).
Stationary phase	(I) Carbowax 1500 (10:30). (II) Dioctyl adipate (10:30). (III) Flexol R-2H (10:50).
Temperatures	(I) 122°C. (II) 138°C. (III) 190°C.
Carrier gas	Helium at (I) 50 ml/min. (II) 45 ml/min. (III) 25 ml/min.
Detector	Thermistor.
Recorder	Leeds and Northrup 0–1 mv.
Sample size	20–50 μl of 1–5% solution.
Analysis time	15 to 30 minutes.

*2. *Ethyl Esters of Lower Dicarboxylic Acids* (Mirocha and DeVay, 1961)

Chromatograph	Aerograph A-100-C equipped with gas sampling valve.
Column dimensions	228.6 × 0.635-cm o.d. coiled copper tubing.
Solid support	C-22 firebrick (60/80 U. S. mesh).
Stationary phase	Poly(diethylene glycol succinate) or poly(1,4-butanediol succinate) (25:75).
Temperatures	Injection: 260°C. Column and detector: 150°C. Collector: 260° to 270°C.
Carrier gas	Helium at 150 ml/min at outlet.
Detector	Four-filament T/C cell operated at 250 ma.
Recorder	Varian G-10, 10 mv; 2.5 seconds; 0.635 cm/min.
Sample size	10 to 60 μl containing 10 to 450 μg of esters.
Analysis time	12.5 minutes to diethyl maleate; about 38 minutes to diethyl malate.

*3. *Methyl Esters of C_3 to C_9 Dicarboxylic Acids* (Nowakowska et al., 1957)

Chromatograph	Laboratory-built.
Column dimensions	190.5 × 0.8-cm i.d. stainless-steel U tube.
Solid support	Johns-Manville Celite 545 (40/120 mesh) acid-washed and size-graded (James and Martin, 1952).
Stationary phase	Dow Corning high-vacuum silicone grease (10:100).
Temperatures	Detector: 197°C. Column: 200°C.
Carrier gas	Helium at 13 ml/min. Inlet pressure: 250 mm Hg. Outlet pressure: atmospheric.
Detector	Gow-Mac TR-II T/C cell.
Recorder	10 mv; 1 second; 16 inches/hour.
Sample size	20 to 40 μl.
Analysis time	About 35 minutes to dimethyl azelate.

III. Summary

Nonvolatile oxygenated and oligobasic organic acids can be chromatographed as their esters on polar or nonpolar columns at temperatures between 120° and 200°C. The C_4 dibasic acids emerge from polar columns in the order following: fumarate, succinate, maleate, and malate, indicating that polarity as well as vapor pressure is a factor governing retention. Esters of oxalic and malonic acids are lost at high temperatures on polyester but not on silicone column packings. Therefore artifacts produced by interactions with the liquid phase are important to watch for in analyzing mixtures of these materials by GLC.

C. Carbohydrates

I. Introduction

Pentoses and hexoses are not volatile, and in fact they char on strong heating. However, if all their hydroxy groups are replaced with methoxy groups, they will pass through chromatographic columns in 20 minutes to 1 hour at a temperature of 150°C without thermal decomposition. Comparatively little work has been done on the gas chromatographic analysis of sugar derivatives, but this is a particularly attractive field for future research because of the large number of sugar isomers possible, coupled with the high resolving power of the method.

Chromatography need not be confined to the monosaccharides, since it is possible to elute octamethyl sucrose from a 6-foot column within 60 to 70 minutes at 200°C. However, its greatest value in the analysis of oligo- and polysaccharides will no doubt stem from the separation and identification of their methanolysis products as a means of characterizing them and establishing structure.

II. METHODS OF ISOLATION

Carbohydrates are extracted from tissues with water, or with 80% ethanol as described previously for amino acids (Section A.II). Exhaustive extraction with ethanol satisfactorily removes mono-, di-, and some higher saccharides, the upper molecular-weight range recoverable by this method being still unknown. Care must be taken to avoid chemical changes produced by enzyme action both before and during extraction. These can be minimized by freeze-drying the sample immediately after harvesting, or by killing the fresh tissue with boiling 95% ethanol. This latter process may result in conversion of some reducing sugars to ethyl glycosides.

After extraction, the solution must be freed from amino and other organic acids. Formerly, this was accomplished by treatment with charcoal and lead acetate, but better results are now obtained with ion-exchange resins. The crude extract is cleared of particulate matter by filtration or centrifugation and then is passed through a column containing a base-binding ion-exchange resin such as Dowex 50-X4 or Amberlite IR-100 H-AG (see Section A for details). These resins retain amino acids and amines. The effluent from this column is next passed through an acid-binding resin such as Dowex 1 (see Section B.I.b). The percolate from the second column contains carbohydrates as well as other neutral materials. If it is not necessary to recover amino acids and other nonvolatile organic acids separately, both groups of compounds can be removed in a single operation by treating the filtered extract with a mixture of anionic and cationic resins (Williams et al., 1950). This can be done by a column or batch process.

Artifacts are sometimes produced by ion-exchange resins. Strongly basic resins can cause decomposition of some carbohydrates resulting in formation of organic acids, or they can promote aldose $\rightleftarrows$ ketose epimerization. Acidic ion-exchange resins are apparently without effect on monosaccharides or aldopyranoside linkages, but they may catalyze the breaking of fructofuranoside bonds. Therefore strongly acid resins should be avoided in the isolation of carbohydrates known to contain them.

Polysaccharides are isolated from plant and animal tissues in a variety of ways depending on their individual properties, so details of specific procedures cannot be given. Often the tissue is dried first, either in a vacuum oven at low temperature, by extraction with successive portions of alcohol, or, preferably, by lyophilization. Water should be withdrawn rapidly at low temperatures. Otherwise, strong secondary valence bonds are formed between adjacent carbohydrate chains, rendering the preparation difficult to redissolve. After drying, the tissue is usually defatted prior to carbohydrate removal. The solvent most widely used for this is an azeotropic mixture of ethanol and benzene. This not only removes lipids but also renders the tissue more permeable to hydrophilic solvents employed in subsequent treatments. Most carbohydrates other than cellulose are then removed from the tissue with water, oxygen-free aqueous alkali, dilute trichloroacetic acid, or chloral hydrate. The crude preparations are finally purified by fractional precipitation. The reader is referred to a paper by Bath (1960) for details on the isolation and fractionation of plant carbohydrates.

a. Removal of Ionic Compounds with Resins

1. *Column Method.* The percolate is taken from the column used for the retention of nonvolatile organic acids (Section B.I.b.1.).

*2. *Batch Method for Clarification of Sugar Solutions* (Williams *et al.*, 1950). Extracts prepared by treatment of the tissue with 80% ethanol (see Section A) are evaporated on a steam bath to remove the alcohol. The concentrate is cooled, filtered through a mat of Celite analytical filter-aid, and enough water is added to give a concentration of about 0.4 mg of reducing sugar per 100 ml. This solution is then treated with Amberlite IR-100H and Duolite A4 at a rate of 4 gm of each resin per 100 ml. The resins and clarified extract are mixed in a flask and agitated every 10 minutes for a period of 2 hours. The solution is filtered through a fluted filter paper, and the first few milliliters of filtrate are discarded.

Prior to use, the resins are activated, washed with water, and air-dried. A number of combinations of anion- and cation-exchange resins can be used, but any mixture selected should first be tested to establish its efficiency as a clarification agent, and to determine whether it alters the concentrations of pure sugar solutions.

III. Preparation of Carbohydrate Derivatives

Reducing sugars and their methyl ethers must be converted to glycosides in advance of GLC. The hemiacetal hydroxyl is more reactive than the true alcohol groups and can be methylated selectively by treatment of the sugar with one equivalent of dimethyl sulfate in the presence of sodium hydroxide. However, it is usually more convenient to carry out the reaction with a solution of hydrochloric acid in anhydrous methanol at reflux temperature (Fischer method). At an acid concentration of 4%, equilibrium is usually reached in 3 to 24 hours with the production of a mixture of α- and β-anomers of the corresponding pyranoside. Furanosides are formed early in the reaction, particularly when it is carried out under mild conditions (room temperature; low, about 0.5%, acid concentration). At high temperatures and higher acid concentration an equilibrium is established in which pyranosides predominate for most sugars. The $\alpha \rightleftarrows \beta$, pyranoside $\rightleftarrows$ furanoside composition at equilibrium varies for each monosaccharide and is also dependent on acid concentration and temperature (Bishop, 1960). In theory, dimethyl acetals could be formed also, but the equilibrium favors the production of methyl glycosides. With D-glucose and D-galactose, the α-pyranose predominates over the β-anomer. Helferich (1926) describes a method for the large-scale production of pure α-methyl D-glucopyranoside. Less elaborate techniques will suffice for the preparation of mixtures of the anomers on a small scale. In carrying out the reaction, it is important that the reagent be anhydrous and free of acetone.

The true hydroxyl groups of carbohydrates can be alkylated with dimethyl sulfate and sodium hydroxide or methyl iodide and silver oxide. If pure α- or β-glycosides are used as starting materials for the production of sugar ethers, the reaction products are also pure anomers. Otherwise mixtures of the two forms will be obtained. Thus West and Holden (1940) state that methyl 2,3,4,6-tetra-O-methyl-α-D-glucopyranoside can be obtained by causing the α-methylglucoside to react with dimethyl sulfate and sodium hydroxide, using four-fifths of the reagents required for the methylation of D-glucose. Simpler techniques can be utilized for the alkylation of small samples, but it is usually necessary to resort to successive additions of the reagents to cause all the hydroxyl groups to react. Dimethyl sulfate and 30% sodium hydroxide are used most generally for alkylation, since they are cheap, and simple sugars and glycosides are soluble in the reagent. Acetyl groups are replaced by methyl groups under the conditions of the reaction; hence acetylated carbohydrates as well as free sugars and glycosides will react. As a result of partial methylation, the sugar may become insoluble in aqueous media, and the rate of reaction will slow down correspondingly. This may be remedied in part by continuing the reaction in an organic solvent such as tetrahydrofuran, with methyl iodide and silver oxide (Purdie method) as reagents. Kuhn et al. (1955) describe an improved method for the permethylation of sucrose with Purdie's reagents and with dimethylformamide as a solvent. Carbohydrates are quite soluble in this solvent, so it is possible to obtain a product by a single methylation step, the infrared spectrum of which shows no OH absorption bands. Reducing sugars must be converted to glycosides before treatment with this reagent because of the oxidizing power of the silver oxide.

Polysaccharides are more difficult to methylate than simple sugars because of lower solubility in aqueous and organic solvents and because of their more complex structures. Techniques required for quantitative methylation vary in individual cases; consequently only a few typical examples can be given. Generally the material is alkylated first with successive portions of dimethyl sulfate and sodium hydroxide until it is no longer soluble in water. Next, it is extracted into an organic solvent and treated in this medium with Purdie's reagents until the product no longer shows absorption in the infrared arising from OH bonds. Alternatively, the polysaccharide is first acetylated to render it soluble in tetrahydrofuran and is treated in this solvent with successive portions of dimethyl sulfate and solid sodium hydroxide. As noted above, this reagent causes replacement of acetyl groups by methyl groups.

The methylated polysaccharides must be hydrolyzed to monoses and these converted to glycosides prior to GLC. Hydrolysis is carried out most conveniently with 90% formic acid, and glycoside formation is carried out with hydrochloric acid in anhydrous methanol. Care must be taken that artifacts are not created during these steps. Thus Kircher (1960), on chromatographing methylated glycosides derived from dextran, observed a peak that could not be accounted for by any of the compounds expected to be present. The same peak was produced on treatment of methyl 2,3,4-tri-*O*-methyl-β-D-glucopyranoside, a normal component of the mixture, with formic acid and HCl–methanol under the same conditions used to prepare the methylated polysaccharide for chromatography. The substance giving rise to the peak was shown to be 2,3,4-tri-*O*-methyl levoglucosan which was formed from the monose by condensation of the hemiacetal hydroxyl with a true hydroxyl to yield a 1,6-anhydro compound.

Hexose monomethyl ethers have not been resolved yet by GLC either as the free sugars or as methyl glycosides. Consequently it is necessary to reduce them to sugar alcohol ethers and to acetylate these to obtain derivatives with sufficient volatility. Sodium borohydride is more convenient than lithium aluminum hydride for this, since it is stable enough for use in water and methanol solutions, whereas the latter reagent is suitable only in nonhydroxylic solvents. Excess reagent is decomposed by acidification, after which the water is evaporated and the dry residue is treated with a mixture of acetic and sulfuric acids. Alternatively, the sugar alcohols can be acetylated with a mixture of acetic anhydride, acetic acid, and perchloric acid (Abdel-Akher et al., 1951).

a. Methylation of Simple Sugars

1. *Formation of Methyl Glycosides.* The carbohydrate (5 gm) is suspended in a 4% solution of hydrochloric acid in acetone-free anhydrous methanol (20 ml) and refluxed for 16 to 24 hours. A tube containing soda lime is attached to the upper end of the reflux condenser to exclude moisture. The solvent is then removed by evaporation. The α-anomer of methyl D-glucopyranoside can be prepared by refluxing D-glucose (500 gm) with 0.25% methanolic hydrochloric acid (2 liters) for 72 hours and crystallizing out the product at 0°C (Helferich and Schäfer, 1926).

2. *Preparative Scale Alkylation with Dimethyl Sulfate* (West and Holden, 1940). The carbohydrate[1] (25 gm) and water (15 ml) are added to a 2-liter flask equipped with a reflux condenser, stirrer, and dropping funnel. The temperature of the mixture is raised to 55°C and kept at this value throughout the duration of the synthesis. Dimethyl sulfate (90 ml) and carbon tetrachloride (125 ml) are added to the flask as rapidly as possible. A 40% solution of sodium hydroxide (400 ml) is then added dropwise at a slow rate to maintain the temperature at 55°C. The evolution of heat diminishes in about 15 to 20 minutes after 70 to 90 ml of alkali has been added. When this occurs, the rest of the alkali is added as rapidly as possible so that the temperature of the reaction mixture increases to 70° to 75°C. Additional dimethyl sulfate (160 ml) is then added drop by drop, and the mixture is heated in a boiling-water bath for 30 minutes with continuous stirring. The solution is cooled, and sufficient water is added to dissolve the sodium sulfate produced during the reaction. The methylated product is extracted with 4 × 150-ml portions of chloroform. The extracts are combined, dried over anhydrous sodium sulfate, and the solvent evaporated.

CAUTION: Dimethyl sulfate is poisonous and must be handled with care. Ammonia is a specific antidote and should be kept on hand to destroy any reagent which may be spilled.

3. *Analytical Scale Alkylation with Dimethyl Sulfate* (Falconer and Adams, 1956). The carbohydrate (0.5 gm) is dissolved in water (3 ml) and treated with dimethyl sulfate (1.5 ml) and 30% sodium hydroxide solution (3 ml).

---

[1] These quantities of reagents are for D-glucose. If the starting material is a methyl glycoside, four-fifths of these amounts will suffice.

After three successive additions of reagents, the pH of the mixture is adjusted to 8.9 with sulfuric acid, and the reaction product is recovered by continuous extraction with chloroform. The solvent is evaporated, and the residue is dissolved in pure (redistilled) tetrahydrofuran. Pulverized sodium hydroxide (2.6 gm) is added, and dimethyl sulfate (3 ml) is introduced drop by drop with stirring over a period of 3 hours. The reaction mixture is digested for 16 hours at 23° to 28°C, after which enough water is added to dissolve the solids. Next, the temperature is raised to 60°C, and the solvent is evaporated under a stream of nitrogen. This temperature is maintained for an additional hour to ensure decomposition of the dimethyl sulfate. The mixture is then cooled, the pH adjusted to 8.9 with sulfuric acid, and the solution extracted with chloroform. The solvent is evaporated, the residue dissolved in methanol, and this solution filtered to remove insoluble impurities.

CAUTION: Dimethyl sulfate is poisonous and must be handled with care. See procedure C.III.a.2. Tetrahydrofuran should be tested for peroxides before distillation.

4. Alkylation with Silver Oxide–Methyl Iodide (Kuhn *et al.*, 1955). The sugar or glycoside (10 gm) is placed in a wide-mouthed flask, dissolved in dimethylformamide (120 ml), and treated at about 20°C with methyl iodide (45 ml). Silver oxide (45 gm) is then added to the flask over a period of 15 minutes with vigorous shaking. After the addition of about 20 gm of silver oxide, the temperature rises to about 30°C; thereupon the flask is cooled so that it goes no higher. When the temperature begins to fall (about 40 minutes after all the silver oxide has been added), the flask is stoppered and placed on a mechanical shaker for 12 hours. Next, the contents of the flask are centrifuged, the supernatant solution is removed by decantation, and the precipitate is washed with chloroform (50 ml). The combined supernatant and washings are treated with water (500 ml) and potassium cyanide (5 gm), and then extracted with 5 × 100-ml portions of chloroform. The combined chloroform extracts are washed with 4 × 100-ml portions of water and dried over anhydrous sodium sulfate. The sugar derivative is obtained on evaporation of the solvent.

b. Methylation and Hydrolysis of Polysaccharides

1. Direct Methylation of Glucan (Bishop *et al.*, 1960). The glucan (1 gm) is methylated five times for 24 hours each time by shaking with 30% sodium hydroxide solution (20 ml) and dimethyl sulfate (10 ml). The product is extracted into chloroform (10 ml) and treated in that solvent with methyl iodide (6 ml) and silver oxide (3 gm) for 24 hours. After three further treatments with methyl iodide–silver oxide, the reaction product is precipitated from the chloroform solution by adding petroleum ether (b.p. 30° to 60°C).

A white powder is obtained that should show no hydroxyl absorption in the infrared.

*2. *Acetylation followed by Methylation* (Bishop and Cooper, 1960b). Glucomannan (1.5 gm) is acetylated with acetic anhydride (30 ml) in pyridine (45 ml). The mixture is quenched with water, and the precipitate is centrifuged, washed with water, and dried under vacuum. The product is dissolved in tetrahydrofuran[2] (25 ml) and treated with sodium hydroxide (17 gm) and dimethyl sulfate (20 ml), the latter reagent being added dropwise with stirring. The mixture is treated a second time with these same quantities of reagents and refluxed for 1 hour. Ten additional portions of reagents are added over a period of 4 days with continuous stirring, tetrahydrofuran being added from time to time to keep the mixture fluid. The solution is then refluxed for 1 hour, cooled, and filtered. The solids are dissolved in water, and this solution and the filtrate are extracted continuously with chloroform for 24 hours. The aqueous phases from the two extractions are evaporated to dryness, and the residues are re-extracted with chloroform and methanol. The extracts are combined and dried, and the solvent is evaporated. The product is methylated six times with the same amounts of methyl iodide (25 ml) and silver oxide (5 gm) for each methylation. The methoxyl content of the product should approach the theoretical value, and there should be no hydroxyl absorption in the infrared.

*3. *Hydrolysis of Methylated Polysaccharides* (Jones and Wilkie, 1959). The polysaccharide (1 gm) is dissolved in 90% formic acid and allowed to stand at room temperature for 12 hours. The temperature is raised to 60°C for 3 hours, and finally to 90°C for 24 to 36 hours. The formic acid is removed under reduced pressure, water being added at frequent intervals. The formyl esters are hydrolized by heating in aqueous solution (125 ml of water per gram of methylated compound) for 6 hours. Water and formic acid are removed by distillation, and the hydrolysis step is repeated an additional three times with 6-hour heating periods, and finally with a 10-hour heating period. The water is evaporated, and the dried sugar derivatives are converted to glycosides by refluxing with a 4% solution of hydrochloric acid in anhydrous methanol for 16 hours (Bishop *et al.*, 1960).

c. Other Sugar Derivatives

*1. *Acetylated Sugar Alcohols* (Abdel-Akher *et al.*, 1951). The sugar or partly methylated sugar (1 gm) is dissolved in water (20 ml) and treated with a 1.5% solution of sodium borohydride in water (10 ml). The reaction mixture is kept at room temperature (20° to 25°C) until a drop of it no longer reduces Fehling solution after acidification with acetic acid to destroy excess

---

[2] Commercial tetrahydrofuran contains antioxidants that should be removed by distillation just prior to use.

reagent. To ensure complete reduction, the mixture can be allowed to stand at room temperature for 24 hours or until its optical rotation becomes constant. Next, the reaction mixture is acidified with acetic acid to destroy excess sodium borohydride and evaporated to dryness under vacuum. The dry residue containing the sugar alcohol is shaken with acetic anhydride (15 ml) containing concentrated sulfuric acid (1 ml) until most of the solid dissolves. The mixture is then warmed for 10 minutes at 50° to 60°C, cooled, and quenched by pouring it with stirring into ice water (50 ml). The acetate of the alcohol is filtered off, washed, dried, and recrystallized. Yields are 70 to 90% of theory.

IV. METHODS OF CHROMATOGRAPHY

Monoses are not volatile, so it is necessary to convert them to methyl ethers prior to chromatography by methods described in the preceding section. However, Kircher (1960) found that tetra-O-methyl glucose did not pass through the gas chromatograph. Similarly, Bishop and Cooper (1960a) observed that sugars in which the anomeric hydroxyl is free or substituted by an acetyl group tend to be adsorbed by columns in which alkali-washed Celite 545 is used as a solid support. Therefore both authors chromatograph sugar ethers as their methyl glycosides.

Kircher (1960) evaluated a number of stationary liquids on the basis of their capacity to separate the fully methylated derivative of β-D-arabino-pyranoside from β-D-glucopyranoside, and the derivative of α-D-manno-pyranoside from that of α-D-glucopyranoside. The best stationary phase was methylated hydroxyethyl cellulose. This material was prepared by acetylat-ing and methylating commercial hydroxyethyl cellulose (Cellosize WP-09, Union Carbide Chemicals Co.) by a modification of the procedure described in Section C.III.b.2. Methylated starch, methylated guar gum, methylated dextran, and commercial columns packed with Craig polyester and LAC-446 were rated as fair; the Apiezons, starch triacetate, hydroxyethyl cel-lulose triacetate, silicone, and Carbowax were rated as poor. Bishop and Cooper (1960a), prior to Kircher's publication, examined a number of liq-uids including Apiezon M, poly(1,4-butanediol succinate), D.C. 550 silicone oil, Carbowax 4000, zinc stearate, D-mannitol, partially benzylated raffinose, methyl cellulose, and mannitol hexastearate. They selected Apiezon M and Craig polyester (the butanediol succinate polymer) as being best suited to the purpose. They found it advantageous to use two columns, one con-taining a nonpolar partition liquid and the other a polar liquid, because some isomeric sugar ethers could be separated on one and not on the other. For example, the methanolysis products from methylated glucomannan gave five peaks when chromatographed on Apiezon M at 150°C (Fig. 4). When the first two peaks to emerge were collected and rechromatographed on the

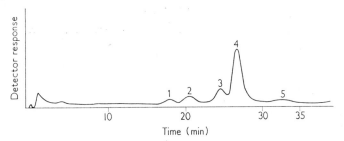

Fig. 4. Gas–liquid partition chromatogram of methanolysis products from methylated glucomannan on Apiezon M at 150°C and 30 ml of argon per minute. (1) Methyl 2,3,4,6,-tetra-O-methyl-α- and β-D-glucopyranosides. (2) Methyl 2,3,4,6-tetra-O-methyl-α- and β-D-galactopyranosides and methyl 2,3,6-tri-O-methyl-β-D-glucopyranoside. (3) Methyl 2,3,6-tri-O-methyl-α-D-glucopyranoside. (4) Methyl 2,3,6-tri-O-methyl-α-D-mannopyranoside. (5) Methyl di-O-methyl-D-galatoside. (Bishop and Cooper, 1960a)

polyester column, eight peaks were obtained (Fig. 5). Insufficient data on the same compounds are given to determine whether the dual-column system employed by Bishop and Cooper is equal in resolving power to the methylated hydroxyethyl cellulose column used by Kircher. It seems likely that some combination of these columns might be useful.

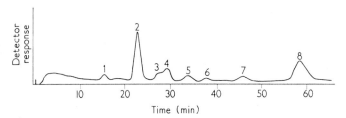

Fig. 5. Chromatogram of peaks 1 and 2 from Fig. 4, collected and rerun on a 4-foot poly(1,4-butanediol succinate) column at 150°C and a flow rate of 60 ml of argon per minute. (1) Methyl 2,3,4,5-tetra-O-methyl-β-D-glucopyranoside. (2) Methyl 2,3,4,6-tetra-O-methyl-α-D-glucopyranoside. (3) Methyl 2,3,4,6-tetra-O-methyl-α-D-galactopyranoside. (4) Methyl 2,3,4,6-methyl-α-D-galactopyranoside. (5, 6, 7) Not identified. (8) Methyl 2,3,6-tri-O-methyl-β-D-glucopyranoside. (Bishop and Cooper, 1960b)

The α- and β-anomers of methyl 2,3,4,6-tetra-O-methyl-D-glucopyranoside can be resolved on Craig polyester, Apiezon M, or methylated hydroxyethyl cellulose. The β-anomer emerges from the column before the α-anomer (Table III) on both the polar and nonpolar liquids, indicating that the compound in which the methoxyl group occupies an axial position is more soluble in both types of liquid. The α-anomers of all the isomeric tri-O-methyl-D-glucopyranosides are retained longer on both columns, so it is evident that this is a general phenomenon. This observation extends to the

TABLE III

RELATIVE RETENTION VOLUMES OF METHYL ETHERS OF METHYL
α- AND β-D-GLUCOPYRANOSIDES ON POLAR AND NONPOLAR
PARTITION LIQUIDS AT 150°C[a]

	Retention volume relative to the α-2,3,4,6-glucoside	
Anomer and positions of methyl groups	On poly(1,4-butanediol succinate)	On Apiezon M
β-2,3,4,6	0.67	0.82
α-2,3,4,6	1.00	1.00
β-2,3,4	1.78	0.98
α-2,3,4	2.19	1.12
β-2,4,6	2.34	1.09
β-2,3,6	2.48	1.12
β-3,4,6	2.62	1.13
α-3,4,6	2.65	1.13
α-2,3,6	3.56	1.26
α-2,4,6	3.56	1.38

[a] From Bishop and Cooper (1960a).

methyl glycosides of D-xylose, which has the same optical configuration as
D-glucose. However, it does not apply to the D-mannopyranosides, where the
α-anomer is eluted first, or to the fully methylated D-galactopyranosides or
D-arabinosides, where the anomers are not resolved. Each of these latter
sugars belongs to a different configurational group, so it is not possible to
tell if there is any correspondence between structure and the order in which
they are eluted from the column. Actually, failure to resolve anomeric pairs
may be an advantage more often than not, since the number of peaks that
appear on the chromatogram would be reduced without loss of vital analytical information.

The separation of anomeric pairs of fully methylated derivatives of five
of the more commonly occurring D-pyranosides is shown in Fig. 6. As expected, the compounds derived from five carbon sugars are eluted first. The
order of emergence is: β-xylose, α-xylose, α- and β-arabinose, β-glucose,
α-mannose, α-glucose, α- and β-galactose, and β-mannose. In all, eight of ten
possible peaks are discernible, the only compounds that are not resolved at
all being two of the anomeric pairs. The separation factors on this liquid
(methylated hydroxyethyl cellulose) are quite good, so it is possible that improved resolution of the peaks could be obtained by using a smaller sample
size coupled with a low liquid/solid packing ratio and an ionization detector. Some configurational isomers could not be resolved under these condi-

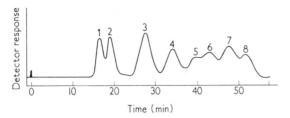

Fig. 6. Chromatogram of fully methylated α- and β-D-pyranosides on methylated hydroxyethyl cellulose at 190°C and 34 ml of helium per minute. Peaks arise from (1) β-xyloside, (2) α-xyloside, (3) α- plus β-arabinoside, (4) β-glucoside, (5) α-mannoside, (6) α-glycoside, (7) α- plus β-galactoside, (8) β-mannoside. (Kircher, 1960)

tions. Thus it was impossible to separate methyl 2,3,4,6-tetra-O-methyl-β-D-arabinopyranoside from its mirror image, the α-L-isomer. More work needs to be done on the separation of optical isomers to extend the usefulness of the method. Similarly, more information is needed on the separation of furanosides and pyranosides. It has been observed that the retention times of furanosides derived from aldohexoses with both the 4- and 5-hydroxy groups free are less than those of the corresponding pyranosides. In such cases, it may be possible to subtract furanoside peaks from the chromatogram by hydrolyzing the glycoside and remethylating under conditions known to favor pyranoside formation. However, this is not possible when the sugars are fully methylated. Consequently, furanoside and pyranoside peaks may sometimes overlap. Thus fully methylated α-D-arabinofuranoside cannot be separated from fully methylated β-D-xylopyranoside on a modified cellulose column.

Free monoses isolated from plant and animal tissues will usually be fully methylated prior to GLC. However, monoses obtained by the hydrolysis of methylated oligo- and polysaccharides may be fully or partly methylated, depending on their positions in the original molecule. Of course the free hydroxyls could be methylated after hydrolysis, but this would result in loss of important information regarding the structure of the carbohydrate. Thus only nonreducing terminal units in polysaccharides yield tetra-O-methyl glycosides on methylation and hydrolysis. Internal hexose units which are part of a straight chain yield different isomeric tri-O-methyl glycosides, depending on whether the units are 1 → 4 linked or 1 → 3 linked. Thus mannan, isolated from Candida albicans, yielded methyl 3,4,6-tri-O-methyl-α-D-mannopyranoside and methyl 2,3,6-tri-O-methyl-α-D-mannopyranoside in a 1.00:0.18 molar ratio on methylation and degradation (Fig. 7). This suggests that about five times as many 1 → 3 glycosidic units occurred in the original carbohydrate as 1 → 4 linkages. Glycoside units in the polysaccharide which serve as branch points yield only di-O-methyl derivatives (if they

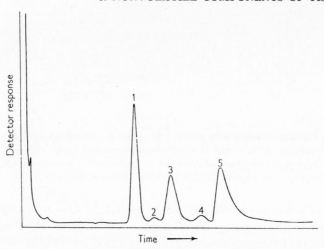

Fig. 7. Chromatogram of methanolysis products from methylated mannan on Apiezon M at 150°C and a flow rate of 140 ml of argon per minute. Molar ratios of compounds in parentheses. (1) Methyl 2,3,4,6-tetra-*O*-methyl-α-D-mannopyranoside (1.65). (2) Unknown (0.13). (3) Methyl 3,4,5-tri-*O*-methyl-α-D-mannopyranoside (1.00). (4) Methyl 2,3,6-tri-*O*-methyl-α-D-mannopyranoside (0.18). (5) Methyl 3,4-di-*O*-methyl-α-D-mannopyranoside (1.90). (Bishop *et al.*, 1960)

are hexoses), since two of the true hydroxy groups as well as the anomeric hydroxyl are involved in primary valence bond formation within the polymer. Including the anomers, two tetramethyl, eight trimethyl, twelve dimethyl, and eight monomethyl derivatives can be obtained theoretically from each isomeric hexose. This does not take into account the possible formation of furanosides. Of course, not all these compounds can be derived from carbohydrates. This makes the task of analyzing methanolyzates much easier than it would be otherwise. Another simplifying fact is that comparatively few of the many sterioisomeric monosaccharides found in nature occur in polysaccharides. Among the hexoses, D-glucose, D-fructose, D-mannose, and D-galactose occur most often, and L-galactose, D-idose, and L-altrose are found less frequently. The most common 5-carbon components of polysaccharides are D-xylose and L-arabinose, but D-arabinose occurs less often. Of course ribose and deoxyribose are constituents of RNA and DNA, but their chromatography leads into another field of biochemistry, which has not yet been explored. Thus the chromatographic separation of the methanolysis products of carbohydrates as a means of identification, characterization, or structure determination is not so complicated as it would seem at first glance. For example, glucomannan isolated from *Pinus banksiana* Lamb. (jack pine) yields only six components, exclusive of the anomers, and cellulose is known to consist only of D-glucopyranose units linked together by β-D-1 $\rightarrow$ 4 bonds (Bishop and Cooper, 1960b).

Retention values of fully and partly methylated D-glucopyranosides are shown in Table III. As noted above, the α- and β-anomers are resolved, the β-compound emerging from the column first in every case. The tetramethyl derivatives are retained longer on both polyester and Apiezon columns than the trimethyl derivatives, and the dimethyl compounds are eluted last. As anticipated, the range of retention values is greater on polyester than on Apiezon.

The methyl mono-O-methyl-D-glucopyranosides are not volatile enough to be separated by GLC. They, as well as methyl hexopyranosides, pass through columns that are conditioned by prior use, but retention volumes are so great that the resolution of mixtures has not been possible as yet. Separation can be obtained by reducing them to the corresponding sugar alcohol monomethyl ethers, acetylating these, and chromatographing the pentaacetates on Apiezon M at 200°C. A mixture of the four possible isomers can be resolved in this way (Fig. 8). Of course α- and β-anomers of these compounds cannot exist, so at first glance reduction and acetylation would seem to be a good way to avoid the formation of complex mixtures during the analysis of carbohydrates. However, there could be difficulty in deciding on the location of a methyl group in the original polymer when the resulting sugar alcohol is symmetrical, since the identities of the head and tail ends of the molecule may be lost.

Free monoses also can be chromatographed as acetates of sugar alcohols (Gunner et al., 1961). Glycose mixtures (0.1 to 10 mg) are reduced to the corresponding glycitols with sodium borohydride. After this, they are fully acetylated by treatment with acetic anhydride containing 2% sulfuric acid at 80°C for 15 hours. The acetylated glycitols are separated by GLC on a mixed stationary phase as described in method C.IV.b.1. Retention values relative to O-L-arabitol pentaacetate are shown in Table IV. Erythritol is used as an internal standard for quantitative measurements. Results are said to be at least as accurate as those obtained by colorimetric or paper chromatographic procedures.

Acetylated monoses and methyl glycosides can be chromatographed without prior reduction by using low liquid/solid ratios (VandenHeuvel and Horning, 1961). Separations according to boiling point are made by using a 6 ft × 0.4 cm column packed with silicone polymer SE-30 on 100/140 mesh Gas-Chrom P. Stereoselective selections can be made on a similar column packed with 1% QF-1 on the same solid support.

D-Mannitol hexaacetate, dulcitol hexaacetate, D-sorbitol hexaacetate, α-methyl-D-mannoside tetraacetate, α-methyl-D-glucoside tetraacetate, α-D-glucose pentaacetate, and β-D-glucose pentaacetate are chromato-

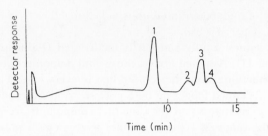

Time (min)

Fig. 8. Separation of mono-O-methylpenta-O-acetyl-D-glucitols on Apiezon M (4 feet), 20% on Celite 545, at 200°C and a flow rate of 60 ml of argon per minute. (1) 6-O-Methyl-D-sorbitol pentaacetate. (2) 2-O-Methyl-D-sorbitol pentaacetate. (3) 3-O-Methyl-D-sorbitol pentaacetate. (4) 4-O-Methyl-D-sorbitol pentaacetate. (Bishop and Cooper, 1960a)

TABLE IV

RETENTION VALUES OF FULLY ACETYLATED GLYCITOLS
RELATIVE TO O-L-ARABITOL PENTAACETATE[a]

Parent alcohol	Relative retention
Glycerol	0.111
Erythritol	0.381
D-Threitol	0.405
L-Rhamnitol	0.739
L-Fucitol	0.810
Ribitol	0.917
L-Arabitol	1.00
Xylitol	1.20
D-Mannitol	2.38
D-Sorbitol	2.68
Dulcitol	2.68

[a] From Gunner *et al.* (1961).

graphed on the SE-30 column at 152°C, and on the QF-1 column at 170°C. α-Cellobiose and sucrose octaacetates can be eluted from the silicone polymer at 220°C and from the QF-1 column at 229°C. Thus the procedure is applicable to a variety of acetylated sugar alcohols, methyl glycosides, reducing sugars, and disaccharides, separations being obtainable according to both boiling point and molecular configuration.

a. Conditions for Chromatography of Methylated Monoses

*1. On Methylated Hydroxyethyl Cellulose (Kircher, 1960)

Chromatograph	Wilkins Aerograph A-100-C.
Column dimensions	6-foot × ¼-inch o.d. coiled copper tubing.
Solid support	Chromosorb (35/80 mesh).

Stationary phase	Methylated hydroxyethyl cellulose (30:70).
Temperatures	(I) 190°C. (II) 220°C.
Carrier gas	(I) Helium at 34 ml/min and 10 psig inlet pressure.
	(II) Helium at 75 ml/min and 20 psig inlet pressure.
Detector	Katharometer.
Recorder	¼ inch/min.
Sample size	0.5 to 20 µl.
Analysis time	About 1 hour.

*2. *On Polar and Nonpolar Columns* (Bishop and Cooper, 1960a)

Chromatograph	Pye Argon.
Column dimensions	4-foot × 0.5-cm i.d. straight glass tube.
Solid support	Celite 545 (80/100 U. S. mesh) treated with methanolic KOH.
Stationary phase	(I) Apiezon M (20:80). (II) Poly-(1,4-butanediol succinate) (20:80).
Temperatures	150°C for sugar derivatives. 200°C for sugar alcohol derivatives.
Carrier gas	Argon at 50 to 100 ml/min.
Detector	Argon ionization with radium D source.
Recorder	Leeds-Northrup, 1 mv; 3 seconds; ½ inch/min.
Sample size	2 to 4 µg.
Analysis time	25 to 100 minutes.

b. Conditions for Chromatography of O-Acetyl Glycitols

*1. *On a Mixed Column Packing* (Gunner et al., 1961)

Chromatograph	Pye Argon.
Column dimensions	120 × 0.5-cm i.d.
Solid support	Chromosorb W (60/80 U. S. mesh) and Chromosorb W (60/80 U. S. mesh) coated with silver (20 to 30%).
Stationary phase	Mixture of 3 parts Apiezon M on silvered Chromosorb (20:80), 1 part of Dow Corning silicone grease on silvered Chromosorb (15:85), and 1 part of poly(1,4-butanediol succinate) (20:80) on Chromosorb.
Temperature	190°C.
Carrier gas	Argon at 60 or 130 ml/min.
Detector	Argon ionization with 80-µc radium D source.
Recorder	10 mv; ½ inch/min.
Sample size	2 to 4 µg.
Analysis time	Up to 1 hour.

V. SUMMARY

Hexoses and pentoses can be chromatographed as their fully methylated glycosides on Apiezon M, Craig polyester, or modified cellulose columns at 150°C. In a number of instances, it is possible to resolve α- and β-anomers of the same sugar, and to separate different sugars having the same carbon number. However, some anomeric pairs, such as those of fully methylated

D-galactoside, and some optical isomers, such as fully methylated β-D- and β-L-arabinopyranosides, are not separated by the conditions employed. Furanosides are eluted more rapidly than pyranosides, but in one case the pyranoside and furanoside peaks from different sugars were coincident.

Polysaccharides can be characterized by methylating them and chromatographing the products obtained on hydrolysis, followed by glycosidation. Tetra-O-methyl, tri-O-methyl, and di-O-methyl glycosides are obtained from hexose units contained in long chains, which yield information on the identities of nonreducing terminal groups, internal glycoside linkages, and branch points, respectively.

D. Glycosides and Aglycones

I. Isothiocyanates

Isothiocyanates, or mustard oils, occur in plants either free or combined with sugars as glycosides. The glycosides can be hydrolyzed by means of enzymes, and the liberated mustard oils isolated from other plant materials by solvent extraction or steam distillation. Among the mustard oils found in nature are allyl isothiocyanate, butene (3)-yl isothiocyanate, phenyl isothiocyanate, and benzyl isothiocyanate. Kjaer and Gmelin (1956) have isolated L(−)-5-methylsulfinyl-pentyl isothiocyanate from seed of *Alyssuum argenteum* where it exists as the aglycone of glucoalyssin.

Kjaer and Jart (1957) investigated gas chromatography as a means of separating volatile isothiocyanates by using a synthetic mixture of five alkyl thiocyanates having 1 to 5 carbon atoms. On a stationary phase of silicone grease and at a temperature of 68.5°C, methyl, ethyl, isopropyl, n-butyl, and isopentyl isothiocyanates were eluted from the column in that order, but the ethyl and isopropyl compounds were not resolved. Some separation of these latter compounds was obtained at 50°C, and at 30.5°C two distant peaks were obtained. The authors state that 3-butenyl and allyl isothiocyanates, as well as the latter and isopropyl isothiocyanate, can be separated at a temperature of 40° to 50°C.

Aliphatic and aromatic isothiocyanates as well as derivatives containing sulfone groups and terminal methylthio groups have been chromatographed on silicone grease, silicone elastomer, squalane, dinonyl phthalate, and tritolyl phosphate (Jart, 1961).

a. Experimental Methods

*1. *Isolation from Seed* (Kjaer *et al.*, 1953, 1955, 1956; Kjaer and Gmelin, 1956). Seeds (200 gm) are crushed and defatted with a mixture of ligroin and ethanol (Kjaer *et al.*, 1953). The ground seed powder is exhaustively extracted with hot 70% methanol, and the alcohol is removed by evaporation under vacuum until the volume is reduced to 500 ml. Impurities are removed by adding an excess of 10% lead acetate solution. After filtration and removal of excess lead ions by precipitation as PbS, the filtered solution is again concentrated to about 500 ml. Solid phosphates are added to buffer the solution at pH 6.6, together with a myrosinase preparation (5 ml), and the mixture is held at room temperature for 18 hours to permit hydrolysis of the glucoside. The aglycone is removed from the water layer by extraction with 3 × 100-ml portions of chloroform, and the solvent is washed twice with sodium carbonate solution and finally with water. After drying, the solvent is removed under vacuum, leaving the aglycone as a colorless vesicant oil.

*2. *Conditions for Chromatography* (Kjaer and Jart, 1957)

Chromatograph	Laboratory-built.
Column dimensions	2 meters × 0.8 cm.
Solid support	Dixon helices (1/16 × 1/16 inch).
Stationary phase	Acetate-washed Dow Corning silicone grease (12:88).
Temperatures	68.5°C, 50°C, and 30.5°C.
Carrier gas	Nitrogen at 10 ml/min.
Detector	Hot-wire T/C cell.
Sample size	4 to 7 mg of mixed isothiocyanates.
Analysis time	About 60 minutes at 68.5°C.

II. Nitriles

Nitriles are found in nature as the aglycones of glycosides. None of them have been analyzed by gas chromatography, but Lysyj (1960) describes a method for the analysis of mixtures of methacrylonitrile, acrylonitrile, acetonitrile, and propionitrile that may be of related interest.

Separation of all four components of the mixture cannot be obtained on one column, but with two columns with different packings a complete analysis can be made. Methacrylonitrile and acrylonitrile are eluted together from Carbowax 400, but acetonitrile and propionitrile are well resolved from this peak and from one another (Table V). On the other hand, acrylonitrile and acetonitrile run together on Craig polyester succinate, but methacrylonitrile and propionitrile are resolved. Acrylonitrile appears as part of a composite peak on both columns, but by subtracting the amount of methacrylonitrile (or acetonitrile) that runs with it as determined on the alternate column, a satisfactory analysis can be made. Results calculated from peak areas agree to within a few per cent.

TABLE V

SEPARATION OF NITRILES ON TWO POLAR LIQUIDS AT FLOW RATE
OF 100 ML OF HELIUM PER MINUTE[a]

| Compound | Retention time (min) | |
	On Carbowax 400 at 70°C	On Craig polyester at 100°C
Methacrylonitrile	8.1[b]	15.7
Acrylonitrile	8.2[b]	10.8[b]
Acetonitrile	10.1	11.5[b]
Propionitrile	12.0	18.2

[a] From Lysyj (1960).
[b] Peaks not resolved.

a. Experimental Methods (Lysyj, 1960)

*1. Chromatography on Carbowax

Chromatograph	Fisher Gulf Partitioner equipped with constant sample injection valve.
Column dimensions	366 × 0.63-cm. o.d. coiled aluminum tubing.
Solid support	Chromosorb W (30/60 U. S. mesh).
Stationary phase	20/80 Carbowax 400, a polyethylene glycol supplied by Union Carbide Chemicals Co.
Temperature	70°C.
Carrier gas	Helium at 100 ml/min. Inlet pressure: 1250 mm Hg. Outlet pressure: atmospheric.
Detector	Two-thermistor T/C cell.
Recorder	0 to 5 mv; 1 second; ½ inch/min.
Sample size	10 μl.
Analysis time	About 12 minutes to propionitrile.

*2. Chromatography on Poly(1,4-butanediol Succinate)

Chromatograph	Cenco gas chromatograph, equipped with gas sampling valve.
Column dimensions	732 × 0.63-cm o.d. coiled aluminum tubing.
Solid support	Chromosorb (30/60 U. S. mesh).
Stationary phase	Poly(1,4-butanediol succinate) (15:85), supplied by Wilkins Instrument and Research Corp.
Temperature	100°C.
Carrier gas	Helium at 100 ml/min. Inlet pressure: 1250 mm Hg. Outlet pressure: atmospheric.
Detector	Two hot-wire T/C cells.
Recorder	0 to 5 mv; 1 second; ½ inch/min.
Sample size	10 μl.
Analysis time	20 minutes to propionitrile.

III. Summary

Glycosides could be characterized by GLC by hydrolysis and separation of the liberated aglycones. Presumably the sugar moiety could also be identified by permethylation and chromatography as described in Section C. Conditions are given for the chromatographic separation of isothiocyanates and nitriles resembling those found as components of glycosides.

References

Abdel-Akher, M., J. K. Hamilton and F. Smith. 1951. The reduction of sugars with sodium borohydride. *J. Am. Chem. Soc.* **73:** 4691–4692.

Ackman, R. G., M. A. Banneman, and F. A. VandenHeuvel. 1960. Decomposition of short-chain dicarboxylic acid esters during separation on polyester gas chromatography media. *Anal. Chem.* **32:** 1209.

Baraud, J. 1960. Dosage de certains amino-acides par chromatographie en phase vapeur. *Bull. soc. chim. France* p. 785.

Bartsch, R. C., F. D. Miller, and F. M. Trent. 1960. Quantitative analysis of some C_{10} dibasic acids associated with monobasic acids by high temperature gas chromatography. *Anal. Chem.* **32:** 1101–1103.

Bath, I. H. 1960. Analysis of the structural carbohydrates of herbage. *J. Sci. Food Agri.* **11:** 560–566.

Bayer, E. 1958. Separation of derivatives of amino acids using gas-liquid chromatography. *In* "Gas Chromatography" (D. H. Desty, ed.), pp. 833–839. New York, Academic Press.

Biemann, K. and W. Vetter. 1960. Separation of peptide derivatives by gas chromatography combined with the mass spectrometric determination of amino acid sequence. *Biochem. Biophys. Research Communs.* **3:** 578–584.

Bier, M. and P. Teitelbaum. 1959. Gas chromatography in amino acid analysis. *Ann. N. Y. Acad. Sci.* **72:** 641–648.

Bishop, C. T. 1960. Personal communication.

Bishop, C. T. and F. P. Cooper. 1960a. Separation of carbohydrate derivatives by gas-liquid chromatography. *Can. J. Chem.* **38:** 388–395.

Bishop, C. T. and F. P. Cooper. 1960b. Constitution of a glucomannan from jack pine (*Pinus banksiana*, Lamb). *Can. J. Chem.* **38:** 793–804.

Bishop, C. T., F. Blank, and P. E. Gardner. 1960. The cell wall polysaccharides of *Candida albicans:* glucan, mannan and chitin. *Can. J. Chem.* **38:** 869–881.

Block, R. J., E. L. Durrum, and G. Zweig. 1958. "A Manual of Paper Chromatography and Paper Electrophoresis," 2nd ed., 710 pp. New York, Academic Press.

Bradford, J. A., W. R. Harlan, and H. R. Hanmer. 1936. Nature of cigaret smoke. Technic of experimental smoking. *Ind. Eng. Chem.* **28:** 836–839.

Bryant, F. and B. T. Overell. 1953. Quantitative chromatographic analysis of organic acids in plant tissue extracts. *Biochim. Biophys. Acta* **10:** 471–476.

Falconer, E. L. and G. A. Adams. 1956. The aldobiouronic acids of hemicellulose B of oat hulls. *Can. J. Chem.* **34:** 338–344.

Fischer, E. 1901. Ueber die Ester der Aminosäuren. *Ber. deut. chem. Ges.* **34:** 433–454.

Gunner, S. W., J. K. N. Jones, and M. B. Perry. 1961. The analysis of sugar mixture by gas-liquid partition chromatography. In press.

Helferich, B. and W. Schäfer. 1926. α-Methyl-*d*-glucoside. *Org. Syntheses* 6: 64–65.

House, H. O., E. J. Grubbs, and W. F. Gannon. 1960. The reaction of ketones with diazomethane. *J. Am. Chem. Soc.* 82: 4099–4106.

Hunter, I. R., K. P. Dimick, and J. W. Corse. 1956. Determination of amino-acids by ninhydrin oxidation and gas chromatography. Separation of leucine and iso-leucine. *Chem. & Ind. (London)*, 294–295.

James, A. T. and A. J. P. Martin. 1952. Gas-liquid chromatography: the separation and micro-estimation of volatile fatty acids from formic acid to dodecanoic acid. *Biochem. J.* 50: 679–690.

Jart, A. 1961. Gas-liquid chromatographic retention data for some isothiocyanates. *Acta Chem. Scand.* 15: in press.

Johnson, D. E., S. J. Scott, and A. Meister. 1961. Gas-liquid chromatography of amino acid derivatives. *Anal. Chem.* 33: 669–673.

Jones, J. K. N. and K. C. B. Wilkie. 1959. Structural studies on clinical dextrans. Part 1. Methylation and periodate oxidation studies. *Can. J. Biochem. Physiol.* 37: 377–390.

Kircher, H. W. 1960. Gas-liquid partition chromatography of methylated sugars. *Anal. Chem.* 32: 1103–1106.

Kjaer, A. and R. Gmelin. 1956. *iso*Thiocyanates XIX. L(−)-5-Methylsulphinylpentyl *iso*thiocyanate, the aglucone of a new naturally occurring glucoside (glucoalyssin). *Acta Chem. Scand.* 10: 1100–1110.

Kjaer, A. and A. Jart. 1957. *iso*Thiocyanates. Part 29. Separation of volatile *iso*thiocyanates by gas chromatography. *Acta. Chem. Scand.* 11: 1423.

Kjaer, A., J. Conti, and I. Larsen. 1953. *iso*Thiocyanates. IV. A systematic investigation of the occurrence and chemical nature of volatile isothiocyanates in seeds of various plants. *Acta Chem. Scand.* 7: 1276–1283.

Kjaer, A. I. Larsen, and F. Gmelin. 1955. *iso*Thiocyanates. XIV. 5-Methylthiopentyl isothiocyanate, a new mustard oil present in nature as a glucoside (glucoberteroin). *Acta Chem. Scand.* 9: 1311–1316.

Kjaer, A., R. Gmelin, and R. B. Jensen. 1956. *iso*Thiocyanates. XXI. (—)-10-Methylsulphinyldecyl *iso*thiocyanate, a new mustard oil present as a glucoside (glucocamelinin) in Camelina species. *Acta Chem. Scand.* 10: 1614–1619.

Kuhn, R., H. Trischmann, and I. Löw. 1955. Zur Permethylierung von Zuckern und Glykosiden. *Angew. Chem.* 67: 32.

Langheld, K. 1909. Über das Verhalten von α-Aminosäuren gegen Natriumhypochlorit. *Ber. deut. chem. Ges.* 42: 2360–2374.

Lysyj, I. 1960. Gas chromatographic analysis of nitriles. *Anal. Chem.* 32: 771.

Melamed, M. and M. Renard. 1960. Analyse de mélanges d'acides aminés par chromatographie gazeuse. *J. Chromatog.* 4: 339–346.

Metcalfe, L. D. and A. A. Schmitz. (1961). The rapid preparation of fatty-acid esters for gas chromatographic analysis. *Anal. Chem.* 33: 363–364.

Mirocha, C. J. and J. E. DeVay. (1961). A rapid gas chromatographic method for determining fumaric acid in fungus cultures and diseased plant tissues. *Phytopath* 51: 274–276.

Nowakowska, J., E. H. Melvin, and R. Wiebe. 1957. Separation of the oxidation products of fatty acids by means of gas-liquid partition chromatography. *J. Am. Oil Chem. Soc.* 34: 411–414.

Prill, E. A., C. A. Porter, R. C. Staples, and H. P. Burchfield. 1960. Methods for the analysis of vanilla extracts for resins, carbonyl compounds, amino acids, and other organic acids. *J. Assoc. Offic. Agric. Chemists* 43: 96–107.

Quin, L. D. 1961. Personal communication.

Quin, L. D. and M. E. Hobbs. 1958. Analysis of the nonvolatile acids in cigarette smoke by gas chromatography of their methyl esters. *Anal. Chem.* **30**: 1400–1406.

Resnick, F. E., L. A. Lee, and W. A. Powell. 1955. Chromatography of organic acids in cured tobacco. *Anal. Chem.* **27**: 928–931.

Rühlmann, K. and W. Giesecke. 1961. Gaschromatographie silylierter Aminosäuren. *Angew. Chem.* **73**: 113.

Saroff, H. A. and A. Karmen. 1960. Gas chromatography of N-trifluoroacetylmethyl esters of the amino acids. *Anal. Biochem.* **1**: 4–5.

Tepe, J. B. and H. J. Wesselman. 1958. Quantitative determination of a series of malonic esters by gas chromatography. *J. Am. Pharm. Assoc., Sci. Ed.* **47**: 457–458.

Thompson, J. F., C. J. Morris and R. K. Gering. 1959. Purification of plant amino acids for paper chromatography. *Anal. Chem.* **31**: 1028–1031.

VandenHeuvel, W. J. A. and E. C. Horning. 1961. Gas chromatographic separations of sugars and related compounds as acetyl derivatives. *Biochem. Biophys. Research Communs.* **4**: 399–403.

Virtanen, A. I. and N. Rautanen. 1946. A micromethod for the estimation of amino acids based on the formation of volatile aldehydes by ninhydrin oxidation. Suomen Kemistilehti **19B**: 56–59; *Chem. Abstr.* **41**: 5566f, 1947.

Wagner, J. 1960. Gas chromatographic separation and determination of amino acids. Ges. deut. Chem., Hauptversammlung, Stuttgart, Germany, April 25–30: Meeting Abstracts, p. 41.

West, E. S. and R. F. Holden. 1940. 2,3,4,6-Tetramethyl-d-glucose. *Org. Syntheses* **20**: 97–100.

Weygand, F., B. Kolb, A. Prox, M. A. Tilak, and I. Tomida. 1960. N-Trifluoroacetyl-aminosäuren, XIX. Gaschromatographische Trennung von N-TFA-Dipeptidmethyl-estern. *Z. Physiol. Chem., Hoppe-Seyler's* **322**: 38–51.

Williams, K. T., A. Bevenue, and B. Washauer. 1950. A study of the use of ion-exchange resins for the removal of non-sugar reducing substances in the analysis of fresh and dehydrated vegetables for reducing sugars. *J. Assoc. Offic. Agric. Chemists* **33**: 986–994.

Youngs, C. G. 1959. Analysis of mixtures of amino acids by gas phase chromatography. *Anal. Chem.* **31**: 1019–1021.

Zlatkis, A. and J. A. Ridgway. 1958. A methane-conversion detector for gas chromatography. *Nature* **182**: 130–131.

Zlatkis, A., J. F. Oro, and A. P. Kimball. 1960. Direct amino acid analysis by gas chromatography. *Anal. Chem.* **32**: 162–164.

Chapter 9

Review of Miscellaneous Applications
Related to Biochemistry

General Introduction

A number of areas in which gas chromatography has been used are related only indirectly to biochemistry. Consequently they will not be covered in detail. On the other hand, they cannot be ignored altogether since many biochemists are working in them or from time to time may find references to the information useful. These areas include methods for the analysis of organic compounds, pesticides, and pharmaceuticals. Although this chapter is written as a review, we lay no claim to having covered the literature completely.

A. Organic Analysis and Structure Determination

I. INTRODUCTION

Gas chromatography is a useful tool for the separation of complex mixtures and the characterization of organic compounds by retention volume. It also has great promise as a means of analyzing organic compounds and determining their structures. Already, it has been applied to elemental analysis, functional group analysis, the location of unsaturation and chain branching, and the identification of hydrocarbon skeletons contained in organic compounds. In time, gas chromatography may well become one of the principal methods in organic analysis and structure determination.

II. ELEMENTAL ANALYSIS

Carbon can be determined with an absolute precision of 0.5% and hydrogen with a precision of 0.1% by gas chromatography (Duswalt and Brandt, 1960). The sample (about 1.5 mg) is burned in a dry carbon dioxide-free oxygen stream to carbon dioxide and water. The vapors are then passed through a tube which contains calcium carbide to convert the water to acetylene. Next, the gases are condensed in a trap cooled with liquid nitrogen. When combustion is complete, the coolant is removed, and the condensed gases are vaporized onto a silica gel column and chromatographed. The area under the carbon dioxide peak is proportional to the carbon content of the sample, and the area under the acetylene peak is proportional to the hydrogen content. The time required for analysis is 20 minutes for a single determination, and about 10 minutes each for a continuous series of analyses. Oxygen and nitrogen do not interfere. However, when halogen- and sulfur-containing compounds are analyzed, a section of silver metal is placed in the combustion tube to remove the products that are formed. In a similar method described by Sundberg and Maresh (1960) the sample is combusted in a tube containing copper and copper oxide at 750°C in a helium atmosphere. This method may offer some advantages over combustion in oxygen because it should be possible to analyze for nitrogen in the same sample without requiring the separation of oxygen from nitrogen on molecular sieve.

A procedure has been developed for the determination of carbon and hydrogen in which the products of combustion are chromatographed directly without prior conversion of the water to acetylene (Vogel and Quattrone, 1960). The sample (8 to 11 mg) is burned by an electrically heated platinum wire in an oxygen atmosphere. The products of combustion are passed through a tube containing granular zinc to remove any oxides of sulfur and nitrogen that may be present. The water and carbon dioxide are separated on a 2-meter column packed with dodecyl phthalate on Celite at a temperature of 104°C. Oxygen is the carrier gas. The analysis time is 17 minutes. Accuracy is said to be within 0.5% for carbon and within 0.8% for hydrogen.

Nitrogen can be determined by gas chromatography by combusting the sample in a $8 \times \frac{1}{4}$-inch tube packed with copper oxide placed before the analytical column (Reitsema and Allphin, 1961). Use of powdered copper oxide mixed with an inert packing works only moderately well because of high resistance to gas flow and the tendency of the powder to settle and pack. Better results are obtained if the tube is packed with thin strands of fine copper wire. The wire is then etched with aqueous ferric nitrate and ignited to CuO in a current of air. At an operating temperature of 700°C, the products of combustion are water, carbon dioxide, and nitrogen dioxide. The water vapor is removed on magnesium perchlorate, and the carbon dioxide and nitrogen dioxide are separated from one another on a 2-meter column packed with silica gel. The area under the CO_2 peak is proportional to the carbon content of the sample, and the area under the NO_2 peak is proportional to the nitrogen content. Thus the ratio of carbon to nitrogen can be computed without weighing the sample. It is possible to determine the nitrogen contents of the components of mixtures by modifications of this method. The mixture is chromatographed on a suitable GLC column to resolve the components. The eluates from this column are passed through the combustion and drying tubes to convert them to CO_2 and NO_2. These gases then are resolved on a silica gel column to determine the amount of each produced by individual components of the mixture. In complex mixtures, the carbon dioxide peak from one compound may overlap the nitrogen dioxide peak from another compound. To avoid this, carbon dioxide can be used as the carrier gas, so that only peaks arising from nitrogen are detected by the thermal conductivity cell. If the analysis is carried out in this manner, it is necessary to know the exact sample weight, and carbon content is not determined.

Ultimately it should be possible to analyze for other elements by already established techniques. The coulometric detection method for chlorine, for example, requires prior combustion of the sample to HCl and other products before measurement (Coulson *et al.*, 1960b). Therefore, if the sample weight is known, it should be possible to compute its chlorine content from the detector response. It also is possible to detect sulfur by a modification of this method.

III. FUNCTIONAL GROUP ANALYSIS

Alkoxy groups can be determined by gas chromatography by a modification of the Zeisel procedure (Vertalier and Martin, 1958; Kratzl and Gruber, 1958). The sample is caused to react with concentrated hydriodic acid, so that alkyl iodides are liberated in accordance with the equation

$$\phi\text{—OR} + \text{HI} \rightarrow \phi\text{—OH} + \text{RI}$$

The alkyl iodides are then introduced into a chromatograph and partitioned in columns containing dioctyl phthalate or polyethylene glycol. The method is rapid and accurate and can be used with samples as small as 0.1 mg. Moreover, methoxy and ethoxy groups can be determined in the same operation. The method has been applied to the analysis of pharmaceuticals and derivatives of lignin.

Combined formyl and acetyl groups also can be determined by gas chromatography (Spingler and Markert, 1959). The sample is interesterified with methanol–HCl or with methanol–*p*-toluenesulfonic acid. The reaction can be carried out at atmospheric pressure or in a sealed tube. Methyl formate and methyl acetate are liberated. These compounds are then separated from each other, and from unreacted methanol on a polyethylene glycol (Carbowax 1500) column at a temperature of 65°C. Thus it is possible to identify and determine quantitatively formyl and acetyl groups in the same sample simultaneously. The method has been applied to the analysis of pharmaceuticals and natural products.

IV. POSITION OF UNSATURATION

The position of a double bond in a hydrocarbon chain can be located by cleaving the chain through oxidation or ozonolysis and chromatographing the reaction products. The chain splits at the double bond, so the position of the latter can be deduced once the identities of the fragments are known.

Oleic acid, for example, yields a 1:1 mixture of pelargonic and azelaic acids, although other materials may be formed through side reactions (Nowakowska et al., 1957). Reagents for oxidation include permanganate in acetic acid (James and Webb, 1957) and a permanganate–periodate mixture (Lemieux and von Rudloff, 1955). James and Webb report that the products of this type of oxidation include numerous lower homologues of the acids resulting from direct cleavage at the double bond. However, ozonolysis followed by oxidation with silver oxide apparently gives clean-cut oxidation to the primary products, contaminated with negligible amounts of lower homologues (Cason and Tavs, 1959). The methyl ester of the fatty acid is dissolved in dry chloroform, and ozone in oxygen is passed through the solution for a few minutes at a temperature of $-60°C$. The primary ozonolysis product is then oxidized with silver oxide in the presence of water, and the product is methylated. The esters are chromatographed on a column packed with silicone grease on Celite at a temperature of 270°C, and a flow rate of 145 ml of helium per minute. It is very difficult if not impossible to oxidize completely the aldehydes obtained on ozonolysis to the acids with this procedure. Therefore, chromatograms of the esterified mixture exhibit two peaks for each cleavage product: one for the ester, and the other for the aldehyde. Apparently the simplest method of handling this problem is to decompose the ozonides with water without oxidation, and chromatograph the aldehydes. These are obtained in good yield accompanied by only traces of acids if the pH of the solution is not too high. Procedures for chromatographing fatty aldehydes as their dimethyl acetals are given in Chapter 7.

The glyceride structures of fats can be determined in part by oxidation at double bonds followed by liquid–liquid and gas–liquid chromatography (Youngs, 1961). The fats are oxidized with permanganate–periodate reagent, and the products are separated into fractions containing no free carboxyl groups, one free carboxyl group, and two or three free carboxyl groups by chromatography on 90% ethanol on silicic acid, the fractions being eluted with Skellysolve B saturated with 90% ethanol followed by diethyl ether. The identities of the mono- and dicarboxylic acids in the various fractions were determined by interesterification of the oxidized glycerides with methanol–HCl, followed by GLC of the methyl esters on a 8-foot × $\frac{3}{16}$-inch column packed with poly(1,4-butanediol succinate) on acid-washed 60/80 mesh C-22 firebrick (10:60). The column temperature was 205°C, and the helium flow rate was 40 ml/min measured at the outlet.

V. CHAIN BRANCHING

Fatty acids and other lipids sometimes contain branched chains as indicated in the introductory section of Chapter 7. The point of branching can be located by GLC preceded by oxidation of the compound by either of two procedures. In the first of these, the fatty acid is oxidized with potassium permanganate (Murray, 1959). The molecule is oxidized from the carboxyl end, yielding a homologous series of branched-chain acids having odd and even carbon numbers. This series continues until the point of branching is reached. When this occurs, the fatty acid with carbon number equal to the fragment at the branch point is not found, an alkyl (usually methyl) ketone being formed in its place. After the branch point is passed, only straight-chain alkanoic acids are produced by further oxidation. Thus the position of the branch point is indicated by the carbon number of the fatty acid that is missing between the branched-chain and straight-chain homologous series, and by the structure of the ketone which appears in its place. These compounds are separated by GLC.

The fatty acid is oxidized by refluxing it with potassium permanganate in acetone overnight. The manganese dioxide is filtered off, and the filtrate is passed through an alumina or silica gel column to purify the ketone fraction. The fatty acids are found in the insoluble fraction as potassium salts. These are extracted, converted to free acids, and methylated prior to chromatography.

The fatty acid esters derived from tuberculostearic acid were chromatographed on a column packed with Silicone Elastomer 301 on Celite 545 (25:75) with the temperature programmed from 60° to 250°C. The ketone fraction derived from this acid was chromatographed on this packing, on benzyldiphenyl and sodium dodecylbenzenesulfonate. Only one peak appeared on all three packings. The compound giving rise to it was shown to be the expected oxidation product, 2-decanone.

An alternative method is available in which the compound is cleaved directly at the branch point without stepwise degradation of the chain from the oxidized end (Cason *et al.*, 1959). Thus 6-methylocatadecanoic acid (I) is cleaved to a C_{14} ketone (II) and a C_5 dibasic acid (III) when treated with chromic acid in glacial acetic acid

$$CH_3—(CH_2)_{11}—\underset{\underset{\text{(I)}}{\overset{|}{CH_3}}}{CH}—(CH_2)_4—COOH$$

$$CH_3—(CH_2)_{11}—\underset{\underset{\text{(II)}}{\overset{|}{CH_3}}}{C}{=}O \qquad\qquad HOOC—(CH_2)_3—COOH$$

$$\text{(III)}$$

Evidently, the reagent attacks the electron-rich tertiary carbon atom, resulting in the formation of a carbonium ion which then may lose a proton to form a mixture of alkenes. Subsequent oxidation of the alkenes could lead to the observed reaction products. The expected cleavage products have been obtained also from 9-methyloctadecanoic acid and 10-methyloctadecanoic acid. However, fatty acids with methyl groups substituted at the α- or γ-positions are not cleaved by this reagent, in the former case owing to the electron-withdrawing power of the carboxyl group, and in the latter perhaps because of *quasi* ring formation resulting from hydrogen bonding of the γ-hydrogen with the carbonyl oxygen.

This procedure may have an important advantage over the permanganate oxidation method in some applications, since the terminal carbon atom of the chain need not be in an oxidized state, so the reaction is applicable even to hydrocarbons. Thus 9,14-dimethyldocosane yielded three of the four expected products resulting from a single cleavage of the chain at the tertiary position. These were: octanoic acid, decanone, and 5-methyl tridecanoic acid. 7-Methyl-2-pentadecanone was not formed. Succinic acid and possibly δ-ketocaproic acid were produced in small amounts by secondary oxidations. The structure could be deduced by chromatographing the oxidation products of a 22-mg sample.

VI. METHODS UTILIZING GLYCOL SPLITTING

Alphatic compounds containing vicinal hydroxyl groups can be cleaved by oxidation with periodate (Sweeley, 1959) or lead tetraacetate, and the aldehydes that are formed can be separated and identified by GLC.

$$R_1—CH—CH—R^2 \rightarrow R_1CHO + R_2CHO$$
$$\begin{matrix} | & | \\ O & O \\ H & H \end{matrix}$$

Modifications of this method have been used also in studies of the structure of polysaccharides by means of the sequence of reactions given here (IV) (Bishop and Cooper, 1960).

The polysaccharide first is oxidized to a polyaldehyde with periodate, and the polyaldehyde is reduced to a polyol with potassium borohydride. The polyol is then subjected to acetolysis, and the alcohol acetates which are formed are separated by GLC. Glucose units connected by $1 \rightarrow 4$ links produce erythritol tetraacetate, and nonreducing terminal units give rise to glyceryl triacetate. Hence the ratio of these compounds as determined by GLC is a measure of the degree of polymerization of a linear polysaccharide.

VII. IDENTIFICATION OF HYDROCARBON SKELETONS

The identification of the hydrocarbon skeleton is an important step in establishing the structure of an unknown compound. Very often, many isomers exist of compounds containing functional groups, so it may be difficult to separate them all or identify them directly. However, if they are converted to hydrocarbons, the number of structural possibilities is reduced greatly, and frequently it is possible to identify the hydrocarbon by compar-

Glycerol triacetate + erythritol pentaacetate

(IV)

ing its chromatographic characteristics and its infrared and mass spectra with those of known compounds. Standard materials for this purpose are available from the Chemical and Petroleum Research Laboratory.

Compounds containing oxygen, sulfur, and nitrogen can be converted to hydrocarbons by catalytic reduction (Thompson *et al.*, 1960a, 1960b). The sample is vaporized and swept by a stream of hydrogen into a heated tube containing pellets composed of 0.5% palladium on alumina. The hydrocarbons which emerge from the tube are condensed in a cold trap and subsequently analyzed by GLC on a column packed with Dow Corning silicone on firebrick. Very often, a single hydrocarbon corresponding in structure to the original compound is formed. Thus 3-pentanol yields pentane, cyclohexanethiol yields cyclohexane, and heptaldehyde yields *n*-hexane. However, in some cases, several compounds are produced, and this must be taken into account in deducing the carbon skeleton of the original material. Thus aniline yields both benzene and cyclohexane, and benzoic acid yields cyclohexane and methylcyclohexane.

In most cases, oxygen or sulfur is removed almost quantitatively, and hydrogen is substituted at the ruptured bond. However, there is likely to be some cleavage of the carbon-to-carbon bond if a —CH_2OH group is attached to a secondary (or tertiary) carbon atom. Thus 2-ethyl-1-butanol yields both *n*-pentane and 3-methylpentane.

The hydrocarbon skeletons of organic phosphates and pyrophosphates often can be identified by pyrolyzing the compound at a temperature of 600°C or lower in a pre-chamber attached to the injection port of a gas chromatograph (Legate and Burnham, 1960). Usually the carbon-to-oxygen bond ruptures, and a proton is abstracted from the position β to it, resulting in the formation of an olefin. The hydrocarbons are then chromatographed, and fractions are collected and analyzed by mass or infrared spectrophotometry.

Reduction to saturated hydrocarbons is often a valuable aid in the identification of alkenes, alkadienes, and alkynes (Smith and Ohlson, 1960). Alkenes boiling at temperatures below 100°C usually can be identified by retention volumes and infrared spectra alone, since their physiochemical properties are well known. However, not so much information is available concerning alkadienes, alkynes, and higher-boiling alkenes. Consequently, hydrogenation to alkanes, or partial reduction to form derivatives with a lower degree of unsaturation is frequently a good means of establishing the structure of the hydrocarbon skeleton. Complete hydrogenation is carried out by using a platinum dioxide catalyst mixed with iron filings. The catalyst is placed in a U tube cooled with acetone–dry ice, and the component of interest is collected as it emerges from the chromatographic column. The tube is disconnected from the chromatograph, filled with hydrogen to a pressure of 3 kg/cm², and heated to 80° to 90°C for 10 minutes. Then the reduced product is rechromatographed, and the tentative identity of the alkane is deduced from its retention volume. Alkadienes are reduced partially by the same procedure except that the collection tube is permitted to remain in the coolant during the time it is being filled with hydrogen. Afterwards it is placed in a water bath heated to 80° to 90°C for 5 to 10 seconds. Alkynes are reduced stepwise in a similar fashion, except that hydrogenation is carried out for 1 minute at room temperature. Alternatively, alkynes are reduced by utilizing metallic sodium covered with a layer of sodium amide. This combination acts both as a catalyst and as a source of hydrogen.

All the unsaturated compounds evaluated yielded the expected alkanes on hydrogenation. However, it proved to be a difficult task to stop reduction of alkadienes at the alkene stage. However, under the conditions described, it was possible to convert enough of the diene to the mono-unsaturated compound for identification. In most cases the expected hydrogenation products were formed. However, during the hydrogenation of *trans*-2-*trans*-4-hexadiene isomerization about the remaining double bond took place. Partial hydrogenation of alkynes with a platinum dioxide catalyst produced alkanes, *cis*-alkenes, and smaller amounts of *trans*-alkenes. Reduction with sodium–sodium amide resulted in the formation of alkanes and *trans*-alkenes.

The hydrocarbon skeletons of unsaturated fatty acids can be identified by similar procedures.

VIII. PYROLYSIS

Complex nonvolatile compounds and polymers can be characterized by chromatographing their pyrolysis products. The patterns obtained are moderately complex (Janák, 1960). Chemical interactions between the fragments produced by thermal decomposition are minimized by keeping the sample size small and by sweeping the products out of the reaction area as rapidly as possible. This can be accomplished by decomposing the sample on an electrically heated wire placed directly in the carrier gas stream. In the apparatus used by Janák, heating is controlled with an electric time switch, which makes it possible to heat the wire at temperatures up to 800°C for periods of time ranging from 0.1 to 5 seconds. The sample size is 10 to 50 μg, and the decomposition products are separated in a squalane column with flame ionization for detection.

With this procedure, chromatograms obtained on plant oils and animal fats were reproducible both quantitatively and qualitatively with relatively large variations in wire temperature and heating time. In the case of macromolecules such as rubber, the qualitative reproducibility of the chromatograms was good, but quantitative composition was not so consistent.

IX. SUMMARY

Gas chromatography can be a valuable asset in elemental analysis and in determining the structures of organic compounds. Methoxyl groups, acetyl groups, position of unsaturation and chain branching, and the nature of hydrocarbon skeletons can be determined rapidly and accurately. Some of the procedures are automatic or nearly so. One great advantage is the extremely small sample sizes that can be employed, particularly with ionization detectors. It is possible that the limiting factor will be the accuracy with which the initial sample can be weighed. However, this difficulty might be circumvented by placing a chromatograph detector before the reaction chamber so that the materials entering it, as well as those eluted from the chromatographic column, are measured in this way. Probably many of the classic methods of organic analysis now in common use ultimately will be adapted to gas chromatography.

B. Pesticides

I. GENERAL

Methods for the analysis of pesticides are becoming increasingly important because of the passage of laws regulating the maximum amounts of residues permissible in foods. In fact, this problem has become so serious that the development of a suitable analytical method must be counted as one of the major expenses of introducing a new agricultural chemical. Consequently, a method having general applicability is desirable, not only from the standpoint of routine residue analysis, but also for use when a candidate pesticide is in an early stage of commercial development, and its future is uncertain. Gas chromatography offers the promise of such a method.

Most organic pesticides are sufficiently volatile to be chromatographed in the vapor phase. Fumigants such as methyl bromide, ethylene dibromide, DD mixture (1,3-dichloropropene and 1,2-dichloropropane), and Nemagon (1,2-dibromo-3-chloropropane) can be chromatographed at temperatures ranging from room to 100°C (Burchfield and Storrs, 1960). Chlorinated hydrocarbon insecticides and esters of chlorinated phenoxyalkanoic, benzoic, and terephthalic acids can be separated on polar or nonpolar stationary liquids at 190° to 250°C. Compounds of this class that have been chromatographed successfully include Thiodan (Zweig and Archer, 1960) lindane, DDT, aldrin, dieldrin, endrin, malathion, parathion, Systox (O,O-diethyl O-2-ethylmercaptoethyl phosphonothioate), and esters of 2,4-dichlorophenoxyacetic acid, 2,4,5-trichlorophenoxyacetic acid, ring-substituted phenoxypropionic and phenoxybutyric acids, naphthaleneacetic acid, and indoleacetic acid. DDT shows some decomposition on the column, but this can be minimized if the solid support is deactivated, and if the packing is preconditioned by running preliminary DDT samples through it (Coulson et al., 1959, 1960b). Chlordan exhibits a number of peaks, and toxaphene a continuum, probably because they are not pure compounds (Coulson et al., 1959). Nevertheless, it seems likely that the great majority of pesticides can be chromatographed successfully in the vapor phase in view of recent developments that are taking place in the chromatography of high-boiling compounds at low temperatures, made possible by supersensitive detection systems.

Gas chromatography possesses a number of advantages for residue analysis that cannot be approached by bioassay or colorimetric methods. It is universal in that a variety of compounds can be separated on a GLC column in a single operation, each component of the mixture yielding a peak at a characteristic location that will provide information on the nature of the material, and the amount of it present. Test organisms used in bioassay often will respond to a large class of compounds, but sensitivity varies enormously, and the response to mixtures is additive, not discriminatory. It is rapid in that six to eight compounds, or more, can be separated in 20 minutes to a half-hour, and quantitative measurements made on them. It is sensitive in that mixtures containing twenty or more components can be analyzed from a 1-μg sample if an ionization detector is employed. Finally, and perhaps most important, it is selective in that detectors can be made that will respond only to compounds containing halogen and sulfur, which includes the great majority of agricultural chemicals. Consequently, analyses in the parts-per-million range can be made on most farm products with essentially no clean-up except for fats, oils, and dairy products. With this method it was possible to measure dieldrin at the 0.06-ppm level in potatoes grown in treated soil. The total elapsed time required for analysis, including extraction of the sample, was 1 to 2 hours (Coulson *et al.*, 1960b).

II. Detector Sensitivity and Selectivity

The development of highly sensitive and selective detection systems has played a major role in the rapid evolution of gas chromatography, but nowhere is this so important as in residue analysis. This is because of the extremely minute amounts of materials that must be dealt with, and the fact that most pesticides contain halogen or sulfur. Therefore if a detector is devised that responds only to compounds containing these elements, interference from plant extracts can be minimized both through separation on the column and failure of the detector to "see" them even when they are eluted with pesticides as unresolved peaks. Of course the column must not be overloaded.

The first procedure utilizing such a detector was described by Coulson *et al.* (1960a). The effluent from the gas chromatograph is mixed with oxygen and passed through a 12 $\times$ $\frac{1}{2}$-inch quartz combustion tube heated to 800°C and containing three 1-inch plugs of platinum gauze. During passage through the tube, chlorinated hydrocarbon pesticides will be burned to water, carbon dioxide, and hydrogen chloride, while almost all naturally occurring components of plants will yield only the first two substances. The effluent from the combustion tube is then bubbled through a titration cell, and the chlorine content is measured coulometrically. The method is based on the continuous automatic titration of chloride with silver ions that are generated electrically in the titration cell. The electric current required to maintain constant concentration of silver ion in the cell is recorded on a strip chart recorder as a function of time. As usual, a series of peaks is recorded, the nature of the pesticide being indicated by the position of the peak on the chart, and the amount present by the area under it. If measurement of sulfur-containing compounds is desired also, the carrier gas entering the combustion tube should be mixed with hydrogen rather than with oxygen, so that the organic compounds are decomposed in a reducing atmosphere. Hydrogen sulfide is formed, which also can be measured coulometrically. Alternatively (and from the standpoint of safety more desirable), the sample can be burned in an oxygen atmosphere, and the sulfur dioxide that is formed measured in a redox cell employing a gold electrode.

Compounds containing halogen atoms and polar functional groups can also be detected selectively by electron capture measurements (Lovelock, 1961). A specially designed ionization cell is used (Jarrell-Ash Co.), or, alternatively, the argon detector supplied with the Shandon Gas Chromatograph can be employed. When the detector is operated at a low voltage, compounds containing halogen atoms give negative peaks, and hydrocarbons give very small positive deflections. This makes it easy to distinguish between these classes of compounds (Goodwin et al., 1960). With this procedure, it is possible to detect aldrin at the 0.05-ppm level, and dieldrin at the 0.1-ppm level in hexane extracts of cabbage, potatoes, tomatoes, gooseberries, and tea without prior clean-up. In the presence of carrot extract, the lower limit of detection is 0.3 ppm of aldrin and 0.6 ppm of dieldrin because of higher background. It is probable that a partial clean-up of the sample is required for detection at the 0.1-ppm level. Even so, it is likely that the technique is much simpler and more reliable than colorimetric and bioassay methods in common use.

The electron capture technique is simpler than the coulometric method and can be adapted to most standard gas chromatographs. However, it has not been investigated extensively and may have some drawbacks, particularly in the measurement of unresolved peaks. The presence of a halogen-containing compound in the detector causes a decrease in ionization current, and hydrocarbons when present in large amounts may tend to increase it. Hence some intermediate effect may occur with a mixture. For this reason it is possible that the electron capture method will require more extensive clean-up or better resolution of the sample components on the chromatographic column than coulometry.

For routine measurements at lower sensitivity, less elaborate techniques are satisfactory (Burchfield and Storrs, 1961). The effluent from the chromatograph is burned in a quartz combustion tube, and the resulting gases are bubbled through an aqueous suspension of mercuric chloranilate for a period known to correspond to the retention time of the component of interest. Hydrogen chloride, if present, will liberate free chloranilic acid which is measured colorimetrically, after removal of the insoluble mercury salt by filtration or centrifugation. A minimum of 10 μg of chloride ion is required for detection. This method has several disadvantages. If internal standards are used or more than one pesticide is present, it is necessary to take several samples during a single run. This requires careful timing. To accomplish this it is necessary to redetermine retention volumes every time operating parameters are changed by chromatographing a known mixture in amounts great enough to elicit responses from a conventional thermal detector. Moreover, shoulders on peaks, or peaks arising from the presence of compounds that are not anticipated would escape detection. The greatest drawback is insufficient sensitivity at the submicrogram level.

Other detection systems selective for chlorine-containing compounds are possible, at least theoretically, that might be both simple and sensitive. One of these involves combustion of the column eluates in an oxidizing atmosphere, and in-stream conversion of the hydrogen chloride to a compound that will yield a response to an argon or flame ionization detector. One possibility would be to pass the effluent from the combustion tube through a column containing a finely divided silver alkylacetylide. This should liberate a stoichiometric amount of alkylacetylene, which would be passed through the detector and measured after removal of water vapor and carbon dioxide by suitable absorbants. Alternatively, the hydrogen chloride might be converted to hydrogen by reaction with a metal or calcium hydride, and the hydrogen measured with a thermistor at low temperature with argon or some other gas with low thermal conductivity as a carrier.

Infrared spectrophotometry has been used for the measurement of Thiodan (6,7,8,9,10,10-hexachloro-1,5,5a,6,9,9a-hexahydro-6,9-methano-2,3,4-benzodioxathiepin 3-oxide) residues, and the method may have general applicability if separation from plant components on the chromatographic column is good enough (Zweig et al., 1960). Samples are collected from the exit line of the chromatograph and dissolved in an infrared solvent, and the solution is transferred to a microcell. The concentration of Thiodan is measured by scanning from 8 to 8.5 μ. Recoveries on known samples are reproducible to within $\pm 10\%$ in the 5-ppm range. The minimum detectable amount of Thiodan is about 4 μg. This method is advantageous in that the identity of the pesticide is established unequivocally by its infrared spectrum. However, it is only semispecific in that normal plant products also may absorb radiation in this region, so good separations on the column are required. This method has been successful in determining the amount of Thiodan added to hexane extracts of alfalfa and peaches prepared by the surface-stripping methods. It is probable that more difficulty would be encountered with plant homogenates and dairy and meat products.

Gas chromatography can also be used in combination with ultraviolet spectrophotometry or colorimetry for residue analysis. Thus Zweig *et al.* (1961) measured the amount of naphthaleneacetic acid in potatoes by methylating the extract with diazomethane and chromatographing it on Dow-11 high-vacuum silicone grease at 220°C. Fractions were collected at appropriate times and the amount of methyl ester determined by absorbance measurements in the ultraviolet at 281 or 224 mμ. Trace amounts of 3-amino-2,5-dichlorobenzoic acid can be determined in a similar manner by trapping fractions, diazotizing them, and coupling with naphthylethylenediamine (Zweig and Breidenbach, 1961). The intensity of the red color which is produced is read with a colorimeter. When used in this manner, gas chromatography becomes an extension of the clean-up process, although trapping the fraction during a definite time interval provides added assurance that the compound being measured is the one sought.

III. Extraction and Analysis of Residues

The procedures for the extraction of pesticide residues from plants are about the same as those for colorimetric analysis or bioassay. Generally, clean-up procedures are much simpler, since the chromatographic column itself takes care of much of this.

In the procedure developed by Coulson *et al.*, (1960a), the chopped sample (300 gm), acetonitrile (150 ml), Skellysolve B (400 ml), and sugar (100 gm) are mixed and blended for 5 minutes in an omnimixer. Water (150 ml) is added, and the homogenate is shaken carefully by hand to avoid the formation of an unbreakable emulsion. After 15 to 30 minutes, the organic layer is withdrawn and evaporated to 2 to 5 ml, and an aliquot is injected into the chromatograph. The column is a 6-foot $\times$ ¼-inch aluminum tube packed with 15 to 30% Dow Corning high-vacuum silicone grease on Chromosorb. The silicone grease first is extracted with ethyl acetate to remove volatiles, and the Chromosorb is deactivated by washing it with hot 6 N hydrochloric acid followed by a water rinse. Chromatography is carried out at 220° to 250°C, with a flow rate of 60 ml of helium per minute. DDT is eluted in about 23 to 25 minutes at the higher temperature. Detection is by coulometry (see above). Analyses have been made in the range of 0.05 to 130 ppm of insecticide on potatoes, lettuce, broccoli, hay, and silage.

In the procedure used by Zweig *et al.* (1960) for the analysis of Thiodan, the sample is surface-stripped with hexane for an hour. A portion of the solvent is evaporated to dryness, and the residue is taken up to 100 μl of toluene. An aliquot of this solution (50 μl) is injected into the chromatograph. The Thiodan eluting from the column is trapped in a collection tube containing a plug of glass wool saturated with carbon disulfide. The sample is transferred to an infrared microcell in this solvent, and the spectrum is scanned from 8 to 8.5 μ with pure carbon disulfide in the reference beam. The absolute absorbance at 8.37 μ is measured, and the amount of Thiodan is calculated.

It is necessary to use more elaborate clean-up procedures for the analysis of dairy products because most pesticides are recovered in the lipid fraction, which is comparatively large. Milk containing 2,4-dichlorophenoxyacetic acid is hydrolyzed enzymatically, and the product is subjected to liquid-liquid extraction with diethyl ether (Burchfield and Storrs, 1961). Next, the solvent is evaporated and the residue is partitioned between hexane and acetonitrile. The 2,4-dichlorophenoxyacetic acid and other polar compounds are found in the acetonitrile, and the lipids in the hexane layer. The acetonitrile is evaporated, the residue methylated, and an aliquot of the methylation products injected into the chromatograph. The methyl esters of 4-chlorophenoxyacetic acid, 2,4-dichlorophenoxyacetic acid (2,4-D), and 2,4,5-trichlorophenoxyacetic acid (2,4,5-T) are easily resolved on a silicone column at 201°C. Hence the method would be applicable to mixtures of herbicides.

Pesticides can be removed from soil samples by steam distillation if they are sufficiently volatile. This technique has been utilized in the gas chromatographic analysis of the pre-emergence herbicide ethyl N,N-dipropyl thiol carbamate (EPTC). Water (80 ml) is added to 100 gm of soil, and the mixture is steam-distilled for 4 hours (Freed and Hughes, 1961). The distillate is extracted continuously with Skellysolve F, and the organic layer is evaporated to a volume of 0.5 ml in a conical centrifuge tube. The solvent is dried over anhydrous sodium sulfate, an internal standard (n-nonyl ketone) is added, and an aliquot of the solution is chromatographed on Apiezon L coated on Celite at 160°C. The amount of EPTC in the effluent is measured with a katharometer.

Steam distillation also has been used to isolate the mold inhibitors biphenyl and o-phenylphenol from orange juice (Thomas, 1960). A 1-ml sample of concentrated orange juice is diluted with water and distilled in a semimicro apparatus. The distillate (1 ml) is extracted with chloroform, and a small amount of column packing is added to the solvent layer. The chloroform is then evaporated, leaving the residue deposited on the packing. This material is then added to the chromatographic column at the end nearest the injection port, and the carrier gas is started as rapidly as possible. Chromatography is on a 6-foot column packed with silicone oil on Celite (20:80) at a temperature of 160°C and a flow rate of 20 ml of argon per minute. Thymol is used as an internal standard. Biphenyl and o-phenylphenol can be analyzed in the range of 1 to 10 ppm to an accuracy of ± 0.5 ppm with a 1-ml sample and an argon ionization detector.

It seems probable that many of the difficulties encountered in pesticide residue analysis could be reduced by adding a known amount of standard to the product being analyzed before extraction of the sample (Storrs and Burchfield, 1962). Ideally, the standard should have physicochemical properties identical to those of the pesticide except for a difference in retention volume great enough to permit good peak resolution. The amount of pesticide in the food product then could be calculated from

$$p = A/A_0 p_0 R \tag{1}$$

where p is the ppm of pesticide, p_0 the ppm of standard, A the area of the pesticide peak, A_0 the peak area of the standard, and R an empirical correction factor determined by adding a fixed amount of standard and various amounts of pesticide to foods and making the analysis. Very likely, R will vary somewhat from crop to crop for each pesticide-standard combination. If R approaches unity, the method becomes equivalent in principle to isotope dilution.

The following criteria are suggested in selecting a standard. (1) The molecular structure and physicochemical properties of the standard should approach those of the pesticide as closely as possible. (2) The retention volumes of the two compounds should be as close as possible while still permitting baseline resolution. (3) The experimentally determined value R should be as close to unity as possible. (4) The standard should not be a compound that is likely to be found as a major impurity in the pesticide. (5) The standard should not be another pesticide, or have the same retention volume as known pesticides that might be carried through the analysis with it.

The most obvious choice would be to select a compound with one more or one less chlorine atom than the pesticide. Thus, dimethyl trichloroterephthalate could be used as an internal standard in the analysis of dimethyl tetrachloroterephthalate, since it emerges from the chromatographic column just before it, and would be expected to have somewhat similar physicochemical properties with regard to solubility, volatility, partition coefficients, etc. However, it could conceivably occur as an impurity in this pesticide which would violate requirement (4). Similarly, either 4-chlorophenoxyacetic acid or 2,4,5-T could be used as a standard in the analysis of 2,4-D, since the methyl esters of the 3 compounds are well resolved when chromatographed on silicone at 201°C. However, 2,4-D and 2,4,5-T are often used in the same formulation, thus violating requirement (5). 4-Chlorophenoxyacetic acid is used in agriculture to a lesser extent, and might be acceptable in many applications.

Another procedure that would satisfy requirement (1) more completely would be to use a compound with the same number of halogens as the pesticide but in different positions. Thus, 2,3,4,5-tetrachlorobenzoic acid would be satisfactory to use in the analysis of 2,3,5,6-tetrachlorobenzoic acid, since the two compounds are well resolved chromatographically and would be expected to resemble each other more in physical properties than the pentachlorobenzoate or any of the trichlorobenzoates. However, the two compounds might coexist in the same formulation, which would, of course, interfere with the analysis. Another example would be the use of 2,5-dichlorophenoxyacetic acid (2,5-D) as an internal standard in the analysis of 2,4-D. Unfortunately, the retention volumes of these compounds are too close to permit resolution with the column and operating parameters employed.

The most promising standards so far investigated have been obtained by replacing a single chlorine atom with a bromine atom. This will shift retention values far enough to permit good resolution even with polyhalogenated compounds. For example, bromopentachlorobenzene can be resolved from hexachlorobenzene, even though the two compounds resemble each other closely in physicochemical properties.

Bromine substitution is advantageous in this application because the structure of the standard is identical to that of the pesticide with respect to the number and positions of the halogen atoms, the only difference being in the size and electronegativity of one of them. This should result in very similar physicochemical properties, a conclusion that is borne out by the well-known fact that the biological activities of bromine compounds are often substantially equivalent to those of their chlorine analogues. Moreover, chromatographically speaking, one bromine atom is equivalent to about 1½ chlorine atoms in its effect on retention volumes. Thus the peaks obtained on bromine analogues are likely to be in between those of the pesticide and the compound containing one more chlorine atom, which would minimize interference caused by the presence of impurities or related pesticides. For example, the peak arising from methyl-2-chloro-4-bromophenoxyacetate is found midway between those of the methyl esters of 2,4-D and 2,4,5-T. Therefore, 2-chloro-4-bromophenoxyacetic acid would be a suitable internal standard in the analysis of both of these herbicides, either alone or when used as mixtures.

IV. Analysis of Herbicide Formulations

Formulations of phenoxyalkanoic acid herbicides can be analyzed by GLC, reportedly within an accuracy of 1 to 5%. The salts are converted to free acids by treatment with aqueous mineral acid, and the herbicides are extracted from the water layer by means of a suitable organic solvent. The free acids are then esterified and chromatographed. Gardner and Overton (1960) use methanol–sulfuric acid for the esterification of 2-methyl-4-chlorophenoxyacetic acid under conditions where interfering compounds do not esterify. Therefore, it is unnecessary to obtain separation on the column, since free acids are not volatile enough to be eluted under the conditions employed. Chromatography is on a 2-meter Apiezon M column at 190°C and a flow rate of 50 ml of hydrogen per minute. Ethyl benzoate is the internal standard.

Martin et al. (1960) have chromatographed unsubstituted monochloro and dichloro derivatives of methyl 2-methylphenoxyacetate, methyl α-(2-methylphenoxy)propionate, and methyl α-(2-methylphenoxy)butyrate on both polar and nonpolar packings. Members of a single family can be separated from one another on either type of stationary liquid. The absence of butyrates in a mixture of acetates and propionates is best shown on a 4-meter column packed with silicone oil on firebrick (25:75) at an operating temperature of 215° to 220°C and a flow rate of 3 to 5 liters of hydrogen per hour. Mixtures of acetates and propionates are best separated on poly(diethylene glycol succinate) under these same conditions. When members of all three families are present, both columns should be used. The complete analysis requires 2 hours, and accuracy is within 5%.

Phenoxy herbicides also can be chromatographed as their butyl esters (Higson and Butler, 1960). Butyl α-(4-chloro-2-methylphenoxy)propionate can be analyzed with an accuracy of 1% with dimethyl phthalate as an internal standard. Chromatography is on a 10-foot column packed with a polyester at 230°C and a flow rate of 1.2 liters of carrier gas per hour.

V. Summary

Gas-liquid chromatography is the most universal and one of the most sensitive methods yet developed for the analysis of pesticides. Much of the customary clean-up can be taken care of on the column, and remaining interferences can be canceled out by using a detector that is sensitive only to compounds containing halogen or sulfur. Residues in fats, oils, and dairy products must be separated from massive amounts of lipids by partition between hexane and acetonirile before they are analyzed by GLC. Most pesticides can be chromatographed without prior chemical modification. However, the phenoxyacetic and benzoic acid herbicides first must be esterified.

GLC also is a promising procedure for the analysis of factory production samples and formulations, since many closely related compounds can be separated from one another if a selective stationary liquid is used. Accuracy should be within 1% by the internal standard method.

C. Pharmaceuticals

I. INTRODUCTION

Gas chromatography has not yet been employed for the analysis of pharmaceuticals to an extent commensurate with its potential value. Moreover, several topics such as the analysis of alkaloids, sterols, and clinical applications have been discussed in earlier chapters. Consequently, only a brief review of progress in this field will be given here.

II. SOLVENTS AND ANESTHETICS

The water content of pharmaceutical preparations is usually measured by the Dean and Stark or the Karl Fisher titration method. However, it can be determined more rapidly and with good accuracy by gas chromatography on a 5-foot column containing Carbowax 1500 coated on Chromosorb (25:75). The sample is mixed with dry acetone, n-propanol is added as an internal standard, and the mixture is chromatographed at an injection port temperature of 150°C and a column temperature of 117°C (Elvidge and Proctor, 1959). Detection is with a katharometer operated at 200 ma. Satisfactory results can be obtained by injecting a 30-μl aliquot containing 1% water. Results are computed by the peak height-internal standard method. Accuracy is good, even though the water peak tails badly.

Ethanol content also can be measured by GLC (Wesselman, 1960). The sample is diluted with an accurately measured volume of acetone and chromatographed on a 6-foot column packed with polyethylene glycol 400 coated on Chromosorb (30:70). The injection port is held at 300°C, and the column at 100°C. A 1- to 2-μl sample is satisfactory with a katharometer for detection. Accuracy is within 1%. Polyethylene glycol was selected as the stationary phase, since it resolves methanol, ethanol, and water, and retention times are short.

The alcohol content as well as the camphor content of spirits of camphor can be measured on a 2-meter column containing Carbowax 1500 coated on C-22 firebrick (Gloesener, 1958a). Alcohol as well as ether can be determined at a column temperature of 140°C. For the elution of camphor, the column temperature is increased to 170°C.

Small amounts of chloroform in pharmaceutical preparations can also be separated on Carbowax 1500 coated on Chromosorb (Brealey et al., 1959). The column length is 3½ feet, the injection block is held at 145°C, and the column temperature at 88°C. Results are computed with n-propanol as an internal standard. Mixtures of ethyl chloride, diethyl ether, and chloroform (Schleich mixture) isolated from tissue can be resolved by using two columns in series (Gloesener et al., 1958). The first column is 1 meter in length and contains solid paraffin; the second is 2 meters long and contains silicone. The column temperatures are 70°C, and the mobile phase is hydrogen at 50 ml/min. The ethyl chloride is eluted first, followed by ether and chloroform in that order. The total time for chromatography is under 10 minutes. Alternatively, a 1-meter column prepared with triethanolamine followed by a 2-meter column packed with silicone will accomplish the same separation at a temperature of 75°C and a flow rate of 70 ml of hydrogen per minute. The latter combination has also been used for the determination of chloroform and ether in bonbons (Gloesener, 1958b). Maricq and Molle (1959) describe the same analysis with a column containing Carbowax operated at 106°C.

Gjaldbaek (1959) has described a number of miscellaneous applications of gas chromatography to pharmaceutical problems. Included are methods for the analysis of mixtures of diethyl ether, chloroform, and methyl chloride, the determination of chloroform in pharmaceutical preparations, and the measurement of alcohol and water in spirits of methanol. Procedures for the gas chromatographic analysis of experimental fluorocarbon anesthetics have been described recently (Fabian et al., 1960). The analysis of mixtures of anesthetics in expired air is described in Chapter 2.

III. Other Compounds

Other compounds of pharmaceutical interest that can be separated by GLC include eucalyptol, linalol, camphor, menthol, and nitroglycerine (Gjaldbaek, 1959). The analysis of alkaloids is discussed in Chapter 4, and the analysis of steroids in Chapter 7. Janák (1960) has characterized the salts of barbituric acid by chromatographing their pyrolysis products. Spingler and Markert (1959) have described a method for determining the number of acetyl groups in digitalis glycosides, and Vertalier and Martin (1958) and Kratzl and Gruber (1958) have described methods for the quantitative determination of alkoxy groups that are applicable to the analysis of pharmaceuticals. These latter procedures are discussed in Section A of this chapter.

References

Bishop, C. T. and F. P. Cooper. 1960. Constitution of a glucomannan from jack pine (Pinus banksiana, Lamb.). Can. J. Chem. 38: 793–804.

Brealey, L., D. A. Elvidge, and K. A. Proctor. 1959. The determination of chloroform in aqueous pharmaceutical preparations. Analyst 84: 221–225.

Burchfield, H. P. and E. E. Storrs. 1960. Unpublished data.

Burchfield, H. P. and E. E. Storrs. 1961. Residue analysis of 2,4-D and other chlorine-containing herbicides in milk. Presented at the 140th meeting of the American Chemical Society, Chicago, Illinois.

Cason, J. and P. Tavs. 1959. Separation of fatty acids from tubercle bacillus by gas chromatography: identification of oleic acid. J. Biol. Chem. 234: 1401–1405.

Cason, J., J. S. Fessenden, and C. L. Agre. 1959. Location of a branch in a saturated carbon chain. *Tetrahendron* **7**: 289–298.

Coulson, D. M., L. A. Cavanagh, and J. Stuart. 1959. Gas chromatography of pesticides. *J. Agr. Food Chem.* **7**: 250–251.

Coulson, D. M., J. E. De Vries, and B. Walther. 1960a. "Pesticide Residues on Fresh Vegetables," 30 pp. Technical Report No. IV to the John A. Hartford Foundation from Stanford Research Inst., Menlo Park, California, January 6, 1960.

Coulson, D. M., L. A. Cavanagh, J. E. De Vries, and B. Walther. 1960b. Microcoulometric gas chromatography of pesticides. *J. Agr. Food Chem.* **8**: 399–402.

Duswalt, A. A. and W. W. Brandt. 1960. Carbon-hydrogen determination by gas chromatography. *Anal. Chem.* **32**: 272–274.

Elvidge, D. A. and K. A. Proctor. 1959. The use of gas chromatography for determining water in pharmaceutical preparations. *Analyst* **84**: 461–463.

Fabian, L. W., H. Dewitt, and M. A. Carnes. 1960. Laboratory and clinical investigation of some newly synthesized fluorocarbon anesthetics. *Anesthesia & Analgesia* **39**: 456–462.

Freed, V. H. and R. E. Hughes, Jr. 1961. The determination of ethyl *N,N-di-n*-propyl thiocarbamate (EPTC) in soil by gas chromatography. *J. Agr. Food Chem.* **9**: 381–382.

Gardner, K. and K. C. Overton. 1960. Analysis of MCPA/TBA herbicide formulations. II. A gas-liquid chromatographic method for the determination of 4-chloro-2-methylphenoxyacetic acid. *Anal. Chim. Acta* **23**: 337–345.

Gjaldbaek, J. Chr. 1959. Gaschromatografisk analyse af nogle farmaceutiske praeparater. *Dansk Tidsskr. Farm* **33**: 158–168.

Gloesener, E. 1958a. Analyse de la solution alcoolique de camphre par chromatographie de partage gaz/liquide. *Farmaco (Pavia) Ed. pract.* **13**: 647–655.

Gloesener, E. 1958b. Application de la chromatographie en phase gazeuse à l'analyse de bonbons au chloroforme et à l'éther. *J. pharm. Belg.* **13**: 585–588.

Gloesener, E., C. L. Lapière, and J. Versie. 1958. Recherche toxicalique du mélange anesthésique de Schleich par chromatographie en phase gazeuse. *Intern. Congr. Pharm. Sci., 18th. Congr., Brussels.*

Goodwin, E. S., R. Goulden, A. Richardson, and J. G. Reynolds. 1960. The analysis of crop extracts for traces of chlorinated pesticides by gas-liquid partition chromatography. *Chem. & Ind. (London)*, pp. 1220–1221.

Higson, H. G. and D. Butler. 1960. The determination of α-(4-chloro-2-methylphenoxy) propionic acid in chloromethylphenoxypropionic acids by gas-liquid chromatography with an internal standard. *Analyst* **85**: 657–663.

James, A. T. and J. Webb. 1957. Determination of the structure of unsaturated fatty acids on a micro-scale with the gas-liquid chromatogram. *Biochem. J.* **66**: 515–520.

Janák, J. 1960. Identification of the structure of non-volatile organic substances by gas chromatography of pyrolytic products. *Nature* **185**: 684–686.

Kratzl, K. and K. Gruber. 1958. Zur quantitativen Trennung und Bestimmung verschiedener Alkoxylgruppen mittels Gas-Flüssig-Chromatographie. *Montash. Chem.* **89**: 618–624.

Legate, C. E. and H. D. Burnham. 1960. Micropyrolytic-gas chromatographic technique for the analysis of organic phosphates and thiophosphates. *Anal. Chem.* **32**: 1042–1045.

Lemieux. R. U. and E. von Rudloff. 1955. Periodate-permanganate oxidations. I. Oxidation of olefins. *Can. J. Chem.* **33**: 1701–1709.

Lovelock, J. E. 1961. Ionization methods for the analysis of gases and vapors. *Anal. Chem.* **33**: 162–178.

Maricq, L. and L. Molle. 1959. Note sur l'analyse par chromatographie gazeuse de bonbons dits "à l'éther." *J. pharm. Belg.* **14**: 156–158.

Martin, F., S. Vertalier, and J. Cramier. 1960. Détermination par chromatographie en phase gazeuse des acids méthyl-2-phénoxy-acétique, méthyl-2-phénoxy-isopropionique, méthyl-2-phénoxy-butyrique et de leurs dérivés monochlorés en 4 on en 6 et dichlorés en 4 et 6. *Bull. soc. chim. France* pp. 2067–2071.

Murray, K. E. 1959. A method for the determination of the structure of saturated branched-chain fatty acids. *Australian J. Chem.* **12:** 657–670.

Nowakowska, J., E. H. Melvin, and R. Wiebe. 1957. Separation of the oxidation products of fatty acids by gas-liquid partition chromatography. *J. Am. Oil Chemists' Soc.* **34:** 411–414.

Reitsema, R. H. and N. L. Allphin. 1961. Determination of nitrogen with gas chromatography. *Anal. Chem.* **33:** 355–359.

Smith, B. and R. Ohlson. 1960. Hydrogenation as an aid in the identification of unsaturated compounds by gas chromatography. *Acta Chem. Scand.* **14:** 1317–1324.

Spingler, H. and F. Markert. 1959. Gaschromatographische Mikrobestimmung von Formyl- und Acetylgruppen, insbesondere in Digitalisglykosiden. *Mikrochim. Acta,* 122–128.

Storrs, E. E. and H. P. Burchfield. 1962. Internal standards in the analysis of phenoxyacetic, benzoic, and terephthalic herbicides by gas chromatography. In press.

Sundberg, O. E. and C. Maresh. 1960. Application of gas chromatography to microdetermination of carbon and hydrogen. *Anal. Chem.* **32:** 274–277.

Sweeley, C. C. 1959. A gas chromatographic method for sphingosine assay. *Biochim. et Biophys. Acta* **36:** 268–271.

Thomas, R. 1960. The detection and determination of diphenyl and *o*-phenylphenol in concentrated orange juice by gas chromatography. *Analyst* **85:** 551–556.

Thompson, C. J., H. J. Coleman, R. L. Hopkins, C. C. Ward, and H. T. Rall. 1960a. Identification of oxygen compounds in gas-liquid chromatographic fractions by catalytic deoxygenation. *Anal. Chem.* **32:** 1762–1765.

Thompson, C. J., H. J. Coleman, C. C. Ward, and H. T. Rall. 1960b. Desulfurization as a method of identifying sulfur compounds. *Anal. Chem.* **32:** 424–430.

Vertalier, S. and F. Martin. 1958. Microdétermination sélective des groupes alcoxy par chromatographie gaz-liquide. *Chim. Anal.* **40:** 80–86.

Vogel, A. M. and J. J. Quattrone, Jr. 1960. Rapid gas chromatographic method for determination of carbon and hydrogen. *Anal. Chem.* **32:** 1754–1757.

Wesselman, H. J. 1960. Quantitative determination of ethanol in pharmaceutical products by gas chromatography. *J. Am. Pharm. Assoc., Sci. Ed.* **49:** 320–322.

Youngs, C. G. 1961. Determination of the glyceride structure of fats. *J. Amer. Oil Chemists' Soc.* **38:** 62–67.

Zweig, G. and T. E. Archer. 1960. Quantitative determination of thiodan by gas chromatography. *J. Agr. Food Chem.* **8:** 190–192.

Zweig, G. and R. W. Breidenbach. 1961. Trace analysis of 3-amino-2,5-dichlorobenzoic acid (Amiben) by combination gas chromatography and colorimetry. Presented at the 140th meeting of the American Chemical Society, Chicago, Illinois.

Zweig, G., T. E. Archer, and D. Rubenstein. 1960. Residue analysis of a chlorinated insecticide (thiodan) by combination of gas chromatography and infrared spectrophotometry. *J. Agr. Food Chem.* **8:** 403–405.

Zweig, G., T. E. Archer and D. Raz. 1961. Residue determination of naphthyleneacetic acid (NAA) and its methyl ester (MENA) in potatoes by a combination of gas chromatography and ultraviolet spectrophotometry. Presented at the 140th meeting of the American Chemical Society, Chicago, Illinois.

Appendix 1

Manufacturers of Gas Chromatographs

American Instrument Co.
8030 Georgia Ave.
Silver Springs, Maryland, U. S. A.

Barber Coleman Co.
Wheelco Instrument Division
Rockford, Illinois, U. S. A.

Beckman Instruments Co.
2500 Fullerton Road
Fullerton, California, U. S. A.

Burrell Corp.
2223 Fifth Ave.
Pittsburgh 19, Pennsylvania, U. S. A.

Carlo Erba S.P.A.
Divisione Apparecchi Speciali
Via Imonati
24-Milan, Italy

Central Scientific Co.
1700 Irving Park Road
Chicago 13, Illinois, U. S. A.

Consolidated Electrodynamics
300-Sierra Madre Villa
Pasadena, California, U. S. A.

D.A.M.
6 Avenue Sidoine Apollinaire
Lyon, France

Dohrmann Instruments Co.
2450 El Camino Real
Palo Alto, California, U. S. A.

Fisher Scientific Co.
711 Forbes Ave.
Pittsburgh 19, Pennsylvania, U. S. A.

F & M Scientific Corp.
Starr Road and Route 41
Avondale, Pennsylvania, U. S. A.

Gas Chromatography Ltd.
Boyn Valley Road
Maidenhead
Berkshire, England

Glowall Corporation
508 Red Oak Drive
Severna Park, Md.

Griffin and George Ltd.
Ealing Road, Alperton
Wembly, Middlesex, England

Herrmann-Moritz, J., Ateliers
40 Rue Pascal
Paris, France

Jarrell-Ash Co.
26 Farwell St.
Newtonville 60, Massachusetts, U. S. A.

Jobin & Yvon
26 Rue Berthollet
Arceuil (Seine), France

Kensington Scientific
1717 Fifth Street
Berkeley 10, California

(National Plant) Laboratory Instruments
Prague, Czechoslovakia

Loe Engineering Co.
2092 N. Lincoln Ave.
Altadena, California, U. S. A.

MECI
123 Blvd. de Grenville XV
Paris, France

Nester & Faust
2401 Ogletown Rd.
Newark, Delaware, U. S. A.

Perkin-Elmer Corp.
Route 7
Norwalk, Connecticut, U. S. A.

Podbielniak, Inc.
341 East Ohio Street
Chicago 11, Illinois, U. S. A.

Promesaur
19 Rue Eugene Carriers
Paris 18°, France

W. G. Pye & Co., Ltd.
Granta Works
P.O. Box 60
Cambridge, England

Radiation Equipment and Accessories
Corporation
665 Merrick Road
Lynbrook, New York, U. S. A.

Research Specialties Co.
200 South Garrard Blvd.
Richmond, California, U. S. A.

Rubarth u. Co.
Hanover, Germany

Shandon Scientific Co., Ltd.
6 Cromwell Place
London S.W.7, England

Dr. Virus KG
Bonn, Rosenburgweg 20
Germany

Well Logging Equipment Manufacturing
Co.
3915 Tharp St.
Houston 3, Texas, U. S. A.

Wilkens Instrument and Research Inc.
P.O. Box 313
Walnut Creek, California, U. S. A.

Manufacturers of Auxiliary Equipment

Aldrich Chemical Co., Inc.
3747 N. Booth Street
Milwaukee 12, Wisconsin, U. S. A.

Diazald for generation of diazomethane

American Cyanamid Co.
Surgical Products Division
1000 Highland Ave.
Needham 92, Mass.

Hypodermic syringes

Analytical Engineering Laboratories, Inc.
P.O. Box 5215
Hamden, Connecticut, U. S. A.

Column packings, solid supports

Applied Science Laboratories
140 North Barnard Street
State College, Pennsylvania, U. S. A.

Polyester stationary liquids
Column packings
Standard fatty acids
Zero retention time marker

Associated Electrical Industries Ltd.
Instrument Division
P.O. Box 1, Harlow
Essex, England

Integrating recorder
Mass spectrometers

Atomic Accessories Inc.
811 West Merrick Road
Valley Stream, New York, U. S. A.

Liquid scintillation counter
Continuous radioactive gas analyzer

Barnes Engineering Co.
30 Commerce Road
Stamford, Connecticut, U. S. A.

Thermal conductivity cell with flake
thermistor

Becton Dickinson and Co.
Rutherford, New Jersey, U. S. A.

Metal surgical stopcocks

Bendix Aviation Corp.
Cincinnati Division
3130 Wasson Road
Cincinnati 8, Ohio, U. S. A.

Time-of-flight mass spectrometer

Berk, F. W., and Co. Ltd.
8 Baker Street
London W.1., England

Modified montmorillonite clay

Biotron Co., The
P.O. Box 22043
Houston, Texas, U. S. A.

Gas sampling valves

British Drug Houses, Ltd., The
B. D. H. Laboratory Chemicals Division
Poole, Dorset, England

Molecular sieves
Amberlite and Permutit ion-exchange
resins
Reagents for gas chromatography

Burroughs Wellcome and Co. The Wellcome Bldg., Euston Rd. London N.W.1., England	Agla micrometer syringe
California Laboratory Equipment Co. 1717 Fifth Avenue Berkeley 10, California, U. S. A.	Micrometer syringe
Cambridge Industries Co., Inc. 101 Potter Street Cambridge 42, Massachusetts, U. S. A.	Polyester stationary liquids (LAC type)
Circle Seal Products Co., Inc. 2181 East Foothill Blvd. Pasadena, California, U. S. A.	Custom selector valves
Chemical and Petroleum Research Laboratory Carnegie Institute of Technology Pittsburgh 13, Pennsylvania, U. S. A.	American Petroleum Institute standard samples of hydrocarbons
Coast Engineering Laboratory 16 14th Street Hermosa Beach, California, U. S. A.	Tubes packed with active solids for drying carrier gas
Connecticut Instrument Corp. Wilton, Connecticut, U. S. A.	Infrared beam condenser and cavity cells GLC fraction collector with cavity cell
Crawford Fitting Co. 884 East 140th Street Cleveland, Ohio, U. S. A.	Swagelok Quick-Connect fittings
Davison Chemical Corp. Baltimore 3, Maryland, U. S. A.	Silica gel
Disc Instrument Co. 3014-B South Haladay St. Santa Ana, California, U. S. A.	Mechanical integrators
Dow Corning Corp. Midland, Michigan, U. S. A.	Silicone stationary liquids Dowex ion-exchange resins
Ealing Corporation 33 University Road Cambridge 38, Mass.	Reagents for chromatography
Electronic Instruments Ltd. Richmond, Surrey, England	Electometers for measurement of ioniza- tion currents
F & B Mfg. Co. 4248 W. Chicago Ave. Chicago 51, Illinois, U. S. A.	FTC-40 induction coil
Fenwall Electronics Inc. 63 Fountain Street Framingham, Massachusetts, U. S. A.	Matched thermistor pairs

Floridin Co.   Florisil
P.O. Box 989
Tallahassee, Florida, U. S. A.

Fluorocarbon, The, Co.   Fluoropak 80—an inert solid support
Polychemicals Division
1754 Clementine St.
Anaheim, California, U. S. A.

Garlock Packing Co., The   Nylon capillary tubes
114 Liberty Street
New York 6, New York, U. S. A.

Gast Manufacturing Co.   Gast pump
P.O. Box 117
121 Hinkley Street
Benton Harbor, Michigan, U. S. A.

General Electric Co.   Silicone rubber gum SE-30
Silicone Products Department
Waterford, New York, U. S. A.

Gow-Mac Instrument Co.   Thermal conductivity cells (hot wire and
100 Kings Road   thermistor)
Madison, New Jersey, U. S. A.   Power supplies
                                                    Gas density balance

Greenbrier Instruments Inc.   Process stream analyzers and accessories
P.O. Box 68
Ronceverte, West Virginia, U. S. A.

Hamilton Co. Inc.   Fraction collectors
11717½ Washington Boulevard   Microliter syringes
P.O. Box 307
Whittier, California, U. S. A.

Honeywell Controls Ltd.   Strip chart recorders
Ruislip Road East   Integrators
Greenford, Middlesex, England

Hopkins and Williams, Ltd.   Stationary liquids
Freshwater Road   Repelcote for treating glassware
Chadwell Heath
Essex, England

Imperial Brass Mfg. Co., The   Tube bender
Chicago 48, Illinois, U. S. A.

Imperial Chemical Industries Ltd.   Lubrol MO (a polyethylene glycol)
Imperial Chemical House
Millbank, London S.W.1., England

Insco Corp.   Controls for chart speeds and heating rates
Groton, Massachusetts, U. S. A.

Jarrell-Ash Co. 26 Farwell St. Newtonville 60, Massachusetts, U. S. A.	Electron capture ionization detector
Johns-Manville Co. 22 East 40th Street New York, New York, U. S. A.	C-22 firebrick Chromosorb W Chromosorb P
Johnson, E. F., Co. Wasica, Minnesota, U. S. A.	Viking navigator radio transmitter
Kirkhill Rubber Co. Cyprus Court Brea, California, U. S. A.	Silicone rubber plugs
Latchat Chemicals Incorporated 2202 West 107th Place Chicago 43, Illinois, U. S. A.	Column packings
Leeds and Northrup Co. 4907 Stenton Ave., Philadelphia 4, Pennsylvania, U. S. A.	Recorders and integrators Process stream analyzers
Leiman Bros. 146-181 Christie St. P.O. Box 1339 Newark 5, New Jersey, U. S. A.	Rotary air pumps
Linde Company Division of Union Carbide Corp. 30 East 42nd Street New York 17, New York, U. S. A.	Molecular sieves
Lockwood and McLorie, Inc. Box 113, Horsham, Pennsylvania, U. S. A.	Custom-built instruments
McGregor Instrument Co. Needham, Massachusetts, U. S. A.	Syringes
Martin, H. S., and Co. 1916 Greenleaf St. Evanston, Illinois, U. S. A.	Four-way twin-V bore stopcock
Matheson Coleman and Bell Division of the Matheson Co., Inc. 2909 Highland Ave. Norwood (Cincinnati), Ohio, U. S. A.	Dimethylsulfolane
May and Baker Ltd. Dagenham, Essex, England	Standard stationary liquids Active solids
Metal Hydrides, Inc. 12–24 Congress St. Beverly, Massachusetts, U. S. A.	Calcium hydride

Metro Industries   Apparatus for microinteresterification
141 Old Country Rd.
Mincola, L.I., N.Y.

Metropolitan-Vickers Electrical Co., Ltd.   Mass spectrometers
Trafford Park
Manchester 17, England

Microbeads, Inc.   Glass microbeads
2505 Albion Street
Toledo 6, Ohio, U. S. A.

Micro-Tek Instruments, Inc.   Chemicals and accessories
550 Oak Villa Blvd.
Baton Rouge, Louisiana, U. S. A.

Minneapolis-Honeywell Regulator Co.   Strip chart recorders and integrators
Wayne and Windrim Avenues
Philadelphia 44, Pennsylvania, U. S. A.

Minnesota Mining and Manufacturing Co.   Glass microbeads
900 Bush Avenue
St. Paul 6, Minnesota, U. S. A.

Moore Products Co.   Flow controllers and pressure regulators
H and Lycoming Streets
Philadelphia 24, Pennsylvania, U. S. A.

Packard Instrument Co., Inc.   Liquid scintillation counters and GLC frac-
P.O. Box 428   tion collectors for radioactivity measure-
LeGrange, Illinois, U. S. A.   ments

Permutit Co. Ltd.   Permutit
Permutit House
Gunnersbury Ave.
London W.4, England

Photovolt Corp.   Recorders and integrators
1115 Broadway
New York 10, New York, U. S. A.

Quintron Instrument Co., Inc.   Recorder range extender
P. O. Box 3184
Milwaukee 18, Wisconsin, U. S. A.

Rhom and Hass Co.   Amberlite ion-exchange resins
Resinous Products Division
Washington Square
Philadelphia 5, Pennsylvania, U. S. A.

Scientific Glass Apparatus Co.   Liquid–liquid extractors
100 Lakewood Terrace
Bloomfield, New Jersey, U. S. A.

Sigmamotor Inc.   Pulsating pump for circulating sweep gas
  3 North Main Street
  Middleport, New York, U. S. A.

Skinner Electric Valve Division of the   Solenoid valves for high-pressure operation
    Skinner Chuck Co.
  95 Edgewood Ave.
  New Britain, Connecticut, U. S. A.

Union Carbide Chemicals Co.   Molecular sieves
  Division of Union Carbide Corporation
  270 Park Avenue
  New York 17, New York

Victory Engineering Co.   Thermistors
  Springfield Ave.
  Springfield, New Jersey, U. S. A.

Zahm and Nagel Co., Inc.   Zahm air tester
  74 Jewett Ave.
  Buffalo 14, New York, U. S. A.

Appendix 3

Comparison Table of U. S., British, and German Sieve Sizes with Tyler Equivalents

(Reprinted from *Handbook of Chemistry and Physics*)

Tyler	U. S.		British standard		I. M. M.		German din		
Equiv. mesh	Mesh no.	Opg. mm.	Mesh no.	Opg. mm.	Mesh no.	Opg mm.	Din. no.	Mesh per sq cm	Opg. mm.
3½	3½	5.66	—	—	—	—	1	1	6.000
4	4	4.76	—	—	—	—	—	—	—
5	5	4.00	—	—	—	—	—	—	—
6	6	3.36	5	3.353	—	—	2	4	3.000
7	7	2.83	6	2.812	—	—	—	—	—
—	—	—	—	—	5	2.540	—	—	—
8	8	2.38	7	2.411	—	—	2½	6.25	2.400
9	10	2.00	8	2.057	—	—	3	9	2.000
10	12	1.68	10	1.676	—	—	4	16	1.500
—	—	—	—	—	8	1.600	—	—	—
12	14	1.41	12	1.405	—	—	—	—	—
—	—	—	—	—	10	1.270	—	—	—
14	16	1.19	14	1.204	—	—	5	25	1.200
—	—	—	—	—	12	1.059	—	—	—
16	18	1.00	16	1.003	—	—	6	36	1.020
20	20	0.84	18	0.853	—	—	—	—	—
—	—	—	—	—	16	0.795	8	64	0.750
24	25	0.71	22	0.699	—	—	—	—	—
—	—	—	—	—	20	0.635	—	—	—
28	30	0.59	25	0.599	—	—	10	100	0.600
—	—	—	—	—	—	—	11	121	0.540
32	35	0.50	30	0.500	—	—	12	144	0.490
35	40	0.42	36	0.422	30	0.424	14	196	0.430
42	45	0.35	44	0.353	—	—	16	256	0.385
—	—	—	—	—	40	0.317	—	—	—
48	50	0.297	52	0.295	—	—	20	400	0.300
60	60	0.250	60	0.251	50	0.254	24	576	0.250

Tyler	U. S.		British standard		I. M. M.		German din		
Equiv. mesh	Mesh no.	Opg. mm.	Mesh no .	Opg. mm.	Mesh no.	Opg. mm.	Din. no.	Mesh per sq cm	Opg mm.
65	70	0.210	72	0.211	60	0.211	30	900	0.200
80	80	0.177	85	0.178	70	0.180	—	—	—
100	100	0.149	100	0.152	80	0.160	40	1600	0.150
—	—	—	—	—	90	0.139	—	—	—
115	120	0.125	120	0.124	100	0.127	50	2500	0.120
150	140	0.105	150	0.104	120	0.104	60	3600	0.102
170	170	0.088	170	0.089	—	—	70	4900	0.088
—	—	—	—	—	150	0.084	—	—	—
200	200	0.074	200	0.076	—	—	80	6400	0.075
250	230	0.062	240	0.066	200	0.063	100	10000	0.060
270	270	0.053	300	0.053	—	—	—	—	—
325	325	0.044	—	—	—	—	—	—	—
400	400	0.037	—	—	—	—	—	—	—

Appendix 4

Hazards Associated with the Use
of Diazomethane

Diazomethane is used as a methylating agent in a number of the procedures described in this book. Consequently the following warning concerning its properties is reprinted in its entirety from *Organic Syntheses*, Vol. 36, page 16a (insert page), 1956.

Diazomethane is not only toxic, but also potentially explosive. Hence one should wear heavy gloves and goggles and work behind a safety screen or a hood door with safety glass, as is recommended in the preparation of diazomethane described by DeBoer and Backer, *Org. Syntheses*, **36,** 16 (1956). As is also recommended there, ground joints and sharp surfaces should be avoided. Thus all glass tubes should be carefully fire-polished, connections should be made with rubber stoppers, and separatory funnels should be avoided, as should etched or scratched flasks. Furthermore, at least one explosion of diazomethane has been observed at the moment crystals (sharp edges!) suddenly separated from a supersaturated solution. Stirring by means of a Teflon-coated magnetic stirrer is greatly to be preferred to swirling the reaction mixture by hand, for there has been at least one case of a chemist whose hand was injured by an explosion during the preparation of diazomethane in a hand-swirled reaction vessel.

It is imperative that diazomethane solutions not be exposed to direct sunlight or placed near a strong artificial light because light is thought to have been responsible for some of the explosions that have been encountered with diazomethane. Particular caution should be exercised when an organic solvent boiling higher than ether is used. Because such a solvent has a lower vapor pressure than ether, the concentration of diazomethane in the vapor above the reaction mixture is greater and an explosion is more apt to occur.

Most diazomethane explosions occur during its distillation. Hence diazomethane should not be distilled unless the need justifies it. An ether solution of diazomethane satisfactory for many uses can be prepared as described by Arndt, *Org. Syntheses*, Coll. Vol. **2,** 165 (1943), Note 3, where nitrosomethylurea is added to a mixture of ether and 50% aqueous potassium hydroxide and the ether solution of diazomethane is subsequently decanted from the aqueous layer and dried over potassium hydroxide pellets (not sharp-edged sticks!). When distilled diazomethane is required, the procedure of DeBoer and Backer (*loc. cit.*) is particularly good because at no time is there much diazomethane present in the distilling flask.

The hazards associated with diazomethane are discussed by C. D. Gutsche, *Org. Reactions* **8,** 391–394 (1954).

AUTHOR INDEX

Numbers in italic show the page on which the complete reference is listed.

SUBJECT INDEX

A

Acetyl groups, determination of, 620
Acid centers, see Rearrangements and Columns, solid supports
α-Acids, 430, 482–487, see also Resin acids pyrolysis of lead salts
β-Acids, 482–487, see also Resin acids
Abies concolor, 419
Abietic acid, 476–482, see also Resin acids chromatography of
Acetals, dimethyl, see also Aldehydes, higher fatty
from terpenoid aldehydes, 404
retention volumes, 523
Active solid, 9
Adjusted retention volume, see Retention volume
Adsorption, see Carrier gas
Agla syringe, 72
Aglycones, see Glycosides
Air, chromatography of, 176–189
organic vapors in, 206–239
sampling in food containers, 147–149
of respiratory gases, 147
Air peak, 11
Air pollutants, 222, 225
chromatography of, 234–237
collection of, 212–214
detectors for, 215–218
hydrocarbons as, 209
Alcohols, higher fatty, 504–511
chromatography as acetates, 508–510
as hydrocarbons, 510–511
direct chromatography, 505–508
isolation and synthesis, 504–505
resolution by unsaturation, 507
lower, 309–329, see also Tailing
chromatography in capillary columns, 314, 317
of derivatives, 326–329
conversion to nitrites, 326–328
to olefins, 328
isolation, 309–310
measurement by combustion, 310
separation from water, 310–311
reduction to hydrocarbons, 328
terpenoid, see Terpenoid alcohols

Aldehydes, higher fatty, 521–526, see also Plasmalogens
chromatography, 522–526
from O-alkyl glycerols, 515
isolation, 520
lower, see Carbonyl compounds
Aldol condensations, 404
Alkaloids, see also Tobacco
chromatography of, 366–369
Alkanes, see also Arenes
separation from alkenes, 227
separation from naphthenes, 227
Alkoxyl groups, determination of, 620
O-Alkyl glycerols, see Glycerols, O-alkyl
Alyssuum argenteum, 612
Amines, aromatic, 353–358
higher fatty, 565–567
Amines, methyl,
chromatography of, 282–285,
polybasic, 289–290
titration of, 28
volatile, 279–289
identification by retention values, 285–289
isolation from plants, 279
Amino acids, 573–588
chromatography of chloro analogues, 587
of deamination products, 586–587
of esters, 576–583
of oxidation products, 583–586
decarboxylation of, 587
isolation of, 574–576
Amino alcohols, 291
Ammonia, chromatography of, 282–285
Andropogon genera, 420
Angiosperma, see Monocotyledoneae and Dicotyledoneae
Anesthetics in respiratory gases, 237–239
Anisoles, see Phenols
Anomers, hexose
separation by GLC, 605–607
Antoine equation, 81–82
Aqueous solutions,
analysis with flame detector, 322–323
chromatography of, 271–272
Arenes, separation from alkanes, 222
Argon, interference in oxygen determination, 179–181

INDEX OF METHODS

INDEX OF STATIONARY LIQUIDS
USED IN METHODS

679